CONSUMER MATH

for Christian Schools®

Larry D. Lemon
Deborah B. Moreno

Bob Jones University Press, Greenville, South Carolina 29614
Textbook Division

Larry D. Lemon, M.S.
Deborah B. Moreno

Consultants
Daniel P. Olinger, Ph.D.
Rebecca H. Davis, M.Ed.
Kathy D. Pilger, M.A.

Note:
The fact that materials produced by other publishers are referred to in this volume does not
constitute an endorsement by Bob Jones University Press of the content or theological
position of materials produced by such publishers. The position of the Bob Jones University
Press, and the University itself, is well known. Any references and ancillary materials are
listed as an aid to the student or the teacher in an attempt to maintain the accepted academic
standards of the publishing industry.

Consumer Math for Christian Schools®

Produced in cooperation with the Bob Jones University
Department of Mathematics of the College of Arts and
Science, the School of Education, and Bob Jones
Academy.

ISBN 0-89084-356-2

20   19   18   17   16   15   14   13   12   11   10   9   8   7   6

Contents

Introduction

Many students think that math is impractical. They ask, "Why do I have to learn these proofs and formulas? I'm never going to use any of this stuff."

They're wrong, of course. They don't realize how often they will need to call on the things they learned in "theoretical" courses like algebra and geometry.

If you, too, have asked yourself questions like this, you'll especially like this course. *CONSUMER MATH for Christian Schools*® is good for many reasons, but perhaps the most obvious is that it's directly practical. No matter where you live, where you work, or how large or small your family is, you will need to know the answers to certain questions:

- How can I best keep track of my finances?
- How do I figure my taxes? How can I avoid paying more than I owe?
- What kind of bank account is best for me? Why?
- What kind of car should I buy? How should I pay for it? How much will a car cost me every day?
- How can I save money on food and clothing?
- Should I rent a home or buy one? How do I decide?
- What do insurance agents mean by all those long words? Do I need insurance? If so, what kind?

This book begins by helping you review the skills you'll need to find the answers to the above questions. Some students may be able to move fairly quickly through the first five chapters; others may need to take more time. In either case, you need to master the skills presented in these chapters before you can completely understand the material in the rest of the text.

By the end of this course, you'll know the answers to the above questions and more. You'll learn what certain terms mean so that you can understand what salespeople and others are talking about. You'll learn how to figure costs, including costs that most of us don't realize are coming. In short, you'll learn to be a good steward of the resources that God has given you—whether those resources be few or many. "Moreover, it is required in stewards, that a man be found faithful" (I Cor. 4:2).

Our Number System

Suppose that someone asks you who you are. You would probably give him your name. But is your name actually *you?* No. It is simply an identification for you. You are a unique person; God created you for a special purpose. God told Jeremiah, "Before I formed thee in the belly I knew thee; and before thou camest forth out of the womb I sanctified thee, and I ordained thee a prophet unto the nations" (Jer. 1:5). God had a special plan for Jeremiah, and He has a special plan for you. No one else can take your place and fulfill the purpose which God has for you. There is only one *you* even though there may be many people who share your name.

As we use names to identify people, we use numerals to represent numbers. If you are asked to think of a number, you may picture in your mind something like this: "7." Then you say that you "see" the number seven. Actually, what you "see" is the numeral seven. This numeral represents any set which has seven members. Numbers cannot be seen; they are abstractions, or ideas. However, since we must have some way to represent numbers, we use numerals. The idea of "sevenness" may be represented by many symbols, including "7," "VII," and "IIIIIII." Since the day God established them, numbers have not changed. What has changed is the different numerals used to represent the numbers. The study of our number system is a study of the numbers that we use and how they work.

The Decimal System

A set is a group, or collection, of objects. Set braces, { }, are the notation for sets. For example, the set of people in a family may be called set F where F = {Jim, Sandy, Todd, Troy}.

Our number system can be separated into several sets. One such set is the natural numbers, or counting numbers. The natural numbers begin with 1 and continue infinitely.

$$\text{Natural numbers} = \{1, 2, 3, 4, \ldots\}$$

Note: The symbol ". . ." is used for "and so forth."

If you include zero with the natural numbers, you have the set of whole numbers. Most of your work in this book will be with the whole numbers.

$$\text{Whole numbers} = \{0, 1, 2, 3, \ldots\}$$

Our number system is a decimal system because it is based on ten digits. (*Decimal* means "numbered by tens.")

Depending on its place in a numeral, a digit takes a certain value. From this concept comes the term *place-value*.

Place-Value Chart

Place Name	1,000,000	100,000	10,000	1,000	100	10	1	0.1	0.01	0.001	0.0001	0.00001	0.000001
Place Value	millions	hundred thousands	ten thousands	thousands	hundreds	tens	ones	tenths	hundredths	thousandths	ten-thousandths	hundred-thousandths	millionths

The *decimal point* is between the ones and tenths place. The values to the right of the decimal point are less than one. Numerals that include digits to the right of the decimal point are called *decimal fractions,* or *decimals.*

To read a decimal . . .
1. Read the whole number (if there is one).
2. Read the decimal point as "and."
3. Read the rest of the decimal as a whole number and end it with the place name of the last digit.

Example 1

2.35 is read as "two and thirty-five hundredths"
0.1 is read as "one tenth"
0.026 is read as "twenty-six thousandths"

A shorter, more common way to read decimals is . . .
1. Read the whole number (if there is one).
2. Read the decimal point as "point."
3. Read the rest of the digits one at a time.

Example 2

59.759 is read as "fifty-nine point seven, five, nine"
.00241 is read as "point zero, zero, two, four, one"

You can find the value of a digit by multiplying the digit times the value of the place it occupies.

Example 3

Consider the numeral 25,634.871.

What place does the digit 6 occupy? the digit 7? the digit 2?

6 is in the hundreds place
7 is in the hundredths place
2 is in the ten-thousands place

What is the value of the digit 5? the digit 3? the digit 1?

5 is in the thousands place
$5 \times 1,000 = 5,000$
3 is in the tens place
$3 \times 10 = 30$
1 is in the thousandths place
$1 \times 0.001 = 0.001$

So,
5 has a value of 5,000
3 has a value of 30
1 has a value of 0.001

Oral Exercises

Read the decimals two different ways.

1. 16.25
2. 35.07
3. 9.218
4. 156.9
5. 231.75

6. 1,416.2
7. 967.004
8. 28.215
9. 540.54
10. 8,192.072

Written Exercises

What place does the digit 4 occupy in each numeral?

1. 426
2. 52,740
3. 689.46
4. 943,376
5. 72.54
6. 65,234

7. 407,236
8. 34,592
9. 0.0124
10. 2,745
11. 4,326,598
12. 6.7953142

Give the value of the underlined digit in each numeral.

13. 86,253
14. 7,199
15. 538
16. 742.31
17. 1,256,738
18. 6.42

19. 62,476
20. 5,132
21. 53.475
22. 0.0045
23. 794
24. 2,631,013

Adding and Subtracting ───────

Throughout this book you will be learning how to solve problems that are like problems you will face every day. You must have some basic tools with which to solve these problems. Two of these tools are addition and subtraction. You have been adding and subtracting numbers for years, but you should always strive to improve your skill. God wants you to do your best in all you do. Ecclesiastes 9:10 tells us, "Whatsoever thy hand findeth to do, do it with thy might." As you review the operations of addition, subtraction, multiplication, and division, determine to do your best to improve these skills.

Parts of an Addition Problem	Parts of a Subtraction Problem
65 ← addend +23 ← addend 88 ← sum	583 ← minuend −27 ← subtrahend 556 ← difference

You can add or subtract only digits that have the same place value. When you write your work out on paper, line up the digits according to place value. An easy way to do this is to line up the decimal points.

thousands	hundreds	tens	ones	tenths	hundredths
6,	3	2	5 .	2	4
+	5	8	9 .	6	
6,	9	1	4 .	8	4

hundreds	tens	ones	tenths	hundredths
9	6	4 .	5	7
−2	1	9 .	4 3	8
7	4	5 .	1 3	2

Exercises

Add or subtract.

1. 387
   +254

2. 2,342
   +695

3. 45,253
   +7,989

4. 77,258
   +63,482

5. 723
   −418

6. 6,452
   −1,377

7. 7,823
   −6,542

8. 29,416
   −15,943

9. $127.5 + 39.68 + 98.413$
10. $3,426 + 6.243 + 35.2$
11. $36.048 + 0.0679 + 7.59$
12. $527 + 69.05 + 36.772$
13. $6.5 - 3.29$
14. $0.07 - 0.063$
15. $183.24 - 69.7$
16. $691.345 - 341.679$

Multiplying

Peter once asked Jesus, "Lord, how oft shall my brother sin against me, and I forgive him? till seven times?" Jesus answered, "I say not unto thee, Until seven times: but, Until seventy times seven." (Matt. 18:21-22). Jesus was teaching that you must forgive someone no matter how many times he sins against you. He used a large number (70 × 7 = 490) to illustrate this principle. If Jesus had used addition to reach this number, He would have had to say "seventy plus seventy plus seventy plus seventy plus seventy plus seventy plus seventy." Multiplication is a shortened form of addition.

Symbols that indicate multiplication

$$5 \times 6 \qquad 5 \cdot 6 \qquad (5)(6)$$

All of these expressions are read "five times six."

Parts of a multiplication problem

$$275 \leftarrow \text{multiplicand (a factor)}$$
$$\times 26 \leftarrow \text{multiplier (a factor)}$$
$$7{,}150 \leftarrow \text{product}$$

Multiplying decimals is just like multiplying whole numbers except that once you have done the computation, you have to decide where to place the decimal point. To decide where to place the decimal point . . .

1. Count the total number of places *to the right of* the decimal point in the factors.
2. Place the decimal point to show the same number of places in the product.

```
 .3  ←              2.5  ← One place        .382  ←
×.9  ←  Two places  ×3                     ×.67  ←   Five places
 .27 ←  Two places  7.5  ← One place       2674
                                           2292
                                          .25594 ← Five places
```

You can use a short cut when multiplying by 10 or any powers of 10. Notice what happens when you multiply by a power of ten.

```
    23        4.75        162.8
   ×10         ×10        ×100
   230       47.50     16,280.0
```

Multiplying by Powers of 10

When multiplying by a power of ten, move the decimal point to the *right* as many places as there are zeros in the power of ten.

$67.5 \times 10 = 675.$ There is one zero in 10, so move the decimal point one place to the right.

$2.37 \times 1,000 = 2,370$ There are three zeros in 1,000, so move the decimal point three places to the right. To get three places, you must add a zero.

Oral Exercises

Multiply.

1. 18×10
2. 362×10
3. 4.98×10
4. 27×100
5. 6.85×100

6. 29.2×100
7. $56 \times 1,000$
8. $3.2 \times 1,000$
9. $436.21 \times 1,000$
10. $89.275 \times 10,000$

Written Exercises

Multiply.

1. 46×21
2. 697×39
3. 563×28
4. $4,621 \times 383$
5. $6,435 \times 2,394$
6. 894×219

7. 42.7×12
8. 362.93×25.4
9. 814.7×123.4
10. 5.006×2.58
11. 62.09×1.48
12. 435.702×561.6

Dividing

Just as subtraction is the opposite of addition, division is the opposite of multiplication. Division "undoes" multiplication.

$$3 \times 5 = 15 \qquad 15 \div 5 = 3$$
$$8 \times 9 = 72 \qquad 72 \div 9 = 8$$

Symbols that Indicate Division

$$15 \div 5 \qquad 5\overline{)15} \qquad \frac{15}{5}$$

All these are read "fifteen divided by 5."

Parts of a Division Problem

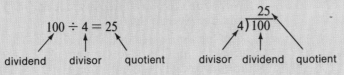

$$100 \div 4 = 25$$

dividend   divisor   quotient   divisor dividend quotient

You can use a short cut when dividing by 10 or a multiple of 10. It is just the opposite of the short cut for multiplying by multiples of 10.

Dividing by a Power of 10

When dividing by a power of ten, move the decimal point to the *left* as many places as there are zeros in the power of ten.

$$638 \div 10 = 63.8$$

There is one zero in 10, so move the decimal point one place to the left.

$$4772.0 \div 100 = 47.72$$

There are two zeros in 100, so move the decimal point two places to the left.

Division involving decimals poses the same problem as multiplication involving decimals: where to place the decimal point. When the divisor is a whole number, simply divide as you would if the dividend were a whole number. Place the decimal point directly above the decimal point in the dividend.

$$14\overline{)36.12} \quad \overset{2.58}{} \qquad 22\overline{)227.128} \quad \overset{10.324}{}$$

When the divisor is not a whole number, you must multiply it by the least multiple of ten that will make it a whole number. Since you are changing the value of the divisor, you must also multiply the dividend by the same power of ten. Look at the examples below to understand why this can be done.

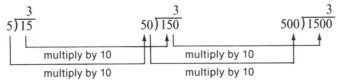

Notice that in each problem you get the same answer. If the divisor and dividend are multiplied by the same number, the quotient will stay the same.

$.26\overline{).14768}$

To make the divisor a whole number, multiply by 100. (Move the decimal point two places to the right.)

$.26\overline{).14768}$

Since the divisor has been multiplied by 100, multiply the dividend by 100.

$26\overline{)14.768}$ with quotient $.568$

Divide as you would when the divisor is a whole number.

Sometimes you may need to annex zeros to the dividend.

$.25\overline{)5.60.0}$ with quotient 22.4

annex zeros

$4\overline{)3.00}$ with quotient $.75$

annex zeros

Oral Exercises

Divide.

1. $75 \div 10$
2. $628 \div 10$
3. $936 \div 100$
4. $2,564 \div 100$
5. $3,624.15 \div 10$
6. $89.6 \div 10$
7. $435.78 \div 100$
8. $992.117 \div 1,000$
9. $722.4 \div 100$
10. $4,336 \div 1,000$

Written Exercises

Write each division problem in three different ways.

1. 48 divided by 6
2. 21 divided by 3
3. 365 divided by 5

Divide.

4. $30 \div 6$
5. $210 \div 6$
6. $276 \div 23$
7. $465 \div 15$
8. $1,170 \div 26$
9. $1,008 \div 36$
10. $14,694 \div 237$
11. $34,484 \div 148$
12. $3,835 \div 65$
13. $7.95 \div 3$
14. $4.548 \div 12$
15. $316.12 \div 14$
16. $9.324 \div 3.6$
17. $279.344 \div 8.84$
18. $13.6059 \div .589$

Rounding and Estimating

Janice bought a dress for $48.99. She told her mother that the dress was "forty-something dollars." She told a friend that the dress was "about fifty dollars." Janice rounded both times, but she rounded in a way that was most convenient for her at the moment. She gave her mother the smaller price to make it appear that she had spent less money. She tried to impress her friend with the expense of the dress by giving her the higher price. Her motives were wrong; she was deliberately deceiving for selfish reasons. "The heart is deceitful above all things," Jeremiah 17:9 tells us. Deception is dishonest and has no place in the Christian's life. Be careful not to use rounding with the intent to deceive.

Rounding numbers, however, is a useful procedure, so it is important that you know how to do it correctly.

To Round Numbers

1. *Mentally* point out the place to which you are going to round the number.

    Round 2,345 to the nearest hundred.

2. Consider the digit to the right of the named place.
    a. If it is equal to or greater than 5, increase the digit in the named place by 1, and replace each digit to the right of the named place with a zero (round up).
    b. If it is less than 5, leave the digit in the named place as it is, but still replace each digit to the right of the named place with a zero (round down).

    In the numeral 2,345, $4 < 5$, so round down.

    $$2,345 \approx 2,300$$

Note: "$\approx$" is read as "is approximately equal to"

Example 1

Round 2,637 to the nearest ten.

3 is in the tens' place
7 is to the right of 3
7 is greater than 5
Round up.
$2{,}637 \approx 2{,}640$

Example 2

Round 341 to the nearest hundred.

3 is in the hundreds' place
4 is to the right of 3
4 is less than 5
Round down.
$341 \approx 300$

Example 3

Round 89.736 to the nearest one.

9 is in the ones' place
7 is to the right of 9
7 is greater than 5
Round up.

(To round up, 9 becomes 10, so add to the tens' column.)
$89.736 \approx 90.0$

Example 4

Round 799.62 to the nearest one.

9 is in the ones' place
6 is to the right of 9
6 is greater than 5
Round up.

(The 9 in the ones place becomes 10, so add 1 to the tens' column, which also becomes 10, so add 1 to the hundreds' column.)
$799.62 \approx 800.0$

Rounding numbers is helpful when you are estimating. An estimate is a rough calculation that you make either to save time or to have some idea of what you will need for the future. For example, you may make an estimate before doing some computation so that you can check your answer.

Example 5

Round both to the nearest hundred.

$$
\begin{array}{r}
427 \\
+368 \\
\end{array}
\quad
\begin{array}{l}
\approx 400 \\
\approx 400 \\
\hline
\approx 800 \leftarrow \text{estimate}
\end{array}
$$

You'll know that your answer should be close to 800. If it is not, you can assume that you probably did something wrong.

$$
\begin{array}{r}
427 \\
+368 \\
\hline
795
\end{array}
$$

795 is close to 800. The answer is reasonable.

Example 6

$$
\begin{array}{r}
148 \\
\times 31 \\
\end{array}
\quad
\begin{array}{l}
\approx 150 \\
\approx \ \ 30 \\
\hline
\approx 4{,}500 \leftarrow \text{estimate}
\end{array}
\qquad
\begin{array}{r}
148 \\
\times 31 \\
\hline
148 \\
4440 \\
\hline
4{,}588
\end{array}
$$

Is the answer close to the estimate?

Exercises

Round each number to the nearest ten.
1. 6,332
2. 76
3. 421
4. 1,985

Round each number to the nearest hundred.
5. 7,384
6. 624
7. 2,356
8. 25,965

Round each number to the nearest hundredth.
9. 65.253
10. .542
11. 37.695
12. .2996

Round each number to the nearest tenth.
13. 2.361
14. 26.728
15. 534.883
16. 47.96

Round 256,372.6843 to the nearest, . . .
17. hundred-thousand.
18. ten-thousand.
19. thousand.
20. hundred.
21. ten.
22. whole number.
23. tenth.
24. hundredth.
25. thousandth.

Find the *approximate* answer by rounding to the nearest tenth, then adding.

26. $1.27	27. $6.95	28. $5.86
3.32	2.81	9.27
.49	1.42	1.33
+.35	+.37	+4.99

First estimate by rounding; then compute the actual answers.

29. 826	30. 6,360	31. 1,245
+259	+598	+381

32. 982	33. 321	34. 2,134
−146	−98	−680

35. 145	36. 682	37. 983
×21	×56	×67

38. 1,176 ÷ 56   **39.** 3,968 ÷ 31   **40.** 4,628 ÷ 89

Opposites and Absolute Value

You can easily solve 8 − 5, but what about 5 − 8?

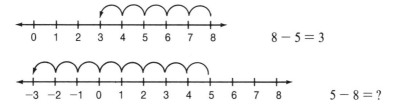

$$8 - 5 = 3$$

$$5 - 8 = ?$$

As you can see, the answer for 5 − 8 is 3 less than zero. This is an example of a negative number: −3. Negative numbers are less than zero on a number line. Since natural numbers and whole numbers do not include negative numbers, we need another set of numbers that does. This is the set of *integers*. Integers include the whole numbers as well as some negative numbers.

$$\text{Integers} = \{\ldots -3, -2, -1, 0, 1, 2, 3, \ldots\}$$

The set of integers can be represented on a number line.

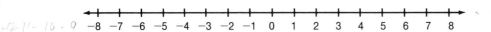

The numbers to the right of zero are called *positive numbers*. The numbers to the left of zero are called *negative numbers*. (Zero is neither positive nor negative.) The arrows at the ends of the number line indicate that the numbers extend without limit in both directions.

Look at 5 and −5 on the number line below.

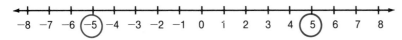

Both numbers are the same distance from zero. They have the same *absolute value*. The *absolute value* of a number is the number of units it is from zero. Absolute value is denoted by vertical parallel bars. For example, $|-2|$ is read "the absolute value of negative two."

$$|-6| = 6 \qquad\qquad |3| = 3$$

Operations can be done with absolute values. Consider the following two examples:

$$|-7| + |2| \qquad\qquad |8 + 2|$$

Figure the absolute value; then add: Add; then take the absolute value:

$$7 + 2 \qquad\qquad |10|$$
$$9 \qquad\qquad\qquad 10$$

Two different numbers that have the same absolute value are called *opposites*. They are the same distance from zero in different directions.

3 and −3 are opposites

−12 and 12 are opposites

Oral Exercises

Find the opposite of each integer.

1. 23	**4.** 36	**7.** −77
2. −64	**5.** 58	**8.** 232
3. −125	**6.** −24	**9.** −481

Written Exercises

Find the absolute value of each integer.

1. $|12|$	**7.** $|92|$
2. $|-16|$	**8.** $|230|$
3. $|-3|$	**9.** $|-309|$
4. $|65|$	**10.** $|-67|$
5. $|34|$	**11.** $|21|$
6. $|-71|$	**12.** $|-342|$

Perform the indicated operation.

13. $|-7| + |-3|$
14. $|5| + |2|$
15. $|-12| + |6|$
16. $|28| - |-13|$
17. $|-62| - |-31|$
18. $|-9| - |6|$
19. $|23| - |-12|$
20. $|-4| \cdot |4|$

21. $|5| \cdot |-10|$
22. $|-25| \div |-5|$
23. $|36 \div 9|$
24. $|52 - 21|$
25. $|23 + 16|$
26. $|6 \cdot 12|$
27. $|8 \cdot 9|$

Adding Integers

Number lines will help you visualize the addition of integers. Remember that a positive number indicates a move to the right and that a negative number indicates a move to the left.

Example 1

Locate -5 on a number line.

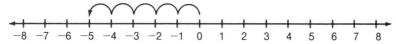

1. Start at 0 (the origin).
2. Move 5 units to the left.

Example 2

Add $(-5) + (-2)$.

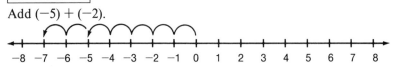

1. Start at 0.
2. Move 5 units to the left.
3. Move 2 units to the left.
4. The answer is -7.

Example 3

Add $4 + 2$.

1. Start at 0.
2. Move 4 units to the right.
3. Move 2 units to the right.
4. The answer is $+6$.

Examples 2 and 3 are examples of adding numbers with like signs. You can apply a rule that will allow you to solve problems like this without using a number line. Simply add the absolute values of the numbers and keep the same sign.

$$(-5) + (-2)$$
$$|-5| + |-2|$$
$$5 + 2 = 7$$
(keep original sign) -7

$$(4) + (2)$$
$$|4| + |2|$$
$$4 + 2 = 6$$
(keep original sign) $+6$

The next two examples illustrate what happens when numbers with unlike signs are added.

Example 4   Add $(-6) + (+3)$.

1. Start at 0.
2. Move 6 units to the left.
3. Move 3 units to the right.
4. The answer is -3.

Example 5

Add $(-5) + (+7)$.

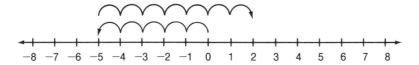

-8   -7   -6   -5   -4   -3   -2   -1   0   1   2   3   4   5   6   7   8

1. Start at 0.
2. Move 5 units to the left.
3. Move 7 units to the right.
4. The answer is +2.

Study the results:

$$(-6) + (+3) = (-3)$$
$$(-5) + (+7) = (+2)$$

What operation is performed on the absolute values of the addends to obtain the absolute value of the sum? When adding numbers with unlike signs, you subtract to find the result.

Rules for the Addition of Integers

1. When adding numbers with like signs, add the absolute values and keep the same sign.

$$(+6) + (+4) \qquad\qquad (-9) + (-5)$$
$$|+6| + |+4| \qquad\qquad |-9| + |-5|$$
$$6 + 4 = 10 \qquad\qquad 9 + 5 = 14$$

(keep original sign) $+10$ (keep original sign) -14

2. When adding numbers with unlike signs, subtract the smaller absolute value from the larger absolute value and keep the sign of the integer with the larger absolute value.

$$(+8) + (-3) \qquad\qquad (+5) + (-9)$$
$$|+8| = 8 \qquad |-3| = 3 \qquad\qquad |+5| = 5 \qquad |-9| = 9$$
$$8 - 3 = 5 = +5 \qquad\qquad 9 - 5 = 4 = -4$$

You can do the work in your head this way:

$(-9) + (-5)$ Think $9 + 5 = 14$; result is negative: -14

$(5) + (-9)$ Think $9 - 5 = 4$; result is negative: -4

Oral Exercises

Use the number line to determine the answers for 1-10.

1. $(5) + (-7)$
2. $(-12) + (6)$
3. $(-6) + (-5)$
4. $(11) + (-8)$
5. $(-3) + (-6)$

6. $(5) + (9)$
7. $(-12) + (10)$
8. $(3) + (-8)$
9. $(7) + (-2)$
10. $(-9) + (4)$

Written Exercises

Add. Use the rules.

1. $(-6) + (28)$
2. $(-21) + (15)$
3. $(-18) + (-26)$
4. $(-29) + (-37)$
5. $(45) + (-32)$
6. $(26) + (-54)$
7. $(63) + (24)$
8. $(92) + (68)$
9. $(-15) + (11)$
10. $(-12) + (8)$

11. $(35) + (-23)$
12. $(21) + (-46)$
13. $(-15) + (-24)$
14. $(-33) + (-47)$
15. $(16) + (48)$
16. $(37) + (76)$
17. $(-82) + (24)$
18. $(-8) + (12)$
19. $(17) + (-9)$
20. $(20) + (-42)$

Subtracting Integers

When you subtract, you find the *distance* from the subtrahend to the minuend. This is illustrated below:

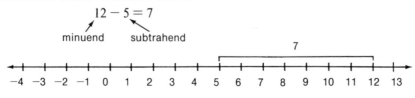

Subtrahend to minuend = 7 units

Whether you realize it or not, you also find the *direction* from the subtrahend to the minuend. Moving from 5 *to* 12 is a move in the positive direction. Hence, the answer is +7.

Consider 5 − 12. The distance between the subtrahend and minuend is 7. The direction is negative.

$$(+5) - (+12) = -7$$

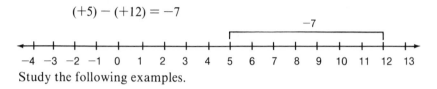

Study the following examples.

$$(+6) - (-2) = +8$$

Subtrahend to minuend = 8
Direction is positive.

$$(-3) - (-5) = (+2)$$

Subtrahend to minuend = 2
Direction is positive.

$$(-7) - (-2) = (-5)$$

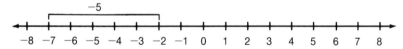

Subtrahend to minuend = 5
Direction is positive.

$$(-4) - (+3) = -7$$

Subtrahend to minuend = 7.
Direction is negative.

You need a rule for subtraction of integers. If you had 0 and you subtracted 6, what would your answer be?

$$0 - 6 = -6$$

-6

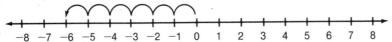

If you had 0 and you added −6, what would your answer be?

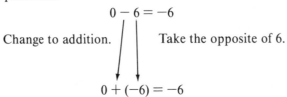

1. Start at 0.
2. Move 6 units to the left.
3. The answer is −6.

Notice that $0 - 6$ yields the same answer as $0 + (-6)$. What is different about the two problems?

$$0 - 6 = -6$$

Change to addition.   Take the opposite of 6.

$$0 + (-6) = -6$$

Adding the opposite of the subtrahend did not change the answer. Will this always work? In an earlier example, we found that $(+6) - (-2) = +8$. Does adding the opposite of the subtrahend yield the same result?

$$(+6) - (-2) = +8$$

same result

$$(+6) + (+2) = +8$$

Example 1

$$(-3) - (-5) = (+2)$$

$$(-3) + (+5) = (+2)$$

As you can see by example, subtraction is the same as adding the opposite of the subtrahend.

Exercises

Subtract.

1. $(6) - (9)$
2. $(-4) - (7)$
3. $(-8) - (13)$
4. $(7) - (12)$
5. $(15) - (6)$
6. $(-24) - (-33)$
7. $(15) - (25)$
8. $(-7) - (-13)$
9. $(-16) - (9)$
10. $(-12) - (-7)$

11. $(27) - (14)$
12. $(-9) - (-14)$
13. $(-11) - (-7)$
14. $(-22) - (8)$
15. $(25) - (12)$
16. $(-6) - (8)$
17. $(-5) - (-13)$
18. $(28) - (36)$
19. $(3) - (12)$
20. $(43) - (-21)$

Multiplying Integers

Remember that there are two rules for adding integers. This is the case because only two conditions exist—either the signs are different, or the signs are the same. The same is true for multiplying integers.

Every multiplication problem involving two factors fits into one of the following categories:

Condition 1: The factors have unlike signs.

Condition 2: The factors have like signs.

First, look at condition 1. As was mentioned earlier, multiplication is a shortened form of addition. Using this information, you can solve multiplication problems with factors having unlike signs.

$$(-3) \cdot (4) \text{ "negative three times four"}$$

means

$$(-3) + (-3) + (-3) + (-3) \text{ "negative three four times"}$$

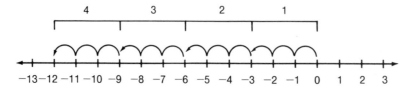

1. Start at 0.
2. Move 3 units to the left four times.
3. The answer is -12.

$$(-3) \cdot (4) = -12$$

If you repeatedly move in a negative direction, will you ever arrive at a positive point? No. So we can say that multiplying factors with unlike signs always gives a negative result.

$$(+5) \cdot (-3) = (-15)$$
$$(-6) \cdot (+4) = (-24)$$

Now consider condition 2. Any time you multiply two positive numbers, the result is positive. But now think about multiplying two negative numbers. You can't write $(-3) \cdot (-4)$ as extended addition because you can't add (-3) a negative number of times. We have to approach this type of problem a different way. In order to understand the multiplication of two negative numbers, study the following pattern:

$$(-3) \cdot (3) = (-9)$$
$$(-3) \cdot (2) = (-6)$$
$$(-3) \cdot (1) = (-3)$$
$$(-3) \cdot (0) = 0$$
$$(-3) \cdot (-1) = ?$$
$$(-3) \cdot (-2) = ?$$
$$(-3) \cdot (-3) = ?$$

As the second factor decreased by one, the product increased by three. Following the pattern, you can see that:

$$(-3) \cdot (-1) = 3$$
$$(-3) \cdot (-2) = 6$$
$$(-3) \cdot (-3) = 9$$

What sign do you get when you multiply two negative numbers?

Rules for Multiplication

1. When multiplying factors with *unlike* signs, the product is negative.
2. When multiplying factors with *like* signs, the product is positive.

Exercises

Multiply.

1. $(+12) \cdot (+5)$
2. $(-15) \cdot (+3)$
3. $(+28) \cdot (-7)$
4. $(-8) \cdot (-9)$
5. $(-23) \cdot (-14)$
6. $(-12) \cdot (+6)$
7. $(+36) \cdot (-21)$
8. $(+21) \cdot (+7)$
9. $(-18) \cdot (-6)$
10. $(-32) \cdot (+14)$

11. $(+25) \cdot (-5)$
12. $(-30) \cdot (-7)$
13. $(+29) \cdot (+23)$
14. $(-40) \cdot (+8)$
15. $(-31) \cdot (-4)$
16. $(+56) \cdot (-9)$
17. $(-38) \cdot (+45)$
18. $(-846) \cdot (-15)$
19. $(-285) \cdot (-43)$
20. $(+192) \cdot (-26)$

Dividing Integers

Based upon what you know about multiplying integers, you can draw conclusions about dividing integers.

$$(+3) \cdot (+4) = +12, \text{ therefore } (+12) \div (+4) = (+3)$$
$$(+3) \cdot (-4) = -12, \text{ therefore } (-12) \div (-4) = (+3)$$
$$(-3) \cdot (-4) = +12, \text{ therefore } (+12) \div (-4) = (-3)$$
$$(-3) \cdot (+4) = -12, \text{ therefore } (-12) \div (+4) = (-3)$$

What sign do you get when the divisor and dividend have like signs? when they have unlike signs?

Rules for Division

1. When dividing numbers with unlike signs, the quotient is negative.
2. When dividing numbers with like signs, the quotient is positive.

Exercises

Solve.

1. $(+35) \div (+7)$
2. $(+46) \div (-2)$
3. $(-54) \div (+9)$
4. $(-72) \div (-8)$
5. $(+21) \div (-3)$
6. $(-78) \div (-6)$
7. $(+108) \div (+12)$
8. $(-135) \div (-9)$
9. $(-210) \div (+15)$
10. $(+576) \div (-32)$

11. $(-128) \div (+16)$
12. $(-264) \div (-24)$
13. $(+70) \div (-7)$
14. $(+180) \div (+10)$
15. $(-608) \div (+38)$
16. $(-105) \div (-21)$
17. $(+396) \div (-18)$
18. $(+252) \div (+7)$
19. $(-380) \div (-20)$
20. $(-966) \div (+42)$

Order of Operations

Mr. Morris gave his math class the following expression and asked them to solve it:

$$4 + 8 \div 2 \times 5 - 3$$

Some of the answers that the students came up with are $1\frac{4}{5}$, 6, 21, 27, and 37. Which is correct? Can you determine how the students arrived at each of these answers? Each answer can be logically explained. However, they can't all be correct. There can be only one correct answer. There must be some guideline that will help you determine the *one* correct answer. This guideline is called the *order of operations*. We accept this guideline because it yields consistent results. Would you consider mathematical guidelines to be absolute? An absolute is something that cannot be doubted. Mathematical guidelines are not absolute, but we must accept them in order to be consistent. What about God's guidelines? Are they absolute? Of course, God's Word is "For ever . . . settled in heaven" (Ps. 119:89)—not to be doubted or questioned.

The order of operations sets a pattern for how to simplify expressions involving more than one operation.

Order of Operations
1. First multiply and/or divide from left to right.
2. Then add and/or subtract from left to right.

Some expressions have parentheses, which are grouping symbols. These may indicate a sequence of operations different from the regular order of operations.

If an expression contains parentheses . . .
1. First perform all operations inside the parentheses.
2. Then follow the order of operations.

Now that you know the order of operations, study the simplification of the expression that Mr. Morris gave his class.

$$4 + 8 \div 2 \cdot 5 - 3$$
$$4 + 4 \cdot 5 - 3$$
$$4 + 20 - 3$$
$$24 - 3$$
$$21$$

Example 1

1. Multiply and divide.
2. Add and subtract.

$$6 + 2 \cdot 5 - 8 \div 4$$
$$6 + 10 - 8 \div 4$$
$$6 + 10 - 2$$
$$16 - 2$$
$$14$$

Example 2

1. Do the operations in the parentheses first.
2. Multiply and divide.
3. Subtract.

$$5 \times (4 + 2) - 9 \div 3$$
$$5 \times 6 - 9 \div 3$$
$$30 - 9 \div 3$$
$$30 - 3$$
$$27$$

Exercises

Solve.

1. $10 + 7 - 3 \cdot 2$
2. $8 + 20 \div 4$
3. $16 \div 2 + 6$
4. $9 - 21 \div 3$
5. $6 \cdot 3 + 12 \div 6$
6. $9 - 15 \div 5 + 6 \cdot 2$
7. $3 \cdot 4 + 7 + 9 \div 3$
8. $18 \div 6 + 9 - 16 \div 4$
9. $12 + 6 - 21 \div 7$
10. $6 \cdot 4 - 5 \cdot 4 + 6 \div 2$

11. $7 \cdot (4 + 2)$
12. $8 \div (2 + 2)$
13. $(6 - 3) \cdot 8$
14. $5 + 6 \cdot (2 + 4)$
15. $(7 + 3) \cdot 4 + 6 \div 2$
16. $12 \div (9 - 5) + 7$
17. $(8 + 6) \cdot 3 \cdot (6 - 4)$
18. $5 \cdot (8 + 2) \div (25 \div 5)$
19. $6 \cdot 3 \div (5 + 4) + 7$
20. $(12 + 3) \div (9 - 6) \cdot 4$

Chapter 1 Review

What place does the digit 3 occupy in each of the following numerals?

1. 632
2. 72.431
3. 3,687.6

Give the value of the underlined digit in each numeral.

4. 3$\underline{6}$4
5. 79.82$\underline{4}$
6. $\underline{5}$2,684

Add.

7. $216 + 728$
8. $5.36 + 25.418$
9. $425 + 318 + 754$
10. $100.46 + 20.7$

Subtract.

11. $847 - 281$
12. $65.2 - 9.67$
13. $34,213 - 7,538$
14. $215.042 - 96.37$

Multiply.

15. 527×36
16. 938×15
17. 45.072×6.58
18. 210.9×32.546

Divide.

19. $1,066 \div 26$

20. $3,055 \div 47$

21. $.9106 \div .29$

22. $136.032 \div 6.24$

Round each number to the nearest hundred.

23. 6,752.34

24. 946.621

25. 491.557

Round each number to the nearest hundredth.

26. 735.8281

27. 65.299

28. 324.754

Find the opposite of each integer.

29. 72

30. -16

31. -2

Find the absolute value of each integer.

32. $|-64|$

33. $|-19|$

34. $|34|$

Perform the indicated operation.

35. $|-6| + |2|$

36. $|-7| \cdot |2|$

37. $|36 \div 6|$

38. $(-12) + (-5)$

39. $(-28) + (+16)$

40. $(+36) + (-8)$

41. $(-21) - (-6)$

42. $(-45) - (+24)$

43. $(+56) - (-12)$

44. $(-6) \cdot (+12)$

45. $(-20) \cdot (-3)$

46. $(-15) \cdot (+2)$

47. $(-18) \div (-3)$

48. $(+25) \div (-5)$

49. $(-21) \div (-7)$

Simplify.

50. $8 + 6 \div 3 - 4 \div 2$

51. $6 \times 3 - 9 \div 3$

52. $6 \div (2 + 1) + 5$

53. $(10 + 2) \div (4 \div 2) + 6$

CHAPTER 2

Fractions

Numbers make wonderful tools; every business uses numbers in one way or another. Obviously, anyone who wants to survive economically must understand how to use numbers in order to keep track of his finances. Unfortunately, it isn't enough for you to understand only whole numbers; many everyday transactions involve *fractions* of numbers. For example, if you and a friend decide to split a pizza, you will each receive one-half the pizza. But how much do you get if you and two other friends decide to split *two* pizzas? To find out, you can either take turns removing a slice at a time (hoping that the slices are all exactly the same size) or you can make a quick calculation and find that you each get two-thirds of a pizza. In these and many other ways, a working knowledge of fractions will serve you well for the rest of your life.

Renaming Fractions

In Chapter 1 you learned about natural numbers, whole numbers, and integers. All these sets are subsets of the set of *rational numbers.* Rational numbers are numbers that can be written by placing one integer over another integer. This means that the set of rational numbers contains the set of integers and the set of all fractions.

A *proper fraction* has a value that is less than one; it represents part of a whole.

$$\frac{5}{7} \qquad \frac{3}{8} \qquad \frac{2}{15} \qquad \text{Proper Fractions}$$

A fraction has three parts: a numerator, a denominator, and a division bar.

division bar $\longrightarrow \dfrac{2}{3}$ — Numerator: tells how many parts are being considered.

Denominator: tells into how many parts the whole has been divided and tells the name of the parts.

Terms: The numerals used to write the fraction.

In this example the whole has been divided into three parts, called thirds. Two of these parts are being considered (two-thirds).

Fractions with a value equal to one or greater than one are called *improper fractions.* An improper fraction has a numerator that is equal to or greater than the denominator.

$$\frac{3}{3} \qquad \frac{5}{4} \qquad \frac{7}{3} \qquad \text{Improper Fractions}$$

A *mixed number* is a number that is the sum of a whole number and a fraction, such as $3\frac{4}{5}$, which is the sum of 3 and $\frac{4}{5}$ ($3\frac{4}{5} = 3 + \frac{4}{5}$). You can rename an improper fraction as either a whole number or a mixed number. To do so, divide the numerator by the denominator.

$$\frac{8}{2} = 8 \div 2 = 4 \qquad\qquad \frac{37}{9} = 37 \div 9 = 4\frac{1}{9}$$

$$4\frac{1}{9} \qquad \text{Write the remainder over the divisor.}$$

$$9\overline{)37}$$
$$\underline{36}$$
$$1$$

This procedure can be reversed to rename a mixed number as an improper fraction.

> To rename a mixed number as an improper fraction . . .
> 1. Multiply the whole number by the denominator of the fraction.
> 2. Add the numerator of the fraction to the product obtained in step 1.
> 3. The sum obtained in step 2 is the new numerator; the denominator stays the same as the original denominator.

Example 1

Rename $4\frac{2}{5}$ as an improper fraction.

$$4 \cdot 5 = 20$$
$$20 + 2 = 22$$
$$4\frac{2}{5} = \frac{22}{5}$$

This procedure can easily be done mentally:

$$4\frac{2}{5} = \frac{22}{5} \qquad 6\frac{4}{9} = \frac{58}{9}$$

Oral Exercises

Identify each as a proper fraction, an improper fraction, or a mixed number.

1. $\frac{5}{4}$

2. $\frac{5}{6}$

3. $\frac{9}{12}$

4. $3\frac{2}{3}$

5. $\frac{7}{3}$

6. $1\frac{1}{2}$

7. $8\frac{9}{10}$

8. $\frac{6}{7}$

Written Exercises

For each fraction, tell (a) into how many parts the whole has been divided, (b) the name of the parts, and (c) how many parts are being considered.

1. $\frac{3}{7}$

2. $\frac{1}{3}$

3. $\frac{4}{5}$

4. $\frac{3}{8}$

5. $\frac{7}{10}$

6. $\frac{2}{9}$

Rename each improper fraction as a whole or mixed number.

7. $\frac{4}{3}$

8. $\frac{12}{4}$

9. $\frac{17}{4}$

10. $\frac{22}{5}$

11. $\frac{72}{8}$

12. $\frac{27}{9}$

13. $\frac{121}{18}$

14. $\frac{253}{42}$

15. $\frac{18}{9}$

Rename each mixed number as an improper fraction.

16. $2\frac{4}{5}$

17. $12\frac{6}{7}$

18. $6\frac{2}{3}$

19. $10\frac{3}{7}$

20. $24\frac{3}{9}$

21. $7\frac{12}{13}$

22. $18\frac{4}{9}$

23. $9\frac{4}{7}$

24. $15\frac{7}{8}$

Prime Factorization

Two or more numbers multiplied together are called factors of the product.

$$5 \cdot 3 = 15$$

factors   product

If you want to find all the whole number factors of a number, you must find all the whole numbers that divide evenly into the number.

Factors of 12: 1, 2, 3, 4, 6, 12
Factors of 36: 1, 2, 3, 4, 6, 9, 12, 18, 36

A *prime number* is a whole number greater than one whose only positive factors are 1 and itself. Two is the first prime number. Its only positive factors are 1 and 2.

Example 1

Tell if each number is prime.

3	factors 1, 3	yes
4	factors 1, 2, 4	no
7	factors 1, 7	yes
9	factors 1, 3, 9	no

Every whole number greater than 1 has a unique *prime factorization*. When all factors of a number are prime numbers, the number has been factored to its prime factors. This list of factors is the prime factorization of the number.

Example 2

Find the prime factorization of 60.

$$60$$
$$2 \cdot 30$$
$$2 \cdot 2 \cdot 15$$
$$2 \cdot 2 \cdot 3 \cdot 5$$

Find two factors of 60. If a factor is not prime, find two factors of it. Continue this process until all the factors are prime numbers.

$$60 = 2 \cdot 2 \cdot 3 \cdot 5$$

Prime factorization can be written using *exponents.* An exponent tells how many times the *base* is used as a factor. If there is no exponent, it is assumed to be "1."

5^3 ◄——— exponent

↑

base

The 3 tells you that 5 (the base) is used as a factor 3 times.

$$5^3 = 5 \cdot 5 \cdot 5 = 125$$
$$3^2 = 3 \cdot 3 = 9$$
$$2 = 2^1 = 2$$

The answer to Example 2 can be written using exponents:

$$2 \cdot 2 \cdot 3 \cdot 5 = 2^2 \cdot 3 \cdot 5$$

Example 3

Find the prime factorization of 600.

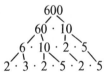

$$600$$
$$60 \cdot 10$$
$$6 \cdot 10 \cdot 2 \cdot 5$$
$$2 \cdot 3 \cdot 2 \cdot 5 \cdot 2 \cdot 5$$

$$600 = 2 \cdot 2 \cdot 2 \cdot 3 \cdot 5 \cdot 5 = 2^3 \cdot 3 \cdot 5^2$$

Oral Exercises

Tell if each number is a prime number.

1. 12
2. 17
3. 29
4. 6
5. 15

6. 43
7. 19
8. 39
9. 57

Written Exercises

List the factors of each number.

1. 16
2. 27
3. 75
4. 92

5. 144
6. 81
7. 132
8. 48

Find the prime factorization of each number.

9. 24
10. 75
11. 441
12. 420
13. 378

14. 180
15. 810
16. 1,500
17. 5,145
18. 13,200

GCF and LCM ─────────────

Now that you know how to find the prime factorization of numbers, you can find the greatest common factor (GCF) and least common multiple (LCM) of two numbers. You will use both of these in your work with fractions.

The greatest common factor of two numbers is the greatest number that will divide evenly into both numbers. One way to find GCF is to list the factors of both numbers and determine the GCF.

Example 1

Find the GCF of 90 and 100.

90: 1, 2, 3, 5, 6, 9, 10, 15, 18, 30, 45, 90   List the factors of each number.
100: 1, 2, 4, 5, 10, 20, 25, 50, 100

1, 2, 5, 10   Find the common factors.

GCF = 10   Find the greatest common factor.

───

You can use prime factorization to find the GCF of two numbers.

Example 2

Using prime factorization, find the GCF of 90 and 100.

$90 = 2 \cdot 3^2 \cdot 5$

$100 = 2^2 \cdot 5^2$

2, 5   Determine what bases are common to both.

$2^1 \cdot 5^1$ Choose the lowest exponent used for each base.

The GCF of 90 and 100 is $2 \cdot 5 = 10$.

Example 3

Using prime factorization, find the GCF of 144 and 270.

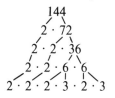

$144 = 2^4 \cdot 3^2$

$270 = 2 \cdot 3^3 \cdot 5$

2, 3   Determine what bases are common to both.

$2^1 \cdot 3^2$ Choose the lowest exponent used for each base.

The GCF of 144 and 270 is $2 \cdot 3^2 = 2 \cdot 9 = 18$

Just as you can list the factors of a number, you can list some of its *multiples*. The multiples of a number are the numbers that it can divide evenly into. You can easily find multiples of a number; just multiply it by the natural numbers.

Multiples of 3: 3, 6, 9, 12, 15, 18, 21, . . .
Multiples of 8: 8, 16, 24, 32, 40, 48, . . .

These lists are not complete because the set of multiples of a number never ends. Can you explain why this is true?

The *least common multiple* of two numbers is the smallest multiple common to both numbers. To find the LCM of two numbers, you can list several multiples of each number and find the LCM.

Example 4

Find the the LCM of 12 and 30.

Multiples of 12: 12, 24, 36, 48, 60, 72, 84 . . .   List some multiples of each number.

Multiples of 30: 30, 60, 90 . . .

LCM = 60   Find the least common multiple.

You can use prime factorization to find the LCM of two numbers.

Example 5

Using prime factorization, find the LCM of 12 and 30.

$12 = 2^2 \cdot 3$ $30 = 2 \cdot 3 \cdot 5$

2, 3, 5,   Determine what bases are used.

$2^2 \cdot 3 \cdot 5$ Choose the highest exponent used for each base.

The LCM of 12 and 30 is $2^2 \cdot 3 \cdot 5 = 4 \cdot 3 \cdot 5 = 60$.

Example 6

Using prime factorization, find the LCM of 1,400 and 2,250.

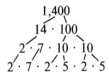   

$1,400 = 2^3 \cdot 5^2 \cdot 7$

$2,250 = 2 \cdot 3^2 \cdot 5^3$

2, 3, 5, 7   Determine what bases are used.

$2^3 \cdot 3^2 \cdot 5^3 \cdot 7$ Choose the highest exponent used for each base.

The LCM of 1,400 and 2,250 is $2^3 \cdot 3^2 \cdot 5^3 \cdot 7 = 8 \cdot 9 \cdot 125 \cdot 7 = 63,000$.

Exercises

List the first 6 multiples of each number.

1. 5

2. 9

3. 12

4. 15

5. 7

6. 22

7. 18

8. 6

Using prime factorization, find the GCF and LCM of each group of numbers.

9. 54 and 36

10. 180 and 225

11. 168 and 196

12. 540 and 360

13. 945 and 648

14. 1,500 and 2,800

15. 2,904 and 1,100

16. 343 and 245

17. 900 and 840

18. 60, 70, and 150

19. 195,425 and 1,045

20. 8,820, 1,512, and 2,835

Equivalent Fractions

Notice in the diagram below that $\frac{1}{2}$, $\frac{2}{4}$, and $\frac{4}{8}$ have the same value.

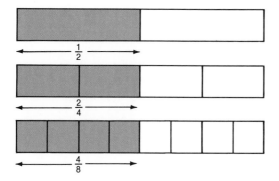

Fractions with the same value are called *equivalent fractions*. An interesting relationship exists between equivalent fractions.

If two fractions are equivalent, the product of the first numerator and the second denominator is equal to the product of the first denominator and the second numerator.

$$\text{If } \frac{a}{b} = \frac{c}{d}, \text{ then } a \cdot d = b \cdot c.$$

Example 1

Since $\frac{2}{3} = \frac{4}{6}$, then $2 \cdot 6 = 3 \cdot 4$, $12 = 12$.

Example 2

Are $\frac{3}{4}$ and $\frac{9}{12}$ equivalent?

$$3 \cdot 12 = 4 \cdot 9$$
$$36 = 36$$

Yes, they are equivalent.

Remember that terms are the numerals used to write a fraction. The terms of $\frac{2}{4}$ are 2 and 4. If you want to write $\frac{2}{4}$ in higher terms, simply multiply the numerator and denominator by the same nonzero number.

$$\frac{2}{4} \cdot \frac{2}{2} = \frac{4}{8} \qquad\qquad\qquad \frac{2}{4} \cdot \frac{3}{3} = \frac{6}{12}$$

You can write a fraction in lower terms by dividing the numerator and denominator by the same nonzero number.

$$\frac{10}{20} \div \frac{5}{5} = \frac{2}{4} \qquad\qquad\qquad \frac{10}{20} \div \frac{2}{2} = \frac{5}{10}$$

Writing fractions in higher and lower terms *renames* the fractions. The renamed fraction and the original fraction are equivalent. To rename a fraction in lower terms, or to reduce it, you need to find the largest number that will divide with no remainder into both the numerator and the denominator. This number is the greatest common factor of the terms.

Example 1

Rename $\frac{8}{12}$ in lowest terms. Find the prime factorization of each term.

$$8 = 2^3 \qquad\qquad\qquad 12 = 2^2 \cdot 3$$

$$\text{GCF} = 2^2 = 4 \qquad\qquad \text{Find the GCF of the terms.}$$

$$\frac{8}{12} \div \frac{4}{4} = \frac{2}{3} \qquad\qquad \text{Divide the numerator and the denominator by the GCF.}$$

$\frac{8}{12}$ in lowest terms is $\frac{2}{3}$

Example 2

Rename $\frac{27}{36}$ in lowest terms.

$$27 = 3^3 \qquad\qquad\qquad 36 = 2^2 \cdot 3^2$$

$$\text{GCF} = 3^2 = 9 \qquad\qquad \text{Find the GCF of the terms.}$$

$$\frac{27}{36} \div \frac{9}{9} = \frac{3}{4} \qquad\qquad \text{Divide the numerator and the denominator by the GCF.}$$

$\frac{27}{36}$ in lowest terms is $\frac{3}{4}$

Improper fractions can also be written in lowest terms. Simply divide; then put the fractional part of the mixed number in lowest terms.

Example 3

Rename $\frac{52}{6}$ in lowest terms.

$$\begin{array}{r} 8\frac{4}{6} \\ 6\overline{)52} \\ \underline{48} \\ 4 \end{array}$$

Divide. Write the remainder over the divisor.

$$\frac{4}{6} \div \frac{2}{2} = \frac{2}{3}$$

Rename the fractional part of the mixed number in lowest terms.

$$\frac{52}{6} = 8\frac{2}{3}$$

Exercises

Rename in higher terms.

1. $\frac{2}{5}$

2. $\frac{5}{7}$

3. $\frac{4}{5}$

4. $\frac{8}{9}$

Rename in lower terms (not necessarily lowest terms).

5. $\frac{16}{24}$

6. $\frac{20}{25}$

7. $\frac{18}{24}$

8. $\frac{6}{9}$

Rename in lowest terms.

9. $\frac{4}{12}$

10. $\frac{16}{24}$

11. $\frac{15}{30}$

12. $\frac{14}{20}$

13. $\frac{18}{36}$

14. $\frac{12}{18}$

15. $\frac{18}{27}$

16. $\frac{75}{100}$

17. $\frac{37}{5}$

18. $\frac{39}{6}$

19. $\frac{98}{8}$

20. $\frac{116}{8}$

Indicate with the symbol $=$ or $\neq$ whether or not the fractions in each pair are equivalent.

21. $\frac{3}{8}$ and $\frac{6}{16}$

22. $\frac{2}{3}$ and $\frac{8}{12}$

23. $\frac{7}{12}$ and $\frac{84}{156}$

24. $\frac{5}{6}$ and $\frac{35}{44}$

25. $\frac{8}{9}$ and $\frac{72}{81}$

26. $\frac{24}{32}$ and $\frac{144}{256}$

27. $\frac{11}{16}$ and $\frac{34}{42}$

28. $\frac{9}{10}$ and $\frac{63}{70}$

Multiplying Fractions

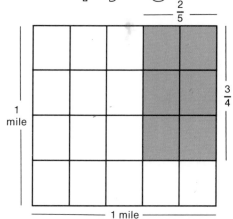

The box at the left represents one square mile. Find the area that the shaded part represents.

To find the area, you multiply $\frac{2}{5}$ and $\frac{3}{4}$. Fractions are easy to multiply. Simply multiply the numerators to find the numerator of the answer, and multiply the denominators to find the denominator of the answer.

$$\frac{2}{5} \cdot \frac{3}{4} = \frac{6}{20} = \frac{3}{10}$$

Does this answer make sense? Look at the diagram above. Is the shaded area $\frac{6}{20}$ of the whole area? Yes. The area that is shaded represents $\frac{3}{10}$ of a square mile.

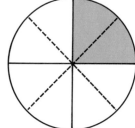

Mrs. Smith baked an apple pie yesterday. One-fourth of it is left. If Joe eats one-half of what is left, what fractional part of the whole pie will he be eating? You need to find $\frac{1}{2}$ of $\frac{1}{4}$.

Can you see from the diagram that $\frac{1}{2}$ of $\frac{1}{4}$ is $\frac{1}{8}$? You can find this answer by multiplying $\frac{1}{2}$ by $\frac{1}{4}$. When a fraction is followed by "of," you should multiply.

Example 1

Find $\frac{3}{4}$ of $\frac{2}{3}$.

$$\frac{3}{4} \cdot \frac{2}{3} = \frac{6}{12} = \frac{1}{2}$$

Note: Be sure to reduce answers to lowest terms and mixed numbers rather than to improper fractions.

Example 2

Find $\frac{2}{3}$ of 8.

$$\frac{2}{3} \cdot \frac{8}{1} = \frac{16}{3} = 5\frac{1}{3}$$

Example 3

Sometimes you can cancel to simplify multiplication of fractions.

$$\frac{\cancel{2}}{\cancel{4}} \cdot \frac{\cancel{2}}{\cancel{2}} = \frac{1}{2}$$

Look for common factors from the numerators and the denominators and divide them out. Then multiply.

Exercises

Multiply.

1. $\frac{2}{3} \cdot 7\frac{14}{3}$

2. $\frac{3}{5} \cdot 15$

3. $\frac{4}{5} \cdot \frac{6}{9}$

4. $\frac{2}{7} \cdot \frac{3}{8}$

5. $\frac{5}{6} \cdot \frac{2}{3}$

6. $\frac{7}{8} \cdot \frac{5}{4}$

7. $\frac{7}{12} \cdot \frac{3}{14}$

8. $\frac{2}{3} \cdot \frac{3}{2}$

9. $\frac{1}{9} \cdot \frac{6}{11}$

10. $\frac{3}{8} \cdot \frac{9}{12}$

11. $\frac{12}{15} \cdot \frac{25}{36}$

Find.

12. $\frac{1}{2}$ of 12

13. $\frac{3}{4}$ of 32

14. $\frac{6}{8}$ of 17

15. $\frac{3}{5}$ of $\frac{4}{9}$

16. $\frac{7}{12}$ of $\frac{8}{13}$

17. $\frac{8}{9}$ of $\frac{5}{6}$

18. Karen is making chocolate chip cookies. The recipe calls for $2\frac{1}{2}$ cups of flour, but Karen is making only half of the recipe. How many cups of flour does she need?

19. John spent $\frac{1}{3}$ of his evening doing homework. If his evening consisted of 4 hours, how much time did he spend doing homework?

20. Fairview Christian Academy has 90 students. $\frac{3}{5}$ of the students are girls. How many girls are in the Academy?

Dividing Fractions

To solve the problem $6 \div 3$, you can think, "How many sets of 3 are there in 6?" Obviously, there are two sets. You can use this same thought process to solve $6 \div \frac{1}{3}$. Think, "How many sets of $\frac{1}{3}$ are there in 6?"

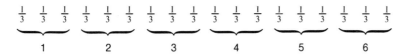

There are 18 sets of $\frac{1}{3}$ in 6. Notice that $6 \div \frac{1}{3}$ yields the same result as $6 \cdot 3$. The principle shown by this example holds true all the time. $\frac{1}{3}$ and 3 are *reciprocals* of each other. Two numbers whose product is 1 are called reciprocals ($\frac{1}{3} \cdot \frac{3}{1} = \frac{3}{3} = 1$). You can find the reciprocal of a fraction by inverting it.

The reciprocal of $\frac{2}{3}$ is $\frac{3}{2}$.

The reciprocal of $\frac{7}{9}$ is $\frac{9}{7}$.

The reciprocal of $\frac{1}{3}$ is $\frac{3}{1}$ or 3.

Dividing by a fraction is the same as multiplying by its reciprocal.

$$4 \div \frac{2}{3} = 4 \cdot \frac{3}{2} = \frac{\cancel{4}^{2}}{1} \cdot \frac{3}{\cancel{2}_{1}} = \frac{6}{1} = 6$$

$$\frac{4}{5} \div \frac{8}{15} = \frac{\cancel{4}^{1}}{\cancel{5}_{1}} \cdot \frac{\cancel{15}^{3}}{\cancel{8}_{2}} = 1\frac{1}{2}$$

Oral Exercises

Give the reciprocal of each number.

1. $\frac{3}{4}$

2. 5

3. $\frac{6}{5}$

4. $\frac{1}{4}$

5. $\frac{7}{12}$

6. $\frac{15}{9}$

Written Exercises

Divide. Put answers in lowest terms.

1. $8 \div \frac{2}{5}$

2. $4 \div \frac{3}{5}$

3. $\frac{1}{3} \div \frac{4}{7}$

4. $\frac{2}{3} \div \frac{2}{6}$

5. $\frac{5}{4} \div \frac{1}{2}$

6. $\frac{7}{8} \div \frac{1}{4}$

7. $6 \div \frac{3}{7}$

8. $3 \div \frac{2}{8}$

9. $\frac{7}{9} \div \frac{1}{4}$

10. $\frac{6}{3} \div \frac{5}{9}$

11. $\frac{3}{7} \div \frac{3}{10}$

12. $\frac{8}{9} \div \frac{4}{5}$

13. $\frac{3}{8} \div \frac{2}{9}$

14. $\frac{1}{4} \div \frac{6}{8}$

15. $\frac{7}{15} \div \frac{2}{5}$

16. $\frac{5}{12} \div \frac{5}{6}$

17. $\frac{9}{13} \div \frac{9}{13}$

18. $\frac{4}{8} \div \frac{8}{4}$

19. How many copies of a book that is $\frac{7}{8}$ inches thick will fit on a 28-inch shelf?

20. Karen has 6 feet of ribbon from which to make awards for a class contest. If each award is made from $\frac{3}{4}$ of a foot of ribbon, how many awards can she make?

Multiplying and Dividing Mixed Numbers

Elizabeth is making some bread. The recipe calls for $4\frac{1}{3}$ cups flour, but Elizabeth is making $2\frac{1}{2}$ times what the recipe calls for. To find out how much flour she needs, she must multiply $4\frac{1}{3}$ and $2\frac{1}{2}$. To multiply or divide mixed numbers, you need to rename the mixed numbers as improper fractions and then perform the operation.

$4\frac{1}{3} \cdot 2\frac{1}{2}$

$\frac{13}{3} \cdot \frac{5}{2}$ Rename as improper fractions.

$\frac{13}{3} \cdot \frac{5}{2} = \frac{65}{6}$ Multiply.

$\frac{65}{6} = 10\frac{5}{6}$ Rename in lowest terms.

Example 1

$6 \cdot 5\frac{2}{3}$

$$\frac{6}{1} \cdot \frac{17}{3} = \frac{34}{1} = 34$$

Example 2

$10\frac{5}{9} \div 3\frac{4}{7}$

$$\frac{95}{9} \div \frac{25}{7}$$

$$\frac{95}{9} \cdot \frac{7}{25} = \frac{133}{45} = 2\frac{43}{45}$$

Exercises

Multiply or divide as indicated.

1. $6 \cdot 5\frac{1}{3}$

2. $2\frac{3}{9} \cdot 3\frac{6}{7}$

3. $16 \cdot 3\frac{3}{10}$

4. $2\frac{1}{2} \cdot 4\frac{2}{3}$

5. $14\frac{1}{4} \cdot 6\frac{2}{5}$

6. $2\frac{6}{9} \cdot 7\frac{1}{3}$

7. $9\frac{2}{6} \cdot 4\frac{3}{10}$

8. $8\frac{1}{2} \div 2$

9. $1\frac{5}{6} \div \frac{11}{12}$

10. $3\frac{3}{4} \div 1\frac{1}{2}$

11. $5\frac{3}{4} \div 2\frac{1}{4}$

12. $4\frac{1}{5} \div 2\frac{1}{3}$

13. $14\frac{3}{4} \div 6\frac{2}{8}$

14. $21\frac{1}{2} \div 7\frac{2}{5}$

15. Mr. Johnson is paneling a 15-foot wall. How many $2\frac{1}{2}$-foot pieces of paneling does he need to buy?

16. Karen is making punch for a party. When she made it before, she put in $3\frac{1}{2}$ liters of lemon-lime soda. This time she is making $2\frac{1}{2}$ times as much punch. How much lemon-lime soda does she need?

Adding and Subtracting Fractions

If you add six cats and four dogs, do you get ten cat-dogs? No. Can you add cats and dogs together? Yes, if you rename them in like terms. You can say that you have ten pets or ten animals.

Believe it or not, adding and subtracting fractions is similar to the problem just described. For example, you can easily add $\frac{3}{8}$ and $\frac{2}{8}$.

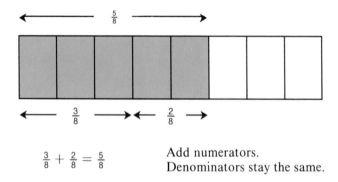

$$\frac{3}{8} + \frac{2}{8} = \frac{5}{8}$$ Add numerators.
Denominators stay the same.

But what about $\frac{1}{8} + \frac{3}{4}$? You must have like terms before you can add or subtract fractions. *Like fractions* are fractions that have the same (or common) denominators. To add or subtract fractions with different denominators, you need to rename one or both of the fractions so that they have the same denominator. The denominator that you choose should be the least common multiple (LCM) of the denominators.

Example 1

Find the common denominator for $\frac{1}{8}$ and $\frac{3}{4}$.

$8 = 2^3 \qquad 4 = 2^2$ $2^3 = 8$	Find the prime factorization of both denominators. Find the LCM of 8 and 4.

The common denominator for $\frac{1}{8}$ and $\frac{3}{4}$ is 8.

Once you know what your common denominator is, you have to rename one or both of the fractions. To rename a fraction into higher terms when you know what you want your new denominator to be, you . . .

1. Figure out what the denominator must be multiplied by to get the new denominator.
2. Multiply the numerator by the number obtained in step 1 to find the new numerator.

Example 2

Change $\frac{3}{4}$ to eighths.

$\frac{3}{4} = \frac{?}{8}$ $\frac{3}{4} \cdot \frac{2}{2} = \frac{6}{8}$	Four was multiplied by 2 to get 8. So multiply 3 by 2.

Now you can add two fractions that have different denominators.

Example 3

Add $\frac{2}{5}$ and $\frac{2}{3}$.

$5 = 5^1 \qquad 3 = 3^1$	Find the prime factorization of 5 and 3.
$5 \cdot 3 = 15$	Find the LCM of 5 and 3.
$\frac{2}{5} = \frac{?}{15} \qquad \frac{2}{3} = \frac{?}{15}$ $\frac{2}{5} \cdot \frac{3}{3} = \frac{6}{15} \qquad \frac{2}{3} \cdot \frac{5}{5} = \frac{10}{15}$	Rename both fractions to fifteenths.
$\frac{6}{15} + \frac{10}{15} = \frac{16}{15}$	Add.
$\frac{16}{15} = 1\frac{1}{15}$	Rename in lowest terms.

$$\frac{2}{5} + \frac{2}{3} = 1\frac{1}{15}$$

Example 4

$$\frac{3}{4} + \frac{5}{18} + \frac{6}{15}$$

$$4 = 2^2$$

$$18 = 2 \cdot 3^2$$

$$15 = 3 \cdot 5$$

Find the prime factorization of 4, 18, and 15.

$$2^2 \cdot 3^2 \cdot 5 = 180$$

Find the LCM of 4, 18, 15.

$$\frac{3}{4} = \frac{?}{180} \qquad \frac{5}{18} = \frac{?}{180} \qquad \frac{6}{15} = \frac{?}{180}$$

Rename each fraction.

$$\frac{3}{4} \cdot \frac{45}{45} = \frac{135}{180} \quad \frac{5}{18} \cdot \frac{10}{10} = \frac{50}{180} \quad \frac{6}{15} \cdot \frac{12}{12} = \frac{72}{180}$$

Add.

$$\frac{135 + 50 + 72}{180} = \frac{257}{180}$$

Rename in lowest terms.

$$\frac{257}{180} = 1\frac{77}{180}$$

To subtract fractions, you must also have a common denominator.

Example 5

$$\frac{5}{6} - \frac{1}{8}$$

$$6 = 2 \cdot 3 \qquad 8 = 2^3$$

Find the prime factorization of 6 and 8.

$$2^3 \cdot 3 = 24$$

Find the LCM of 6 and 8.

$$\frac{5}{6} = \frac{?}{24} \qquad \frac{1}{8} = \frac{?}{24}$$

Rename both fractions to twenty-fourths.

$$\frac{5}{6} \cdot \frac{4}{4} = \frac{20}{24} \qquad \frac{1}{8} \cdot \frac{3}{3} = \frac{3}{24}$$

$$\frac{20}{24} - \frac{3}{24} = \frac{17}{24}$$

Subtract. Make sure that your answer is in lowest terms.

Exercises

Rename the fractions as indicated.

1. $\frac{2}{3}$ to sixths

2. $\frac{5}{8}$ to twenty-fourths

3. $\frac{3}{5}$ to fifteenths

4. $\frac{4}{9}$ to twenty-sevenths

5. $\frac{6}{10} = \frac{?}{40}$

6. $\frac{14}{12} = \frac{?}{60}$

7. $\frac{7}{9} = \frac{?}{108}$

8. $\frac{6}{15} = \frac{?}{120}$

Add or subtract as indicated.

9. $\frac{2}{5} + \frac{1}{5}$

10. $\frac{3}{7} + \frac{2}{7}$

11. $\frac{6}{9} + \frac{2}{9}$

12. $\frac{3}{4} - \frac{2}{4}$

13. $\frac{6}{8} - \frac{4}{8}$

14. $\frac{7}{10} - \frac{2}{10}$

15. $\frac{9}{16} + \frac{3}{4}$

16. $\frac{1}{2} + \frac{4}{5}$

17. $\frac{2}{3} + \frac{6}{9}$

18. $\frac{5}{12} - \frac{1}{3}$

19. $\frac{1}{2} - \frac{1}{4}$

20. $\frac{5}{8} - \frac{4}{12}$

21. $\frac{3}{10} + \frac{1}{6}$

22. $\frac{5}{13} + \frac{2}{3}$

23. $\frac{5}{8} + \frac{1}{3}$

24. $\frac{17}{26} - \frac{11}{65}$

25. $\frac{3}{5} - \frac{1}{8}$

26. $\frac{4}{9} - \frac{5}{16}$

27. Find the thickness of a window that consists of two panes of glass each $\frac{4}{15}$ in. thick and an airspace of $\frac{1}{3}$ in. between them.

28. In the 1864 presidential election, Abraham Lincoln received $\frac{11}{20}$ of the popular vote. What fraction of the popular vote did the other candidates receive?

29. For a home-economics project, Kim bought remnants of material measuring $\frac{3}{8}$ yd., $\frac{1}{2}$ yd., $\frac{5}{8}$ yd., and $\frac{3}{4}$ yd. How many yards did she buy?

Adding and Subtracting Mixed Numbers

You can use what you learned about adding and subtracting fractions to help you add and subtract mixed numbers.

$$\begin{array}{r} 3\frac{3}{5} \\ +2\frac{1}{5} \\ \hline 5\frac{4}{5} \end{array}$$
1. Add the fractions.
2. Add the whole numbers.

$$\begin{array}{r} 7\frac{4}{9} \\ -3\frac{2}{9} \\ \hline 4\frac{2}{9} \end{array}$$
1. Subtract the fractions.
2. Subtract the whole numbers.

Sometimes you'll need to rename fractions in order to add or subtract mixed numbers. Study the following examples of renaming.

Example 1

$$4\tfrac{1}{4} = 4\tfrac{1}{4}$$
$$+2\tfrac{1}{2} = 2\tfrac{2}{4}$$
$$\overline{6\tfrac{3}{4}}$$

Rename $\tfrac{1}{2}$ as $\tfrac{2}{4}$ so that the denominators are the same.

Example 2

$$7\tfrac{5}{7}$$
$$+2\tfrac{4}{7}$$
$$\overline{9\tfrac{9}{7}} = 9 + 1\tfrac{2}{7} = 10\tfrac{2}{7}$$

Rename $\tfrac{9}{7}$ as $1\tfrac{2}{7}$; then add $9 + 1\tfrac{2}{7}$ to put answers in lowest terms.

Example 3

$$5\tfrac{3}{4} = 5\tfrac{6}{8}$$
$$-2\tfrac{3}{8} = 2\tfrac{3}{8}$$
$$\overline{3\tfrac{3}{8}}$$

Rename $\tfrac{3}{4}$ as $\tfrac{6}{8}$ so that the denominators are the same.

Example 4

$$8\tfrac{2}{5} = 7\tfrac{7}{5}$$
$$-3\tfrac{4}{5} = 3\tfrac{4}{5}$$
$$\overline{4\tfrac{3}{5}}$$

Rename $8\tfrac{2}{5}$ as $7\tfrac{7}{5}$ so that you can subtract $\tfrac{4}{5}$ from $\tfrac{7}{5}$.
Note: $8\tfrac{2}{5} = 7 + 1 + \tfrac{2}{5}$
$$= 7 + \tfrac{5}{5} + \tfrac{2}{5}$$
$$= 7 + \tfrac{7}{5} = 7\tfrac{7}{5}$$

Example 5

$$6 = 5\tfrac{3}{3}$$
$$-5\tfrac{2}{3} = 5\tfrac{2}{3}$$
$$\overline{\tfrac{1}{3}}$$

Rename 6 as $5\tfrac{3}{3}$ so that you can subtract $\tfrac{2}{3}$ from $\tfrac{3}{3}$.
Note: $6 = 5 + 1$
$$= 5 + \tfrac{3}{3}$$
$$= 5\tfrac{3}{3}$$

Exercises

Add or subtract as indicated. Put answers in lowest terms.

1. $3\frac{2}{5}$
   $+7\frac{1}{5}$

2. $8\frac{3}{8}$
   $+4\frac{2}{8}$

3. $6\frac{5}{6}$
   $-2\frac{2}{6}$

4. $12\frac{8}{9}$
   $-7\frac{3}{9}$

5. $25\frac{3}{4}$
   $+36\frac{3}{4}$

6. $8\frac{2}{4}$
   $+3\frac{3}{8}$

7. $13\frac{5}{6}$
   $+6\frac{2}{3}$

8. $16\frac{4}{5}$
   $-7\frac{3}{10}$

9. $26\frac{5}{6}$
   $-18\frac{2}{8}$

10. $45\frac{4}{6}$
    $+61\frac{9}{12}$

11. $84\frac{2}{3}$
    $+22\frac{3}{4}$

12. 16
    $-14\frac{3}{5}$

13. $94\frac{5}{7}$
    $-16\frac{1}{3}$

14. $108\frac{5}{6}$
    $+91\frac{1}{18}$

15. $65\frac{9}{12}$
    $+34\frac{1}{3}$

16. $12\frac{4}{7}$
    $-8\frac{6}{7}$

17. $61\frac{2}{5}$
    $-25\frac{3}{5}$

18. $24\frac{1}{2}$
    $+16\frac{4}{5}$

19. $238\frac{6}{8}$
    $+116\frac{5}{9}$

20. $28\frac{2}{9}$
    $-13\frac{2}{3}$

21. Ashley has a part-time job at Barbara's Bakery. Last week she worked the following number of hours: Mon—$2\frac{1}{2}$ hr., Tues—$3\frac{1}{4}$ hr., Wed—2 hr., Thur—$3\frac{3}{4}$ hr., Fri—$1\frac{1}{2}$ hr. How many hours did Ashley work?

22. The sophomores at Faith Christian Academy ordered some pastry for a class party from Barbara's Bakery. Ashley is making the pastry. She needs $20\frac{2}{3}$ cups of flour for pies and $16\frac{3}{4}$ cups of flour for tarts. How much flour will she use on this order?

23. Ashley had $86\frac{1}{4}$ cups flour before she started baking the pies and tarts mentioned in problem 23. How much flour was left after she finished her baking?

Converting Decimals to Fractions

Can you add .875 and $\frac{3}{4}$? You can if you express both as either decimals or fractions. Any decimal can easily be written as a fraction with a denominator that is a multiple of 10. You simply write the part of the decimal that is to the right of zero as the numerator. The denominator is the place value of the last digit.

Example 1

Express .3 as a fraction.

Part of the decimal that is to the right of the decimal point → $\frac{3}{10}$

Place value of the 3

$$.3 = \frac{3}{10}$$

Example 2

Express .65 as a fraction.

Part of the decimal that is to the right of the decimal point → $\frac{65}{100} = \frac{13}{20}$

Place value of the 5

$$.65 = \frac{13}{20}$$

You can use a shortcut that will make your work easier. Keep in mind that the number of digits after the decimal point will equal the number of zeros in the denominator.

$$.5 = \frac{5}{10} \qquad\qquad .49 = \frac{49}{100} \qquad\qquad .6381 = \frac{6,381}{10,000}$$

You can convert mixed decimals to mixed numbers the same way. Leave the whole number the same and convert the decimal to a fraction.

$$3.4 = 3\frac{4}{10} = 3\frac{2}{5} \qquad\qquad 16.15 = 16\frac{15}{100} = 16\frac{3}{20}$$

This section began with the question "Can you add .875 and $\frac{3}{4}$?" You should be able to add them now that you know how to convert .875 to a fraction.

$$.875 = \frac{875}{1,000} = \frac{7}{8}$$

$$
\begin{array}{rcl}
\frac{7}{8} & = & \frac{7}{8} \\
+\frac{3}{4} & = & \frac{6}{8} \\
\hline
\frac{13}{8} & = & 1\frac{5}{8}
\end{array}
$$

Exercises

Convert to fractions. Reduce answers to lowest terms.

1. .7

2. .25

3. .5

4. .36

5. .124

6. .76

7. .375

8. .50

9. .625

10. .600

11. .75

12. .1824

Convert to mixed numbers with fractions. Reduce answers to lowest terms.

13. 6.2

14. 18.6

15. 23.42

16. 15.70

17. 26.05

18. 158.125

19. 12.575

20. 648.62

21. 43.004

22. 65.85

23. 28.144

24. 5.00006

Add by converting the decimals to fractions. Reduce answers to lowest terms.

25. $\frac{2}{5} + .45$

26. $6.5 + \frac{3}{4}$

27. $\frac{7}{8} + .875$

28. $.08 + \frac{3}{5}$

29. $\frac{5}{6} + .25 + \frac{2}{3}$

30. $.7 + \frac{1}{3} + \frac{1}{5}$

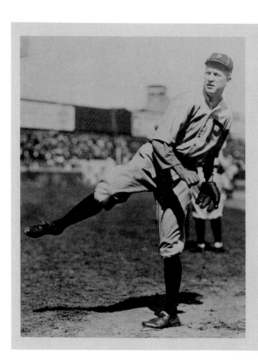

Grover Cleveland Alexander
(1887-1950)
Pitcher
Philadelphia, Phillies (1911-1917, 1930); Chicago, Cubs (1918-1926); St. Louis, Cardinals (1926-1929)
Elected to the Baseball Hall of Fame in 1938

Games Pitched	Wins	Losses	Winning Percentage	Complete Games
696	373	208	.642	437
	Third all-time			Natl. League Record

Shut Outs	Total Innings Pitched	Strike Outs	Base on Balls	Earned Run Average
90	5,189	2,199	951	2.56
Natl. League Record	Second all-time		Sixth all-time	

Converting Fractions to Decimals

You can convert fractions to decimals several ways. Once you are familiar with the different ways, you will be able to choose the one that is most convenient for the particular fraction you are dealing with.

You can convert every fraction to a decimal by division. The numerator is the dividend and the denominator is the divisor. If the remainder is zero after several steps, the resulting decimal is called a *terminating decimal*. If the remainder is never zero, the resulting decimal is called a *repeating decimal*.

Terminating Decimal

$$\frac{3}{4} = 4\overline{)3.00}$$
$$\begin{array}{r} .75 \\ \underline{2\ 8} \\ 20 \\ \underline{20} \\ 0 \text{ remainder} \end{array}$$

Repeating Decimal

$$\frac{5}{6} = 6\overline{)5.000}$$
$$\begin{array}{r} .833 \\ \underline{4\ 8} \\ 20 \\ \underline{18} \\ 20 \\ \underline{18} \\ 2 \text{ remainder} \end{array}$$

Draw a bar over the repeating digit or digits in a repeating decimal.

$$\tfrac{5}{6} = .8\overline{3}$$ $$\tfrac{4}{11} = .\overline{36}$$

Some fractions can be converted to decimals more easily. If the denominator is a multiple of 10, simply write the fraction as a decimal.

$$\tfrac{5}{10} = .5$$ $$\tfrac{28}{100} = .28$$ $$\tfrac{634}{1,000} = .634$$

If the denominator is not a multiple of 10, you may be able to change the fraction to an equivalent fraction whose denominator is a multiple of 10. Then simply write the fraction as a decimal.

$$\tfrac{3}{5} \cdot \tfrac{2}{2} = \tfrac{6}{10} = .6$$ $$\tfrac{7}{25} \cdot \tfrac{4}{4} = \tfrac{28}{100} = .28$$ $$\tfrac{5}{8} \cdot \tfrac{125}{125} = \tfrac{625}{1,000} = .625$$

Exercises

Convert to decimals.

1. $\tfrac{3}{10}$

2. $\tfrac{15}{100}$

3. $\tfrac{35}{100}$

4. $\tfrac{6}{100}$

5. $\tfrac{3}{1,000}$

6. $\tfrac{45}{10,000}$

Convert to decimals by renaming the fraction to an equivalent fraction with a denominator that is a multiple of ten.

7. $\tfrac{3}{5}$

8. $\tfrac{9}{25}$

9. $\tfrac{3}{8}$

10. $\tfrac{36}{50}$

11. $\tfrac{137}{250}$

12. $\tfrac{986}{2,000}$

Convert to decimals by division.

13. $\tfrac{7}{25}$

14. $\tfrac{21}{40}$

15. $\tfrac{1}{40}$

16. $\tfrac{5}{11}$

17. $\tfrac{6}{9}$

18. $\tfrac{5}{16}$

Add by converting the fractions to decimals.

19. $\tfrac{2}{5} + .731$

20. $\tfrac{7}{32} + 3.54$

21. $.7 + \tfrac{13}{25} + .613$

22. $\tfrac{3}{4} + .2 + \tfrac{7}{8}$

Comparing Decimals

Which numeral represents the greater number, 2.6 or 2.54? You can make the comparison easier by annexing zeros to the right of the decimal point until both numerals have the same number of digits. Decimals with the same number of places to the right of zero are like fractions with a common denominator.

$$2.6 = 2.60$$
60 is greater than 54, so
2.60 is greater than 2.54

Comparisons are often made with numbers. Certain symbols are used to show the result of the comparison.

$=$ "is equal to"
$<$ "is less than"
$>$ "is greater than"

Example

Compare the following pairs of numbers.

16.2 and 16.23   9.08 and 9.1
$16.20 < 16.23$ $9.08 < 9.10$

3.67 and 3.6   5.7 and 5.70
$3.67 > 3.60$ $5.70 = 5.70$

Exercises

Compare each pair of numbers by giving one of the symbols $(=, >, <)$ to replace the word *and*.

1. 6.24 and 6.2
2. 17.3 and 17.300
3. 3.07 and 3.1
4. 5.675 and 5.68
5. 8.70 and 8.7
6. 12.5 and 12.49

7. 6.03 and 6.026
8. 9.004 and 9.03
9. 8.02 and 8.020
10. 72.685 and 72.7
11. 31.46 and 31.459
12. 46.075 and 46.07

Arrange the numbers in order from greatest to least.

13. 0.03, 0.30, 0.003
14. 5.24, 5.2, 5.02
15. 7.075, 7.7, 7.75
16. 8.6, 0.86, 0.086

17. 12.7, 12.63, 12.73
18. 6.0739, 6.164, 6.1098
19. 400.48, 401.25, 399.87
20. 0.460, 0.0468, 0.097

Chapter 2 Review

Rename each improper fraction as a whole or mixed number.

1. $\frac{5}{2}$

2. $\frac{25}{3}$

3. $\frac{16}{4}$

4. $\frac{28}{5}$

5. $\frac{72}{12}$

6. $\frac{183}{16}$

Rename each mixed number as an improper fraction.

7. $6\frac{2}{5}$

8. $12\frac{1}{9}$

9. $35\frac{4}{7}$

10. $15\frac{2}{8}$

11. $18\frac{3}{4}$

12. $26\frac{7}{9}$

Find the prime factorization of each number.

13. 270

14. 1,540

15. 1,575

16. 17,640

Using prime factorization, find first the GCF and then the LCM of each group of numbers.

17. 300 and 270

18. 126,000 and 280

19. 1,170 and 1,400

20. 1,080 and 1,008

Rename in lowest terms.

21. $\frac{5}{15}$

22. $\frac{6}{8}$

23. $\frac{18}{36}$

24. $\frac{16}{20}$

25. $\frac{25}{38}$

26. $\frac{12}{42}$

Indicate with the symbols $=$ or $\neq$ whether the fractions are equivalent.

27. $\frac{6}{7}$ and $\frac{18}{21}$

28. $\frac{4}{5}$ and $\frac{14}{17}$

29. $\frac{12}{22}$ and $\frac{30}{55}$

30. $\frac{27}{36}$ and $\frac{6}{8}$

31. $\frac{4}{9}$ and $\frac{30}{67}$

32. $\frac{4}{14}$ and $\frac{26}{91}$

Rename as indicated.

33. $\frac{6}{7} = \frac{?}{28}$

34. $\frac{2}{3} = \frac{?}{21}$

35. $\frac{7}{13} = \frac{?}{65}$

36. $\frac{6}{15} = \frac{?}{120}$

37. $\frac{4}{9} = \frac{?}{36}$

38. $\frac{8}{17} = \frac{?}{153}$

Perform the indicated operation. Reduce answers to lowest terms.

39. $\frac{3}{8} + \frac{2}{8}$

40. $\frac{7}{9} + \frac{1}{3}$

41. $\frac{2}{5} + \frac{3}{8}$

42. $\frac{7}{9} - \frac{2}{9}$

43. $\frac{16}{20} - \frac{3}{4}$

44. $\frac{8}{10} - \frac{4}{5}$

45. $\frac{2}{3} \cdot \frac{4}{6}$

46. $\frac{6}{7} \cdot \frac{4}{9}$

47. $\frac{9}{13} \cdot \frac{1}{6}$

48. $\frac{6}{7} \div \frac{3}{8}$

49. $\frac{5}{9} \div \frac{10}{18}$

50. $\frac{4}{7} \div \frac{6}{9}$

51. $6\frac{2}{3} + 5\frac{1}{3}$

52. $7\frac{2}{9} + 4\frac{2}{3}$

53. $12\frac{2}{5} + 6\frac{1}{6}$

54. $10\frac{9}{12} - 8\frac{3}{12}$

55. $16\frac{2}{8} - 5\frac{5}{8}$

56. $26\frac{1}{3} - 14\frac{5}{6}$

57. $5\frac{2}{3} \cdot 3\frac{4}{7}$

58. $13\frac{5}{8} \cdot 6\frac{2}{4}$

59. $12\frac{1}{9} \cdot 3\frac{1}{4}$

60. $16\frac{2}{5} \div 2\frac{3}{4}$

61. $23\frac{3}{7} \div 6\frac{1}{8}$

62. $28\frac{9}{10} \div 16\frac{2}{3}$

Convert to fractions. Reduce answers to lowest terms.

63. .5

64. .06

65. .74

66. 6.40

67. 12.025

68. 23.238

Convert to decimals.

69. $\frac{7}{10}$

70. $\frac{69}{100}$

71. $\frac{3}{20}$

72. $\frac{5}{8}$

73. $\frac{1}{30}$

74. $\frac{6}{16}$

Compare each pair of numbers, using the symbols $=$, $>$, and $<$.

75. 9.6 and 9.59

76. 12.028 and 12.03

77. 32 and 32.00

78. 49.693 and 49.7

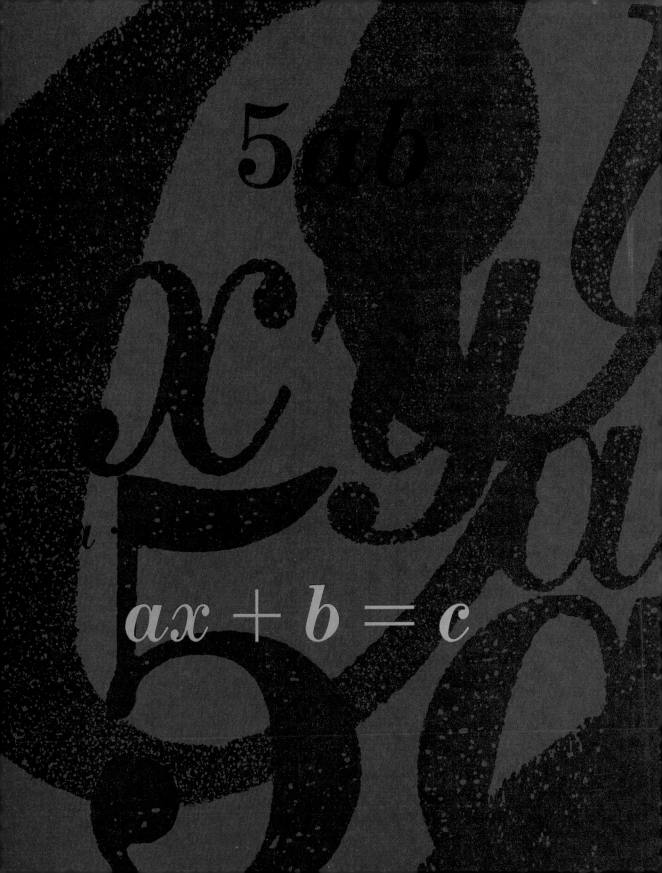

CHAPTER 3

Algebra

Have you ever tried to solve a seemingly impossible riddle?
You may, for example, have tried your hand at one of those
puzzles in which you are supposed to slip a cord through a small
metal ring—except that the ends of the cord are tied to pieces of
wood larger than the ring. Such puzzles can be frustrating at first.
However, once you know the secret behind the trick, it's fun to
watch the astonished faces of spectators who just can't
understand how you do it.

If you're like many people, algebra—like an "impossible"
puzzle—may seem like a great mystery: something terribly
difficult and better left to experts. But if you follow the steps to
solving equations, algebra soon becomes simple common sense.
Then you, too, will be a master mathematician, tracking down
hidden answers for problems that you once considered
impossible to solve!

Variables

What comes to your mind when you think of algebra? Perhaps you think of the use of letters in problems. Letters are used in algebra to represent unknown numbers. When used in this way, they are called *variables*. A variable does not have to be a letter; it can be any symbol. Sometimes a question mark is used for the variable.

Variable: a symbol used to represent a number

Suppose that $x = 5$ in one algebra problem. This *does not* mean that x always equals 5. Variables can *vary,* or change. James 1:17 tells us that there is "no variableness" with God. This means that God *never* changes. He is "the same yesterday, and to day, and for ever" (Heb. 13:9).

Symbols whose values do not change are called *constants.* Our numerals (0, 1, 2, 3, etc.) are constants.

Constant: a symbol that represents a fixed number

When constants and variables are put next to each other with no sign between them, you *multiply* them.

$$2x \text{ means } 2 \cdot x$$
$$8ab \text{ means } 8 \cdot a \cdot b$$

Note: Do not use $\times$ to indicate multiplication in algebra because it can be confused with the variable x.

Algebraic Expression: a string of one or more variables and constants

Example

Examples of algebraic expressions:
$$2x + 5y$$
$$12p$$
$$16ab + 2b - 3ac$$

The parts of an algebraic expression are called *terms*. Terms are separated by $+$ and $-$ signs. A term may be a variable, a number, a product, or a quotient. The following algebraic expression has five terms:

$$2x + \frac{3}{xy} + 5xz + y - 3$$

The numeral in a term has a special name. It is called the *coefficient*.

Coefficient: the numerical factor accompanying the variable in a term.

Term	Coefficient
$2x$	2
$\frac{3}{xy}$	3
$5xz$	5
y	1

Note: If there is no numeral accompanying a variable, the coefficient is 1.

Exercises

Name the coefficient of each expression.

1. $3a$
2. $5xy$
3. z
4. $16abc$
5. $21y$

6. mn
7. $19a$
8. $60xy$
9. x
10. $26ab$

List the terms of each expression.

11. $15x + 2y$
12. $132ab - 4a + 2b$
13. $26xyz + 16xy - 4x + 5y$
14. $7x + 3y - 4z$
15. $53a + 21b - 5c$
16. $16m + 3mn - 4n$
17. $25x + 5y$
18. $18abc - 2ab + 3b$
19. $61xy - 32y$
20. $6xyz + 3xy - 5z$

Evaluating Algebraic Expressions

When you evaluate something, you examine or judge it to determine its value. Every Christian needs to evaluate his life daily in the light of Scripture. He should examine his actions and motives to see whether they are in line with God's standards. This self-evaluation is profitable only if he takes time to confess and forsake the things that are not pleasing to the Lord.

You must evaluate an algebraic expression in order to find its numerical value. When you are asked to evaluate an algebraic expression, you will be given values for the variables. Replace the variables with the given values and simplify the expression. When you simplify the expression, be sure to follow the order of operations.

Example 1

Evaluate $5 + x$ when $x = 7$.

$$5 + x$$
$$5 + 7$$
$$12$$

Example 2

Evaluate $2x + 3$ when $x = 4$.

$$2x + 3$$
$$2(4) + 3$$
$$8 + 3$$
$$11$$

Example 3

Evaluate $a(b + c)$ when $a = 5$, $b = 2$, and $c = 6$.

$$a(b + c)$$
$$5(2 + 6)$$
$$5(8)$$
$$40$$

Exercises

Evaluate the following expressions when $x = 3$, $y = 5$, and $z = 8$.

1. $6x$
2. $3xyz$
3. $4y - 2x$
4. $z - y$
5. $x + 8yz$
6. $x(y + z)$
7. $5x + \frac{15}{5}$
8. $2y(5 + x) - 6z$
9. $7x - y$
10. $z(2x + y) - 4y$

Evaluate the following expressions when $a = 4$, $b = 3$, and $c = 7$.

11. $3a + 2b$
12. $c + a(b + c)$
13. $(a + b) \cdot (b + c)$
14. $\frac{c + 5}{a}$
15. $\frac{a}{2} + \frac{9}{3}$
16. $5a - 2b$
17. $6abc$
18. $b(a + c) - 2a$
19. $\frac{21}{c} + b + 5ab$
20. $c(a - b) + a(c - b)$

Formulas

A phrase is a group of words that does not express a complete thought. A sentence is a group of words that does express a complete thought.

Phrases	**Sentences**
on the table	The plate is on the table.
coming home	Susan is coming home.

Using numerals and math symbols, you can write mathematical phrases and sentences.

Phrases	**Sentences**
$2 + 3$	$12 + 3 = 15$
$2 \cdot 8$	$2 \cdot 8 > 15$

The "verb" in a mathematical sentence is the equal sign ($=$) or inequality sign ($>$, $<$, or $\neq$). A mathematical sentence that has an equal sign is called an equation.

Equation: a mathematical sentence stating that two expressions are equal.

A formula is a special kind of equation.

Formula: an equation that describes a rule or principle.

Formulas are tools that are used in solving some word problems. A few formulas are given below:

$A = l \cdot w$ formula for area of a rectangle:
area = length · width

$P = 2 \cdot l + 2 \cdot w$ formula for perimeter of a rectangle:
perimeter = 2 · length + 2 · width

$d = r \cdot t$ formula for distance:
distance = rate · time

To solve a problem using a formula, replace the variables in the formula with the values given. (One variable should be left.) Then evaluate the expression to find the value of the remaining variable.

Example 1

Find the perimeter of a rectangle that measures 25 yards by 38 yards.
$$P = 2 \cdot l + 2 \cdot w$$
$$P = 2 \cdot 38 + 2 \cdot 25$$
$$P = 76 + 50$$
$$P = 126 \text{ yards}$$

Example 2

Find the distance a car will travel in 4 hours if it travels at the rate of 50 m.p.h.
$$d = r \cdot t$$
$$d = 50 \cdot 4$$
$$d = 200 \text{ miles}$$

Exercises

1. Find the area of a rectangle that measures 64 feet by 31 feet.
2. Find the area of a rectangle that measures 21 cm by 16 cm.
3. Find the perimeter of a rectangle that measures 53 inches by 16 inches.
4. Find the perimeter of a rectangle that measures 9 meters by 6 meters.
5. Find the distance a car will travel in 5 hours if it travels at the rate of 45 m.p.h.
6. Find the distance a car will travel in 3 hours if it travels at the rate of 55 m.p.h.
7. Jerry wants to enclose a plot of land for a garden. He wants the garden to measure 12 feet by 8 feet. How many feet of fencing does he need in order to make the garden?

8. Mrs. Franklin wants to carpet the family room of her home. The room measures 15 feet by 12 feet. How many square feet of carpet does she need to buy?

9. A car traveling at the rate of 52 m.p.h. will travel how many miles in 5 hours?

10. The formula for the circumference of a circle is $C = 2\pi r$ where $r =$ the radius of the circle and $\pi = 3.14$. Find the circumference of a circular swimming pool whose radius is 8 feet.

Translating Phrases and Sentences

The Bible was originally written in Hebrew, Aramaic, and Greek. These originals have been translated into many other languages. To "translate" means to express in another language.

Mathematics is a language. It is a language that utilizes numerals and other symbols to form math phrases and sentences. In order to solve word problems, you must be able to *translate* the words into mathematical symbols. The chart below will help you choose what symbol to use when translating.

Term	Symbol to Use
add, plus, sum, increased by, more than, greater than	+
subtract, difference, minus, decreased by, less than, diminished, take away	−
multiply, product, times, of	× or ·
Divided by, quotient	÷
is equal to, equals, is	=
is greater than	>
is less than	<
the quantity	( )

Translate the following into math phrases. Use any variables for unknown numbers.

Example 1

The sum of a number and 6

$$x + 6$$

Example 2

A number decreased by 12

$$n - 12$$

Example 3

Three-fourths of a number

$$\tfrac{3}{4} \cdot n$$

Example 4

The quotient of a number and 5

$$\tfrac{x}{5}$$

Translate the following into math sentences.

Example 5

The product of 6 and a number is 18.

$$6 \cdot x = 18$$

Example 6

Twice the quantity 2 plus 9 is greater than a number.

$$2(2 + 9) > n$$

Example 7

The product of a number and 3 divided by the sum of the number and 4 is equal to 2.

$$\frac{3x}{x + 4} = 2$$

Exercises

Translate the following into mathematical phrases or sentences. Let x equal the unknown numbers.

1. a number increased by 6

2. the product of three and a number

3. the quotient of a number and 4

4. a number diminished by 5

5. four greater than a number

6. the sum of twice a number and 3 times the number

7. a number divided by 9

8. the difference between the product of 8 and a number and the sum of 6 and the number

9. three-fifths of a number

10. 12 less than a number

11. The product of a number and 7 is 28.

12. A number decreased by 15 is less than the number increased by 4.

13. The sum of a number and 28 times the number is 174.

14. Five less than the product of a number and 3 more than the number is less than 85.

15. Four times the quantity 7 plus a number is equal to the product of 5 and 8.

16. The difference between the product of a number and 3 and the quotient of the number and 3 equals 56.

17. One-third of a number added to one-half of the number is greater than 4.

18. The quotient of the quantity 9 plus a number and twice the number is 1.

19. The sum of the product of 5 and a number and the product of 4 and the number is less than 40.

20. Two-thirds of the quantity of a number minus 3 equals the product of 2 and 5.

Open Sentences

Is the following statement true or false?

$$x + 5 = 9$$

You can't tell, can you? If $x = 4$, the statement is true. If $x = 3$, the statement is false. But if the value of x isn't given, it's impossible to know whether the statement is true or false. This is an *open* sentence.

> **Open Sentence:** a mathematical sentence that contains at least one variable and as a result is neither true nor false.

An equation that needs to be solved is an open sentence. To solve it, you must find the solution set.

> **Solution:** the number(s) that make(s) an open sentence true.

The solution of the equation $x + 5 = 9$ is 4 because if you replace x with 4 in the equation, you have a true statement. The equation $4 + 5 = 9$ is true.

Exercises

Tell whether the following statements are true, false, or open.

1. $x + 7 = 15$
2. $6 + 8 = 13$
3. $n - 3 > 5$
4. $15 + 23 < 40$
5. $38 \cdot 4 = 152$

6. $12 + 35 = 46$
7. $6x = 24$
8. $27 - 11 < 16$
9. $18 \div 3 > 5$
10. $54 - x = 21$

Name the solution of each equation.

11. $5 + x = 8$
12. $7 - x = 5$
13. $16 + x = 17$
14. $6x = 12$
15. $5x = 20$

16. $3x = 21$
17. $12 - x = 9$
18. $25 - x = 20$
19. $8 + x = 14$
20. $x + 4 = 10$

Solving Equations of the Form a + b = c

Since an equation states that two expressions are equal, it is balanced. It may help you to think of an equation as a horizontal see-saw or a balanced scale.

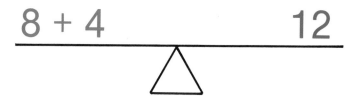

If you subtract 4 from the left side, you would have something like the following:

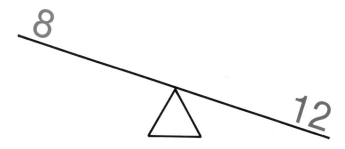

This is no longer balanced. But if you subtract 4 from *both* sides of the equation, you still have a balanced equation.

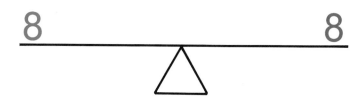

It is very important to remember that *whatever you do to one side of an equation, you must do to the other side.* Otherwise, your equal sign is no longer true.

Perhaps you are wondering why you would need to perform operations on an equation. You do so in the process of solving equations. To find a solution or solutions to an equation means to find those values that replace the variable so that the sentence is true. The goal in solving equations is to *isolate the variable*. In other words, you get the variable by itself on one side of the equal sign and its numerical value (the solution) on the other side.

In order to solve an equation, you need to figure out what operation is being done to the variable. You then "undo" this operation to isolate the variable.

Thus, if an equation shows a number being *added* to the variable, you *subtract* the number from both sides of the equation to "undo" it, because subtraction is the opposite of addition. Similarly, you add to "undo" subtraction.

Example 1

Solve $x + 15 = 38$ for x.

$$
\begin{array}{rl}
x + 15 &= 38 \\
-15 &-15 \\
\hline
x + 0 &= 23 \\
x &= 23
\end{array}
$$

"Undo" addition by subtraction.
Subtract 15 from both sides.

Check: $23 + 15 = 38$
$38 = 38$

Check your solution by substituting it for the variable. If the resulting equation is true, the solution is correct.

Example 2

Solve $y - 21 = 46$ for y.

$$
\begin{array}{rl}
y - 21 &= 46 \\
+21 &+21 \\
\hline
y + 0 &= 67 \\
y &= 67
\end{array}
$$

Check: $67 - 21 = 46$
$46 = 46$

Exercises

What operation would you need to perform in order to isolate the variable?

1. $x + 5 = 21$
2. $x + 16 = 38$
3. $x - 6 = 20$
4. $x + 15 = 19$
5. $x - 8 = 42$
6. $x - 20 = 15$
7. $x + 36 = 45$
8. $x - 19 = 62$
9. $x - 12 = 34$
10. $x + 40 = 67$

Solve the following for x. Show your work.

11. $x + 34 = 72$
12. $x + 19 = 43$
13. $x - 16 = 58$
14. $x - 23 = 61$
15. $x + 95 = 134$
16. $x + 18 = 124$
17. $x - 29 = 84$

18. $x - 56 = 93$
19. $x + 27 = 142$
20. $x + 375 = 521$
21. $x - 134 = 244$
22. $x - 98 = 98$
23. $x + 50 = 167$
24. $x + 83 = 222$

Solving Equations of the Form $a \cdot b = c$

What is being done to the variable in the following equation?

$$6x = 30$$

The variable is being *multiplied* by 6. To "undo" multiplication, you divide. If you divide $6x$ by 6, you are left with x because $\frac{6x}{6} = \frac{6}{6} \cdot x = 1 \cdot x = x$. This procedure will accomplish the goal of isolating the variable. Remember that whatever you do to one side of an equation, you must do to the other side.

Example 1

Solve $6x = 30$ for x.

$\frac{6x}{6} = \frac{30}{6}$ "Undo" multiplication by division.

$x = \frac{30}{6}$ Divide both sides by 6.

$x = 5$

Check: $6x = 30$
$6 \cdot 5 = 30$
$30 = 30$

Example 2

Solve $9x = 135$ for x.

$$\frac{9x}{9} = \frac{135}{9}$$ "Undo" multiplication by division.

$$x = 15$$ Divide both sides by 9.

Check: $9x = 135$

$9 \cdot 15 = 135$

$135 = 135$

To "undo" division, you multiply.

Example 3

Solve $\frac{x}{6} = 21$ for x.

$$6 \cdot \frac{x}{6} = 21 \cdot 6$$ "Undo" division by multiplication.

$$x = 126$$ Multiply both sides by 6.

Check: $\frac{x}{6} = 21$

$\frac{126}{6} = 21$

$21 = 21$

Example 4

Solve $\frac{x}{3} = 24$ for x.

$$3 \cdot \frac{x}{3} = 24 \cdot 3$$ "Undo" division by multiplication.

$$x = 72$$ Multiply both sides by 3.

Check: $\frac{x}{3} = 24$

$\frac{72}{3} = 24$

Exercises

What operation would you need to perform in order to isolate the variable?

1. $\frac{x}{5} = 35$
2. $x - 6 = 27$
3. $5x = 85$
4. $\frac{x}{16} = 24$
5. $x + 34 = 75$

6. $x - 19 = 36$
7. $12x = 192$
8. $21x = 483$
9. $\frac{x}{7} = 49$
10. $x + 84 = 137$

Solve the following for x. Show your work.

11. $15x = 135$
12. $9x = 216$
13. $\frac{x}{6} = 42$
14. $\frac{x}{7} = 82$
15. $4x = 28$
16. $13x = 104$
17. $\frac{x}{9} = 81$
18. $\frac{x}{4} = 17$
19. $8x = 128$

20. $x + 47 = 93$
21. $x - 81 = 126$
22. $12x = 84$
23. $\frac{x}{19} = 6$
24. $20x = 240$
25. $x + 73 = 461$
26. $x - 64 = 87$
27. $31x = 806$
28. $\frac{x}{27} = 86$

Solving Equations of the Form $ax + b = c$

Suppose that you must solve an equation that has two different operations performed on the variable. In the equation $6x + 12 = 84$, the variable has a number being multiplied by it and a number being added to it. You must know what operation to "undo," or reverse, first. The order in which to reverse operations is the opposite of the order of operations. To reverse operations, reverse addition or subtraction first; then reverse multiplication or division.

Example 1

Solve for x.

$$6x + 12 = 84$$
$$\underline{-12 \quad -12}$$
$$6x + 0 = 72$$
$$\frac{6x}{6} = \frac{72}{6}$$
$$x = 12$$

Reverse addition by subtracting 12 from both sides.

Reverse multiplication by dividing both sides by 6.

Check: $6x + 12 = 84$

$6(12) + 12 = 84$

$72 + 12 = 84$

$84 = 84$

Example 2

Solve for x.

$$7x - 21 = 42$$
$$\underline{+21 \quad +21}$$
$$7x + 0 = 63$$
$$\frac{7x}{7} = \frac{63}{7}$$
$$x = 9$$

Reverse subtraction by adding 21 to both sides.

Reverse multiplication by dividing both sides by 7.

Check: $7x - 21 = 42$

$7(9) - 21 = 42$

$63 - 21 = 42$

$42 = 42$

Example 3

Solve for x.

$$\frac{x}{6} + 19 = 26$$

$$\underline{-19 \quad -19}$$

$$\frac{x}{6} + 0 = 7$$

$$\frac{x}{6} = 7$$

$$6 \cdot \frac{x}{6} = 7 \cdot 6$$

$$x = 42$$

Reverse addition by subtracting 19 from both sides.

Reverse division by multiplying both sides by 6.

Check: $\frac{x}{6} + 19 = 26$

$$\frac{42}{6} + 19 = 26$$

$$7 + 19 = 26$$

$$26 = 26$$

Example 4

Solve for x.

$$36 + \frac{x}{6} = 51$$

$$\underline{-36 \qquad -36}$$

$$\frac{x}{6} = 15$$

$$6 \cdot \frac{x}{6} = 15 \cdot 6$$

$$x = 90$$

Since the 36 has no operation sign in front of it, it is addition.

Reverse addition by subtracting 36 from both sides.

Reverse division by multiplying both sides by 6.

Check: $36 + \frac{x}{6} = 51$

$$36 + \frac{90}{6} = 51$$

$$36 + 15 = 51$$

$$51 = 51$$

Exercises

Solve the following for x. Show your work.

1. $3x + 9 = 30$
2. $12x + 17 = 113$
3. $25x + 4 = 179$
4. $15x - 23 = 172$
5. $8x - 18 = 126$
6. $17x - 46 = 39$

7. $9x + 14 = 68$
8. $11x - 22 = 132$
9. $4x + 19 = 83$
10. $24 + 6x = 60$
11. $18 + 7x = 158$
12. $8 + 15x = 68$

13. $\frac{x}{9} + 7 = 12$

14. $\frac{x}{6} + 24 = 42$

15. $\frac{x}{7} - 13 = 10$

16. $\frac{x}{12} - 5 = 13$

17. $34 + \frac{x}{4} = 55$

18. $19 + \frac{x}{15} = 28$

19. $23 + \frac{x}{8} = 57$

20. $31 + \frac{x}{7} = 35$

21. $14x + 92 = 204$

22. $83 + 61x = 327$

23. $\frac{x}{21} + 38 = 94$

24. $48 + \frac{x}{7} = 130$

25. $43x - 75 = 54$

26. $\frac{x}{17} - 32 = 11$

27. $27x - 42 = 174$

28. $84 + \frac{x}{7} = 118$

29. $61 + 9x = 430$

30. $75x - 52 = 548$

Word Problems

Referring to what you know about translating and solving equations, you should now be able to solve problems like the following:

The product of a number and 6 is 108. Find the number.

The first step in solving problems of this sort is to translate the words into an equation with a variable. Then solve the equation.

1. Translate: Let x = the number.

$$6 \cdot x = 108$$
$$6x = 108$$

2. Solve for the variable.

$$\frac{6x}{6} = \frac{108}{6}$$
$$x = 18$$

Check: $6x = 108$
$6(18) = 108$
$108 = 108$

Example 1

If 38 is added to 5 times a number, the result is 73. Find the number.

1. Translate: Let x = the number.

$$5x + 38 = 73$$

2. Solve for the variable.

$$5x + 38 = 73$$
$$\underline{-38 \quad -38}$$
$$5x + 0 = 35$$

Check: $5x + 38 = 73$ $\qquad \frac{5x}{5} = \frac{35}{5}$
$5(7) + 38 = 73$ $\qquad\qquad x = 7$
$35 + 38 = 73$
$73 = 73$

Example 2

The number of boys in Mr. Johnson's algebra class is 6 less than twice the number of girls. If there are 12 boys, how many girls are there?

1. Translate: Let n = the number of girls.

$$2n - 6 = 12$$

2. Solve for the variable.

$$2n - 6 = 12$$
$$\underline{+6 \qquad +6}$$
$$2n + 0 = 18$$

Check: $2n - 6 = 12$ $\qquad \frac{2n}{2} = \frac{18}{2}$
$2(9) - 6 = 12$ $\qquad\qquad n = 9$
$18 - 6 = 12$

Exercises

Translate into an equation. Then solve for the variable.

1. The sum of a number and 33 is 84. Find the number.

2. Nine less than a number is 27. Find the number.

3. The product of 12 and a number equals 96. What is the number?

4. The quotient of a number and 6 is 14. Find the number.

5. A number decreased by 23 is 47. Find the number.

6. Twelve more than a number equals 46. Find the number.

7. Twenty-two times a number is 132. What is the number?

8. A number divided by 17 is 23. Find the number.

9. A number increased by 24 equals 42. What is the number?

10. The difference between a number and 15 is 31. Find the number.

11. The sum of 18 plus 6 times a number is 66. Find the number.

12. The product of a number and 7 increased by 23 is 114. Find the number.

13. The quotient of a number and 9 added to 15 is 78. Find the number.

14. A number divided by 8 minus 32 equals 5. What is the number?

15. Twelve less than the product of 5 and a number is 68. Find the number.

16. The product of a number and 16 decreased by 32 equals 48. What is the number?

17. Jim is 7 years less than twice the age of his sister, Karen. If Jim is 15 years old, how old is Karen?

18. Susan is 12 years older than the quotient of her brother's age and 2. If Susan is 18, how old is her brother?

19. The number of boys attending a certain soccer game was 17 more than three times the number of girls. If 59 boys attended the game, how many girls attended?

20. One number is 12 less than 4 times another number. If the first number is 48, what is the second number?

Ratios

Suppose that you want to compare two quantities. You could use words such as "larger," "smaller," "older," and "longer." To be more precise, you could use expressions like "twice as old" and "half as many." But the most precise way to compare two quantities is to use a *ratio*.

Ratio: a comparison of two numbers or quantities

If there are 14 boys and 16 girls in a class, the ratio of boys to girls is 14:16 or $\frac{14}{16}$. The ratio can be renamed in simplest terms by renaming the fraction in lowest terms.

$$\frac{14}{16} = \frac{7}{8} = 7:8$$

This ratio means that for every 7 boys in the class there are 8 girls. You can see that this comparison is more precise than saying, "The number of boys is less than the number of girls" or, "There are more girls than boys."

A ratio is never to be written as a whole or mixed number because a ratio is a comparison of *two* numbers, not a fraction. The ratio 3:1 is left as $\frac{3}{1}$, *not* 3. Similarly, the ratio 7:5 is left as $\frac{7}{5}$, *not* $1\frac{2}{5}$.

Exercises

Express each of the following ratios in simplest form.

1. 4:8
2. 10:5
3. 25:100
4. 91:21
5. 16:24
6. 320:140
7. 75:250
8. 132:144
9. 135:240
10. 150:90

Write the ratios which the following comparisons represent. (Express in simplest form.)

11. Judy is 15 years old, and her mother is 40 years old. What is the ratio of Judy's age to her mother's age?

12. Jeff weighs 148 lb., and Tim weighs 132 lb. What is the ratio of Jeff's weight to Tim's weight?

13. Mr. Kuryakin's salary is $28,000 per year and Mr. Lee's salary is $35,000 per year. What is the ratio of Mr. Kuryakin's salary to Mr. Lee's salary?

14. The Tigers won 12 games and lost 7. What is the ratio of games won to games lost?

15. Forty-six students went on a field trip. Twenty-four of them were boys. What is the ratio of girls to boys who went on the field trip?

Proportions

Judy went to the grocery store to pick up some potato chips for a class party. The potato chips came in two different sizes and she wanted to figure out which would be the best buy. The 8-oz. package was $1.19, and the 16-oz. package was $2.89. Set up a ratio for each package comparing cost to ounces.

$$119:8 \qquad 289:16$$
$$\frac{119}{8} \qquad \frac{289}{16}$$

The ratio that names the smaller "fraction" is the better buy. If the ratios are equal, the packages are priced at the same rate. We say that these ratios are proportional. The ratios will have units $ per ounce ($\frac{\text{cost}}{\text{ounce}}$).

> **Proportion:** an equation that states that two ratios are equal

In every proportion, two of the numbers are called *means,* and two are called *extremes.*

$$\text{means}$$
$$4:8 = 12:24$$
$$\text{extremes}$$

$$\text{means}$$
$$\frac{4}{8} = \frac{12}{24}$$
$$\text{extremes}$$

An interesting relationship exists between the means and extremes of every proportion. *The product of the means equals the product of the extremes.* Therefore, it can be said that if two ratios are equal, the product of the means is equal to the product of the extremes.

Example 1

Are the following ratios equal?

$$\frac{9}{15} \text{ and } \frac{12}{20}$$
$$9 \cdot 20 = 12 \cdot 15?$$
$$180 = 180$$

yes

$$\frac{3}{5} \text{ and } \frac{4}{6}$$
$$3 \cdot 6 = 4 \cdot 5?$$
$$18 \neq 20$$

no

If you use the following procedure, you will be able to tell which ratio is the greater.

Example 2

Which ratio is the greater?

$$\frac{5}{6} \text{ or } \frac{7}{9}$$

45   42

45 > 42

$$\frac{5}{6} > \frac{7}{9}$$

$\frac{5}{6}$ is the greater ratio

1. Multiply the extremes, and put your answer on the *left* side.
2. Multiply the means and put your answer on the *right* side.
3. Compare the two products and insert the proper symbol (=, >, or <).
4. This symbol can be inserted between the two ratios.

Example 3

Compare the two ratios below and decide which symbol (=, >, <) would best replace the word *and*.

$$\frac{19}{23} \text{ and } \frac{25}{29}$$

product of extremes $\longrightarrow 551 < 575 \longleftarrow$ product of means

$$\frac{19}{23} < \frac{25}{29}$$

Now you should be able to determine which bag of potato chips is the better buy.

$$\frac{119}{8} \text{ or } \frac{289}{16}$$
$$1,904 < 2,312$$

The 8-oz. bag names the smaller fraction. Therefore buying two 8-oz. bags would be less expensive than buying a 16-oz. bag.

Exercises

Compare each pair of ratios and insert the proper symbol ($=, >, <$).

1. $\frac{3}{4}$ and $\frac{15}{20}$

2. $\frac{5}{8}$ and $\frac{14}{23}$

3. $\frac{16}{26}$ and $\frac{8}{13}$

4. $\frac{4}{13}$ and $\frac{5}{16}$

5. $\frac{6}{7}$ and $\frac{9}{11}$

6. $\frac{57}{76}$ and $\frac{12}{16}$

7. $\frac{2}{9}$ and $\frac{3}{10}$

8. $\frac{12}{7}$ and $\frac{35}{16}$

9. $\frac{12}{5}$ and $\frac{23}{8}$

10. $\frac{16}{25}$ and $\frac{14}{23}$

11. $\frac{12}{32}$ and $\frac{45}{120}$

12. $\frac{45}{81}$ and $\frac{10}{18}$

13. $\frac{7}{4}$ and $\frac{8}{5}$

14. $\frac{15}{21}$ and $\frac{25}{35}$

15. $\frac{34}{51}$ and $\frac{32}{46}$

16. $\frac{42}{77}$ and $\frac{78}{143}$

17. $\frac{39}{92}$ and $\frac{26}{78}$

18. $\frac{24}{54}$ and $\frac{34}{64}$

19. $\frac{42}{147}$ and $\frac{36}{126}$

20. $\frac{57}{83}$ and $\frac{76}{97}$

Chapter 3 Review

algebraic expression
coefficient
constant
equation
formula
open sentence

proportion
ratio
solution
term
variable

Evaluate the following expressions when $x = 3$, $y = 4$, and $z = 5$.

1. $7x$

2. $18xy$

3. $3z - 2y$

4. $y(2x + 4)$

5. $\frac{25}{z} + \frac{12}{2}$

6. $2z(x + 3y)$

7. $\frac{8+y}{x}$

8. $16xy - 5z$

Find the following, using the formulas you have learned.

9. Find the area of a rectangle that measures 73 feet by 46 feet.

10. Find the perimeter of a rectangle that measures 17 cm by 9 cm.

11. Find the distance a car will travel in 6 hours if it travels at the rate of 53 m.p.h.

Translate the following into mathematical phrases or sentences.

12. a number decreased by 5

13. a number plus 8

14. the product of 9 and a number

15. the sum of a number and 18

16. the quotient of 15 and a number

17. Six more than a number is 19.

18. A number diminished by 7 is 23.

19. A number divided by 3 equals 7.

20. Six times the quantity 5 plus a number is equal to the sum of 19 and 23.

Tell whether the following statements are true, false, or open.

21. $18 + 24 = 42$

22. $x + 15 = 32$

23. $73x > 292$

24. $28 \div 4 = 9$

25. $93 - 47 < 53$

Solve the following for x.

26. $x + 36 = 79$

27. $x - 64 = 93$

28. $6x = 90$

29. $\frac{x}{7} = 4$

30. $x + 82 = 156$

31. $x - 21 = 237$

32. $12x = 168$

33. $\frac{x}{5} = 20$

34. $5x + 9 = 49$

35. $16x - 7 = 105$

36. $18 + 23x = 110$

37. $\frac{x}{3} + 52 = 66$

38. $\frac{x}{14} - 5 = 4$

39. $19 + \frac{x}{7} = 31$

Translate into an equation. Then solve for the variable.

40. The sum of a number and 7 is 36. Find the number.

41. The product of a number and 6 is equal to 144. What is the number?

42. A number decreased by 15 is 34. Find the number.

43. The product of a number and 3 plus 6 is 30. Find the number.

44. The quotient of a number and 5 decreased by 11 is 3. Find the number.

Express each ratio in simplest form.

45. 24:48

46. 60:108

47. 42:24

48. 192:288

Compare each pair of ratios and insert the proper symbol ($=, >, <$).

49. $\frac{29}{31}$ and $\frac{7}{8}$

50. $\frac{63}{36}$ and $\frac{112}{64}$

51. $\frac{10}{15}$ and $\frac{14}{21}$

52. $\frac{5}{8}$ and $\frac{16}{25}$

53. $\frac{13}{17}$ and $\frac{4}{6}$

54. $\frac{12}{15}$ and $\frac{35}{39}$

55. $\frac{21}{16}$ and $\frac{10}{9}$

56. $\frac{18}{30}$ and $\frac{33}{55}$

Percents

How many years are in a century? How many soldiers did a Roman centurion command? How many cents are in a dollar? Of course, "One-hundred" is the answer to all of these questions. But even if you didn't know the answers, you could have figured them out if you knew the origin of the word *cent*. This term comes from the Latin word *centum,* which means "hundred." Knowing that, you can correctly assume that one French *franc* equals one hundred *centimes* and that one Italian *lira* equals one hundred *centesimi*. And even though a centipede doesn't really have one hundred feet, you'll know that somebody once thought so when he gave it a name that means just that.

In the twentieth century, one hundred forms an important unit of measure. Just about everything that can be divided is referred to as portions of one hundred—percents. As a consumer, you will need to know how to work with percents to communicate with others and to handle your own daily business.

What Is *Percent?*

The word *percent* means "per hundred" or "for each hundred." Percent is simply another way of expressing "hundredths." A percent is a ratio of a given number to 100 ($25\% = \frac{25}{100}$). Thus, $100\% = 1$ because $\frac{100}{100} = 1$. One-hundred percent represents "the whole." Have you given 100% of your life to the Lord? Does He control every area of your life? Or are you holding back something for yourself?

Exercises

Express each percent as a ratio. (Rename answer to lowest terms.)

1. 30%
2. 55%
3. 16%
4. 99%
5. 75%

6. 20%
7. 38%
8. 5%
9. 50%
10. 100%

Commonly Used Percents

$\frac{1}{2} = 50\%$ $\frac{2}{3} = 66\frac{2}{3}\%$ $\frac{3}{4} = 75\%$ $\frac{2}{5} = 40\%$ $\frac{4}{5} = 80\%$

$\frac{1}{3} = 33\frac{1}{3}\%$ $\frac{1}{4} = 25\%$ $\frac{1}{5} = 20\%$ $\frac{3}{5} = 60\%$ $\frac{1}{10} = 10\%$

Converting Percents and Decimal Fractions

Have you ever tried to figure the tip to give a waitress at a restaurant? Suppose you want to find 15% of the bill. In solving problems that involve percents, you do not work with the percent but with its fractional equivalent.

For example, you do not multiply the bill by 15 to figure the tip. (If you did, the tip on a $16.50 dinner would be $247.50!) Rather, you multiply the bill by 0.15, the decimal-fraction equivalent of 15%. ($0.15 \times \$16.50 = \$2.475$, or $2.48—a little more reasonable!)

Since *percent* means "per hundred" or "hundredths," the conversion of a percent to a decimal fraction is very simple.

$7\% = 7$ hundredths $= 0.07$

$18\% = 18$ hundredths $= 0.18$

$26.5\% = 26.5$ hundredths $= 0.265$

$352\% = 352$ hundredths $= 3.52$

Changing a Percent to a Decimal

To change a percent to an equivalent decimal fraction, omit the "%" symbol and divide by 100. (Remember the short cut for dividing by 100: move the decimal point two places to the left.)

$28\% = 0.28$

$473\% = 4.73$

$2\% = 0.02$

$76\frac{1}{2}\% = 76.5\% = 0.765$

$\frac{1}{2}\% = \frac{5}{10}\% = 0.5\% = 0.005$

The conversion of a decimal fraction to a percent is just as easy.

$0.6 = 0.60 = 60$ hundredths $= 60\%$

$0.09 = 9$ hundredths $= 9\%$

$0.56 = 56$ hundredths $= 56\%$

$0.498 = 49.8$ hundredths $= 49.8\%$

Changing a Decimal to a Percent

To change a decimal fraction to a percent, multiply by 100 and add on a "%" symbol. (Remember the short cut for multiplying by 100: move the decimal point two places to the right.)

$0.4 = 40\%$

$0.03 = 03\%$

$2.95 = 295\%$

$7.365 = 736.5\%$ or $736\frac{1}{2}\%$

Many students have a hard time remembering whether to multiply or divide, whether to move the decimal point to the right or left. To avoid this problem, try to *think* about what you are doing. If you only memorize short cuts without understanding what you are doing, you will have trouble applying these principles to real-life problems.

Exercises

Convert to decimal fractions.

1. 28%

2. 56%

3. 5%

4. 99%

5. 4%

6. $62\frac{1}{2}\%$

7. $84\frac{1}{2}\%$

8. 12%

9. 76%

10. 83%

11. 16%

12. 8%

13. 125%

14. 634%

15. 946%

Convert to percents.

16. 0.68

17. 0.21

18. 0.7

19. 0.03

20. 0.96

21. 0.07

22. 0.5

23. 0.73

24. 0.40

25. 0.672

26. 4.163

27. 9.6

28. 24.31

29. 0.025

30. 0.001

Converting Percents and Common Fractions

The conversion of percents to common fractions is very much the same as converting percents to decimal fractions.

$3\% = 3$ hundredths $= \frac{3}{100}$

$15\% = 15$ hundredths $= \frac{15}{100} = \frac{3}{20}$

$155\% = 155$ hundredths $= \frac{155}{100} = 1\frac{55}{100} = 1\frac{11}{20}$

Note: Express fractions in lowest terms.

Changing a Percent to a Common Fraction

To change a percent to a common fraction, omit the "%" symbol and write the numeral as the numerator of a fraction whose denominator is 100. Express the fraction in lowest terms.

$7\% = \frac{7}{100}$

$25\% = \frac{25}{100} = \frac{1}{4}$

$250\% = \frac{250}{100} = 2\frac{50}{100} = 2\frac{1}{2}$

The conversion of common fractions to percents is more complicated because there is more than one way to do it. Here are three ways:

Procedure 1: If the fraction has a denominator of 100, it can be converted directly to a percent.

$$\frac{5}{100} = 5\% \qquad\qquad \frac{38}{100} = 38\%$$

Procedure 2: If the denominator of the fraction is a factor of 100, rename the fraction as an equivalent fraction with a denominator of 100. Then simply write the percent.

$$\frac{1}{2}\frac{(\times 50)}{(\times 50)} = \frac{50}{100} = 50\% \qquad\qquad \frac{9}{25}\frac{(\times 4)}{(\times 4)} = \frac{36}{100} = 36\%$$

Procedure 3: If procedures 1 and 2 do not apply, convert the fraction to a decimal fraction by division; then change the decimal to a percent.

When dividing, carry the answer two places to the right of the decimal point and express the remainder as a common fraction.

Example

$\frac{7}{8} =$

$$.87\frac{4}{8} = .87\frac{1}{2} = 87\frac{1}{2}\%$$

$$
\begin{array}{r}
8\overline{)7.00} \\
\underline{6\ 4} \\
60 \\
\underline{56} \\
4
\end{array}
$$

$\frac{2}{3} =$

$$.66\frac{2}{3} = 66\frac{2}{3}\%$$

$$
\begin{array}{r}
3\overline{)2.00} \\
\underline{1\ 8} \\
20 \\
\underline{18} \\
2
\end{array}
$$

$\frac{4}{7} =$

$$.57\frac{1}{7} = 57\frac{1}{7}\%$$

$$
\begin{array}{r}
7\overline{)4.00} \\
\underline{3\ 5} \\
50 \\
\underline{49} \\
1
\end{array}
$$

Exercises

Convert to common fractions.

1. 5%	**6.** 93%
2. 12%	**7.** 125%
3. 63%	**8.** 2%
4. 50%	**9.** 36%
5. 28%	**10.** 245%

Convert to percents.

11. $\frac{34}{100}$

12. $\frac{61}{100}$

13. $\frac{3}{8}$

14. $\frac{4}{10}$

15. $\frac{3}{6}$

16. $\frac{17}{20}$

17. $\frac{4}{9}$

18. $\frac{18}{100}$

19. $\frac{420}{100}$

20. $\frac{7}{25}$

21. $\frac{3}{5}$

22. $\frac{7}{4}$

23. $\frac{19}{100}$

24. $\frac{6}{7}$

25. $\frac{1}{4}$

26. $\frac{5}{6}$

27. $\frac{1}{3}$

28. $\frac{72}{100}$

29. $\frac{5}{8}$

30. $\frac{3}{7}$

$r \times b = p$

You have studied all of the computational skills needed to solve problems involving percent. Now you must develop skill in interpreting percent-related problems. You cannot perform the mathematical computation unless you can first figure out what to do.

Percent problems involve a comparison between numbers or quantities. The numbers are compared in such a way that one is said to be a certain percentage of the other. Percent problems can be broken down into three parts: the rate, the base, and the percentage.

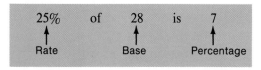

The *base* is the standard of comparison. It represents the whole or all of some quantity. Another quantity, the *percentage,* is compared to the base. *Caution:* The number called the "percentage" is *not* the number written with the percent symbol. The word *percentage* means "part." The percentage is a part of the base.

The *rate* shows what *part* of the base is being taken to make the percentage. It is a percent and needs to be converted to a decimal before computation. The product of the rate and the base is the percentage.

The formula to use when solving percent-related problems is as follows:

$r \times b = p$ where:

r = rate
b = base
p = percentage

When you are faced with a percent problem, plug the given information into this formula; then solve for the unknown.

Example 1

What percent of 24 is 18?

$$? \text{ of } 24 \text{ is } 18$$
$$r \times 24 = 18$$
$$\frac{24r}{24} = \frac{18}{24}$$
$$r = 0.75 = 75\%$$

Remember: Translate "of" as "$\times$" and "is" as "$=$."

Example 2

9 is 45% of what number?

$$9 \text{ is } 45\% \text{ of } ?$$
$$9 = 0.45 \times b$$
$$\text{or}$$
$$0.45 \times b = 9$$
$$\frac{0.45b}{0.45} = \frac{9}{0.45}$$
$$b = 20$$

Example 3

What is 62% of 50?

$$? = 62\% \text{ of } 50$$
$$p = 0.62 \times 50$$
$$\text{or}$$
$$0.62 \times 50 = p$$
$$31 = p, \text{ or } p = 31$$

A very important step in solving word problems is to check your answer to see if it makes sense. Consider Example 2, which reads "9 is 45% of what number?" You can estimate that your answer will be a little more than 18 because 45% is almost 50%, and 9 is 50% of 18. The answer, 20, is a logical answer. If you arrived at an answer of 2, you would know that you had done something wrong because 9 could not possibly be 45% of 2.

Exercises

Solve for the variable.

1. $.12 \times b = 6$
2. $.28 \times b = 7$
3. $.65 \times b = 13$
4. $.84 \times b = 126$
5. $r \times 24 = 12$
6. $r \times 25 = 20$
7. $r \times 50 = 23$
8. $r \times 12 = 9$
9. $.16 \times 28 = p$
10. $.39 \times 100 = p$
11. $.34 \times 59 = p$
12. $.26 \times 150 = p$
13. What percent of 5 is 4?
14. 19 is 76% of what number?
15. 6 is what percent of 15?
16. What is 40% of 65?
17. 29 is 25% of what number?
18. 99 is 30% of what number?
19. What is 22% of 50?
20. Find 75% of 400?
21. What percent of 45 is 27?
22. 66 is 75% of what number?
23. 48 is 150% of what number?
24. 4 is what percent of 25?
25. What is 94% of 50?
26. What is 13% of 84?
27. What percent of 115 is 23?
28. 15 is what percent of 20?
29. 13 is 4% of what number?
30. 147 is 98% of what number?
31. 73% of 10 is what number?
32. Find 77% of 13.
33. Find 56% of 87.
34. What percent of 92 is 47?

Applying Percentages

Whatever you plan to do after high school, you must know how to solve percent-related problems. Even if your job does not require this knowledge, you will need it for completing an income tax form, for figuring shipping and handling costs on an order, and for comparing interest on investments, to name a few. Do not let word problems frighten you—they are simply practical applications of what you have been studying. Remember that Christians are to do everything "heartily, as to the Lord" (Col. 3:23). You must do your best to understand and be able to apply this information.

Example 1

Barbara has $450 invested in a savings bond. She earned $25.20 in interest on the bond last year. What rate of simple interest does that represent?

$$\text{rate of interest of } \$450 = \$25.20$$

$$r \times \$450 = \$25.20$$

$$\frac{\$450 \times r}{\$450} = \frac{25.20}{\$450}$$

$$r = 0.05\tfrac{3}{5} = 5\tfrac{3}{5}\%$$

Example 2

The sophomore class of Temple Christian School raised $1,826.00 selling candy bars. Of all the money raised, 15% goes into the general fund. How much money from this fund raiser will go into the general fund?

$$15\% \text{ of money raised} = \text{money put into general fund}$$

$$0.15 \times \$1,826.00 = p$$

$$\$273.90 = p$$

Example 3

A 7% sales tax on a purchase of groceries was $3.92. What was the before-tax cost of the groceries?

$$7\% \text{ of price of groceries} = \text{tax}$$

$$7\% \text{ of } b = \$3.92$$

$$\frac{0.07 \times b}{0.07} = \frac{\$3.92}{0.07}$$

$$b = \$56.00$$

Exercises

1. Jeff answered 24 questions correctly on a 30-question quiz. What percent of the total number of questions did Jeff answer correctly?

2. Mrs. McBride announced that 6 students, or 20% of those in the class, failed a certain test. How many students are in the class?

3. Miss Johnson gives 12% of her salary to the Lord. If she earns $280 each week, how much does she give to the Lord each week?

4. How much would Miss Johnson give each week if she gave a tithe on her salary? (A tithe is 10%.)

5. Janice saved $14.70 on a new dress. The store was having a sale and all dresses were 30% off the regular price. How much did the dress originally cost?

6. Calvary Christian School has 480 students. If 24 students are absent one day, what percent of the students are absent?

7. Mr. Andretti sells appliances on a 17% commission basis. How much would he make on a refrigerator that sells for $789?

8. The Hansens borrowed $1,500 to buy a used car. By the time the loan was paid off, they had paid $210 in interest. What rate of interest did they pay? (one-year loan with simple interest)

9. Leslie has $324.00 in her savings account. How much interest will she earn in one year on this money if the rate of simple interest is 6%?

10. Mrs. Azarov paid a sales tax of $.96 on a $24.00 purse. What percent of the price of the purse did she pay in sales tax?

More Application

An iron with a regular price of $23.00 is on sale at 15% off the regular price. What is the sale price of the iron?

This problem involves more than one step. First you must find the percentage, which is 15% of the regular price. Then you must subtract the percentage from the regular price to find the sale price.

$$15\% \text{ of } \$23.00 = p$$
$$0.15 \times 23.00 = 3.45$$
$$\$23.00 - \$3.45 = \$19.55$$

The key to solving problems involving more than one step is to make sure that you understand the question. Read the problem carefully and determine what the question is. Then study the information given and decide what to do. Perform the necessary operations and always check your answer to see whether it is logical.

The following examples will illustrate two types of percent problems involving more than one operation.

Type 1: Amount problems are percent increase. These problems involve finding the percentage and *adding* it to the base.

Example 1

A department store had sales of $35,000.00 in November. The management of the store is expecting a 20% increase in sales in December due to Christmas. What are the projected sales for December?

$$20\% \text{ of } \$35,000.00 = \text{increase}$$
$$0.2 \times \$35,000.00 = p$$
$$\$7,000.00 = p$$

The sales are expected to increase by $7,000.00. To find the projected sales for December, add $7,000.00 to the November sales.

$$\$35,000.00 + \$7,000.00 = \$42,000.00$$

Example 2

The inventory clerk wants to price some radios that cost the store $25.00 each. The store uses a markup rate of 18%. What price should the radios sell for?

$$18\% \text{ of } 25.00 = \text{markup}$$
$$0.18 \times 25.00 = p$$
$$4.50 = p$$
$$\text{price} = 25.00 + 4.50$$
$$\text{price} = \$29.50$$

Type 2: Amount problems for percent decrease. These problems involve finding the percentage and *subtracting* it from the base.

Example 3

Mr. Anderson bought stock for $10,000.00, and its value has decreased by 5%. What is it worth now?

$$5\% \text{ of } \$10,000.00 = \text{decrease}$$
$$0.05 \times \$10,000.00 = p$$
$$\$500.00 = p$$

The value of the stock has decreased by $500.00. To find the present value of the stock, subtract $500.00 from the original price of the stock.

$$\$10,000.00 - \$500.00 = \$9,500.00$$

Does the problem at the beginning of this section fit under type 1 or type 2?

Exercises

1. Miss Woods has a salary of $23,000.00 per year. If she is given a 5% increase in her salary, what will her annual income be?

2. A bicycle shop is having a sale on all bicycles in the store. A $79.00 bicycle is on sale for 20% off. What is the sale price?

3. A business firm currently has 325 employees. They plan to lay off 8% of their workers due to financial difficulties. How many employees will they have after the layoff?

4. Longview Christian Academy had 740 students enrolled at the beginning of last school year. This year there has been a 15% increase in enrollment. How many students are enrolled this year?

5. A suit that regularly sells for $189.00 is on sale at a 30% discount. What is the sale price of the suit?

6. The Vogt family is buying a washing machine that costs $359.00. They have paid 32% of the total cost. How much do they owe on the washing machine?

7. If Miss Allen pays her electric bill two weeks late, she must pay a late fee which is 13% of the bill. She is paying a $25.00 electric bill two weeks late. How much money does she owe?

8. A maker of small appliances is offering a rebate of 28% on several appliances. The coffee maker included in this rebate costs $32.00. What is the actual cost after rebate?

9. Mr. Davis recently bought a new car for $9,249.00. He needs to pay a sales tax of 4%. How much will the car cost including sales tax?

10. Kim has a part-time job at a dress shop. She receives $2.30 per hour plus a commission of 6%. If she worked 23 hours last week and sold $538.00 worth of clothing, how much money did she earn last week?

Chapter 4 Review

Convert to decimal fractions.

1. 36%
2. 27%
3. 6%
4. 51%

5. $48\frac{1}{2}\%$
6. 4%
7. 385%
8. $73\frac{1}{2}\%$

Convert to percents.

9. 0.86
10. 0.4
11. 0.27
12. 0.03

13. 5.62
14. 265.
15. 0.96
16. 0.002

Convert to common fractions.

17. 6%
18. 25%
19. 27%
20. 4%

21. 24%
22. 395%
23. 116%
24. 80%

Convert to percents.

25. $\frac{71}{100}$
26. $\frac{13}{15}$
27. $\frac{4}{5}$
28. $\frac{9}{10}$

29. $\frac{3}{50}$
30. $\frac{33}{100}$
31. $\frac{3}{4}$
32. $\frac{17}{18}$

Solve for the variables.

33. $0.47 \times b = 16.92$
34. $0.65 \times b = 26$
35. $r \times 25 = 3$
36. $r \times 16 = 12$
37. $0.64 \times 25 = p$
38. $0.32 \times 81 = p$

39. What percent of 15 is 6?
40. 23 is what percent of 85?
41. 42 is 56% of what number?
42. 53% of what number is 22.26?
43. What is 89% of 63?
44. Find 95% of 60.

45. A 4% sales tax on a shirt was $.60. What was the marked price of the shirt?

46. Susan missed 9 days of school last year. If there were 180 school days in the year, what percent of days did she miss?

47. During a basketball game, Dave shot 20 free throws and made 14 of them. What percent of throws did he make?

48. An accounting firm has 350 employees, 36% of whom are women. How many female employees does the firm have?

49. A 200-lb. wrestler lost 12% of his weight. How much does he weigh now?

50. Jim's Sporting Store has a markup of 90% on all items. If they buy basketballs for $22.00 each, how much do they sell them for?

Measurement

   "Congratulations! You are now the parent of a beautiful baby girl. She weighs 3½ kilograms and is 50 centimeters long!" Although these metric figures are standard in foreign countries, they would puzzle most Americans. But Americans also have trouble understanding their own system of pounds and inches. For example, in the United States the units of length are a jumble of unrelated numbers: 12 inches in a foot, 3 feet in a yard, 5½ yards in a rod, and 320 rods in a mile. To make measurements easier to use and remember, most countries have adopted what is called the International System, or "S.I." for short (abbreviated from the French, "Système International").

   Although the United States adopted S.I. back in 1866, Americans stuck to the old system. Now you must grasp both systems before you can solve everyday problems. Grocery shopping, cooking, sewing, building furniture, yard work, and the purchase of property all require the ability to handle measurements. Imagine what dinner would taste like if your mother did not know how to follow a recipe. Or what if your dad tried to build cabinets, a desk, or your bed frame without understanding a little geometry? How much grass seed and fertilizer should you spread next fall? A mistake could yield lush red clay and dead shrubs the following spring! You might be surprised how often you will need a table of weights and measures, a conversion table, and geometric equations in your daily life.

The Customary System

When you describe things around you, you often describe them by their size or weight. You may say that a dog is "huge." But "huge" to you may not be what someone else considers "huge." In order to be more precise, you must use units of measure that are familiar and agreed upon. Two systems of measurement are currently being used in the United States: the United States customary system and the International System (commonly referred to as the metric system). A summary of the customary system is given below:

Length	Capacity	
12 inches (in.) = 1 foot (ft.)	*Dry*	*Liquid*
36 inches = 1 yard (yd.)	2 pints (pt.) = 1 quart (qt.)	8 ounces (oz.) = 1 cup (c.)
3 feet = 1 yard	8 quarts = 1 peck (pk.)	2 cups = 1 pint (pt.)
$5\frac{1}{2}$ yd. = 1 rod (rd.)	4 pecks = 1 bushel (bu.)	2 pints = 1 quart (qt.)
320 rods = 1 mile (mi.)		4 quarts = 1 gallon (gal.)
5,280 feet = 1 mile		

Mass

16 ounces (oz.) = 1 pound (lb.)

2,000 pounds = 1 ton (T.)

If you want to express a quantity in a different unit, you must know a conversion factor. A *conversion factor* is a number used to multiply or divide a quantity in order to express it in a different unit. The conversion factor is simply the number of smaller units needed to make up one of the larger units. For example, when converting between feet and inches, the conversion factor is 12 because it takes 12 inches (smaller units) to make 1 foot (larger unit).

Once you know the conversion factor, you must determine whether you are to multiply or divide by it. First of all, decide whether you are converting from smaller to larger units or from larger to smaller.

	Length	**Mass**	**Capacity**	
			Dry	*Liquid*
Larger	mile	ton	bushel	gallon
↑	rod	pound	peck	quart
↕	yard	ounce	quart	pint
↓	foot		pint	cup
Smaller	inch			ounce

When converting from smaller to larger, DIVIDE.

When converting from larger to smaller, MULTIPLY.

Example 1

Convert 5 yd. to inches.

1. The conversion factor is 36 because there are 36 inches (smaller unit) in one yard (larger unit).
2. You multiply because you are converting from larger to smaller units.

$$5 \cdot 36 = 180$$
$$5 \cdot 36 = 180 \text{ inches}$$

Example 2

Convert 160 oz. to quarts.

1. Determine the conversion factor in the following way:

$$\text{ounces to cups} = 8$$
$$\text{cups to pints} = 2$$
$$\text{pints to quarts} = 2$$
$$8 \cdot 2 \cdot 2 = 32$$

2. You divide because you are converting from smaller to larger units.

$$160 \div 32 = 5$$
$$160 \text{ oz.} = 5 \text{ qt.}$$

Example 3

Convert 17,160 feet to miles.

1. Conversion factor is 5,280.
2. Smaller to larger indicates division.

$$
\begin{array}{r}
3.25 \\
5{,}280\overline{)17{,}160.00} \\
\underline{15{,}840} \\
1\ 320 \\
\underline{1\ 056} \\
26400 \\
\underline{26400} \\
0
\end{array}
$$

17,160 ft. = 3.25 mi.

Exercises

Determine (a) what operation you would use to convert, and (b) what the conversion factor would be if converting.

1. inches to feet
2. cups to pints
3. miles to rods
4. quarts to gallon
5. pounds to ounces
6. quarts to bushels
7. quarts to pints
8. gallons to quarts
9. ounces to tons
10. miles to yards
11. quarts to ounces
12. peck to pints
13. feet to rods
14. cups to quarts
15. tons to pounds

Convert to the units indicated. (Use the answers to 1-15 as reference.)

16. 60 qt. = _____ gal.
17. 9 lb. = _____ oz.
18. 22 mi. = _____ rd.
19. 36 c. = _____ pt.
20. 378 in. = _____ ft.
21. 128,000 oz. = _____ T.
22. 12 pk. = _____ pt.
23. 553.6 qt. = _____ bu.
24. 115.5 ft. = _____ rd.
25. 3 T. = _____ lb.
26. 19 qt. = _____ oz.
27. 9 mi. = _____ yd.
28. 26 gal. = _____ qt.
29. 24.84 c. = _____ qt.
30. 21 qt. = _____ pt.

Introduction to the International System (S.I.)

The International System is being incorporated into our society more and more. This means that you need to be familiar with it and you need to feel comfortable using it. You may prefer the customary system because you are accustomed to it. But, in reality, S.I. is much simpler than the other system. One nice thing about it is that there is consistency among the three types of measurement: length, mass, and capacity. Each type has one basic unit and several prefixes which, together, can represent different units. The prefixes are the same for all three types of measurement.

Type of Measurement	Basic Unit	Abbreviation
length	meter	m
mass	gram	g
capacity	liter	l

Some well-meaning people claim that it is wrong for Christians to use S.I. because it will be advancing one-world government and Antichrist. A measurement system is not evil because it is used or will be used by those that are evil. Christians do not promote evil by using the implements of trade and commerce.

PREFIXES

Prefix	Meaning	Symbol
kilo-	1,000	k
hecto-	100	h
deka-	10	dk
(BASIC UNIT)	1	
deci-	.1 or $\frac{1}{10}$	d
centi-	.01 or $\frac{1}{100}$	c
milli-	.001 or $\frac{1}{1,000}$	m

Consider the measure of length. The meter is the basic unit of length. A meter is a little more than the length of a yardstick. Suppose that you are measuring the distance across Kansas. You would want a unit larger than a meter. To find a unit larger than a meter, you choose a prefix *above* the basic unit, for example, a dekameter (ten meters) is the length of 10 meters. Similarly, a kilometer is equal to 1,000 meters. To measure the distance across Kansas, you would probably use the kilometer. (One kilometer is approximately two-thirds the length of a mile.) If you wanted units smaller than a meter, you would choose a prefix *below* the basic unit. For example, the decimeter is one-tenth of a meter, which means that 10 decimeters are equal to 1 meter.

These prefixes are used in the same way for measurement of mass and capacity. The difference is the basic unit: the liter for capacity and the gram for mass. A liter is the volume of a cube, each side of which is one decimeter in length. It is slightly more than a quart. A gram is equal to the mass of the water needed to fill up a cube with sides 1 centimeter in length. The customary-system pound is closer in mass to the kilogram than the gram. One kilogram equals approximately 2.2 pounds, whereas it takes about 454 grams to equal one pound.

The International System is easy to work with once you know these basic units and prefixes. Take time to memorize them now; it will save you work later.

Exercises

Tell what each abbreviation stands for.

1. cm
2. dkl
3. kg
4. mm
5. cg

6. hl
7. dm
8. dkg
9. ml
10. km

S.I. Conversions

Jesus tells us in Matthew 18:3 that "except ye be converted, . . . ye shall not enter into the kingdom of heaven." Have you been converted? To convert means "to alter into a different form; change." When a person is truly saved, he is changed. "He is a new creature: old things are passed away; behold, all things are become new" (II Cor. 5:17). Conversion involves more than simply saying a prayer; it involves a changed life. A Christian will live a different life from an unsaved person. Has there been a true conversion in your life?

You have recently studied how to convert from one unit of measure to another within the customary system. When you convert to different units, you are changing into another form, but the value does not change. Conversion within S.I. is similar to that of the customary system. Yet, it is easier because all of the conversion factors are multiples of ten. So all you have to do when converting within the metric system is move the decimal point to the left or right. As with conversion within the customary system, you determine whether to multiply or divide by whether you are converting from smaller to larger units or from larger to smaller.

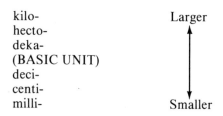

kilo-   Larger
hecto-
deka-
(BASIC UNIT)
deci-
centi-
milli-   Smaller

> When converting from smaller to larger, DIVIDE.
> When converting from larger to smaller, MULTIPLY.

Since each unit is ten times the one below it and one tenth of the one above it, you can easily determine the conversion factor. For a move of one unit, the conversion factor is 10; for a move of two units, it is 100, etc. Consider converting meters to centimeters.

kilometer
hectometer
dekameter
• meter   } 1 Begin at meters.
  decimeter   2 Two moves indicates that the
• centimeter   conversion factor is 100.
  millimeter

Example 1

Convert 5.279 meters to centimeters.

5.279   Larger to smaller indicates multiplication.

                            Two moves indicates that the conversion factor
                            is 100.

5.279 = 527.9 cm   When multiplying by 100, move the decimal
                            point two places to the right.

Example 2

Convert 375.4 centiliters to hectoliters.

375.4   Smaller to larger indicates division.

                            Four moves indicates that the conversion factor
                            is 10,000.

0375.4 = .03754 hl   When multiplying by 10,000, move the decimal
                            point four places to the left.

Exercises

Determine (a) what operation you would use to convert, and (b) what the conversion factor would be if converting.

1. kg to g
2. mm to dm
3. cl to kl
4. m to mm
5. hg to dkg
6. l to cl
7. dg to kg
8. mm to cm

Convert to the units indicated.

9. 3.47 m = _____ hm
10. 645 cg = _____ dkg
11. 43.2 kl = _____ dkl
12. 7 cm = _____ mm
13. 34.2 g = _____ mg
14. 38.5 l = _____ dkl
15. 64.2 dg = _____ cg
16. 930 mm = _____ dm
17. 4,675 cg = _____ kg
18. .0053 kl = _____ ml
19. 983 dg = _____ hg
20. 7.95 m = _____ mm
21. .8462 dkl = _____ cl
22. 3312.7 cg = _____ kg

Converting Between Systems ────

Since both the customary system and S.I. are used in the United States, you must become familiar with both of them. You have worked with both systems independently, but this is not always possible. Take, for instance, the following example:

Janice plans to make a dress to wear to a banquet. The pattern calls for 3 meters of material. At the store, material is sold by the yard. Before she can know how much material to buy, Janice must convert meters to yards.

Converting between systems is complicated because the conversion factors are so awkward. To simplify things, you are given only two conversion factors from each type of measurement. Memorize these; they will be your link between the two systems.

Approximate Conversions

Length	Mass	Capacity
Larger to Smaller	**Larger to Smaller**	**Larger to Smaller**
1 in. ≈ 2.54 cm	1 oz. ≈ 28.33 g	1 oz. ≈ 2.96 cl
1 mi. ≈ 1.61 km	1 lb. ≈ 0.45 kg	1 gal. ≈ 3.79 l

Example 1

Convert 16 dm to yd.

1. First, convert 16 dm to cm or km.

    Converting to cm is easier.

    16 dm = ? cm

    Larger to smaller indicates multiplication.

    Conversion factor = 10

    $16 \cdot 10 = 160$ cm

2. Next, convert 160 cm to in.

    Smaller to larger indicates division.

    Conversion factor = 2.54

    $160 \div 2.54 \approx 63$ in.

3. Finally, convert 63 in. to yd.

    Smaller to larger indicates division.

    Conversion factor = 36

    $63 \div 36 = 1.75$

4. 16 dm ≈ 1.75 yd.

Example 2

Convert 110 lb. to hg.

1. First, convert lb. to kg.

    Larger to smaller indicates multiplication.

    Conversion factor = 0.45

    $110 \cdot 0.45 \approx 49.5$

2. Next, convert kg to hg.

    Larger to smaller indicates multiplication.

    Conversion factor = 10

    $49.5 \cdot 10 = 495$

3. 110 lb. ≈ 495 hg

Example 3

Convert 42 dl to quarts.

1. First, convert dl to l.

Smaller to larger indicates division.
Conversion factor = 10
$42 \div 10 = 4.2$

2. Next, convert l to gal.

Smaller to larger indicates division.
Conversion factor = 3.79
$4.2 \div 3.79 \approx 1.11$ gal.

3. Finally, convert gal. to qt.

Larger to smaller indicates multiplication.
Conversion factor = 4
$1.11 \cdot 4 = 4.44$ qt.

4. 42 dl $\approx$ 4.44 qt.

Exercises

Convert as indicated. (Round off to the nearest hundredth.)

1. 35 dm $\approx$ _____ ft.
2. 210 mi. $\approx$ _____ km
3. 16 oz. $\approx$ _____ g
4. 12 l $\approx$ _____ gal.
5. 6 lb. $\approx$ _____ g
6. 18 m $\approx$ _____ ft.
7. 24 pt. $\approx$ _____ dl
8. 2 T. $\approx$ _____ kg
9. 13 c. $\approx$ _____ l
10. 215 mm $\approx$ _____ ft.

Perimeter and Circumference

When God told Noah to build an ark, He gave him specific instructions to follow. Turn in your Bible to Genesis 6 and read verses 13-16. In verse 15, God gives Noah the measurements for the length, width, and height of the ark. The ark was probably not shaped the way boats and ships are today. Let's suppose it was a big rectangular "box." Since you know the length, width, and height, you can determine the perimeter and the area of the floor and the capacity of the ark.

Let's begin with perimeter. The *perimeter* of a figure is the distance around it. Consider the floor of the ark. The length is 300 cubits, and the width (breadth) is 50 cubits. (A cubit is approximately a foot and a half.)

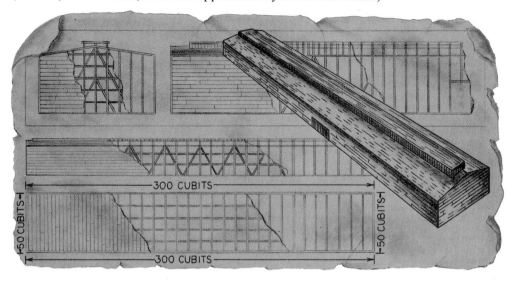

To find the perimeter of a rectangle, you add the length of the sides.

$$300 + 300 + 50 + 50 = 700 \text{ cubits}$$

Since a rectangle has two lengths that are equal and two widths that are equal, the following formula can be used to find the perimeter of a rectangle.

$$p = 2l + 2w$$

A square has four equal sides. It is a special kind of rectangle. The formula for the perimeter of a square is given below.

$$p = 4s, \text{ where } s = \text{length of a side}$$

Example 1

Find the perimeter of a rectangle whose length = 12 m and whose width = 7 m.

$$p = 2l + 2w$$
$$p = 2(12) + 2(7)$$

Using the order of operations, multiply first.

$$p = 24 + 14$$
$$p = 38 \text{ m}$$

Example 2

Find the perimeter of a square with each side equal to 6 cm.

$$p = 4s$$
$$p = 4(6)$$
$$p = 24 \text{ cm}$$

You can also find the distance around a circle, but it is not called perimeter. The distance around a circle is called the *circumference* of the circle. In order to understand the formula for the circumference of a circle, you need to know the basic parts of a circle.

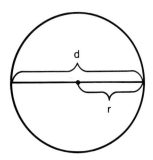

d = diameter: a line segment that connects two points on a circle and passes through the center

r = radius: a line segment that connects the center of a circle with a point on the circle.

The formula for the circumference of a circle is as follows:

$$C = d\pi, \text{ where } \pi = 3.14$$

Since the diameter is always twice as long as the radius, here is another way to express the formula:

$$C = 2\pi r$$

Example 3

Find the circumference of a circle whose diameter = 5 cm.

$$C = d\pi$$
$$C = (5)(3.14)$$
$$C = 15.7 \text{ cm}$$

Example 4

Find the circumference of a circle whose radius is 8 m.

$$C = 2\pi r$$
$$C = (2)(3.14)(8)$$
$$C = 50.24 \text{ m}$$

Exercises

Find the perimeter of the following rectangles. When necessary, convert so that the units are the same.

1. $l = 15$ m, $w = 11$ m
2. $l = 7$ cm, $w = 3$ cm
3. $l = 18$ ft., $w = 15$ ft.
4. $l = 21$ yd., $w = 6$ yd.
5. $l = 28$ m, $w = 22$ m

6. $l = 25$ cm, $w = 14$ cm
7. $l = 4.8$ dkm, $w = 32$ m
8. $l = 3$ km, $w = 250$ dkm
9. $l = 385$ cm, $w = 22.5$ dm
10. $l = 27$ cm, $w = 186$ mm

Find the perimeter of the squares whose sides are given.

11. $s = 12$ cm
12. $s = 26$ ft.
13. $s = 7$ mm

14. $s = 32$ km
15. $s = 19$ in.

Find the circumference of the circles represented below. Let $\pi = 3.14$.

16. $d = 19$ ft.
17. $d = 12$ cm
18. $d = 21$ mi.
19. $d = 35$ dm

20. $r = 14$ mm
21. $r = 33$ m
22. $r = 8$ cm
23. $r = 29$ km

24. Tom's father asked him to determine how many meters of fencing they would need to enclose their rectangular garden. Rather than measure around the entire garden, Tom measured one long side and one short side. He found that the garden measured 45 m by 28 m. How many meters of fencing are needed to enclose the garden?

25. Gary's dog, Husky, must stay on a leash because the yard is not fenced in. Husky's leash is 8 feet long and is hooked to a pivot stake in the ground. When Husky runs, he is forced to run in a circle because of the leash. If Husky runs around the circle 14 times, how far has he run?

26. Gary feels sorry for Husky, so he plans to fence in a play area for him. Gary decided to make the area the length of 4 leashes and the width of 3 leashes. What is the distance around the area?

27. Some ladies at First Baptist Church are planning to decorate for a banquet. They want to cover the tops and sides of four serving tables that are 30 in. high, 30 in. wide, and 8 ft. long. The paper for this comes in rolls which are 36 in. wide and can be purchased in any length needed. The excess width of the paper is used as an overlap and for attachment.

   (a) How many linear feet of paper do they need to cover the top of a table?

   (b) How many linear feet of paper do they need to cover the sides of 1 table? (Hint: find the perimeter of the table.)

   (c) How many linear feet of paper do they need to completely cover all four tables?

   (d) If the paper is to have a 3-in. overhang at each end of each table, how many linear feet should be added to the total paper requirements?

Statistics

Have you ever wondered how the TV networks can predict the winner of an election when only about one-third of the voters have cast their ballots? Some predictions are possible through the tools of a mathematical science called *statistics*.

The methods of statistics allow us to study samples of data that represent a much larger collection of data, called the *universe,* or the *population.* In the case of elections, a carefully chosen sample of voters from the whole population of voters are asked whom they voted for or whom they will vote for. If the voters who make up this sample approximate, or represent, all the voters, then the answers that the voters give will be approximately the same as the answers for the whole population. The process of getting a *representative sample* is complicated, and occasionally the predictions are not decisive. It may be easy to take a sample of blood from your arm and expect it to be like the rest of your blood, but selecting a sample of 2,000 voters from a population of two million requires some careful work.

Sometimes statisticians refer to the samples they take as *random samples.* A random sample is so selected that any data from the total population are just as likely to be chosen as any other. For instance, suppose that a company was making bolts. They are usually required to give the tensile strength of the bolts. To do this, they take a random sampling and test those bolts with a special machine that gives their breaking point in pounds of force. (It's obvious why the company can break only a small random sample—

they wouldn't have any bolts to sell if they tested them all. Futhermore, if the sample weren't random, they couldn't be confident that the remaining bolts were of the same strength.)

Besides helping us to predict characteristics of a population, statistical methods also allow us to describe a set of data that has been collected. We call this *descriptive statistics.* After a class takes a test, the teacher has a set of scores to "describe." One way to describe them is to find the average score. There are three kinds of "averages." The *mean* is found by adding all the scores and dividing by the number of scores. The *median* is the middle score; the *mode* is the score that occurs most often.

If on a certain test 100% was the most frequent score, then it is the mode. The teacher could technically say that the "average" on this test was 100%. However, most of us expect the average score to be the mean, not the mode.

Descriptive statistics not only gives information about the average or central points but also tells how the data are scattered or dispersed. Two common measures of dispersion are the *range* and the *standard deviation.*

The standard deviation is especially useful for statisticians to determine how much of the population falls within certain values. They often call these values *confidence limits.* They are important to manufacturers in determining the kind of guarantee offered for their products. If an automobile battery is guaranteed for 48

months, and the 95% confidence limits are 42 to 54 months, then the company will need to price the batteries so that it doesn't lose money on those lasting only 42 months.

People who use statisics have found that statistical measures and lists of data are not very meaningful to nontechnical personnel. Therefore the use of graphic presentations has made it possible to communicate useful information to most groups of people. Graphs help us make mental comparisons and concentrate on relationships that are meaningful. You may find it interesting to look in newspapers and magazines for descriptive statistics presented as graphs. Your textbooks also contain graphs for population statistics and geographical relationships, among other things.

Perhaps without realizing it, you have been deluged by all kinds of statistics. Every major sport has its "stats," such as batting averages and shooting percentages. The weather forecasters press many statistics into service to tell us there is a 40% chance of rain today. Traffic and highway engineers need statistics to

design and improve the roads you ride on. Insurance people also use this remarkable science to determine premiums and benefits. The insurance company can use mortality tables to determine the risk involved in selling life insurance to a person at any certain age. Likewise, automobile-insurance companies have found through statistical analysis that unmarried male drivers under 25 are high-risk drivers; yet when these same young men are honor students, the risk is much lower.

You may be surprised at the many statistical ideas we use to make statements in our everyday conversation. Do you use any of these?

What are my *chances* of passing this course?

She's just an *average* student.

That's Jack—he's late *90%* of the time.

CBS predicts the winner in the Senate race to be . . .

Like all information, however, statistics must be interpreted correctly to be valid. People who have already made up their minds not to believe in the Bible may quote statistics, trying to convince you that evolution, astrology, or something else is true. Don't be deceived by such efforts, though. While statistics present information in an organized fashion, it's up to you to determine whether *all* the relevant information is being given and whether the facts quoted are even worth heeding.

Area

A meter does not have any width or height; it has only length. As a result, a meter can be used only to measure one dimension: length. You can use a meter to measure perimeter, but not area, which is two-dimensional. Suppose that you are buying carpet with which to cover the floor of a room. If you tell the salesman that your floor is 56 meters, he will have trouble helping you. The perimeter may be 56 meters, but not the area. Area is measured in square units.

1 cm

length: measured in *linear units*
(Examples: meter, centimeter)

1 sq. cm

area (length × width): measured in *square units*
(Examples: square meter, square centimeter)

The *area* of a region is the number of square units needed to cover the region completely.

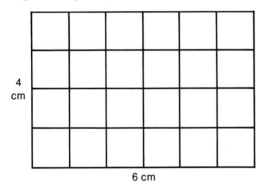

4 cm

6 cm

This rectangular region has been covered with square centimeters. Count the number of squares. The area of the region is 24 sq. cm.

Formulas make it much easier to find the area of regions. The two dimensions of a rectangular region (length and width) are referred to as *base* and *height*. In the rectangle above, the base is 6 cm, and the height is 4 cm. Notice that multiplying these two numbers gives the area of the region.

Area of a Rectangular Region

$A = b \cdot h$, where b = base and h = height.

Since a square is a special kind of rectangle, the formula for area of a rectangular region can be used for a square region. However, the base and height are always equal in a square. So instead of $A = b \cdot h$, you'll have $A = b \cdot b$ ($A = b^2$).

Area of a Square Region

$A = b^2$, where b = base (length of all sides)

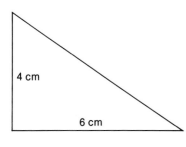

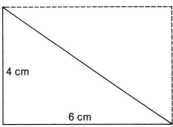

You may have trouble covering this triangle region with square centimeters. Fortunately, the formula for the area of a triangular region permits you to by-pass such a procedure.

Notice that a rectangle is formed when a triangle of equal size is placed next to the original. You can see that the area of a triangular region is equal to half of the area of a rectangular region.

Area of a Triangular Region

$$A = \tfrac{1}{2}b \cdot h$$

The height of a triangular region is not always a side of the triangle. Some examples are shown below:

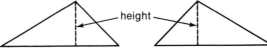

Example 1

Find the area of a square region, each side of which = 6 m.

$$A = s^2$$
$$A = 6^2$$
$$A = 36 \text{ m}^2$$

Example 2

Find the area of a triangular region whose base is 8 cm and whose height is 6 cm.

$$A = \tfrac{1}{2}b \cdot h$$
$$A = \tfrac{1}{2}(8)(6)$$
$$A = \tfrac{1}{2}(48)$$
$$A = 24 \text{ cm}^2$$

Exercises

Find the areas of the following rectangular regions. When necessary, convert so that the units are the same.

1. $b = 9$ cm; $h = 3$ cm
2. $b = 12$ m; $h = 7.5$ m
3. $b = 16$ dkm; $h = 11.3$ dkm
4. $b = 24$ ft.; $h = 19$ ft.
5. $b = 21.4$ yd.; $h = 16$ yd.
6. $b = 14$ m; $h = 75$ dm
7. $b = 230$ cm; $h = 18$ dm
8. $b = 247$ in.; $h = 152$ in.
9. $b = 370$ hm; $h = 25$ km
10. $b = 8$ m; $h = 7,350$ mm

Find the areas of the following square regions.

11. $b = 7$ in.
12. $b = 9$ m
13. $b = 12$ dm
14. $b = 15$ km
15. $b = 20$ ft.

Find the areas of the following triangular regions.

16. $b = 16$ m; $h = 9$ m
17. $b = 22$ yd.; $h = 18$ yd.
18. $b = 36$ dm; $h = 28$ dm
19. $b = 9$ mm; $h = 6$ mm
20. $b = 41$ cm; $h = 35$ cm

Determine the areas of the following regions.

21.

22.

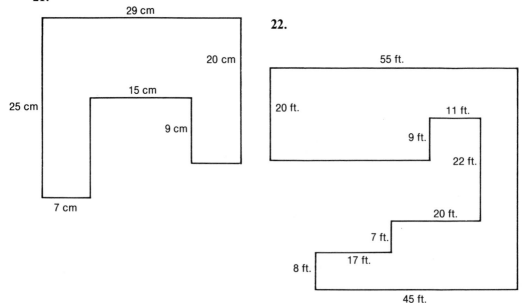

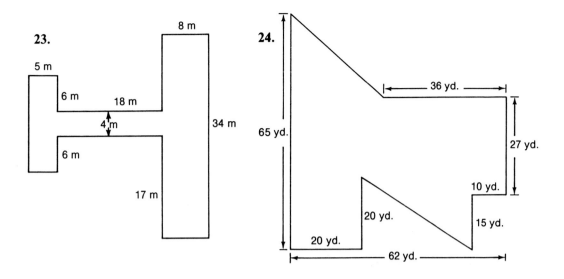

23.

24.

25. The Pasternaks plan to carpet their living room and two bedrooms. The living room measures 12 ft. by 20 ft., and the bedrooms measure 12 ft. by 14 ft. and 10 ft. by 15 ft. How much carpet do they need to purchase?

26. Mr. Robinson is having a new house built for his family. The house is almost complete, and he wants to order some sod for the lawn. Using the scale drawing below, determine how many square meters of sod he will need to order. (All of the property not covered by the house or the sidewalk will be sodded.)

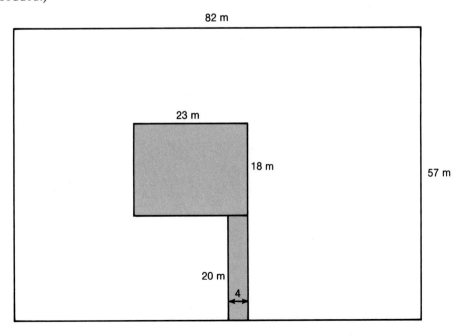

Volume

The *capacity* of a container is the amount that it can hold. Capacity is measured in liters with S.I. and in ounces, cups, pints, etc., with the customary system.

Volume is closely related to capacity. *Volume* is the measure of a solid object in cubic units.

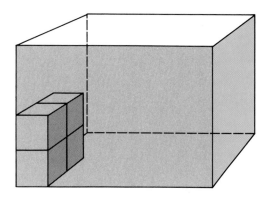

Volume (length · width · height) is measured in cubic units. Volume is the number of cubic units needed to fill up the interior of a figure.

To find the volume of a rectangular box, simply multiply length times width times height.

Volume of a Rectangular Box

$$V = l \cdot w \cdot h$$

Since the length, width, and height are the same in a cube, the volume of a cube is found by "cubing" a side.

Volume of a Cube

$$V = s^3$$

Example 1

Find the volume of a rectangular box whose length = 6 cm, width = 4 cm, and height = 5 cm.

$$6 \cdot 4 \cdot 5 = 120 \text{ cm}^3 \text{ (cubic centimeters)}$$

Example 2

Find the volume of a cube, each side of which = 8 in.

$$8^3 = 8 \cdot 8 \cdot 8 = 512 \text{ in.}^3$$

Exercises

Find the volumes of the following three-dimensional figures. When necessary, convert so that the units are the same.

1. $l = 12$ ft.
   $w = 10$ ft.
   $h = 9$ ft.

2. $l = 8$ m
   $w = 5$ m
   $h = 7$ m

3. $l = 36$ cm
   $w = 24$ cm
   $h = 28$ cm

4. $l = 16$ in.
   $w = 12$ in.
   $h = 20$ in.

5. $l = 21$ km
   $w = 18$ km
   $h = 2$ km

6. $l = 35$ yd.
   $w = 21$ yd.
   $h = 16$ yd.

7. $l = 42$ ft.
   $w = 38$ ft.
   $h = 27$ ft.

8. $l = 26$ cm
   $w = 22$ cm
   $h = 29$ cm

9. $l = 15$ m
   $w = 900$ cm
   $h = 70$ dm

10. $l = 23$ km
   $w = 1600$ dkm
   $h = 120$ hm

Find the volumes of the following cubes.

11. $s = 6$ in.
12. $s = 12$ cm
13. $s = 9$ m
14. $s = 15$ ft.
15. $s = 23$ dm

16. Determine the volume of the ark in Genesis 6:15 if you assume that it is shaped like a rectangular box.

Chapter 5 Review

capacity
circumference
conversion factor
customary system
International System (S.I.)

linear units
perimeter
square units
volume

Convert to the units indicated.

1. 16 ft. = _____ in.
2. 76 yd. = _____ ft.
3. 240 oz. = _____ lb.
4. 32 c. = _____ qt.
5. 9 mi. = _____ in.
6. 16 rods = _____ yd.
7. 72 kl = _____ dkl
8. 342 mm = _____ m
9. 41.6 dg = _____ hg

10. 9.3 g = _____ dg
11. 43 l = _____ cl
12. 210 cm = _____ hm
13. 12 oz. ≈ _____ g
14. 79.59 l ≈ _____ gal.
15. 19 cm ≈ _____ ft.
16. 86 lb. ≈ _____ kg
17. 6 qt. ≈ _____ l
18. 180 km ≈ _____ mi.

Find the perimeters of the following rectangles and squares.

19. $l = 19$ ft.
    $w = 14$ ft.
20. $l = 24$ in.
    $w = 21$ in.
21. $l = 9$ m
    $w = 7$ m

22. $l = 36$ dm
    $w = 24$ dm
23. $s = 6$ cm
24. $s = 21$ in.
25. $s = 14$ yd.
26. $s = 30$ m

Find the circumference of each circle. Let $\pi = 3.14$.

27. $d = 11$ cm
28. $d = 13$ ft.

29. $r = 5$ in.
30. $r = 15$ m

Find the areas of the following rectangular regions.

31. $b = 12$ cm; $h = 4$ cm
32. $b = 6$ ft.; $h = 4.5$ ft.

33. $b = 17$ m; $h = 16$ m
34. $b = 27$ in.; $h = 21$ in.

Find the areas of the following square regions.

35. $b = 6$ ft.
36. $b = 18$ cm

37. $b = 11$ m
38. $b = 8$ in.

Find the areas of the following triangular regions.

39. $b = 12$ in.; $h = 11$ in.
40. $b = 24$ dm; $h = 18$ dm

41. $b = 28$ cm; $h = 21$ cm
42. $b = 30$ ft.; $h = 26$ ft.

Find the volume of the following three-dimensional rectangular figures.

43. $l = 14$ in.
   $w = 9$ in.
   $h = 12$ in.
44. $l = 25$ cm
   $w = 20$ cm
   $h = 30$ cm
45. $s = 26$ m

46. $l = 34$ mm
   $w = 29$ mm
   $h = 24$ mm
47. $l = 84$ in.
   $w = 76$ in.
   $h = 68$ in.
48. $s = 18$ ft.

Income

Should a Christian be concerned with money? Of course he should. A Christian is accountable to God for the management of his money. There is nothing wrong with having money; money is not wrong in itself. The evil comes from love of money. I Timothy 6:10 informs us that "the love of money is the root of all evil." When people begin to love money for what it can give them, they are an easy prey for Satan. You can see many examples of this truth in our society. People's love of money leads them to hate, to covet, to steal, and even to kill.

If a Christian views money from the proper perspective, he is not wrong to have it and use it. But he should be a wise steward of his money so that he will have the maximum amount possible with which to serve God. A Christian's ultimate goal in making money should be to use it to help the Lord's work. If a Christian is not willing to give his money away, he is loving it.

In order for a person to have money to use for the Lord, he must have a source of income. Any money that a person takes in is *gross income,* but the primary source of income is pay for work or service. When you take a job to earn money, the person you work for is your *employer,* and you are the *employee.* Depending on the type of work you do, you will be paid a certain way. This chapter will introduce you to the ways that people are paid for their work.

Hourly Wages
Timecards
Hourly Wages and Tips
Salary
Commission and Piecework
Including Graduated Commission
Review

Hourly Wages

If an employee is paid according to how many hours he works, he earns hourly wages. A full-time hourly worker usually works 40 hours per week. The number of hours he is expected to work each week is called *regular time*. Any time worked in excess of regular time is called *overtime*. One pay scale is used for regular time and another for overtime. The overtime pay scale is usually $1\frac{1}{2}$ or 2 times the regular pay scale (sometimes referred to as "time and a half" and "double time.")

Example 1

Complete the overtime pay rate if it is "time and a half" and the regular pay rate is $4.15 per hour. (Do not round the result.)

$$\$4.15 \cdot 1.5 = ? \qquad \$6.225$$

To find an hourly worker's regular-time pay, multiply the number of regular hours worked by the regular pay rate. To find his overtime pay, multiply the number of overtime hours worked by the overtime rate. The sum of these two amounts equals the gross pay.

Example 2

One week, Candy worked 25 regular hours. Her regular pay rate is $5.25 per hour. What was her gross pay for this particular week?

$$\text{hours} \cdot \text{rate} = \text{pay}$$
$$25 \cdot \$5.25 = \$131.25$$

Example 3

Mr. Lewis is paid $7.55 per regular hour and receives time and a half for overtime hours. Any hours over 40 per week are considered overtime. Last week, Mr. Lewis worked 44 hours. What was his gross pay?

$44 - 40 = 4$	Figure out how many overtime hours he worked.
$\$7.55 \cdot 1.5 = \$11.325$	Figure the overtime pay rate. (Do not round off.)
$\$7.55 \cdot 40 = \$302.00$	Figure pay for regular hours.
$\$11.325 \cdot 4 = \$45.30$	Figure pay for overtime hours.
$\$302.00 + \$45.30 = \$347.30$	Add to find gross pay.

Exercises

1. Jack McDowell earns $9.00 per hour as a mechanic. Last week, he worked 38 hours. What was his gross pay for the week?

2. Janessa has a part-time job as a salesclerk. She is paid $3.65 per hour. One particular month, she worked the following hours:

   Week 1: 21 hours
   Week 2: 17 hours
   Week 3: 19 hours
   Week 4: 13 hours

   Compute her gross pay for this month.

3. Mrs. Wright earns $5.70 per hour as a file clerk. She receives time and a half for any hours over 40 per week. One week, she worked 44 hours. What was her gross pay for the week?

4. Larry earns $5.00 per hour as a welder. For any hours over 40 per week, he earns time and a half. If he works on Sundays or holidays, he earns double time. Compute his pay for the following week:

   Monday, July 4 (holiday)—7 hours
   Tuesday, July 5—8 hours
   Wednesday, July 6—8 hours
   Thursday, July 7—8 hours
   Friday, July 8—7 hours

	Regular Hourly Pay Rate	Overtime Pay Rate (hours over 40) (time and a half)	No. of Hours Worked in One Week	Regular Wages	Overtime Wages	Total Weekly Wages
5.	$4.10		38			
6.	$5.25		43			
7.		$9.45	45			
8.			35			$204.40
9.	$12.46			$461.02	$0	
10.	$3.85			$154.00	$11.55	
11.			28			$119.28
12.		$7.77	44			

Timecards

An hourly worker usually completes a timecard or a time sheet to keep track of the hours he works. The time of day is recorded each time he starts and stops working. Some companies have a time clock that stamps the time on a timecard when it is inserted. Other companies have the employees record the time by hand. Timecards and time sheets come in a variety of forms, but basically they are the same. The time that the employee begins working is recorded in the "IN" column; the time he leaves is marked in the "OUT" column. The difference between "Time In" and "Time Out" is the amount of time worked.

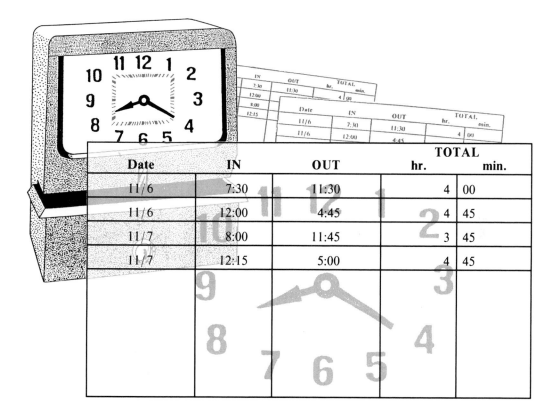

Date	IN	OUT	TOTAL hr.	min.
11/6	7:30	11:30	4	00
11/6	12:00	4:45	4	45
11/7	8:00	11:45	3	45
11/7	12:15	5:00	4	45

To find the difference between two times, you subtract. When filling out a timecard or time sheet, it saves time to use some shortcuts by doing the figuring mentally.

To figure the amount of time worked . . .

1. Start with "Time In."
2. Mentally count the number of whole hours between "Time In" and "Time Out."
3. Figure out the number of minutes left to reach "Time Out."

Example 1

Find the amount of time worked if . . .

Time In = 8:15 A.M.   Time Out = 12:50 P.M.

1. Start with 8:15 A.M.
2. Mentally count from 8:15 to 12:15, which is 4 hours.
3. Figure out the number of minutes between 12:15 and 12:50, which is 35 minutes.
4. The amount of time worked is 4 hours, 35 minutes.

Example 2

Find the amount of time worked if . . .

Time In = 9:35 A.M.   Time Out = 2:05 P.M.

1. Start with 9:35 A.M.
2. Mentally count from 9:35 to 1:35, which is 4 hours.
3. Figure out the number of minutes between 1:35 and 2:05, which is 30 minutes.
4. The amount of time worked is 4 hours, 30 minutes.

To calculate daily and weekly totals, you must add the list of times worked. There are three procedures for doing this.

Example 3

Compute the weekly total from the daily totals given.

Mon. 6 hr., 30 min.
Tues. 7 hr., 15 min.
Wed. 8 hr., 0 min.
Thurs. 7 hr., 45 min.
Fri. 6 hr., 35 min.

Procedure I:

1. Add the minutes.

$$30 + 15 + 45 + 35 = 125 \text{ minutes}$$

2. Divide by 60 to find the number of hours in 125 minutes.

$$
\begin{array}{r}
2 \text{ hr., } 5 \text{ min.} \\
60 \overline{)125} \\
120 \\
\hline
5
\end{array}
$$

3. Add the hours, including the 2 hours obtained from the minutes.

$$
\begin{array}{r}
2 \text{ hr. } 5 \text{ min.} \\
6 \\
7 \\
8 \\
7 \\
+6 \\
\hline
36 \text{ hr., } 5 \text{ min.}
\end{array}
$$

Procedure II: (This procedure is practical only if the times are rounded off to the nearest 5, 10, or 15 minutes.)
1. Group the minutes into sets that equal whole hours.

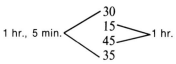

Total: 2 hr., 5 min.

2. Add the hours, including the 2 hours obtained from the minutes.

$$
\begin{array}{l}
2 \text{ hr., } 5 \text{ min.} \\
6 \\
7 \\
8 \\
7 \\
\underline{+6} \\
36 \text{ hr., } 5 \text{ min.}
\end{array}
$$

Procedure III: (This procedure will work even if the times are not rounded off.)
1. Add the ones' column of the minutes.

$$
\begin{array}{ll}
6 \text{ hr.} & 30 \text{ min.} \\
7 & 15 \\
8 & 0 \\
7 & 45 \\
\underline{6} & \underline{35} \\
& 5 \text{ min.}
\end{array}
$$

2. Mentally, add the tens' column of the minutes.

$1 + 3 + 1 + 4 + 3 = 12$

3. Divide the number obtained in Step 2 by 6. Place the answer in the hours' column and the remainder below the tens' column of the minutes.

$12 \div 6 = 2$, remainder 0

$$
\begin{array}{ll}
& 2 \\
6 \text{ hr.} & 30 \text{ min.} \\
7 & 15 \\
8 & 0 \\
7 & 45 \\
\underline{6} & \underline{35} \\
36 \text{ hr.} & 5 \text{ min.}
\end{array}
$$

4. Add the hours' column.

Example 4

Using Procedure III, compute the weekly total from the daily totals given.

Mon. 5 hr., 36 min.
Tues. 7 hr., 9 min.
Wed. 6 hr., 53 min.
Thurs. 5 hr., 42 min.
Fri. 8 hr., 57 min.

Solution:

$$\begin{array}{rr} \overset{3}{} & \overset{2}{} \\ 5 \text{ hr.} & 36 \\ 7 & 9 \\ 6 & 53 \\ 5 & 42 \\ +8 & 57 \\ \hline 34 \text{ hr.} & 17 \text{ min.} \end{array}$$

$19 \div 6 = 3$, remainder 1

In the working world, there is a great opportunity for Christians to help or hurt the cause of Christ. Unsaved people will watch a professing Christian to see whether he is honest in recording his work time and whether he is doing his job. I Peter 2:12 admonishes Christians to have their "conversation [life-style] honest among the Gentiles: that . . . they may by your good works, which they shall behold, glorify God." Always remember that dishonesty is not worth a few extra dollars.

Man is wicked by nature. "The heart is deceitful above all things, and desperately wicked " (Jer. 17:9). Man's inclination is to do wrong. Even after a person becomes a Christian, he still must battle his old sinful nature. If men were perfect and always honest, there would be no need for rules. But, since this is not the case, men live under laws and regulations.

Employers know that people are naturally selfish and lazy. So they place regulations on their employees. Often a penalty is given for arriving late or leaving early. For example, some companies whose employees punch a time clock will take off 15 minutes of pay for arriving late or leaving early. Companies have different regulations regarding the calculation of work time. Sometimes, to keep workers on a regular schedule, no credit is given for arriving early or leaving late. If you work an hourly wage job, you need to become familiar with your employer's procedures.

Example 5

Mrs. Bentley punches a time clock in order to keep track of her work hours. She is supposed to work a 40-hour week, 8:00 A.M. to 5:00 P.M. every day with a 1-hour lunch. She is not paid for any time worked before 8:00 A.M. or after 5:00 P.M. She is penalized by losing 15 minutes of pay time for arriving after 8:00, for leaving before 5:00, and for being absent before or after the allotted hour for lunch. The hours that she worked are shown below.

Day	In	Out	In	Out	
1	7:57	12:03	12:52	5:00	
2	8:04	12:05	1:02	5:01	left early
3	7:55	11:53	12:50	5:06	
4	8:00	12:01	12:58	4:52	
5	8:00	12:00	1:05	5:02	

arrived late

The times that Mrs. Bentley will be penalized are treated as follows:

8:04 as 8:15
1:02 as 1:15
11:53 as 11:45
4:52 as 4:45
1:05 as 1:15

The times that Mrs. Bentley arrived early or left late will be treated as follows:

7:57 as 8:00   7:55 as 8:00
12:03 as 12:00   12:50 as 1:00
12:52 as 1:00   5:06 as 5:00
12:05 as 12:00   12:01 as 12:00
5:01 as 5:00   12:58 as 1:00
                      5:02 as 5:00

To find Mrs. Bentley's hours for the week, find the daily totals and then add them to get the weekly totals.

Day	In	Out	Total		Daily Total		Weekly Total	
1	8:00	12:00	4	00				
	1:00	5:00	4	00	8	00		
2	8:15	12:00	3	45				
	1:15	5:00	3	45	7	30		
3	8:00	11:45	3	45				
	1:00	5:00	4	00	7	45		
4	8:00	12:00	4	00				
	1:00	4:45	3	45	7	45		
5	8:00	12:00	4	00				
	1:15	5:00	3	45	7	45	38	45

If Mrs. Bentley earns $4.85 per hour, calculate her gross pay for this week.

$$45 \text{ min.} = \frac{45}{60} \text{ of an hour} = \frac{3}{4} \text{ of an hour} = .75$$

$$\$4.85 \times 38.75 = \$187.9375 = \$187.94$$

Sometimes an employer will allow a certain number of minutes that workers may arrive late or leave early without a penalty. In the example below, the employer permits 2 minutes without a penalty. For how much time will the worker receive credit?

Example 6

	In	Out
	8:02	11:56

Solution:

8:02 = 8:00 because 2 minutes are allowed without penalty.

11:56 = 11:45

8:00 to 11:45 is 3 hr., 45 min.

Exercises

Find the amount of time worked. The first time indicates "Time In"; the second indicates "Time Out." Do the work mentally.

1. 9:00 A.M.   1:15 P.M.
2. 8:30 A.M.   2:45 P.M.
3. 1:10 P.M.   5:00 P.M.
4. 7:50 A.M.   11:35 A.M.
5. 1:30 P.M.   4:45 P.M.
6. 10:20 A.M.   2:15 P.M.
7. 9:45 A.M.   1:10 P.M.
8. 6:30 A.M.   11:45 A.M.
9. 8:25 A.M.   12:30 P.M.
10. 7:55 A.M.   11:45 A.M.

Use the following information for exercises 11-13.

The Waverly Steel Company has three shifts of factory workers. The shifts are as follows:

First shift, 7:00 A.M.—3:00 P.M.
Second shift, 3:00 P.M.—11:00 P.M.
Third shift, 11:00 P.M.—7:00 A.M.

The employees punch a time clock to record their work hours. Their time is calculated under the following regulations:

- The employees work an 8-hour shift and can take a half-hour break for which they are paid.
- No credit is given for arriving early or leaving late.
- Time less than a quarter of an hour does not count.
- The employees earn $6.50 per hour.

11. Ken McArthur works first shift. Tell what each time on his timecard will be when his hours are figured.

Day	In	Out
1	7:00	2:56
2	6:53	3:04
3	7:02	3:00
4	7:05	2:58
5	6:57	3:01

12. Mr. Arnold works third shift. Tell (a) what each time on his timecard will be treated as when his hours are figured. Then give (b) the number of hours for which he will receive credit. Finally, calculate (c) his gross income for the week.

Day	In	Out
1	11:06	7:02
2	10:58	7:00
3	11:00	6:54
4	11:03	6:53
5	10:59	6:56

13. Mr. Stivinsky works second shift. Calculate (a) the number of hours for which he will receive credit, and (b) his gross income for the week.

Day	In	Out
1	3:00	11:00
2	2:56	10:58
3	3:04	11:05
4	3:00	11:02
5	2:57	10:55

Use the following information for exercises 14-17.

Nancy Jamison works from 8:00 A.M. to 12:00 noon and from 1:00 P.M. to 5:00 P.M. She does not receive credit for arriving early or leaving late. Time less than a quarter hour does not count, but three minutes are allowed without penalty for arriving late or leaving early. Find the number of hours for which Nancy will receive credit.

	IN	OUT
14.	7:56	12:01
15.	8:01	11:59
16.	1:05	5:03
17.	1:01	4:55

Use the following information for exercises 18-24.

Kathy Mayville works as a typist for several executives. She can work any hours she wants as long as she does not exceed 25 hours per week. When her hours are credited, the time is rounded backward to the nearest 15 minutes. Find the number of hours for which Kathy will receive credit.

	In	Out	
18.	8:15	10:41	8:15—10:30
19.	9:20	10:36	9:15—10:30
20.	1:05	4:30	1:00—4:30
21.	2:16	5:00	2:15—5:00
22.	7:53	11:21	7:45—11:15

23. If 18-22 represent the days of one particular week, find the number of hours for which Kathy will receive credit.

24. If Kathy earns $5.20 per hour, find her gross income for this particular week.

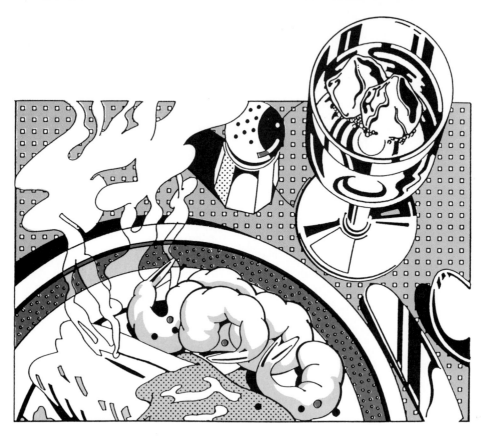

Hourly Wages and Tips

When you eat at a restaurant, you leave a tip for your waiter or waitress. Waiters, waitresses, bellboys, and maids are among the hourly workers who receive part of their wages in tips. They have an hourly rate from which their hourly wages are figured, and they add their tips to the hourly wage to find their gross pay.

A worker who receives part of his wages in tips must realize that his quality of work and his attitude have a direct influence on the amount of money people will give him. If he is pleasant and courteous, people will leave larger tips. This fact should not be his sole motivation for being polite, though; a Christian should always display a Christ-like attitude. But keeping these facts in mind will be a good reminder to be courteous.

Example

Martha works as a waitress and earns $3.85 per hour plus tips. She worked 25 hours last week and received $75 in tips. What was her weekly gross income?

$$\$3.85 \cdot 25 = \$96.25$$
$$\$96.25 + \$75.00 = \$171.25$$

Exercises

Find each person's gross pay for the week.

	Name	Hourly Rate	Hours Worked	Tips
1.	Maria	$3.95	37	$186
2.	Jeff	$3.05	40	$163
3.	Peter	$3.30	26	$143
4.	Gloria	$3.63	32	$159

5. Jerry is a bellboy at the Carriage House Hotel. He earns $2.50 per hour plus tips. One week, he worked 35 hours and was given $86.50 in tips. What was his gross income for this particular week?

6. Nancy, a waitress, earns $2.85 per hour plus 80% of her tips. She gives the other 20% of her tips to other employees who help her. One week she worked 37 hours and received $245 in tips. Find her gross income for this week.

7. Carol is a beautician. The beauty shop where she works charges customers $8.00 for a haircut, of which Carol earns half. Find her gross income for one week if she gave 62 haircuts and was given $42.50 in tips.

Use the following information for exercises 8-12.

The waiters and waitresses at Bob's Family Restaurant earn $3.15 per hour. They pool their tips together and divide the sum evenly among themselves. Find the gross weekly income for each of the restaurant's waiters and waitresses.

	Name	Hours Worked	Tips
8.	Jane	25	$152
9.	Mike	23	$163
10.	Susan	30	$204
11.	Keith	28	$187
12.	Janice	32	$196

A Tip for the Tipper

Have you ever found yourself at a restaurant computing 15% of your bill with a pen and a napkin? Or maybe you make a wild guess for the tip. Next time you need to compute a tip, try the following shortcut:

$$15\% = 10\% + 5\%$$

So, find 10% of your bill. This is easily done mentally by "moving" the decimal point one place to the left.

For example . . .

10% of \$7.60 is \$.76

To find the remaining 5%, simply take half of the 10%.

half of \$.76 is \$.38

Add the 10% and 5% to find 15%.

\$.76 + \$.38 = \$1.14

15% of \$7.60 = \$1.14

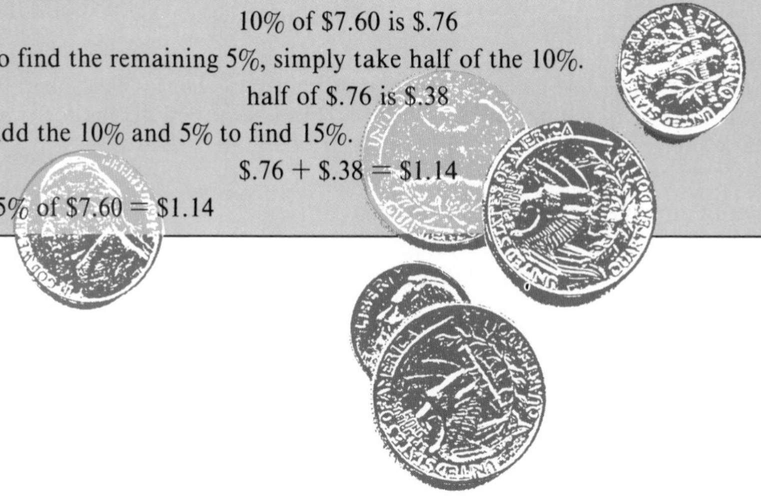

Salary

A *salary* is a fixed amount of money paid to an employee in equal payments. These payments are usually made weekly, every two weeks, twice a month, or monthly. A salaried employee is expected to work a certain number of hours or to accomplish certain objectives. Since he does not punch a time clock or turn in a time sheet, he is largely on his own to get his work done. A Christian must remember that he is accountable to God for the way he uses his time. He must be honest in performing what tasks are required of him.

A *payroll period* indicates how often an employee receives a paycheck. The chart below indicates the common payroll periods and how many paychecks are received per year with each period.

Payroll Period		Number of Paychecks Received per Year
Weekly	(receive a paycheck once each week)	52
Biweekly	(receive a paycheck once every two weeks)	26
Semimonthly	(receive a paycheck twice each month—often on the 1st and 15th of the month)	24
Monthly	(receive a paycheck once each month)	12

Example 1

Mrs. Johnson is paid semimonthly, and each paycheck is $710. Find her annual salary.

$$\$710.00 \cdot 24 = \$17,040.00$$

Example 2

Mr. Rollins earns an annual salary of $22,872, and he is paid monthly. Find the amount of his monthly paycheck.

$$\$22,872 \div 12 = \$1,906$$

Example 3

Mr. Schoening is a banker and is looking for a new job. He has been offered two positions. State Bank has offered him $280.00 weekly. National Bank has offered him $590 semimonthly. What is the annual salary offered by each bank?

State Bank	National Bank
$280 · 52 = $14,560	$590 · 24 = $14,160

Exercises

Find the gross pay for each paycheck with the given annual salary and payroll period.

1. $14,112; semimonthly
2. $19,318; biweekly
3. $16,120; weekly
4. $25,440; monthly

5. $15,548; weekly
6. $40,040; biweekly
7. $24,600; semimonthly
8. $34,224; monthly

Find the annual salary with the given payroll period and gross pay per paycheck.

9. weekly; $192
10. monthly; $2250
11. semimonthly; $489
12. biweekly; $564

13. monthly; $1915
14. biweekly; $740
15. semimonthly; $675
16. weekly; $246

17. Bill Bolander has recently graduated from college as an engineer. He has been offered several jobs and is considering three of them. If the benefits are the same for all three jobs, which one pays the most?

Gross Pay per Paycheck	Payroll Period
A: $1,458	semimonthly
B: $1,379	biweekly
C: $2,855	monthly

18. Evanna Key is considering two different secretarial jobs. If the benefits are the same for both jobs, which one pays the most? (Hint: Find the annual amount earned for each job.)

A: Pays $6.25 per hour for a
    40-hour week
B: Pays $565 biweekly

19. Jason's employer has been paying him $455 monthly. He has decided to pay him weekly at the same annual rate. How much will Jason's gross pay be per week? (Hint: Do not assume that each month has four weeks.)

Commission and Piecework

Many salesmen earn all or part of their income by commission. A *commission* is a certain percentage of total sales. A person works *straight commission* if his commission is the only money he earns. Often a salesman is paid a guaranteed sum of money in addition to a commission. This payment may be a salary or an hourly wage.

Example 1

Jack Green is paid a straight commission of 30% on the appliances that he sells at the department store where he works. Last month, he sold $5,700.00 worth of appliances. What was his commission for the month?

$$30\% \text{ of } \$5,700 = P$$
$$0.3 \cdot 5,700 = \$1,710.00$$

Example 2

Suzanne works at a dress shop where she earns $2.85 an hour plus a commission of 10% on all of her sales above $2,000 per week. One week Suzanne worked 26 hours, and her sales were $2,500. What was her gross income for this week?

$\$2.85 \cdot 26 = \$74.10$	Compute her hourly wages.
$\$2,500 - \$2,000 = \$500$	Determine her sales above $2,000.
$10\% \text{ of } \$500 = P$ $0.1 \cdot 500 = \$50$	Compute her commission.
$\$74.10 + \$50 = \$124.10$	Add hourly rate and commission to find gross income.

Some sales people are paid a *graduated commission,* by which the rate of commission increases as the sales increase. The purpose behind this method is to give the employee more incentive to sell as much as possible.

Example 3

Mr. Duvalier earns a base salary of $200 per month, 6% on the first $25,000 of monthly sales, and 8% on all monthly sales over $25,000. In October, his sales were $27,500. Find his gross monthly income for the month.

$0.06 \cdot \$25,000 = \$1,500$	Compute 6% of $25,000.
$\$27,500 - \$25,000 = \$2,500$	Determine sales above $25,000.
$0.08 \cdot \$2,500 = \$200$	Compute 8% of $2,500.
$\$200 + \$1,500 + \$200 = \$1,900$	Add to find gross income.

An employer uses commission as an incentive for his employees to work harder. If a salesman does not sell anything, he does not receive a commission. The more he sells, the more money he makes. The employer knows that his employees will work harder if what they sell affects how much money they make. Employers use this same principle when they pay their employees piecework wages. *Piecework wages* are paid according to the number of items (pieces) of work completed. A person employed under this wage system is paid a fixed amount for each item produced. The product of the number of items completed and the rate per item equals his wage.

number of items completed · rate per item = wage

Example 4

Maryanne works in a clothing factory making ties. She is paid $.16 for each tie that she makes. What was her gross weekly income for the week shown below?

Monday: 280 ties
Tuesday: 266 ties
Wednesday: 300 ties
Thursday: 295 ties
Friday: 254 ties

$280 + 266 + 300 + 295 + 254 = 1,395$	Add to find how many ties she completed in the week.
$1,395 \cdot \$.16 = \$223.20$	Multiply the number of ties she made by the rate for each tie.

Exercises

Find the gross monthly income for each salesman.

Salesman	Base Rate/ Salary	Commission	Sales
1. Johnson	None	15% on all sales	$10,250
2. Henderson	$450	12% on all sales	$4,300
3. Lemon	$800	8% above $5,000	$9,250
4. Baily	None	4.5% on all sales	$17,600
5. Witten	$3.50 per hour (40-hour week; 4 weeks in the month)	6% on all sales	$4,700

Find the gross weekly income for the following employees of Wilson Apparel. They are all paid piecework wages.

Employee	Number of Pieces Completed	Pay per Item
6. Atwood	156 shirts	$1.30
7. Carey	1,014 ties	$.17
8. Lewis	125 dresses	$1.50
9. Deas	79 coats	$2.50
10. Peterson	1,463 scarfs	$.13

11. Mrs. Meyers sells jewelry on a straight commission basis. She earns 40% of all her sales. From the following order, find the total price of the order and find Mrs. Meyers' commission on the sale.

Item	Quantity	Price for One
necklace	1	$12.50
ring	2	$6.95

12. Mr. Haverty earns a base salary of $290 per month, 5% on the first $20,000 of monthly sales and 7% on all monthly sales over $20,000. In March, his sales were $25,000, and in April they were $14,000. Find his gross monthly income for both months.

Chapter 6 Review

overtime
payroll period
regular time
salary

timecard
time clock
time sheet

1. Mrs. Larson earns $9.80 per hour as a nurse. Last week, she worked 37 hours. What was her gross pay for the week?

2. Mr. Kline earns $4.80 per regular hour, and he receives time and a half for any hours over 40 per week. One particular week, Mr. Kline worked 45 hours. What was his gross pay for the week?

Compute the weekly totals from the daily totals given. You may use any procedure you choose.

3. M: 6 hr., 30 min.
   T: 5 hr., 15 min.
   W: 7 hr., 25 min.
   Th: 8 hr., 0 min.
   F: 7 hr., 45 min.

4. M: 7 hr., 38 min.
   T: 5 hr., 49 min.
   W: 8 hr., 25 min.
   Th: 6 hr., 13 min.
   F: 7 hr., 52 min.

Use the following information for 5-7.

Ed Rostpovich is a part-time salesclerk at a department store. He does not receive credit for arriving early or leaving late. Time less than a quarter hour does not count, but Ed is allowed 3 minutes without penalty for arriving late or leaving early. Ed's timecard is shown below. Find the number of hours for which he will receive credit.

	In	Out
5.	7:58 A.M.	12:04 P.M.
6.	8:03 A.M.	11:56 A.M.
7.	1:05 P.M.	5:00 P.M.

8. Karen is a waitress at Jim's Café. She earns $2.65 per hour plus tips. She worked 32 hours one particular week and received $96 in tips. What was her gross income?

9. Mr. Lakey is a taxi driver. He earns $3.00 per hour plus tips. One week he worked 40 hours, receiving $87 in tips. Find his weekly gross income.

10. Ted Hale is a cost accountant for a major accounting firm. He has an annual salary of $30,168 and is paid semimonthly. Find his gross pay for one paycheck.

11. Mrs. Bardinelli is a medical receptionist, and she earns an annual salary of $13,000. If she is paid weekly, find her gross pay for one paycheck.

12. Dr. McCormick is a college professor. He receives his paychecks monthly and grosses $3,750 per paycheck. Find his annual salary.

13. Mrs. Harrison sells cosmetics for extra income. She is paid a straight commission of 35% on all that she sells. One customer made the following order. Find the total price of the order and the commission earned. (Round commission off to nearest cent.)

Item	Quantity	Price for One
eye liner	1	$2.95
hand lotion	3	$3.80
perfume	2	$6.98

14. Mr. Yates sells furniture for a living. He earns a base salary of $350 per month. He earns a commission of 6% on the first $15,000 of monthly sales and 9% on all monthly sales over $15,000. In July, his sales were $18,500. Find his gross income for the month.

15. Jennifer works part time making crafts. She is paid $4.80 for each plaque that she completes. One particular week, she made 15 plaques. Find her gross income for the week.

Taxes

Taxes—to many consumers the word represents a useless but inescapable evil. After all, taxes affect virtually everyone's pocketbook; you cannot hold a job, make purchases, or own property without being affected by one of the many different government-decreed taxes. Even as a youngster, the first time you walked into a drugstore to buy a candy bar you couldn't get your treat without paying a little extra for tax.

Of course, no one likes to part with his hard-earned wages for nothing, but the Scriptures admonish believers willingly to support their government through taxes. Romans 13:1, 6-7 says, "Let every soul be subject unto the higher powers. For there is no power but of God: the powers that be are ordained of God. . . . For for this cause pay ye tribute also: for they are God's ministers. . . . Render therefore to all their dues: tribute to whom tribute is due; custom to whom custom; fear to whom fear; honour to whom honour."

Try to imagine what life would be like if there were no taxes at all. First of all, without tax-paid salaries there would be no government—no president, no foreign ambassadors, no congressmen, no senators, no governors, and no mayors. Fire departments and paved highways would not exist. Because there would be no police departments to discourage evildoers, crime would run rampant, and anarchy would result. Finally, in the midst of this confusion, some militaristic government *with* taxes would invade to plunder the nation's natural resources and levy its own taxes on you to help finance itself.

Viewed in this light, taxes don't seem quite so bad after all. They are simply the price we pay for civilized society, whether it be in the United States or in imperial Rome.

You will be faced with a wide variety of taxes during your lifetime, both direct and indirect. So if you ever plan to work, buy food, or own a home, you need to be prepared to pay taxes.

Forms for Taxes

For tax purposes, you must fill out some forms when you start working. First of all, if you do not already have a social security number, you must apply for one at a Social Security Office. After you fill out a Form SS-5, Application for a Social Security Card, the Social Security Administration will issue you a card and a 9-digit number. This number is *your* number; no one else has the same number, and this number remains yours for the rest of your life. The number issued to you is actually your account number. Your employer withholds money from your paycheck and sends it to the Social Security Administration, where it is credited to your account.

When you start a new job, your employer will have you fill out a Form W-4, *Employee's Withholding Allowance Certificate*. The information on this form helps your employer figure how much of your gross income to withhold for federal income tax. On the form, you figure out the number of withholding allowances that you may claim. Each allowance that you claim lowers the amount of tax that your employer will withhold from your paycheck. You may claim allowances for several things: exemptions, deductions and credits, etc. Only allowances for exemptions will be discussed here.

There are two types of exemptions: personal and dependency. You can always claim yourself as a personal exemption. You can also claim your spouse if you have one. A dependency exemption is allowed for each dependent that you have. Basically, a *dependent* is a member of your household or a relative who depends upon you for more than half of his support and whose gross income is very small. Right now, your parents or guardians probably claim an exemption for you because you are their dependent—you depend upon them for support.

A sample copy of a Form W-4 is shown here.

Form **W-4** Department of the Treasury Internal Revenue Service	**Employee's Withholding Allowance Certificate** ► For Privacy Act and Paperwork Reduction Act Notice, see instructions.	OMB No. 1545-0010 **1987**

1 Type or print your full name

Home address (number and street or rural route)

City or town, state, and ZIP code

2 Your social security number

3 Marital Status
- ☐ Single   ☐ Married
- ☐ Married, but withhold at higher Single rate

Note: *If married, but legally separated, or spouse is a nonresident alien, check the Single box.*

4 Total number of allowances you are claiming (from the Worksheet on page 3) . . . .

5 Additional amount, if any, you want deducted from each pay (see Step 4 on page 2) . . . . $

6 I claim exemption from withholding because (see Step 2 above and check boxes below that apply):

a ☐ Last year I did not owe any Federal income tax and had a right to a full refund of **ALL** income tax withheld, **AND**

b ☐ This year I do not expect to owe any Federal income tax and expect to have a right to a full refund of **ALL** income tax withheld. If both a and b apply, enter the year effective and "EXEMPT" here . . . . . ► Year 19

c If you entered "EXEMPT" on line 6b, are you a full-time student? . . . . ☐ Yes ☐ No

Under penalties of perjury, I certify that I am entitled to the number of withholding allowances claimed on this certificate or, if claiming exemption from withholding, that I am entitled to claim the exempt status.

Employee's signature ►   Date ► _____, 19___

7 Employer's name and address (Employer: Complete 7, 8, and 9 only if sending to IRS)

8 Office code

9 Employer identification number

Withholdings: FICA Tax

Suppose that Joshua earns $3.65 per hour and works 20 hours one particular week. His gross income would be $73.00. But his paycheck would not be $73.00. Each payroll period, certain amounts of money are deducted from an employee's gross income before his check is written. These amounts are known as *withholdings*. The amount left after the withholdings are subtracted from the gross income is known as *net income* or "take-home pay." The net income is the amount written on the check.

Some withholdings are required by law. The Federal Insurance Contributions Act (FICA), passed in 1935, requires employers to deduct a certain percent of the employee's earnings to go toward the support of the social-security program. Under this program, employees pay a social-security tax (FICA tax) during their working years. When they retire or become disabled, they receive social security benefit payments.

The social security tax rate and base figure increase every few years. In January of 1986, the rate increased from 7.05% to 7.15%, and the base figure increased from $39,600 to $42,000. (Any earnings above the base figure are not taxable.) As of January, 1987, the rate remained at 7.15%, but the base figure increased to $43,800. When an employer withholds FICA tax from an employee, he is required by law to pay the same amount toward the employee's social security benefits. This amounts to approximately 14.3% of a person's gross income being credited toward his social security account annually. A self-employed person must pay the entire 14.3% himself, but he figures the tax from his net income.

Social security is supposed to provide security for your future. This program, however, like all man-made programs, has its shortcomings. The program may go bankrupt and be unable to pay you by the time you reach retirement age. You cannot put your trust in social security, but you can trust in the security that you have in Christ. If you are a Christian, your future is secure. You are promised eternal life with your heavenly Father. You can trust in the eternal security that God gives you, not in man's "social security."

Example 1

Amy earned $210 one particular week. Find the amount that was withheld for FICA tax.

$$\$210 \times 7.15\%$$
$$\$210 \times 0.0715 = 15.015 \approx \$15.02$$

Example 2

Mr. Howard earned $56,000 in 1986. Find the FICA tax that was withheld.

$56,000 is more than the base figure, so the base figure is used.

$$\$42,000 \times 7.15\%$$
$$\$42,000 \times 0.0715 = \$3,003$$

Exercises

Find the FICA tax that should be withheld from each of the monthly salaries shown below. Use the tax rate of 7.15% and round to the nearest cent.

1. $2,580
2. $2,250
3. $1,500
4. $3,166

5. $1,648
6. $900
7. $1,287
8. $2,050

Find the FICA tax that should be withheld from each of the 1987 annual salaries shown below. Use a tax rate of 7.15% and round to the nearest cent.

9. $38,000
10. $64,000
11. $27,000

12. $73,580
13. $36,210
14. $82,000

15. Mr. Green owns a farm. His net earnings in 1986 were $25,240. Find the FICA tax that he owed in 1986.

16. One month, the Johnson Jewelry Company paid combined gross wages of $96,200 to its three employees. Find the company's share of the FICA tax owed. (Use the 1987 tax rate.)

Withholdings: Federal Income Tax

The federal government requires an employer to withhold and pay an income tax for each employee. This income tax provides the federal government with more than half of its income. The amount of income tax to withhold is determined by three things: the employee's gross pay, his marital status, and the number of withholding allowances that he has claimed.

An employer can choose one of several ways to compute the amount of federal income tax to withhold. One way is called the percentage method. Tables like those following are used to figure the income tax.

Table 7.1

Percentage Method Income Tax Withholding Table

Amount of One Withholding Allowance (for Wages Paid after December 1986)

Payroll Period	Value of One Withholding Allowance
Weekly	$ 36.54
Biweekly	73.08
Semimonthly	79.17
Monthly	158.33
Quarterly	475.00
Semiannually	950.00
Annually	1,900.00
Daily or Miscellaneous (each day of the payroll period)	7.31

Table 7.2
Tables for Percentage Method Withholding

(For Wages Paid after December 1986)
Remember: *The wage amounts on this page are after withholding allowances have been subtracted.*

If the Payroll Period with Respect to an Employee Is Weekly

(a) SINGLE person—including head of household:

If the amount of wages is:		The amount of income tax to be withheld shall be:	
Not over $12 0			
Over—	But not over—		of excess over
$12	—$47	11%	—$12
$47	—$335	$3.85 plus 15%	—$47
$335	—$532	$47.05 plus 28%	—$335
$532	—$1,051	$102.21 plus 35%	—$532
$1,051	....	$283.86 plus 38.5%	—$1,051

(b) MARRIED person—

If the amount of wages is:		The amount of income tax to be withheld shall be:	
Not over $36 0			
Over—	But not over—		of excess over
$36	—$93	11%	—$36
$93	—$574	$6.27 plus 15%	—$93
$574	—$901	$78.42 plus 28%	—$574
$901	—$1,767	$169.98 plus 35%	—$901
$1,767	....	$473.08 plus 38.5%	—$1,767

If the Payroll Period with Respect to an Employee Is Biweekly

(a) SINGLE person—including head of household:

If the amount of wages is:		The amount of income tax to be withheld shall be:	
Not over $25 0			
Over—	But not over—		of excess over
$25	—$94	11%	—$25
$94	—$671	$7.59 plus 15%	—$94
$671	—$1,063	$94.14 plus 28%	—$671
$1,063	—$2,102	$203.90 plus 35%	—$1,063
$2,102	....	$567.55 plus 38.5%	—$2,102

(b) MARRIED person—

If the amount of wages is:		The amount of income tax to be withheld shall be:	
Not over $72 0			
Over—	But not over—		of excess over
$72	—$187	11%	—$72
$187	—$1,148	$12.65 plus 15%	—$187
$1,148	—$1,802	$156.80 plus 28%	—$1,148
$1,802	—$3,533	$339.92 plus 35%	—$1,802
$3,533	....	$945.77 plus 38.5%	—$3,533

If the Payroll Period with Respect to an Employee Is Semimonthly

(a) SINGLE person—including head of household:

If the amount of wages is:		The amount of income tax to be withheld shall be:	
Not over $27 0			
Over—	But not over—		of excess over
$27	—$102	11%	—$27
$102	—$727	$8.25 plus 15%	—$102
$727	—$1,152	$102.00 plus 28%	—$727
$1,152	—$2,277	$221.00 plus 35%	—$1,152
$2,277	....	$614.75 plus 38.5%	—$2,277

(b) MARRIED person—

If the amount of wages is:		The amount of income tax to be withheld shall be:	
Not over $78 0			
Over—	But not over—		of excess over
$78	—$203	11%	—$78
$203	—$1,244	$13.75 plus 15%	—$203
$1,244	—$1,953	$169.90 plus 28%	—$1,244
$1,953	—$3,828	$368.42 plus 35%	—$1,953
$3,828	....	$1,024.67 plus 38.5%	—$3,828

If the Payroll Period with Respect to an Employee Is Monthly

(a) SINGLE person—including head of household:

If the amount of wages is:		The amount of income tax to be withheld shall be:	
Not over $53 0			
Over—	But not over—		of excess over
$53	—$203	11%	—$53
$203	—$1,453	$16.50 plus 15%	—$203
$1,453	—$2,303	$204.00 plus 28%	—$1,453
$2,303	—$4,553	$442.00 plus 35%	—$2,303
$4,553	....	$1,229.50 plus 38.5%	—$4,553

(b) MARRIED person—

If the amount of wages is:		The amount of income tax to be withheld shall be:	
Not over $155 0			
Over—	But not over—		of excess over
$155	—$405	11%	—$155
$405	—$2,488	$27.50 plus 15%	—$405
$2,488	—$3,905	$339.95 plus 28%	—$2,488
$3,905	—$7,655	$736.71 plus 35%	—$3,905
$7,655	....	$2,049.21 plus 38.5%	—$7,655

To figure the federal income tax by the percentage method . . .

1. Multiply the appropriate withholding allowance by the number of allowances (exemptions) claimed.
2. Subtract the amount obtained in step 1 from the employee's wage. The result is called the amount subject to withholding.
3. Use the tables to determine the amount to withhold.

Example

Jane Holland is single and claimed one exemption for herself on her W-4 Form. She is paid weekly. One week she earned $285. Using the percentage method, determine the amount that was withheld for federal income tax.

1. Using the withholding table, determine the amount of one withholding allowance.

$$\$36.54$$

2. Multiply the amount from step 1 by 1 because Jane has claimed 1 exemption.

$$1 \times \$36.54 = \$36.54$$

3. Subtract $36.54 from Jane's weekly income.

$$\$285 - \$36.54 = \$248.46 \text{ (income subject to withholding)}$$

4. Use Table 7.2 to determine the amount to withhold.

$$\$3.85 + 15\% \text{ of excess over } \$47$$

(a) Determine the excess over $47.

$$\$248.46 - \$47 = \$201.46$$

(b) Find 15% of $201.46.

$$0.15 \times \$201.46 \approx \$30.22$$

(c) Add the amount from step "b" to $3.85.

$$\$3.85 + \$30.22 = \$34.07$$

Conclusion: $34.07 is the amount withheld.

Exercises

Use Table 7.1 to determine the amount subject to withholding in exercises 1 through 5.

Gross Income	Payroll Period	Number of Exemptions Claimed
1. $1,250	monthly	2
2. $215	weekly	1
3. $790	semimonthly	3
4. $7,000	quarterly	4
5. $923	biweekly	5

Use the biweekly-payroll-period section of Table 7.2 to figure the amount of income tax to be withheld if the amount subject to withholding is . . .

6. $600 for a single person
7. $1,450 for a single person
8. $987 for a married person
9. $750 for a married person
10. $43.50 for a single person
11. $1,290 for a married person

Using the percentage method, determine the amount of federal income tax that should be withheld for each person.

Name	Gross Income	Payroll Period	No. of Exemptions Claimed	Marital Status
12. Robert	$195	weekly	1	single
13. Janet	$350	biweekly	2	single
14. Mr. Hill	$1,425	semimonthly	4	married
15. Mr. Cook	$1,162	semimonthly	5	married
16. Mr. Manz	$415	weekly	3	married

Withholdings: State Income Tax

In addition to federal income tax, most states require their residents to pay an income tax to the state. Like the federal income tax, these taxes are collected through withholdings. The employer withholds the tax from each paycheck and sends it to the state. States differ on the methods they use to figure taxes, but most use a flat rate, a graduated rate, or a variation of one of these. Only the two major methods will be discussed here.

If the flat-rate method is used, the tax is a set percentage of all taxable income.

Example 1

Jerry must pay Michigan income tax. In 1986, Michigan had a flat-rate income tax of 4.35% of taxable income. If Jerry's taxable income for that year was $36,700, find the income tax that he owed the state of Michigan.

$$4.35\% \text{ of } \$36,700$$
$$0.0435 \times 36,700 = \$1,596.45$$

Most states use a graduated income tax. Using this method, the incomes are divided into segments, or brackets, and each bracket is taxed at a different rate. The following is a sample table for figuring graduated income tax:

Table 7.3

Bracket	Annual Income	Tax
1	$0—$2,000	2% of income
2	$2,001—$4,000	$40 plus 3% of the amount over $2,000
3	$4,001—$6,000	$100 plus 4% of the amount over $4,000
4	$6,001 and over	$180 plus 5% of the amount over $6,000

Example 2

In 1985, the residents of Maryland paid a graduated income tax according to the Table 7.3. Find the state income tax of a resident whose taxable income was $7,200.

Find the amount over $6,000.

$$7,200 - 6,000 = \$1,200$$

Find 5% of $1,200.

$$0.05 \times 1,200 = 60$$

Add $60 to the base of $180.

$$\$180 + \$60 = \$240$$

Exercises

Figure the state income tax on the following taxable incomes. Use the flat-rate method. (Round to the nearest cent.)

	Taxable Income	Rate		Taxable Income	Rate
1.	$15,200	$2\frac{1}{2}$	6.	$18,250	$3\frac{1}{4}$
2.	$21,650	3.25%	7.	$9,230	3.6%
3.	$12,785	3%	8.	$31,500	2.95%
4.	$23,400	4.15%	9.	$7,200	$4\frac{1}{2}$
5.	$36,788	$2\frac{3}{4}$	10.	$25,400	3.85%

Use Table 7.3 to figure the state income tax for the following taxable incomes.

11. $5,800
12. $12,400
13. $26,530
14. $895
15. $4,580

16. $18,200
17. $970
18. $34,350
19. $2,450
20. $15,200

Income Tax Returns

Each resident of the United States who has an income above a designated minimum must file an annual federal income tax return. In most states this same resident will also be required to file a state income tax return. Many of the states are standardizing their tax forms to match or closely parallel the federal forms. In previous sections you have seen how federal and state withholding taxes are calculated. A tax return reconciles the amount of money withheld for taxes with the taxpayer's actual tax obligation. In other words, if the amount withheld from the taxpayer's income matches his tax obligation, his tax return will indicate this fact for the Internal Revenue Service (IRS), the tax-collection agency of the federal government. Any difference between withholding and obligations is reconciled by a refund from the IRS or by an additional payment by the taxpayer.

By April 15 of every year income tax returns must be in the mail to the regional office of the IRS or to the respective state treasurer's office. Taxpayers who do not file a return or who file a late return without a time extension are subject to a penalty along with interest charges.

Each year the IRS is informed about your income through a Form W-2, Wage and Tax Statement, filed by your employer. This statement has three copies for the taxpayer plus the copy sent directly to the IRS. The taxpayer's three copies of the W-2 provide one each for the federal tax return, state tax return, and employee's records. By January 31, the employee will receive his W-2 forms from all employers. Once all the W-2 forms are in hand, he may file his return. In the sample W-2 in Figure 7.2 you will notice that, besides carefully identifying the employee and employer, his form gives the total wages, the federal tax withheld, the Social Security tax withheld, and state tax withheld.

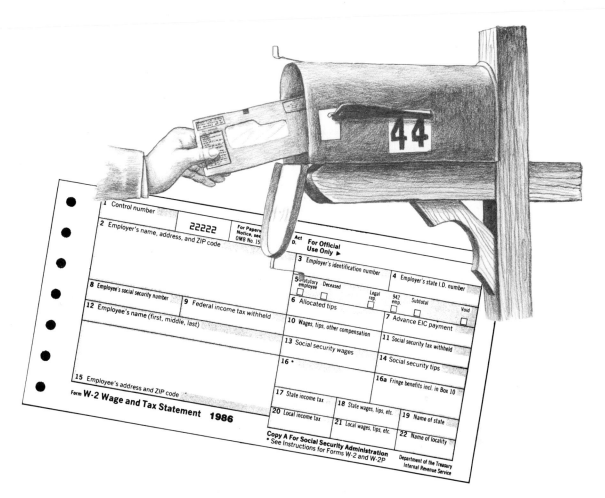

The form shown contains the following fields:

- 1 Control number
- 2 Employer's name, address, and ZIP code — 22222
- For Paperwork Reduction Act Notice, see OMB No. 15...
- Act D. For Official Use Only ▶
- 3 Employer's identification number
- 4 Employer's state I.D. number
- 5 Statutory employee / Deceased / Legal rep. / 942 emp. / Subtotal / Void
- 6 Allocated tips
- 7 Advance EIC payment
- 8 Employee's social security number
- 9 Federal income tax withheld
- 10 Wages, tips, other compensation
- 11 Social security tax withheld
- 12 Employee's name (first, middle, last)
- 13 Social security wages
- 14 Social security tips
- 16 *
- 16a Fringe benefits incl. in Box 10
- 15 Employee's address and ZIP code
- 17 State income tax
- 18 State wages, tips, etc.
- 19 Name of state
- 20 Local income tax
- 21 Local wages, tips, etc.
- 22 Name of locality
- Form W-2 Wage and Tax Statement 1986
- Copy A For Social Security Administration
- See Instructions for Forms W-2 and W-2P
- Department of the Treasury Internal Revenue Service

Prior to the Tax Reform Act of 1986, there were three basic filing forms used for federal income tax returns: Form 1040 EZ, 1040 A, and 1040. The taxpayer's use of a given form depends on a number of criteria, such as marital status, income level, dependents, sources of income, and itemization of deductions. Because the changes resulting from tax reform will continue to occur over several tax years, this study centers on the principles of a federal tax return rather than a specific tax form. If you learn the principles and vocabulary of tax returns, you can easily fill out a tax return just by reading the directions.

You should become familiar with the following tax return vocabulary. This list is shorter than what you would find in a tax manual, but it concentrates on the key ideas. The process of establishing your tax liability will follow the list of terms.

income: This includes wages, bonuses, commissions, tips, dividends, interest, and profits from business or sale of real property. The total of all income is called *gross income*. (*Note:* A dividend is income from ownership of stocks such as IBM or General Motors.)

income exclusions: The following are not considered income: welfare, insurance benefits because of death or property loss, gifts, interest on tax-free bonds, and child support.

adjustments to income: Certain costs incurred by the taxpayer can be subtracted directly from the gross income. These include employee business expenses that are not paid by the employer, payments to retirement plans up to a maximum amount, alimony, and interest penalties for early withdrawals.

adjusted gross income: The difference between gross income and all allowable adjustments to income. This value is used to establish income level for tax forms and to calculate certain deductions and credits.

filing status: There are five different categories for filing status: single, single—head of household, married with joint return, married with separate returns, and widow or widowers with dependents.

exemptions: Identify the members of a household and include the taxpayer, his spouse, dependent children or others who depend on the taxpayer for at least half of their support. Table 7.4 gives the amount allowed for each personal exemption.

Table 7.4
Personal Exemptions

Year	Amount
1987	$1,900
1988	$1,950
1989+	$2,000

deductions: These are amounts that can be subtracted from the adjusted gross income before calculating tax liability. Those who do not itemize deductions on Form 1040 can claim the standard deduction, which is based on the filing status of the tax payer. See Table 7.5 for the amounts allowed as the standard deduction. Those who itemize deductions will use the total of allowable medical expenses, tax payments, certain interest charges, charitable contributions, moving expenses, and certain portions of miscellaneous items such as union dues and professional fees. If the total of itemized deductions exceeds the standard deduction, then the taxpayer can benefit from itemizing.

Table 7.5
Standard Deductions

Filing Status	1987	After 1987
Joint return*	$3,760	$5,000
Married—separately	$1,880	$2,500
Single	$2,540	$3,000
Head of household	$2,540	$4,400

*includes widows or widowers with dependents

taxable income: This amount is the adjusted gross income minus all allowable deductions.

tax liability: The tax liability for a given taxpayer is found by using a table listing taxable income by increments and by filing status.

The steps below give the process that any tax return uses to establish tax liability. You may think that it looks much simpler than the tax forms you have seen your parents use because just the key steps are outlined here. One step may require several lines or even several pages on an actual tax form. Remember, every tax form will involve these principles.

Calculation of Tax Liability

Step 1.   List all income. Interest income may have the first $200 to $400 as tax-free. The total of all income is called *gross income*.

Step 2.   List all adjustments to income.

Step 3.   Find adjusted gross income by subtracting the total in Step 2 from the total in Step 1.

Step 4.   Find the standard deduction from a table such as 7.5.

Step 5.   Find the total of all itemized deductions. If this is larger than the standard deduction, use it; otherwise use the standard deduction.

Step 6.   Find the total deductions due to the number of exemptions.

Step 7.   Find the taxable income by subtracting all allowable deductions from Steps 4, 5, and 6 from the adjusted gross income.

Step 8.   Find the tax liability using the table based on appropriate filing status and using the taxable income from Step 7.

Step 9.   Find the difference between the tax liability and the federal tax paid through withholding or estimated pre-payments.

Step 10. If withholding is larger, you get a *refund*. If tax liability is larger, you pay additional taxes.

Note: There are three types of income, related as follows:

Gross income = the sum of all sources of income
Adjusted gross income = gross income minus adjustments
Taxable income = adjusted gross income minus deductions

Example 1

Find the adjusted gross income for Mr. Ezra Goldberg.

wages: $29,250
interest: $4,900
dividends: $1,820
IRA contribution: $2,000
business expenses: $450

Solution:

$$\begin{aligned}
\text{gross income} = 29{,}250 + 4{,}900 + 1{,}820 = &\quad 35{,}970 \\
\text{total adjustments} = 2{,}000 + 450 = &\quad \underline{-2{,}450} \\
\text{adjusted gross income} = &\quad 33{,}520
\end{aligned}$$

Example 2

Find Mr. Goldberg's 1987 taxable income, given the following deductions:

5 exemptions @ $1,900 each
itemized deductions of $5,230
filing status: married with joint return

Solution:

$$\begin{aligned}
\text{total deductions} = 5 \times 1{,}900 = &\quad 9{,}500 \\
&\quad \underline{+5{,}230} \\
&\quad 14{,}730
\end{aligned}$$

$$\begin{aligned}
\text{taxable income} \;&= \text{adjusted gross income} - \text{total deductions} \\
&= \$33{,}520 - \$14{,}730 \\
&= \$18{,}790
\end{aligned}$$

Example 3

Use the following tax table to find Mr. Goldberg's tax liability for 1987.

Table 7.6
1987 Tax Rates

Married Couples Filing Joint Returns*					SINGLE INDIVIDUALS*				
Taxable Income					*Taxable Income*				
Over:	*But not over:*	*Pay*	*+ % on excess*	*of the amount over*	*Over:*	*But not over:*	*Pay*	*+ % on excess*	*of the amount over*
$ 0–	$ 3,000	$ 0	11%	$ 0	$ 0–	$ 1,800	$ 0	11%	$ 0
3,000–	28,000	330	15	3,000	1,800–	16,800	198	15	1,800
28,000–	45,000	4,080	28	28,000	16,800–	27,000	2,448	28	16,800
45,000–	90,000	8,840	35	45,000	27,000–	54,000	5,304	35	27,000
Over	90,000	24,590	38.5	90,000	Over	54,000	14,754	38.5	54,000
* This schedule also applies to a qualified surviving spouse with dependents.					* This schedule also applies to unmarried taxpayers other than a qualified surviving spouse or head of household.				

1988+ Tax Rates
Married Couples Filing Joint Returns*

	Taxable Income				
Over:	But not over:	Pay	+ % on excess	of the amount over:
$ 0—	$ 29,750	$ 0	15%	$ 0
Over	29,750	4,462.50	28	29,750

* This schedule also applies to a qualified surviving spouse with dependents.

1988+ Tax Rates
Single Individuals*

	Taxable Income				
Over:	But not over:	Pay	+ % on excess	of the amount over:
$ 0—	$ 17,850	$ 0	15%	$ 0
Over	17,850	2,677.50	28	17,850

* This schedule also applies to unmarried taxpayers other than a qualified surviving spouse or head of household.

Solution:

Mr. Goldberg's taxable income falls in the bracket $3,000 to $28,000, so his tax liability is . . .

$$\$330 + 15\%(18,790 - 3,000)$$
$$\$330 + 0.15(15,790)$$
$$\$330 + 2,368.50$$
$$\$2,698.50$$

Exercises

For each problem, use the given information to find the adjusted gross income.

Compensation & Income	Adjustments
1. wages: $9,263.20 interest: $520.00	IRA: $500 interest penalty: $182
2. wages: $21,536.00 dividends: $122.00	retirement fund: $620 business expense: $1,150
3. wages: $19,977.45 insurance settlement: $10,000	alimony: $1,200 interest penalty: $2,400 business expense: $850
4. wages: $3,040 dividends: $1,800 interest: $2,900 land-sale profit: $8,100	interest penalty: $1,600
5. wages: $7,240.70 graduation gift: $10,000 interest: $79 Christmas bonus: $500	IRA: $2,000 business expense: $150

For each problem, use the given information to find the taxable income. Always pick itemized or standard deduction to give the most benefit to the taxpayer. Use Tables 7.4 and 7.5.

	Adjusted Gross Income	Tax Year	Filing Status	Exemptions	Itemized Deductions
6.	$10,400	87	single	1	none
7.	$20,550	87	married—joint	2	$3,850
8.	$15,800	88	head of household	3	$4,100
9.	$23,480	89	married—separately	3	$4,720
10.	$34,250	89	single	1	$3,850

Use Table 7.6 to calculate the tax liability for each tax return.

	Taxable Income	Year	Filing Status
11.	$6,580	1987	single
12.	$44,240	1987	married—joint
13.	$8,350	1988	widow—dependents
14.	$18,500	1989	married—joint
15.	$31,760	1989	single

For exercises 16-18, use the methods and allowances as in exercises 1-15 to find the tax liability and refund or additional tax owed.

16. Find the tax liability for Tony Battaglia. He has a wife and 3 grade-school children, and he earned $18,529.80 during 1987 on a construction job. Other information from his financial records are as follows: $320 interest income, $580 paid to an IRA, $185 business expense, and the federal withholding on his W-2 was $1,043.35.

17. Using the financial records below and a standard deduction allowance for 1988, find the tax liability of Anita Ramseur, age 26, single.

IBM stock dividend .... $	350.00
sales commissions—Intex Corp.	16,800.00
interest income—First National	1,425.86
insurance check—car accident	8,450.00
business expense	423.50
interest withdrawal penalty	85.00
deposit to IRA—mutual fund	1,260.00
W-2 withholding—Intex Corp.	2,352.60

18. Mrs. Randolph Danforth is a widow with 2 dependent children and earns $21,500 per year as a legal secretary. She owns a home and itemizes her deductions for tax returns. Find her tax liability from the following financial information. Use the 1988 deductions and rates.

> interest income: $150
> business expenses: $240
> medical allowance: any amount above 7% of adjusted gross income
> W-2 federal withholding: $1,493.80

> *Itemized deductions*
> medical expenses: $1,753.82
> taxes: $1,141.20
> interest paid: $1,512.00
> charitable contributions: $1,950.00
> professional fees: $200.00

Sales Tax

In many cities and states, you pay a sales tax when you purchase merchandise or services. This sales tax is usually from 4% to 8% of the amount of the purchase. The seller of the merchandise collects the tax from the buyer and sends it to the appropriate government agency. In some states, exclusions from tax are allowed. For example, food and medicine may be excluded from sales tax because these things are necessities.

A 5% sales tax means that the buyer pays $.05 tax for every dollar spent. To compute sales tax, simply find the percent of the price and round it to the nearest cent.

Example

Mr. Cooper purchased the following items at the hardware store:

        hammer: $12.95

        box of nails: $4.49

        paintbrush: $5.99

Find his total bill if he must pay a sales tax of 6%.

1. Add to find the subtotal.

$$\$12.94 + \$4.49 + \$5.99 = \$23.43$$

2. Find 6% of $23.43.

$$.06 \times \$23.43 = \$1.4058 = \$1.41$$

3. Add the subtotal and the sales tax to find the total bill.

$$\$23.43 + \$1.41 = \$24.84$$

Today, most cash registers are programmed to figure sales tax automatically. This makes things easy on the clerk, but as a customer you should know how to figure sales tax so that you can estimate and check your bill.

Exercises

Find the sales tax on the following subtotals. (Use a rate of 4%.)

1. $6.00	**5.** $3.25
2. $19.26	**6.** $16.97
3. $31.20	**7.** $38.36
4. $11.89	**8.** $52.18

Find the total bill for each list of prices if the sales tax rate is 5%.

9. $2.12	**11.** $24.00
$7.38	$13.56
$4.26	$ 9.49
10. $14.25	$ 6.98
$ 7.99	**12.** $239.00
$ 6.49	$ 17.98
$10.85	$ 6.37

Find the total bill for each list of prices if the sales tax rate is 7%.

13. $15.35	**15.** $89.99
$ 8.99	$52.50
$ 2.39	$12.75
14. $38.17	**16.** $110.00
$ 9.59	$ 95.00
$13.36	$ 62.29
$ 4.76	

Michigan has a 4% sales tax rate that excludes food from tax. The people in problems 17-20 are shopping at a Michigan department store that carries everything from clothing to hardware to groceries. Part of the receipt is shown. Calculate the total bill. (*Note:* Food items are labeled *GROC* for "grocery item.")

17. Charlotte:

```
$21.99 CLOTH
$ 6.26 HARDW
$ 7.99 GROC
$  .89 GROC
$12.55 HOUSEW
```

19. Mr. Koth:

```
$59.00 APPLI
$26.89 HOMEIM
$ 2.49 GROC
$ 7.85 GROC
```

18. Mrs. Highfield:

```
$ 2.69 GROC
$13.46 TOYS
$5.73 TOYS
$ .39 GROC
$ 6.19 GROC
$10.88 HARDW
```

20. Nathan:

```
$18.97 SPORT
$23.49 CLOTH
$29.99 SHOES
```

Property Tax

If you own real estate, you may be required to pay a property tax to your local government. This tax differs from income tax and sales tax in that you are billed once or twice a year for property tax. Your local tax collector sends you this bill.

It is the *assessed valuation* of property that is taxed, not the market value. Local tax assessors determine the assessed valuation of the property, which is a certain percentage of the market value.

Example 1

The assessed valuation of the Hartmans' house and land is 40% of the market value. If the market value is $83,400, find the assessed valuation.

$$40\% \text{ of } \$83,400$$
$$0.4 \times 83,400 = \$33,360.00$$

A tax rate and the assessed valuation are used to determine the property tax. Often the rate is expressed as a certain number of dollars for each $100 unit of the assessed valuation.

Example 2

If the tax rate is $4.15 per $100 unit of assessed valuation, find the property tax on real estate assessed at $26,570.00

Figure how many $100 units there are in $26,570.

$$\$26,570 \div 100 = 265.7$$

Figure the amount of tax.

$$265.7 \times \$4.15 = \$1,102.655 \approx \$1,102.66$$

Exercises

Figure the assessed valuation for each of the following:

Percent of Assessment	Market Value	Percent of Assessment	Market Value
1. 30%	$36,400	6. 40%	$92,116
2. 45%	$97,384	7. 25%	$23,726
3. 50%	$25,200	8. 55%	$42,190
4. 35%	$89,677	9. 60%	$65,213
5. 60%	$108,215	10. 45%	$52,955

Find the property tax for each of the following. (Round answers to the nearest cent.)

Assessed Valuation	Tax Rate
11. $10,870	$2.56 per $100
12. $12,595	$3.24 per $100
13. $32,719	$3.85 per $100
14. $36,742	$4.75 per $100
15. $47,243	$3.92 per $100
16. $15,387	$4.36 per $100
17. $64,526	$2.79 per $100
18. $9,260	$5.10 per $100
19. $31,840	$4.63 per $100
20. $27,166	$3.99 per $100

Chapter 7 Review

adjusted gross income	gross income
adjustments to income	income
deduction	income exclusion
dependent	Internal Revenue
exemption	Service (IRS)
filing status	net income
Form W-2, Wage and Tax Statement	taxable income
Form W-4, Employee's Withholding	tax liability
Allowance Certificate	withholding

Find the FICA tax that should be withheld from each of the following annual salaries. Use a tax rate of 7.15% and round to the nearest cent.

1. $32,500   **3.** $18,285

2. $27,650   **4.** $36,342

Using the percentage method, determine the amount of federal income tax that should be withheld for the people below:

Gross Income	Payroll Period	No. of Exemptions Claimed	Marital Status
5. $265	weekly	1	single
6. $1,350	semimonthly	3	married

Using the flat-rate method, determine the amount of state income tax to withhold.

Taxable Income	Rate
7. $9,246	4.25%
8. $18,355	3.5%

Use Table 7.3 to determine amount of state income tax to withhold for the following taxable incomes.

9. $8,740

10. $13,582

Find the total bill for each list of prices if the sales tax rate is 4%.

11. $7.21   **12.** $21.50

     $9.75 $12.99

     $ .49 $ 6.45

     $3.99

Find the property tax for each of the following:

Percent of Assessment	Market Value	Tax Rate
13. 35%	$56,250	$4.25 per $100
14. 55%	$87,190	$3.95 per $100

BEAUMONT
HORIZO
257 789 79
ANDRA T LOCKS
Accon Oil Company
National Credit Card
Al S. Drackston
Not valid unless signed, in ink, by cardholde
469 50 584 78
AL S DRACKSTON
reverse side
Credit Card
Marshall's
OOT 62TO800
AA
SANDRA L STOCK
MEMBER SINCE 1986
HARTY L HART
EXP DATE 05/98
STAN L
Serving You S

Borrowing Money

Romans 13:8 says, "Owe no man any thing, but to love one another." Some Christians take this verse to mean that we should never go into debt under any circumstances. Others believe that it is acceptable to go into debt only for items whose value does not depreciate. What do you think?

Consider for a moment how a loan works. You borrow a sum of money and agree to pay it back over a certain length of time. You also pay interest, the price paid for the use of someone else's money. Interest, then, is the cost of the use of money. When you take out a loan, you are paying for a convenience—the use of money. At the time you secure a loan, you sit down with your creditor and agree upon payments that you will make in order to pay back the loan. He then expects you to pay a specified amount of money at regular intervals, usually monthly. After you have made all these payments, you no longer owe him anything. You have satisfied the obligation to meet the terms of the loan.

As a Christian, however, you must be careful not to get into excessive debt or to agree upon payments that you cannot make. You are dishonest if you agree to make payments, knowing that you are not financially able to meet that obligation. This is not only a matter of stewardship, but also of testimony. Your testimony is at stake when you do not pay what you have agreed to pay.

Some of the ideas discussed in this chapter may not apply to you, but it is good to be familiar with them. In each section, try to develop some principles for your life. For example, decide whether you believe it is wise to use credit cards. If so, determine how you will limit yourself with their use. Many people get into trouble with credit cards because they are not disciplined with them. Ask the Lord to help you make some decisions regarding your financial future.

Simple Interest and Promissory Notes

Someday you may be in the position of wanting to purchase something but not having the funds available. Before you run out and borrow the money, you need to examine your situation carefully. It is not wise to borrow money in order to live beyond your means. The writer of Hebrews admonishes us, "Be content with such things as ye have." In other words, don't give in to every desire that you have. Determine whether the item you are considering is a need or merely a want.

When you borrow money, you must promise that you will repay the amount borrowed *plus* interest within a specified length of time. Loans between individuals are usually legally established by a signed paper, called a *promissory note.* Loans from banks and credit unions, however, are usually set down legally on a signed paper, called a *contract.* Each of these documents will state the amount borrowed, the date of repayment or length of time before repayment, the rate of interest, and the person (or institution) to be repaid.

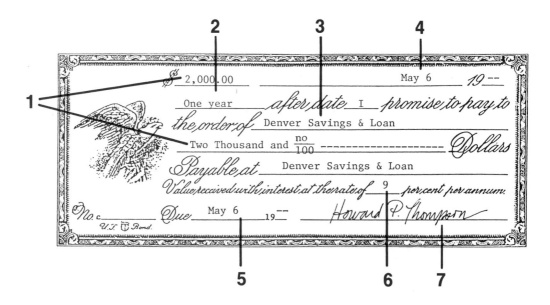

Figure 8.1

1. *Face value* or *principal*—amount borrowed
2. *Term*—time for which the money is borrowed
3. *Payee*—person or institution from whom the money is borrowed
4. *Date of the note*—date the note is signed
5. *Maturity date*—date the money must be repaid
6. *Rate of interest*—percentage of principal added to payments
7. *Maker*—signature of the person or people borrowing the money

Figure 8.2

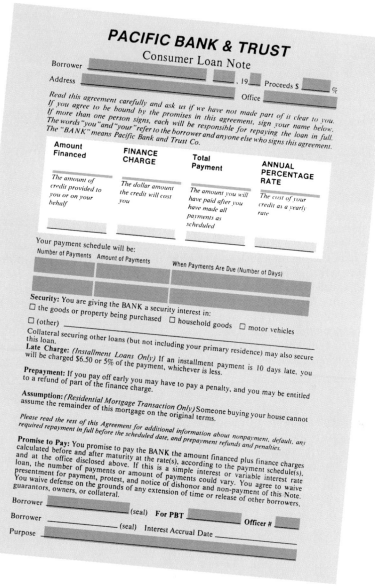

A *simple-interest* loan has the interest computed on the original principal. The *interest rate* is a percent of the principal that must be paid for its use. Simple-interest rates are usually stated as a rate per year. You can compute the simple interest as the product of principal, rate, and time.

$$I = Prt, \text{ where } \dots$$

I = simple interest in dollars
P = principal borrowed in dollars
r = interest rate (percent) per year
t = time in years.

Example 1

Find the simple interest on a $5,000 loan, borrowed for 15 months at 9%.

Solution:

Substitute the given number into the simple interest formula after changing 15 months to years.

$$I = P \times r \times t$$
$$= \$5,000 \times 0.09 \times \tfrac{15}{12}$$
$$= \$562.50$$

Remarks:

1. If the term of the loan is stated in days instead of months or years, you will have to divide by the number of days in a year to convert time to years. Banks and other lending institutions often use a 360-day year. The use of 360 to convert time to years is called *ordinary interest*. The use of a 365-day year is called *exact interest*.

2. When the time for a loan is given in days or when the date of the note and the maturity date are given, the time is called *exact time*. Using months or years is called *approximate time*.

3. *Banker's Rule* makes use of ordinary interest and exact time. The name has obviously come about because it is used so much by bankers.

Example 2

Use Banker's Rule to find the interest charges for the following loan:

$4,850 borrowed at 12%
Date of note: April 14, 1986
Due date: June 25, 1986

Solution:

The first step is to find the time. Use the serial table from the back of the book to find the two dates:

$$
\begin{array}{lr}
\text{June 25} = & 176 \\
\text{April 14} = & \underline{104} \\
\text{time in days} = & 72
\end{array}
$$

Now substitute your values into the simple-interest formula:

$$I = P \times r \times t$$
$$= \$4,850 \times 0.12 \times \tfrac{72}{360}$$
$$= \$116.40$$

Besides needing the interest charges for a simple-interest loan, you will need to know the amount to be repaid, called the *maturity value*. This amount will be the sum of the original principal and the interest. The letter S is usually used for the amount of the maturity value. It comes from the word *sum*.

$$S = P + I, \text{ where } \ldots$$

S = maturity value
P = principal
I = simple interest

If you replace I by its formula and use the distributive law, another form of the maturity value can be used.

$$S = P + Prt$$
$$= P(1 + rt) \text{ maturity value, or amount at simple interest}$$

Example 3

Find the maturity value of a $2,500 simple-interest loan at 8% for 18 months.

Solution:
Substitute into the amount formula:

$$S = P(1 + rt)$$
$$= \$2,500[1 + (0.08)(\tfrac{18}{12})]$$
$$= \$2,500[1 + 0.12]$$
$$= \$2,500[1.12]$$
$$= \$2,800$$

Example 4

Find the maturity value of the following promissory note.

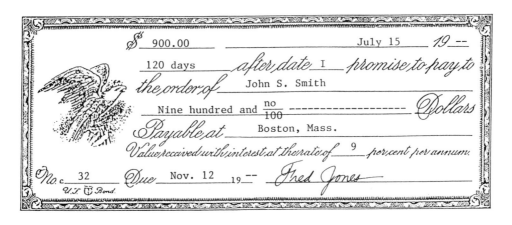

$ __900.00__   July 15   19 --

__120 days__ _after date_ I _promise to pay to_

the order of   John S. Smith

Nine hundred and $\tfrac{no}{100}$ ----------------- _Dollars_

Payable at   Boston, Mass.

Value received with interest at the rate of __9__ _percent per annum._

No. c __32__   _Due_ __Nov. 12__ 19 --   _Fred Jones_

U.S. ⓣ Bond.

Solution:
Use the maturity-value formula and substitute numbers from the note.

$$S = P[1 + rt]$$
$$= 900[1 + (0.09)(\tfrac{120}{360})] \quad \text{(Use Banker's Rule.)}$$
$$= 900[1 + 0.03]$$
$$= 900[1.03]$$
$$= \$927$$

Exercises

Find the exact time for the term of each simple interest loan. Use the serial table.

1. Date of note: Feb. 22, 1980
   Maturity date: Aug. 22, 1980

2. Date of note: March 1, 1984
   Maturity date: April 15, 1984

3. Date of note: July 20, 1985
   Maturity date: Dec. 17, 1985

4. Date of note: Jan. 14, 1845
   Maturity date: March 11, 1845

5. Date of note: Oct. 28, 1929
   Maturity date: Jan. 21, 1930

6. Date of note: Dec. 3, 1967
   Maturity date: May 2, 1968

Find the interest to be paid for each simple-interest loan. If the exact time is given in days or as dates, use the Banker's Rule.

7. principal: $500
   term: $1\frac{1}{2}$ years
   rate: 5%

8. principal: $1,000
   term: 16 months
   rate: $8\frac{1}{2}$%

9. principal: $3,500
   term: 120 days
   rate: $9\frac{1}{2}$%

10. principal: $485
    term: 21 months
    rate: 7%

11. principal: $850
    term: May 19 to Aug. 4
    rate: 6%

12. principal: $4,700
    term: March 15 to Nov. 16
    rate: 10%

Find the exact interest and maturity value for each promissory note.

	Face Value of Note	Term	Rate of Interest
13.	$950	2 years	$9\frac{1}{2}$%
14.	$1,300	8 months	12%
15.	$750	90 days	$9\frac{3}{4}$%
16.	$1,250	1 year	$8\frac{1}{4}$%
17.	$800	5 months	14%
18.	$2,500	120 days	$10\frac{1}{2}$%
19.	$4,000	5 years	12%
20.	$1,500	180 days	$14\frac{1}{4}$%
21.	$695	7 months	$10\frac{1}{4}$%
22.	$1,450	18 months	13%

23. Mr. Jackson had a loan for $1,600 at $7\frac{1}{2}$% dated March 9, 1986. If the term of the loan was 120 days, what date did he have to pay back the loan and what was the maturity value? (Use Banker's Rule.)

24. Jenny noticed an advertisement stating that the Genn Finance Co. would lend $2,000 for 15 months with an interest charge of $312.50. What interest rate were they charging?

25. If Reggie Smith paid off his 90-day simple-interest loan with a payment of $897.60, how much did he borrow at a rate of 8%? (Use Banker's Rule.)

26. When Stan Jones borrowed $2,000 for his motorcycle, he knew that the interest would be $108.50. Find the maturity date of his simple-interest loan if the rate is $10\frac{1}{2}\%$ and he signed the note on May 6, 1986. (Use Banker's Rule.)

Add-on Loans and Annual Percentage Rate

You saw in the last section how a simple-interest loan was handled. The borrower received the money in the amount of the principal and paid it back with interest after an agreed-on time called the "term." But suppose that the borrower pays it back as several smaller payments until all the principal and interest are paid off. A simple-interest loan that is paid off by installments is called an *add-on loan*. If you consider that the lender has a certain portion of the principal back in his possession partway through the term, it will be clear that the true interest rate is not the stated simple-interest rate.

The Truth-in-Lending Act requires anyone offering credit (a creditor) to provide certain information in writing to the borrower. He must show the total finance charges and the annual percentage rate (APR). The APR makes a true comparison between different loan arrangements. The methods of calculating APR, as used by banks, are beyond the scope of this text, but some formulas can be used to give good approximations. We will employ the *constant-ratio formula* to learn how the APR can be considerably more than the stated note of an add-on loan.

Example 1

City Bank offers a $10,000 add-on loan at 8% with 36 monthly payments. What is the total finance charge and the monthly payment?

Solution:

First find the interest using $I = Prt$.

$$I = \$10,000 \times 0.08 \times \tfrac{36}{12}$$
$$= \$10,000 \times 0.08 \times 3$$
$$= \$2,400 \text{ finance charge (interest)}$$

Now find the maturity value.

$$S = P + I$$
$$= \$10,000 + \$2,400$$
$$= \$12,400$$

Finally, divide the maturity value by the number of payments.

$$\text{payment} = \frac{\$12,400}{36}$$
$$= \$344.44$$

The constant-ratio formula allows you to make a good approximation of the annual percentage rate (APR).

$$\text{APR} = \frac{2mI}{P(n+1)}, \text{ where } \ldots$$

m = number of payments per year
I = amount of interest (finance charge)
P = amount of the loan (principal)
n = total number of payments

Example 2

Use the constant-ratio formula to find the APR that City Bank charges for their add-on loans (Example 1).

Solution:

Substitute the values from Example 1 into the formula.

$$\text{APR} = \frac{2mI}{P(n+1)}$$

$$= \frac{2(12)(2400)}{\$10,000(37)}$$

$$= 0.156$$
$$= 15.6\% \text{ (actually 14.56\%; this is about 1\% high)}$$

Exercise

Find the finance charges (interest) and the monthly payment for each add-on loan.

1. principal: $965
   rate: $7\frac{1}{2}\%$
   term: 18 months

2. principal: $1,500
   rate: $9\frac{1}{4}\%$
   term: 15 months

3. principal: $2,500
   rate: 12%
   term: 2 years

4. principal: $4,500
   rate: $6\frac{1}{2}\%$
   term: 30 months

5. principal: $750
   rate: 14%
   term: 9 months

6. principal: $1,882
   rate: $8\frac{3}{4}\%$
   term: 10 months

Use the constant-ratio formula to approximate the APR for each loan. Round answers to the nearest percent.

	Principal	Finance Charges	To Be Paid In:
7.	$500	$135	18 equal monthly installments
8.	$1,000	$170	equal installments, 1 every 3 months for 1 year
9.	$950	$285	equal monthly installments for 2 years
10.	$2,500	$900	equal installments twice a year for 3 years
11.	$1,500	$850	equal installments, 1 every 4 months for 4 years
12.	$600	$84	a single installment at the end of 1 year
13.	$825	$132	a single installment at the end of 1 year
14.	$3,500	$1,050	30 equal monthly installments
15.	$4,000	$2,100	equal installments, 1 every 6 months for 5 years
16.	$3,600	$1,053	equal monthly installments for 3 years
17.	$1,800	12% of the principal	equal monthly installments for 1 year

Discount Interest and Discount Loans

Another common loan instrument, besides simple interest, is *discount interest,* sometimes called *discounting.* Many commercial financial transactions use discounting. United States Treasury Bills are sold by auction as discount loans to the United States government. Banks regularly buy promissory notes or other securities by discount interest. Discount interest works this way: first a loan is made to a customer with a contract for repayment of a specific amount of money at a future date. The bank then calculates the interest charges, using their interest rate and the time or length of the loan. These interest charges are subtracted from the face value of the loan, and the customer receives the balance, called the *proceeds.* The formula for the discount works just like the one for simple interest:

$$D = S \times d \times t, \text{ where } \ldots$$

D = discount in dollars
S = face value of the loan (amount to be repaid)
d = discount rate (per annum)
t = time in years

Example 1

Find the discount for a $500 loan for 15 months at a discount rate of 8%.

Solution:
Write the formula down and substitute.

$$D = S \times d \times t$$
$$= 500 \times 0.08 \times \tfrac{15}{12}$$
$$= \$50$$

Example 2

Find the proceeds (money the borrower receives) for Example 1.

Solution:

$$P(\text{proceeds}) = S(\text{amount}) - D(\text{discount})$$
$$= S - D$$
$$= \$500 - \$50$$
$$= \$450$$

Remarks:
1. The customer will receive $450 and 15 months later will pay back $500 to the lender.
2. The customer who needs the whole $500 will obviously have to borrow more with a discount loan in order to receive $500 as the proceeds.

Using the ideas of Examples 1 and 2, you can make up a formula for the proceeds similar to the one developed for simple interest.

$$\text{Proceeds} = \text{Amount} - \text{Discount}$$
$$= S - D \quad \text{(Now substitute for discount.)}$$
$$= S - Sdt$$
$$= S(1 - dt)$$
$$= S(1 - dt)$$

If this formula is solved for S (the amount), then the face value of a discount loan can be calculated for the desired proceeds.

Example 3

Find the proceeds for a $900 loan for 18 months at a discount rate of $6\tfrac{1}{2}\%$.

Solution:
Substitute the numbers into the proceeds formula.

$$P = S(1 - dt)$$
$$= \$900[1 - (0.065)(\tfrac{18}{12})]$$
$$= \$900[0.9025]$$
$$= \$812.25$$

Example 4

Find the amount of a discount loan that will give $500 proceeds at a discount rate of 8% and a term of 15 months.

Solution:

Solve the formula for S.

$$P = S(1 - dt)$$

$$\frac{P}{(1-dt)} = \frac{S\cancel{(1-dt)}}{\cancel{(1-dt)}} \quad \text{(Divide by } 1 - dt \text{ and cancel.)}$$

$$\frac{P}{(1-dt)} = S \quad \text{(Put the solved variable on the left of the "=.")}$$

$$S = \frac{P}{(1-dt)} \quad \text{(Now substitute values.)}$$

$$S = \frac{\$500}{1 - (0.08)(15/12)}$$

$$S = \frac{\$500}{0.9}$$

$$S = \$555.56$$

Note: The borrower will receive $500 as proceeds, but he will pay back $555.56 after 15 months.

The following two examples show how discounting is used in financial transactions that are more commercially oriented.

Example 5

At a United States Treasury Bill auction, a $1,000,000 90-day treasury bill was purchased for $968,000. Find the discount rate.

Solution:

You can use the formula for discount $D = Sdt$ and solve for d, giving

$$d = \frac{D}{St}$$

The difference between the purchase price (proceeds) and the face value (amount) represents the discount.

$$D = \$1,000,000 - \$968,000$$
$$= \$32,000$$

Now substitute.

$$D = \frac{32,000}{(1,000,000)(0.25)} = 0.128 = 12.8\% \text{ discount rate}$$

Example 6

Many banks buy promissory notes from merchants and small companies who need cash before the maturity date of the note. Suppose that a truck farmer has a promissory note that matures in 120 days with a maturity value of $5,000. How much can he get for the note at a bank that charges 9% discount?

Solution:

The proceeds formula $P = S(1 - dt)$ can be used, with the amount being the maturity value of the promissory note.

$$
\begin{aligned}
P &= S(1 - dt) \\
&= \$5,000[1 - (0.09)(\tfrac{120}{360})] \\
&= \$5,000[0.97] \\
&= \$4,850
\end{aligned}
$$

Remarks:
1. In 4 months the banker will receive $5,000 for the note he paid $4,850 to buy. He makes $150 interest.
2. It may look like the truck farmer paid the whole $150 interest charges; however, he probably charged the original borrower 6% to 7% simple interest.
3. If the original promissory note was for 6 months at 6%, the truck farmer lent only $4,854 as the principal on the promissory note.

Exercises

Find the proceeds that would be received for each of the following discount loans. (Use a 365-day year when days are given.)

	Amount	Rate of Discount	Time
1.	$500	11%	1 year
2.	$850	$8\frac{1}{2}\%$	1 year
3.	$650	$9\frac{1}{4}\%$	6 months
4.	$1,000	10%	3 months
5.	$900	12%	4 months
6.	$750	$11\frac{3}{4}\%$	6 months
7.	$1,200	15%	3 months
8.	$1,500	$12\frac{1}{2}\%$	75 days
9.	$2,000	$13\frac{1}{4}\%$	50 days
10.	$1,350	$16\frac{3}{4}\%$	140 days

Find the amount (face value) of each discount loan. Use a 365-day year when days are given.

Proceeds	Discount Rate	Time
11. $850	$6\frac{1}{2}\%$	1 year
12. $524	8%	9 months
13. $1,200	10%	15 months
14. $5,000	$7\frac{1}{2}\%$	6 months
15. $2,500	$9\frac{1}{2}\%$	80 days
16. $1,000	11%	120 days
17. $1,800	14%	180 days
18. $4,200	12%	$1\frac{1}{2}$ years

Find the discount rate d for each discount loan.

19. amount: $850
time: 9 months
discount: $54.19

20. amount: $1,500
time: 16 months
discount: $120

21. amount: $250,000
proceeds: $225,000
time: 180 days

22. proceeds: $2,500
discount: $500
time: 1 year

23. proceeds: $1,200
discount: $200
time: 15 months

24. amount: $9,000
proceeds: $8,000
time: 2 years

25. Jack Malker made a promissory note for money owed to him by a sales representative. The loan was for $4,500 at 8% simple interest and a term of 9 months. After 3 months he sold the note to a bank, using a discount rate of 10%. What were Jack's proceeds for the note?

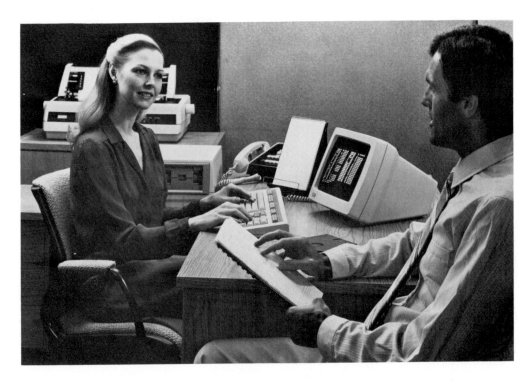

Amortized Loans

Many loans that consumers get from banks and loan companies involve monthly payments, but they are not add-on loans. The borrower receives a loan, which is recorded as a balance owed the lender. One month later the borrower pays the interest that has accrued plus a portion of the balance (principal). He continues to make equal payments, but each month the principal is slightly smaller, so a little more of the payment goes to principal and a little less to interest as time passes. This method of paying back a loan is called *amortization*. Home loans and many automobile loans are amortized. The monthly payment is calculated by knowing the size of the loan, the interest rate per month, and the number of payments. The formula for computing the payment (or the amount borrowed) is developed using compound interest. In the next chapter you will be introduced to compound interest, and the amortization-loan formula will be shown in a special section for calculator methods.

Loan officers at banks usually find out the payments for amortized loans with a table or a company computer. You will find an extensive set of finance tables at the back of this book. The following table is an excerpt to show you how the finance table can be used to get either the monthly payment for each $1.00 borrowed or to get the amount that can be borrowed for each $1.00 of payment. Each page of the tables is for an interest rate, usually called i. The numerals down the side represent the number of payments. To find the term for loans, find the number of payments by multiplying years times twelve.

Table 8.1

Amortized Loan Payments

Pres. Value of $1 at Comp. Int.	Amount Borrowed for $1 Payment	Payment to Borrow $1	n	
0.9876543210	0.9876543210	1.0125000000	1	**Rate**
0.9754610578	1.9631153788	0.5093944099	2	
0.9634183287	2.9265337074	0.3417011728	3	**1.25%**
0.9515242752	3.8780579826	0.2578610233	4	
0.9397770619	4.8178350446	0.2075621084	5	
0.9281748760	5.7460099206	0.1740338102	6	
0.9167159269	6.6627258475	0.1500887209	7	
0.9053984463	7.5681242938	0.1321331365	8	
0.8942206877	8.4623449815	0.1181705546	9	
0.8831809262	9.3455259077	0.1070030740	10	
0.8722774579	10.2178033656	0.0978683935	11	
0.8615086004	11.0793119660	0.0902583123	12	
0.8508726918	11.9301846578	0.0838209993	13	
0.8403680906	12.7705527485	0.0783051462	14	
0.8299931759	13.6005459244	0.0735264603	15	
0.8197463466	14.4202922710	0.0693467221	16	
0.8096260213	15.2299182924	0.0656602341	17	
0.7996306384	16.0295489307	0.0623847873	18	
0.7897586552	16.8193075859	0.0594554797	19	
0.7800085483	17.5993161342	0.0568203896	20	**ANNUALLY**
0.7703788132	18.3696949474	0.0544374854	21	*If compounded*
0.7608679636	19.1305629110	0.0522723772	22	***annually,***
0.7514745320	19.8820374430	0.0502966561	23	*nominal annual rate is*
0.7421970686	20.6242345116	0.0484866480	24	
0.7330341418	21.3572686534	0.0468224667	25	$1^1/4\%$
0.7239843376	22.0812529910	0.0452872851	26	
0.7150462594	22.7962992504	0.0438667693	27	
0.7062185278	23.5025177782	0.0425486329	28	
0.6974997805	24.2000175587	0.0413222841	29	
0.6888886721	24.8889062308	0.0401785434	30	**SEMIANNUALLY**
0.6803838737	25.5692901045	0.0391094159	31	*If compounded*
0.6719840728	26.2412741773	0.0381079056	32	***semiannually,***
0.6636879731	26.9049621504	0.0371678650	33	*nominal annual rate is*
0.6554942944	27.5604564448	0.0362838693	34	
0.6474017723	28.2078582171	0.0354511141	35	$2^1/2\%$
0.6394091578	28.8472673749	0.0346653285	36	
0.6315152176	29.4787825925	0.0339227035	37	
0.6237187334	30.1025013259	0.0332198308	38	
0.6160185021	30.7185198281	0.0325536519	39	
0.6084133355	31.3269331635	0.0319214139	40	**QUARTERLY**
0.6009020597	31.9278352233	0.0313206327	41	*If compounded*
0.5934835158	32.5213187390	0.0307490606	42	***quarterly,***
0.5861565588	33.1074752978	0.0302046589	43	*nominal annual rate is*
0.5789200581	33.6863953558	0.0296855745	44	
0.5717728968	34.2581682527	0.0291901188	45	**5%**
0.5647139722	34.8228822249	0.0287167499	46	
0.5577421948	35.3806244196	0.0282640574	47	
0.5508564886	35.9314809083	0.0278307483	48	
0.5440557913	36.4755366995	0.0274156350	49	
0.5373390531	37.0128757526	0.0270176251	50	**MONTHLY**
0.5307052376	37.5435809902	0.0266357117	51	*If compounded*
0.5241533211	38.0677343114	0.0262689655	52	***monthly,***
0.5176822925	38.5854166038	0.0259165272	53	*nominal annual rate is*
0.5112911530	39.0967077568	0.0255776012	54	
0.5049789166	39.6016866734	0.0252514497	55	**15%**
0.4987446090	40.1004312824	0.0249373877	56	
0.4925872681	40.5930185505	0.0246347780	57	
0.4865059438	41.0795244943	0.0243430276	58	
0.4804996976	41.5600241919	0.0240615837	59	
0.4745676026	42.0345917945	0.0237899301	60	
$\dfrac{1}{(1+i)^n}$	$p_{\overline{n}}$	$\dfrac{1}{p_{\overline{n}}}$	n	

Example 1

Find the monthly payment to borrow $6,000 for 5 years at $i = 1\frac{1}{4}\%$ per month.

Solution:
First find the number of payments.   5 years $\times$ 12 = 60

You will need to find the payment-to-borrow factor for $n = 60$. This is then multiplied by the amount borrowed.

$$
\begin{aligned}
\text{payment} &= \$6,000 \times \text{payment-to-borrow factor} \\
&= \$6,000 \times 0.02378993 \\
&= \$142.73958 \\
&= \$142.74 \text{ per month (rounded off)}
\end{aligned}
$$

Remarks:
1. This payment represents principal and interest paid each month. The total paid = 60 $\times$ 142.74 = $8,564.40.
2. The principal paid off over the life of the loan was $6,000. This means the total interest paid = $8,564.40 − $6,000 = $2,564.40.

Example 2

Jesse Oakman wants to know how much he can borrow with a $125-per-month payment for 3 years at $i = 1\frac{1}{4}\%$ per month.

Solution:
Find the number of payments. $n = 12 \times 3 = 36$

Next find the *amount borrowed* factor for $n = 60$. This factor is multiplied by the desired payment.

$$
\begin{aligned}
\text{amount borrowed} &= \$125 \times \text{amount borrowed factor} \\
&= \$125 \times (28.84726738) \\
&= \$3,605.91
\end{aligned}
$$

Remark: The interest that will be charged can also be found in the following way:

$$
\begin{aligned}
\text{total paid out} = 36 \times 125 = &\quad \$4,500.00 \\
\text{amount borrowed} = &\quad \underline{-\$3,605.91} \\
\text{interest} = &\quad \$\ \ 894.09
\end{aligned}
$$

Sometimes the interest rate is stated as an annual rate, even though it is calculated monthly. When this occurs, the monthly rate i can be determined by dividing by 12. An 8% rate that is calculated monthly would have a monthly rate . . .

$$ i = \tfrac{8\%}{12} = \tfrac{2}{3}\% $$

A convenient notation to state how often per year this interest is calculated is the symbol 8%(12). You will see this method of notation used for expressing rates and compounding periods in the section on compound interest in the next chapter.

Example 3

Randy Greenwald financed $7,500 for his pickup at 10%(12) for 36 months. What was his monthly payment?

Solution:

First get the monthly rate. $i = \frac{10\%}{12} = \frac{5}{6}\%$

Since there are 36 payments, $n = 36$. Now turn to the finance tables in the back of the book and locate the page for $i = \frac{5}{6}\%$. Find the *payment to borrow* factor for $n = 36$.

$$
\begin{aligned}
\text{payment} &= \$7,500 \times (\text{factor}) \\
&= \$7,500 \times (0.032267187) \\
&= \$242.0039 \\
&= \$242.00 \text{ per month}
\end{aligned}
$$

The next example gives a situation in which the payments and interest calculations occur other than monthly. Such loans occur frequently when businesses secure loans to improve their equipment or building.

Example 4

Several years ago the Franklin Tool Company borrowed $25,000 for a major expansion. The 10-year loan was based on an interest rate of 14%(4). What is their quarterly payment?

Solution:

The symbol 14%(4) means that interest is calculated four times a year; so the payments are quarterly, and $i = \frac{14\%}{4} = 3\frac{1}{2}\%$ per quarter. In the finance tables, find the page for $i = 3\frac{1}{2}\%$. The number of payments will be 4 times 10 years = 40. Look down the *payment to borrow* column to $n = 40$.

$$
\begin{aligned}
\text{payment} &= \$25,000 \times (\text{factor}) \\
&= \$25,000 \times (0.046827282) \\
&= \$1,170.68 \text{ per quarter}
\end{aligned}
$$

Example 5

The Wilson family learned from a financial guide that a home mortgage payment should not be more than one-fourth of their monthly income. If their monthly income is $1,600 and the bank charges 12%(12), what amount of money can they borrow for a 25-year loan?

Solution:

Their payment should not exceed $\frac{1}{4}(\$1,600)$, which equals $400 per month. The mortgage will require $25 \times 12 = 300$ payments. Look in the tables on the page for $i = 12\% \div 12 = 1\%$, and look down the *amount borrowed* column to $n = 300$ to find the correct factor.

$$
\begin{aligned}
\text{Amount borrowed} &= \$400 \times (94.94655126) \\
&= \$37,978.62
\end{aligned}
$$

Remark: You might be surprised to learn how much interest the Wilsons would pay out over the term of their loan. Find out how much it is.

Exercises

Use the finance tables in the back of the book to find each payment and the total interest charges over the term of the loan. Round answers to the nearest cent.

Amount Borrowed	Interest Rate	Term
1. $900	9%(12)	6 months
2. $1,800	12%(12)	$1\frac{1}{2}$ years
3. $3,000	18%(12)	$2\frac{1}{2}$ years
4. $4,500	10%(12)	3 years
5. $7,900	8%(12)	42 months
6. $21,000	8%(4)	6 years
7. $42,500	15%(12)	15 years
8. $185,000	10%(4)	20 years

Use the finance tables to find the amount of money that can be borrowed for the given monthly payment, interest rate, and term. Round answers to the nearest dollar.

Payment	Interest Rate	Term
9. $85	6%(12)	18 months
10. $125	7%(12)	2 years
11. $182	8%(12)	3 years
12. $318	9%(12)	15 years
13. $512	10%(12)	25 years
14. $1,285	14%(4)	6 years
15. $10,500	15%(12)	10 years
16. $425	16%(4)	30 months

17. Compare the payment size and total interest paid for a home loan of $47,000 at 14%(12) when the term is . . .

   (a) 20 years

   (b) 30 years

18. Calculate the total interest charges that the Wilson family would pay for the home loan in Example 5.

19. Leroy Green borrowed $2,300 at 12%(12). He agreed to repay the loan in $2\frac{1}{2}$ years by making monthly installments.

   (a) What will his monthly payments be?

   (b) What is the total amount that he will pay by the end of $2\frac{1}{2}$ years?

   (c) How much of what Leroy pays back will be interest?

20. The Andersons borrowed $3,500 at 9%(12). They will repay the loan in 3 years with monthly installments.

   (a) What will their monthly payments be?

   (b) What is the total amount that they will pay by the end of 3 years?

   (c) What would be the total amount that they would pay if they repaid the loan with a single-payment at the end of three years?

   (d) Which loan is less expensive for the Andersons, a simple-interest loan or the amortized loan? How much do they save?

Credit Cards: Minimum Payment

The use of credit cards is a form of borrowing money. When you use a credit card, you purchase merchandise with the presentation of your card. For the time between when you make the purchase and when you pay for it, you are borrowing the money. Once you are billed by the credit-card company, you have about 25 days to pay the bill. When you are considering whether to use a particular credit card, you need to keep in mind several things:

1. **Annual or Monthly Fees.** Some companies charge anywhere from $5.00 to $25.00 annually simply to let you own the card. Consider whether the convenience of the card is worth this amount of money.
2. **Rate of Interest.** The interest that you pay the credit-card company is often called a finance charge. In recent years, the rate of interest on credit cards has been close to 1.5% monthly, which amounts to 18% annually. This is a rather high rate of interest. If you decide to use a credit card, you may want to avoid finance charges for this reason.

3. **Finance Charges.** Some companies start charging interest from the day a charge is made on your credit card. In this case, whenever you charge something with the card, you will begin paying a finance charge. Other companies charge interest only if you do not pay your bill by the date it is due, or if you don't pay in full. If this is the case, the credit card can actually work for you. For instance, if you pay each bill on time and in full, you do not have to pay any finance charges. So you actually have free use of the money for a few weeks.

If you have a checking account that pays $5\frac{1}{4}\%$ and you can use your card to delay payments for goods and services, you must have an average charge-card bill of $457 per month for 12 months to offset an annual card service charge of $24 per year.

Reason:

$$\$24 \text{ per year} = \$2 \text{ per month}$$

$$I = Prt$$
$$P = \frac{I}{rt} = \frac{2}{(0.0525)(1/12)} = 457.14$$

Some computation dealing with credit cards will be presented in this section and in the next section. One thing that you must know how to compute is the minimum payment.

When you receive your statement (bill), you are given a date indicating when payment is due. You usually can choose how much you want to pay. However, most companies require that the customer make a *minimum payment*. This means that the total bill does not *have* to be paid, but interest will be charged if it isn't.

Your credit-card statement will indicate your minimum payment, or it will tell you how to compute it.

Example

Jeffrey Hopkins received a credit-card statement indicating that he owed $363.72. The minimum payment can be figured by using Table 8.2.

Table 8.2

Balance	Minimum Payment
$0 — $25	amount of balance
$25.01 — $100	$25.00
$100.01 — $300	$35.00
$300.01 — $500	15% of balance
over $500	20% of balance

Find the minimum payment that Jeffrey must make.

$$\$363 \times 0.15 = \$54.45$$

Paying only the minimum balance may sound like a good idea, but you may not think so if you take a closer look. You must pay a finance charge on the unpaid balance. As you seek to be a good steward of your money, you should keep in mind that it is wise to pay off as much of the balance as you possibly can.

Exercises

Use Table 8.2 to determine the minimum payment for each balance. (Round to the nearest cent.)

1. $73.61
2. $12.95
3. $672.31
4. $412.86
5. $475.25
6. $793.47
7. $228.64
8. $9.43
9. $1,498.16
10. $372.94
11. Dick Parish has an unpaid balance of $536.18 on his credit card. This month he has made the following charges: $12.65, $21.19, $54.86, $35.92. Determine his new unpaid balance and the minimum payment. (Use Table 8.2.)
12. Mr. Kelly has made the following charges this month: $38.25, $79.82, $27.94, $146.87. He had no previous balance. Determine his balance for this month and the minimum payment if it is $10.00 plus 15% of the balance.

Credit Cards: Finance Charges

As a Christian, you need to be especially careful with credit cards, not only for your own reputation's sake but also for the Lord's. It's easy to let bills accumulate because the cards are so convenient to use. If you use credit cards, you should always keep track of how much you charge and make sure that you have the money to cover the charges. If you let yourself get into the habit of making only minimum payments, finance charges will soon be overwhelming.

To get an idea of how quickly finance charges accumulate, consider the following example:

Example 1

Mr. Harrison's credit-card bill for one particular month was $259.80. He decided to pay only the minimum payment, which was $35.00. Find the finance charge if the monthly interest rate is 1.5%. Then find Mr. Harrison's new unpaid balance.

Solution:
Find the balance after the payment.
$$\$259.80 - \$35.00 = \$224.80$$
Find the finance charge at 1.5% (round to the cent).
$$\$224.80 \times 0.015 = \$3.37$$
Find the new unpaid balance (including interest).
$$\$224.80 + 3.37 = \$228.17$$

Remark: Mr. Harrison will receive a statement for this unpaid balance, plus new charges, later in the month.

Example 2

Suppose that during the month Mr. Harrison used his charge card to make another $265.21 worth of purchases. Find his minimum payment, the new balance, and the accumulated interest for these two months if he makes a minimum payment.

Solution:
Find the total of the last balance plus new charges.
$$\$228.17 + \$265.21 = \$493.38$$
Use Table 8.2 to find the minimum payment.
$$\$493.38 \times 0.15 = \$74.01$$
If Mr. Harrison makes only the minimum payment, the new balance is found by subtracting.
$$\$493.38 - \$74.01 = \$419.37$$
During the next month this balance will accrue interest at 1.5%.
$$\$419.37 \times 0.015 = \$6.29$$

In just two months, Mr. Harrison has accrued $9.66 in finance charges. If he doesn't charge any other goods, his next statement will be $419.37 + 6.29 = $425.66.

Exercises

Complete the following grid. The finance charge is computed on the unpaid balance at the end of the month, and it is figured at a rate of 1.5% monthly.

	Balance	Payment	Unpaid Balance After Payment	Amount of Finance Charge
1.	$356.28	$ 60.00		
2.	$182.35	$ 30.00		
3.	$ 97.64	$ 25.00		
4.	$418.76	$ 65.00		
5.	$ 53.18	$ 10.00		
6.	$289.95	$ 45.00		
7.	$116.12	$ 25.00		
8.	$ 27.36	$ 10.00		
9.	$733.77	$100.00		
10.	$216.25	$ 35.00		
11.	$796.42	$150.00		
12.	$421.86	$ 60.00		

13. Calculate the December balance, December payment, and total interest charges on Maria Marconi's charge-card account if she makes only the minimum payment indicated on Table 8.2 and the unpaid balance accrues interest at 1.75% per month.

    September 30 balance: $212.65
    October purchases: $183.80
    November purchases: $65.21
    December purchases: $326.79

14. Calculate the April balance, April payment, and total interest charges on Larry Whitmire's charge account. Assume that he makes double the minimum payment as indicated on Table 8.2 and that any unpaid balance accrues interest at 1.5% per month.

    January 30 balance: $86.15
    February purchases: $42.62
    March purchases: $121.80
    April purchases: $95.18

The Rule of 78

When you borrow and then repay the loan before it is due, you save interest. But do you know how to calculate the amount of interest you save? Lenders collect most of the interest from the earliest payments of the loan. That means that by paying off an obligation early, you may not save as much as you would expect.

The bank or person who makes the loan normally divides your payment into both principal and interest—assigning a portion of every payment to each. That means that, as the payments are being applied, part of each payment goes for interest. The remainder of each payment goes to pay back the money you borrowed.

Obviously, lenders must have a "system" for computing exactly how much of your payment is assigned to each purpose. One common method is called the *rule of 78*. It takes its name from a hypothetical loan of 12 months. By adding the numbers 1, 2, 3, 4, 5, 6, 7, 8, 9, 10, 11, and 12, you get a total of 78. This figure becomes the denominator of a fraction you will use to multiply times the total interest charge. The numerator is simply the number of months remaining on the loan.

For instance, imagine that you have taken out a 12-month loan for which the total interest charges are $500; this is the first month, and you have not yet made a payment. Some borrowers assume that the interest for the first month is simply $\frac{1}{12}$ of $500, or $41.67. However, the interest portion of that payment is actually $\frac{12}{78} \times$ $500, or $76.92—almost twice as much. As a result, even if you pay the loan in full during the second month, you will still have paid almost $\frac{1}{6}$ the total interest due. The interest you don't pay will be $500 − $76.92, or $423.08.

You can use the same rule for longer or shorter loans. In addition, a formula exists to eliminate the need to compute the sum of the months for the denominator. Instead, you can compute the amount of interest remaining on the loan with the following procedure:

$$\frac{p(p+1)}{n(n+1)} \times I, \text{ where . . .}$$

$p =$ payments remaining
$n =$ original (or total) number of monthly payments
$I =$ total interest charges.

After the first payment on the 12-month loan above, we could substitute . . .

$$\frac{11(11+1)}{12(12+1)} \times 500$$

and get $423.08, or exactly the amount we calculated earlier by multiplying $\frac{12}{78}$ times $500 to get $76.92, and then subtracting $76.92 from $500.

Chapter 8 Review ───────────

add-on loan
amortization
annual interest rate
annual percentage rate (APR)
approximate time
Banker's Rule
constant ratio formula
contract
credit card
discount formula
discounting
exact interest

exact time
finance charge
maturity date
maturity value
minimum payment
ordinary interest
principal
proceeds
promissory note
simple interest
term
total accrued interest

Review Exercises

1. Find the exact time, given the signing date and the maturity date of each loan.
   (a) Jan. 5, 1972—July 10, 1972
   (b) Mar. 9, 1989—Sept. 15, 1989
   (c) April 24, 1980—Dec. 20, 1980
   (d) Aug. 13, 1989—March 30, 1990
   (e) June 30, 1968—Dec. 27, 1968
   (f) Feb. 3, 1984—May 16, 1984

2. For each simple-interest loan, find the interest charge and the maturity value. If exact time is given, use Banker's Rule.

Principal	Interest Rate	Term
(a) $2,500	9.5%	3 years
(b) $1,250	11%	9 months
(c) $900	14%	180 days
(d) $3,250	8.5%	96 days

3. Find the annual interest rate for the following loans being advertised by the Gem Finance Co.

You Borrow	Pay Back	Pay-back Time
(a) $500	$550	7 months
(b) $1,000	$1,120	1 year
(c) $1,800	$2,025	15 months

4. For each add-on loan find the finance charge and the monthly payment.

(a) principal: $1,800
rate: 7.5%
term: 18 months

(b) principal: $2,500
rate: 9%
term: 24 months

(c) principal: $3,600
rate: 10%
term: 30 months

(d) principal: $1,250
rate: 14%
term: 12 months

(e) principal: $10,000
rate: 8.5%
term: 15 months

(f) principal: $4,500
rate: 11%
term: 48 months

5. Using the constant ratio formula, find the annual percentage rate (APR) for each loan in problem 4.

6. Find the proceeds for each discount loan. If the term is given in days, use a 360-day year (ordinary interest).

(a) amount: $950
rate: 8.5%
term: 87 days

(b) amount: $1,800
rate: 12%
term: 15 months

(c) amount: $2,750
rate: 15%
term: 418 days

(d) amount: $4,800
rate: 10.5%
term: 20 months

7. Find the monthly payment and the total accrued interest for each amortized loan.

(a) $3,000 at 12%(12) for 18 months

(b) $6,500 at 15%(12) for 3 years

(c) $18,000 at 9%(4) for 6 years

(d) $42,000 at 10%(12) for 25 years

8. Use Table 8.2 to determine the minimum payment for each credit statement.

(a) $226.30
(b) $456.78

(c) $12.91
(d) $790.00

(e) $500.00

9. Mike Brame arranged a loan for home improvements. He needs $4,500, and his bank will write a 24-month discount loan at 13%. Find the interest charges and the amount to be paid back in 24 months.

10. At a Treasury Bill auction, a $1,000,000 90-day Treasury Bill could be purchased for 96.8% of face value. Find the discount rate for this bill. (Use a 360-day year.)

11. Rodney Richards accepted a promissory note from one of his best customers. The note was written for $5,000 at 8% for 181 days. Sixty-five days later Mr. Richards needed money and sold the note to the Western Bank and Trust, which discounted the note at a discount rate of 10%. What did Mr. Richards receive for the note?

12. If Robin Weatherspoon can afford a $135-per-month car payment, how much can she borrow for 4 years at 14%(12)? If this represents 80% of the value of the car, what price range would she be looking at, provided she had the down payment?

Personal Banking

When you think of banking, your first thought should not be of loans or borrowing. Banks provide many other services. The most important features for you as an individual are protection of your money and accumulation of assets through savings programs and earned interest. If you don't already have a checking account, you will eventually need one. A checking account allows you to pay obligations safely by mail. Furthermore, it provides valuable legal records of expenditures related to taxes, contributions, and budgeting. People who pay bills and premiums with cash have only the receipt from the payee as legal proof, but those who pay by check have both their check and the company's receipt.

Most of a person's accomplishments in life are realized by developing good habits and sticking to them. This may seem obvious for learning to play a musical instrument or developing athletic skills, but it is equally important for saving money. As an old saying tells us, a fool and his money are soon parted. When someone works hard and enjoys the financial benefit of that labor, it's foolish for him to let the money slip away on trivial buying. You must develop good habits of saving part of all you earn. Saving requires self-discipline and self-denial, but it eventually brings worthwhile returns. Not only can you save for a car or house, but you can drastically reduce the amount of money you must borrow. In fact, you will actually save money two ways. You will earn interest on what you save, and you will not have to pay the interest on borrowed money. In Chapter 10 this principle will result in a significant savings on the purchase of a car.

The principle of saving regularly can be made as routine as the government's deducting taxes and your giving offerings to the Lord's work. Every check you bring home should automatically have three deductions—taxes, the Lord, and yourself. The last two depend on *your* self-discipline.

Checking Accounts

An important service that financial institutions offer is checking accounts. If you will be paying bills, especially by mail, you'll be wise to start a checking account. Paying by check is safer and more convenient than paying with cash.

When you open a checking account, you purchase a certain number of checks. When you write and issue a check, it is actually an order to your financial institution to pay a certain amount of money to the person you have designated. This sum of money is then subtracted from your account.

A sample check is shown below. The parts pointed out are printed on your checks when you order them.

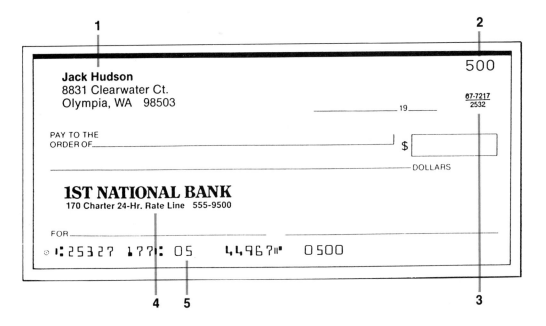

1—Name, address, and phone number of the owner of the checks (the *drawer*). Many people have their driver's-license number on the checks.

2—Number of the check. Checks are numbered consecutively.

3—American Banking Association numbers. These numbers are used to get your check to the proper place to be processed after you have issued it.

4—Name and address of the financial institution (the *drawee*).

5—Magnetic numbers at the bottom of the check allow the check to be processed by electronic data processing.

The parts pointed out on the next check are to be completed by the owner of the check when he pays for something with it.

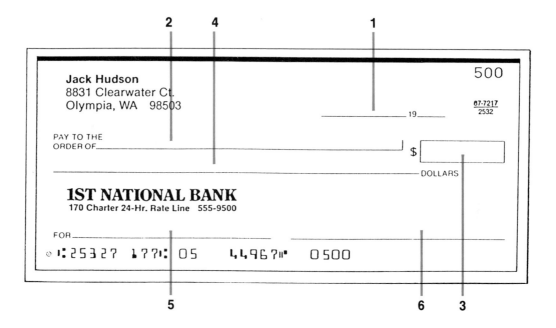

1—The date the check is written.

2—The name of the person or organization to whom the check is written *(payee)*.

3—Amount of the check, printed in numerals.

4—Amount of the check, written out in words.

5—Purpose of the check (optional).

6—Signature of the writer of the check.

Study the following examples of how to write the amount of the check in words. Note that the word *and* represents the decimal point.

$96.00   *Ninety-six and $\frac{No}{100}$*

$30.05   *Thirty and $\frac{05}{100}$*

$643.23   *Six hundred forty-three and $\frac{23}{100}$*

At the time you write a check, record the information in your checkbook register. This is your record of the check.

Entries in the deposit column are added to the balance. Entries in the withdrawal column are subtracted from the balance. Amounts added to your account are known as *credits*. Amounts subtracted are known as *debits*.

Now suppose that you are writing a check and make a mistake. Don't try to write over and change the mistake, or your bank will not honor it; it will look like the payee is trying to cheat you out of money. You should void the check and write a new one. To *void* a check means that you destroy it and write the word *void* next to that check's number in your checkbook register. If you simply destroy a check and don't make a record that you did so, you may forget and wonder what happened to that check. The following is a sample check that has been voided.

Jack Hudson
8831 Clearwater Ct.
Olympia, WA 98503

500

March 5 19 —

67-7217
2532

PAY TO THE
ORDER OF _Kelly Lewis_____ $ | 25 00 |

_Twenty and No/100_____ DOLLARS

1ST NATIONAL BANK
170 Charter 24-Hr. Rate Line 555-9500

FOR _Birthday gift_____   _Jack Hudson_

⑆ ⑈25327 1771⑈ 05   449671⑈ 0500

Written value and numerals do not match.

Exercises

Write the following amounts out in words as you would on a check.

1. $35.00

2. $26.32

3. $253.00

4. $628.19

5. $58.84

6. $2,347.16

Use the sample checks provided by your teacher to write checks for the following. Use the current date and sign the check with your name.

7. $15.00 to Karen Highfield for a gift

8. $26.92 to Sherwood Shoes for a pair of shoes

9. $79.27 to Anson Oil Company for your gasoline credit-card payment

10. $150.00 to Wilson County Credit Union for your loan payment

11. $16.36 to Union Hardware for painting supplies

12. Fill out the sample checks and sample checkbook register provided by your teacher to reflect the following transactions for the month of September.

- Last check issued: no. 215; forwarding balance: $28.50
- On Sept. 2, deposit your paycheck of $85.00 from your part-time job.
- On Sept. 3, write a check to your church (use your church's name) for $11.00.
- On Sept. 6, write a check to Wayne's Apparel for a shirt and tie costing $29.10, including tax.
- On that same day, write a check to Carl's Service Station for $10.75 worth of gas.
- On Sept. 15, deposit your paycheck of $135.92.
- On Sept. 17, write a check to your church for $15.00.
- On Sept. 22, write a check to Jeff Hutton for $5.00.

Deposits and Electronic Transfers

When you deposit money into your checking account, you must fill out a deposit slip. Your personalized deposit slips are found in your checkbook behind your checks.

DEPOSIT TICKET		C A S H	CURRENCY		
			COIN		
Walter H. Warton		CHECKS			
Pine Mountain Place					
Las Horas, CA					87-7217
					2532
		TOTAL from reverse side			
DATE 19		TOTAL			
		LESS CASH RECEIVED			USE OTHER SIDE FOR ADDITIONAL LISTING
SIGN HERE FOR LESS CASH RECEIVED		NET DEPOSIT			BE SURE EACH ITEM IS PROPERLY ENDORSED.

1ST NATIONAL BANK
170 Charter 24-Hr. Rate Line 555-9500

⑈ ⑆ 25327 177⑆ 05   44967⑈   0226

CHECKS AND OTHER ITEMS ARE RECEIVED FOR DEPOSIT SUBJECT TO THE TERMS AND CONDITIONS OF THIS FINANCIAL INSTITUTION'S COLLECTION AGREEMENT

Currency, coins, and checks are listed separately and then added for a total. If you wish to make a withdrawal from the amount you are depositing, write the amount of cash you want next to "Less cash received" (if your particular bank's slips include such a blank). Subtract this amount from the total for the total deposit.

Example 1

Wilma Sears deposited these items in her bank: 4 five-dollar bills, 3 ten-dollar bills, 5 nickels, 3 dimes, 7 quarters, a check for $42.87, and a check for $12.50. Her deposit slip should look like the following:

Currency: 4 five-dollar bills ($20) + 3 ten-dollar bills ($30) = $50.00
Coins: 5 nickels ($.25) + 3 dimes ($.30) + (7 quarters) $1.75 = $2.30
Checks: $42.87 + $12.50 = $55.37

DEPOSIT TICKET			
	CASH CURRENCY	50	00
Wilma Sears	COIN	2	30
9263 Starr Ave.	CHECKS	42	87
Pontiac, MI 48054		12	50
		67-7217	
		2532	
DATE _June 14_ 19 —	TOTAL from reverse side		
	TOTAL	107	67
	LESS CASH RECEIVED		USE OTHER SIDE FOR ADDITIONAL LISTING
SIGN HERE FOR LESS CASH RECEIVED	**NET DEPOSIT** 107 67		BE SURE EACH ITEM IS PROPERLY ENDORSED.
1ST NATIONAL BANK			
170 Charter 24-Hr. Rate Line 555-9500			

⑆ 532 17 ⑆ 05 44967⑈ 022

CHECKS AND OTHER ITEMS ARE RECEIVED FOR DEPOSIT SUBJECT TO THE TERMS AND CONDITIONS OF THIS FINANCIAL INSTITUTION'S COLLECTION AGREEMENT.

Example 2

Jack Hudson has three checks to deposit, but he wants to withdraw $50.00 before he deposits the rest. Here is a deposit slip to indicate this transaction; the amounts of the checks are $348.20, $27.96, and $43.62.

DEPOSIT TICKET			
	CASH CURRENCY		
Jack Hudson	COIN		
8831 Clearwater Ct.	CHECKS	348	20
Olympia, WA 98503		27	96
		43	62
		67-7217	
		2532	
DATE _Aug 7_ 19 —	TOTAL from reverse side		
	TOTAL	419	78
Jack Hudson	LESS CASH RECEIVED	50	00	USE OTHER SIDE FOR ADDITIONAL LISTING
SIGN HERE FOR LESS CASH RECEIVED	**NET DEPOSIT** 369 78		BE SURE EACH ITEM IS PROPERLY ENDORSED.
1ST NATIONAL BANK			
170 Charter 24-Hr. Rate Line 555-9500			

⑆ 25327 177 ⑆ 05 4967⑈ 226

CHECKS AND OTHER ITEMS ARE RECEIVED FOR DEPOSIT SUBJECT TO THE TERMS AND CONDITIONS OF THIS FINANCIAL INSTITUTION'S COLLECTION AGREEMENT

When you deposit or cash a check, you must endorse it. You *endorse* a check by signing your name on the back. You must sign your name exactly as it is made out to you. For example, if your name is misspelled, spell it the way it appears on the check; then sign it correctly below the first signature. There are three general types of endorsements, as illustrated below.

Blank Endorsement

Restricted Endorsement

Special or Full Endorsement

A *blank endorsement* is simply your signature. This type of endorsement is used to cash or deposit a check; and once endorsed, it allows anyone to cash the check. For this reason, you should never endorse a check in this manner until you are actually at the bank, ready to make the deposit or to cash the check.

A *restricted endorsement* limits what can be done with the check. If a check has been designed "for deposit only," nobody else can cash it in case you lose it.

A *special* or *full endorsement* transfers ownership of the check. The person to whom you have signed over the check must endorse it himself before cashing it.

All modern banking institutions have electronic teller systems. If you wish to make use of this system, you are issued a special card, similar to a credit card, which allows you access to your funds in the bank. You place the card into the machine, and instructions appear on a screen (like a computer display or television). You must enter a secret code that no one else but you knows. This way no one can steal your card and withdraw money from your bank accounts. If you enter the correct code, the computer will ask the type of transaction you desire. You can transfer between accounts, deposit, withdraw, or just inquire about your balance. (When you make a deposit at a teller machine, though, you will still need one of your encoded deposit slips.)

When you simply want to get some cash, teller machines save money because you don't have to write a check that you pay for. If you give the wrong code, however, many teller machines will take your card, making you return to the bank during regular hours to get it back. Another safety feature of electronic tellers is a maximum of about $300 that can be withdrawn on a given day.

When you use an electronic teller, however, you must also be careful to write the amount of cash withdrawn from the machine on your checkbook register. Otherwise, you may later think that you have more money than you really do.

Exercises

Determine the amounts you would put in the "currency" and "coin" columns of a deposit slip if you had the following to deposit:

1. 9 nickels, 6 dimes, 3 quarters; 3 one-dollar bills, 6 five-dollar bills, 2 ten-dollar bills, 4 twenty-dollar bills

2. 8 pennies, 7 dimes, 12 quarters; 3 five-dollar bills, 12 ten-dollar bills, 1 fifty-dollar bill

3. 28 pennies, 15 nickels, 12 dimes, 21 quarters; 6 one-dollar bills, 8 five-dollar bills, 4 ten-dollar bills, 3 twenty-dollar bills

4. 9 nickels, 23 dimes, 14 quarters; 20 one-dollar bills, 12 five-dollar bills, 6 ten-dollar bills

For exercises 5-8, complete the deposit slips that your teacher gives you. Fill in your name and the current date.

5. You want to deposit the following:
   3 five-dollar bills
   3 ten-dollar bills
   a $297.23 check
   a $15.78 check

6. You want to deposit the following:
   a $370.26 check
   a $23.00 check
   a $32.85 check

7. You want to deposit the following:
   a $528.36 check
   a $43.72 check
   and withdraw $25.00

8. You want to deposit the following:
   16 dimes
   12 quarters
   a $152.96 check
   a $36.00 check
   and withdraw $40.00

9. Charlene A. Brown is at Heritage Savings and Loan, and she wants to cash her paycheck. How would she endorse the check?

10. How should Harold M. Ingersoll endorse a check that he wants to give to Carolyn K. Reed?

11. Francis Sawyer wants to deposit her paycheck in her bank. Her husband is going to the bank, so she will send the check with him. How should she endorse the check?

12. Pastor Lawrence W. Rose received a check made out to Laurence Rose. If he is at his bank, ready to cash the check, how should he endorse it?

Reconciling Bank Statements ⎯⎯⎯

Once a month your financial institution will send you a bank statement. It is your responsibility to reconcile your statement. Basically to *reconcile* means "to settle or resolve." When you reconcile your bank statement, you compare your checking-account records with the bank statement and resolve any conflicts. You want to make sure that both records agree. A bank statement will generally include the following:

- your previous balance
- your current balance
- deposits and withdrawals made during the month
- interest your account has earned
- service charges
- charges for checks
- a list of your checks that have cleared the bank (deducted from your account)

Reconciled Yet?

Your checkbook isn't the only thing you need to have reconciled. II Corinthians 5:18 says that "God . . . hath reconciled us to himself by Jesus Christ." If you are a Christian, God has settled the problem of your sin because of Christ's death for you. You can have fellowship with God because your sin problem has been resolved—reconciled. However, if you have never repented of your sin and put your trust in Christ's substitutionary death, you are still loaded down with a debt of sin—a debt that will cost your very soul for eternity.

Usually your bank statement and your checkbook register will not agree. This is no cause for worry. You must do a little computation to reconcile the two. Suppose that the statement records that you have more money in your account than your register records. This could mean that one or both of the following are true: (1) one or more of your checks are *outstanding;* that is, they have not yet cleared the bank, or (2) interest has been added to your account.

Suppose, on the other hand, that your register records more money than the statement. This situation might occur if charges have been subtracted from your account, if you have failed to record a check or an electronic-teller withdrawal on the register, or if one or more of your deposits have not yet been credited *(outstanding deposits)*.

Along with your statement, you will receive your cancelled checks. A *cancelled check* is a check that the financial institution has paid. These will match the checks listed by number and amount on the bank statement. They are marked or punched so that no one may use them again. With the cancelled checks you receive, you can determine which, if any, of your checks have not yet cleared the bank.

To reconcile your statement, first adjust your checkbook register balance. To do this, verify all deposits and withdrawals by comparing them to the statement. Add any credits that have not yet been recorded in your register. Subtract any debits that have not been recorded.

Date	Number	Transaction Description	Deposit or Interest (+)		√	Withdrawal or fee (-)		Balance 473 06	
4	24	Nancy's Boutique			√	17	36	455	70
5	2	Interest	1	45	√			457	15
5	2	Checks Charge			√	5	00	452	15

Mark checks that have drawn
and deposits that are credited.

Next, you need to adjust the bank-statement balance. Add any outstanding deposits listed in your register that aren't on the statement. Subtract any outstanding checks or withdrawals listed in your register that aren't on the statement. Often there will be a place on the back of your bank statement where you can do your computation. It may look something like the following example.

CHECKS OUTSTANDING NOT CHARGED TO YOUR ACCOUNT

	$	
TOTAL	$	

MONTH _____ 19 _____

YOUR CHECK BOOK BALANCE	$ _____
† LESS SERVICE CHARGE (IF ANY) OR ANY AUTOMATIC PAYMENTS	$ _____
† ADD INTEREST IF EARNED THIS MONTH	$ _____
† ADD AUTOMATIC ADVANCES NOT LISTED IN YOUR CHECK BOOK	$ _____
NET CHECK BOOK BALANCE*	$ _____
† [BE SURE TO LIST THESE AMOUNTS IN YOUR CHECK BOOK]	
CHECKING ACCOUNT BALANCE THIS STATEMENT	$ _____
ADD DEPOSITS MADE AFTER DATE OF THIS STATEMENT	$ _____
SUBTRACT OUTSTANDING CHECKS	$ _____
*BALANCE	$ _____
* THIS FIGURE SHOULD AGREE WITH YOUR NET CHECK BOOK BALANCE	

This adjusted balance should be the same as your adjusted checkbook register balance. If it is, you have reconciled the two.

What if the adjusted bank statement and your checkbook register do not agree? Here are some steps you can take to find the problem:

1. Carefully go through your checkbook register, adding and subtracting all the deposits and checks. Most of the time this is where you will find some calculation error. If you and the bank disagree by numbers like $9.00, 90¢, or $99, you have made a decimal-point error. For example:

You meant to do . . .	But actually did . . .
$123.65	$123.65
−$10.00	−$1.00
$113.65	$122.65

Notice: $122.65 − $113.65 = $9.00

2. Make sure there are no checks on the bank statement that don't correspond to what you wrote. It's rare that a bank makes errors in arithmetic because computers do the work; however, certain errors can happen that the computer won't recognize. Remember, computers read only numbers, not names and signatures. It's possible, for example, that someone else's check will draw on your account due to a misprinting of the numbers on his check. Also, banks sometimes make errors in deposits as human tellers write down the numbers or punch computer keys.

Exercises

Reconcile the following bank statements and checkbook balances. Give the adjusted balance.

	Checkbook Balance	Bank Statement Balance	Outstanding Checks	Outstanding Deposits	Interest	Service Charges
1.	$237.45	$260.72	$23.67		$ .98	$1.38
2.	$652.39	$723.28	$120.18	$50.00	$2.71	$2.00
3.	$716.90	$746.71	$26.82		$2.99	
4.	$2,346.27	$2,521.65	$240.60	$75.00	$9.78	
5.	$319.12	$329.22	$15.10			$5.00
6.	$425.73	$327.50		$100.00	$1.77	
7.	$678.00	$620.83		$60.00	$2.83	
8.	$519.56	$525.71	$9.15			$3.00

NUMBER	DATE	TRANSACTION DESCRIPTION	PAYMENT (-) WITHDRAWAL	√	FEE IF ANY	(+) AMOUNT OF DEPOSIT	BALANCE
	4-2	–	Deposit Paycheck				934 26
	4-4	–	Withdrawal			255 80	1190 06
223	4-7	Credit Card Payment	25 00				1165 06
	4-8	–	Deposit	77 96			1087 10
224	4-10	Big M Supermarket			75 00		1162 10
	4-20	–	Deposit Paycheck	25 00			1137 10
225	4-25	Repairs on Car-Auto Shop Jacks	265 30			265 30	1402 40
			49 37				1353 03
	4-26	–	Withdrawal				
226	4-26	Nancy's Dress Shop	50 00				1303 03
227	4-27	The Shoe Shop	75 92				1227 11
			32 15				1194 96

BLE. ADD ANY INTEREST EARNED.

Michael K. Lee
5678 Oak St.
Lithonia, GA   30058

Checking account number:	0404 050461
Previous Balance:	$934.26
Total Deposits and other credits:	$601.52
Total Checks and other debits:	$294.48
Current Balance:	$1,241.30

Credits:

04-02	Deposit	$255.80
04-08	Deposit	$ 75.00
04-20	Deposit	$265.30
04-30	Interest	$ 5.42

Debits:

04-04	Withdrawal	$ 25.00
04-12	Withdrawal	$ 30.00
04-26	Withdrawal	$ 50.00
04-30	Printing charge for checks	$ 5.00

Checks:

Check Number	Amount
223	$77.96
224	$25.00
225	$49.37
227	$32.15

Refer to the checking-account statement for Michael K. Lee to answer the following questions:

9. Find the difference between the current balance in the register and on the statement.

10. Have any checks not yet cleared the bank?

11. Verify deposits and withdrawals in the register. Are any deposits or withdrawals not recorded in the checkbook register?

Are any deposits or withdrawals not recorded on the statement?

12. Are any other credits or debits not recorded in the register?

13. Update the register by recording any information you found in problems 11 and 12.

14. Finish the work necessary to reconcile the statement and register. Does the checkbook balance?

Compound Interest

If you thought that simple interest gets its name from the fact that it's easy to calculate, you might assume that compound interest must really be rough! Actually, though, compound interest isn't much more complicated than simple interest.

When money is invested, "compounding" the interest just means adding it to the existing principal. With a simple-interest loan or investment, interest is compounded just once. For instance, $3,000 invested at 6% simple interest will earn $180 at the end of one year. If the same amount of principal is invested at 6% compounded *quarterly,* then interest would be credited to the account four times a year. But the compound interest would grow faster than simple interest because in the second, third, and fourth quarters you also get interest *on the money that was added as interest* in each earlier quarter. The following diagram shows how the $3,000 will grow at 6% compounded quarterly. Remember, a year has four quarters, or four interest periods.

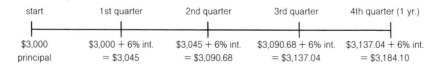

start	1st quarter	2nd quarter	3rd quarter	4th quarter (1 yr.)
$3,000 principal	$3,000 + 6% int. = $3,045	$3,045 + 6% int. = $3,090.68	$3,090.68 + 6% int. = $3,137.04	$3,137.04 + 6% int. = $3,184.10

Notice that the $3,000 earned $184.10 in one year using compound interest. Certainly the calculating of compound interest could be complicated if you had to do it this way. Just imagine the work if the time period were 8 or 10 years! But those who first began this concept were quick to see that a formula would be helpful.

The Compound-Interest Formula

$$S = P(1 + i)^n, \text{ when } \ldots$$

$S =$ the amount of money after n compounding periods
$P =$ the principal invested
$i =$ the interest rate per interest period
$n =$ the total number of interest periods

The interest rate for compound-interest problems is usually given as an annual rate with the statement of how often interest is compounded.

6% compounded quarterly gives $i = \frac{6\%}{4} = 1\frac{1}{2}\%$.

8% compounded semiannually gives $i = \frac{8\%}{2} = 4\%$

12% compounded monthly gives $i = \frac{12}{12} = 1\%$

In this text the above statements will be abbreviated to 6%(4), 8%(2), and 12%(12).

The number of interest periods, denoted by n, can be found as the product of compounding periods per year and the number of years. For example,

6%(4) for 6 years gives $n = 4 \times 6 = 24$ periods

8%(2) for 3 years gives $n = 2 \times 3 = 6$ periods

12%(12) for 5 years gives $n = 12 \times 5 = 60$ periods

The compound amount S will be found as the product of the principal P and the amount factor $(1 + i)^n$. This factor can be found in the finance tables under the first column of each page. In Example 3 you will see how to determine this factor with a hand-held calculator.

Example 1

Find the amount of an investment of $895 for 2 years at 6%(4).

Solution:

First find i.

$$i = \frac{6\%}{4} = 1\frac{1}{2}\%$$

Next find n.

$$n = 4 \times 2 \text{ years} = 8 \text{ periods}$$

Substitute into the formula:

$$S = P(1 + i)^n$$
$$= 895(1.015)^8$$

Now look up $(1.015)^8$ in the finance tables on the page where $i = 1\frac{1}{2}\%$ under column one, **Amount of $1 at Compound Interest.**

$$S = \$895(1.126492587)$$
$$S = \$1,008.21$$

Remark: To determine the interest earned, subtract the original principal:

$$i = \$1,008.21 - \$895 = \$113.21$$

Sometimes people need to know the principal (present value) to invest in order for their money to grow through compound interest to a value needed in the future. You can solve the compound interest formula for the principal P, called the present value.

$$S = P(1 + i)^n \qquad \text{Now divide by } (1 + i)^n.$$

$$\frac{S}{(1+i)^n} = \frac{P\cancel{(1+i)^n}}{\cancel{(1+i)^n}} \qquad \text{Canceling leaves } P \text{ alone.}$$

$$\text{So } P = \frac{S}{(1+i)^n}$$

Often we use the equivalent expression $P = S(1 + i)^{-n}$. Factors for the present value formula are found in the finance tables under **Present Value of $1.**

Example 2

A thoughtful father wants to invest some money in a trust for his 3-year-old son's college education. He would like to have $10,000 in the trust when the boy reaches age 18. He can invest at 8%(12).

Solution:
Find the rate i.
$$i = \frac{8\%}{12} = \frac{2}{3}\% = 0.006$$

Find the number of periods.
$$18 - 3 = 15 \text{ years}$$
$$15 \text{ years} \times 12 = 180 \text{ periods}$$

Substitute into the formula:
$$P = S(1 + i)^{-n}$$
$$= 10,000(1.006)^{-180}$$
$$= 10,000(0.302396088)$$
$$= \$3,023.96$$

Example 3

Find the amount of a $2,500 investment for 5 years at 10%(4).

Solution:
Find i.
$$i = \frac{10\%}{4} = 2\frac{1}{2}\%$$

Find n.
$$n = 4 \times 5 \text{ years} = 20 \text{ periods}$$

Substitute into the amount formula:
$$S = P(1 + i)^n$$
$$= 2,500(1.025)^{20}$$

You can use a calculator with an exponential button. It looks like this: $\boxed{y^x}$

Calculator steps:

1.025 $\boxed{y^x}$

20 $\boxed{=}$

$\boxed{\times}$

$2,500$ $\boxed{=}$ Answer: \$4,096.54

Example 4

Use a calculator to find the principal invested at 12%(4) for 8 years if the compounded value is $6,000.

Solution:

Find i.

$$i = \frac{12\%}{4} = 3\%$$

Find n.

$$n = 4 \times 8 \text{ years} = 32 \text{ periods}$$

Substitute:

$$P = S(1 + i)^{-n}$$
$$P = \$6,000(1.03)^{-32}$$

Calculator Steps:

1.03 $\boxed{y^x}$

32 $\boxed{^+/_-}$ $\boxed{=}$

$\boxed{\times}$

6,000 $\boxed{=}$ Answer: $2,330.02

Remark: Note that in 8 years $2,330.02 will grow to $6,000.

Exercises

Complete the following table on your own paper.

	Interest Rate	Term	Rate Per Period i	Total Number of Points n
1.	8% compounded annually	5 years	8%	
2.	10% compounded monthly	15 years	5/6%	
3.	12% compounded quarterly	2 years	3%	
4.	9% compounded semiannually	8 years	4½%	
5.	36% compounded monthly	1½ years	3%	
6.	15% compounded quarterly	15 months	3¾%	
7.	6% compounded semiannually	20 years	3%	
8.	11% compounded daily	1½ months	11/365% ≈ 0.03%	

Use the finance tables to determine the amount and interest earned for each investment.

	Principal	Interest Rate	Term	Compound Amount	Compound Interest
9.	$960	5% (2)	3		
10.	$1,435	8% (4)	2		
11.	$795	6% (4)	4		
12.	$867	4% (4)	2		
13.	$2,560	7% (2)	3		
14.	$2,462	7% (1)	3		
15.	$1,397	6% (1)	4		
16.	$3,753	9% (2)	5		

Find the principal (present value) that must be invested to obtain the desired compound amount, given the rate and term. Use either the finance tables or your calculator.

	Amount Desired	Interest Rate	Years of Investment	Principal (Present Value)
17.	$500	6%(4)	4 years	
18.	$1,000	8%(4)	6 years	
19.	$1,500	9%(12)	2.5 years	
20.	$2,000	10%(2)	8 years	
21.	$20,000	10%(12)	15 years	
22.	$30,000	8%(12)	20 years	

23. How much money should be deposited in a college-education trust fund when a child is 6 years old in order to have $20,000 when he is 18 years old? Assume that the account pays 9%(12).

24. If Jonathan Edwards left $1,000 in a foundation trust on June 1, 1750, what would have been the value of the fund on June 1, 1980? Assume that both invested and loaned moneys earned 4%(1) interest for the first 100 years, 5%(1) for the next 100 years, and 6%(1) to June 1, 1980.

Banking

From your first day of life, the bank plays a significant part in your finances. Since its beginnings in the Middle Ages, the modern bank has become essential in the flow of money among Western nations. Without banks, economic activity as we know it would cease. Although banks exist to make a profit through investments, they offer a wide range of services to attract customers. If you have ever wondered why downtown banks usually reside in huge skyscrapers, the following explanation of services should explain the need for so many offices.

Banks help you invest your income. Your first thought concerning your local bank may be your *savings account,* but many other services are available. For example, the *direct deposit* plan sends your payroll check or Social Security check directly to the bank, without its ever entering your hands. A *payroll savings* plan makes automatic transfers of a fixed sum to United States savings bonds or to your savings account. Experienced financiers will help manage investment portfolios of stocks, bonds, etc. (usually charging 0.5% of the capital's market value). Brokerage services buy and sell directly through the bank, saving you up to 70% on commissions. Banks also help you plan for private expenses. *Christmas clubs* and *vacation clubs* transfer a certain amount of money from your account, and the clubs prevent you from withdrawing the funds until Christmas or vacation time. *Bank loans* permit you to purchase items for which you do not yet have the money. Most homes and many cars and appliances are purchased through bank loans. Many families start a private business or farm using bank loans. Then professional counselors give advice on how to spend the money. Some major banks also offer *payroll services:* the bank's computers will process payroll accounts, write the checks, analyze the information, and prepare statements. Many banks go so far as to prepare and collect the business's bills!

Bank *credit cards* (Visa, Mastercard, American Express, and others) provide easy temporary loans for anything from gasoline to clothes and music equipment.

One of the most ancient services of "money-changers" was the safeguarding of valuables and the exchange of cash for checks or foreign currency. Banks still provide these services. A bank's *safety deposit* box serves as a safe place for important papers and other valuables, such as wills, jewelry, or birth certificates. If you go on vacation, you can buy *foreign money* as well as *travelers' checks,* which require a signature at the time of purchase and a new signature at the time of exchange. *Bank checks* (also called *cashier's checks*) are slips of paper guaranteeing that the bank will pay the specified amount. *Bank drafts* are similar, but they guarantee money at another bank that has been deposited to the first bank's account. If you need to guarantee that

you can cover the amount on your check, you can buy a *certified check,* which the bank stamps and signs.

As you grow older, you can choose from many *trust funds* to protect your possessions. Some *insurance* options are available through banks (particularly supplements to Medicare coverage). You can also set up a *pension trust* to support you during retirement. The most popular new retirement plan is the *IRA* (Individual Retirement Account), which permits you to invest up to $2,000 in any bank each year with tax-deferred interest. Other trusts provide for a bank official (executor) to manage your estate after your death: the *sheltering trust* guarantees support for your children's education and welfare; the *charitable trust* places your estate in the hands of a charitable organization; and the *spendthrift trust* protects unwise beneficiaries of your will (such as minors) from bungling your finances. After you die, bank officials will probably take care of the details of your will.

As technology grows, banks will continue to offer more for your financial needs, from your first savings account to your last will. The future list of services is limited only by the imagination and resources of bank executives.

Effective-Interest Rates

In the previous sections, you saw that compounding gives a better return than simple interest for the same rate. However, when the interest rate for compound interest is to be compared to a different simple-interest rate, it's hard to decide which gives the best return. For example, is 6% compounded monthly as good as or better than $6\frac{1}{4}$% simple interest? To make a proper judgment, you will need to change the compound-interest rate to an equivalent simple-interest rate, called the *effective interest rate*.

To change a compound-interest rate to simple-interest rate, compare a known compound rate to an unknown simple rate that gives the same return. Recalling that i represents the rate per period, S the compound amount, P the principal, and r the simple-interest rate, let m be the number of compounding periods per year. The value of an investment of P dollars for one year can be expressed as:

$$S = P(1 + i)^m \qquad \text{by compound interest}$$

$$S = P(1 + r) \qquad \text{by simple interest}$$

Since the return is to be equal, set these equal to each other.

$$P(1 + r) = P(1 + i)^m$$

Now cancel the value P from each side, and solve for r.

$$\frac{\cancel{P}(1 + r)}{\cancel{P}} = \frac{\cancel{P}(1 + i)^m}{\cancel{P}}$$

$$1 + r = (1 + i)^m$$

$$\boxed{r = (1 + i)^m - 1} \qquad \text{(Effective-interest-rate formula)}$$

In the finance tables you will find $(1 + i)^m$ in the first column under **amount of $1** at compound interest.

Example 1

Find the effective rate for 6% compounded monthly.

Solution:

Note that $i = \frac{6\%}{12} = \frac{1}{2}\%$ and that $m = 12$ (periods per year).

In the finance table for $\frac{1}{2}$%, look up the factor $(1 + \frac{1}{2}\%)^{12}$ or $(1.005)^{12}$. You will find it equals 1.061677812. Now subtract 1.

$$\begin{array}{r} 1.061677812 \\ \underline{-1.0} \\ r = \quad 0.061677812 \text{ (as a decimal)} \\ r = \quad 6.1677812\% \\ \text{or rounded, } r = \quad 6.17\% \end{array}$$

Remark: It's now clear that $6\frac{1}{4}\%$ (6.25%) simple interest gives a better return than 6.17%.

Example 2

Find the effective rate for 12% compounded daily.

Solution:
Since the rate $i = \frac{12\%}{365}$ isn't in the finance tables, this must be a calculator problem.
Set up the factor $(1 + i)^m$ using $i = 0.000328767$.

$$r = (1.000328767)^{365} - 1$$

$$1.000328767 \quad \boxed{y^x}$$

$$365 \quad \boxed{=}$$

$$\boxed{-}$$

$$1 \quad \boxed{=}$$

$$0.127474614$$

Change to percent: $r = 12.75\%$

Exercises

Complete the following table on your own paper. All of these effective rates can be calculated with the finance tables.

	Nominal Annual Rate	Effective Rate if the compounding is . . .		
		Semiannual	Quarterly	Monthly
1.	6%			
2.	7%			
3.	8%			
4.	9%			
5.	10%			
6.	12%			
7.	14%			
8.	16%			

Complete the following table on your own paper. Most of these effective rates will require a calculator with an exponential button.

	Nominal Annual Rate	Effective Rate if the compounding is . . .		
		Quarterly	Monthly	Daily
9.	5¼%			
10.	11%			
11.	13%			
12.	15%			
13.	18%			
14.	21%			
15.	24%			

16. Which rate of interest gives the better annual yield, 9% compounded daily or $9\frac{1}{2}$% simple interest?

17. Suppose that a bank uses Banker's Rule for daily compound interest. That is, they get i using ordinary interest (360 days), but they use 365 for n. How much more in earnings would an investor make in one year on $10,000 at 8% compounded daily?

Passbook Savings ⸻⸻⸻⸻⸻

When you open a savings account, you usually receive a passbook. You keep the passbook and present it each time you make a transaction. A transaction on a savings account is always a deposit or a withdrawal. Your financial institution records in your passbook your deposits, withdrawals, earned interest, and the balance.

Carol Henry's passbook is shown below:

		Upstate Savings and Loan		
		In Account with _Carol Henry_		
Date	**Deposit**	**Withdrawal**	**Interest**	**Balance**
Jan. 5	$350.00			$350.00
Jan. 21		$55.00		$295.00
Feb. 2	$200.00			$495.00
Feb. 16		$20.00		$475.00
Mar. 6	$300.00			$775.00
Apr. 1			$7.44	$782.44

Date of transaction

Withdrawals are *subtracted* from the balance.

Amount in the account

Deposits and interest are *added* to the balance.

The interest problems you did in the previous sections involved accounts in which the principal remained the same for the entire compound period. This is not usually the case in a passbook savings account because the account holder makes deposits and withdrawals during the compound period. Obviously, these transactions change the principal. There are several methods for computing interest on an active account. Two of these are the minimum-balance method and the daily-interest method.

Minimum-Balance Method

When interest is figured by the minimum-balance method, interest is paid on the lowest balance in the account during the compound period. One disadvantage of this method is that additional deposits made during the period don't earn interest until the next compound period. Another disadvantage is that interest is lost whenever money is withdrawn.

Example 1

Use the minimum-balance method to find the interest on the following account; then find the new balance as of June 30. Interest is paid at the rate of 5%(4).

Date	Deposit	Withdrawal	Interest	Balance
April 1	$250.00			$680.00
April 23		$150.00		$530.00
May 2	$320.00			$850.00
June 2	$200.00			$1,050.00
June 15		$250.00		$800.00
June 30			?	?

The lowest balance during the quarter is $530.00, so this amount is used as the principal:

$$S = P(1 + i)^n$$
$$= \$530(1.0125)^1 \quad \text{(Remember, } i = \tfrac{0.05}{4} = 0.0125.\text{)}$$
$$= \$536.63 \text{ (the balance)}$$
$$\text{interest} = \$536.63 - \$530.00$$
$$\text{interest} = \$6.63$$

Daily-Interest Method

The *daily-interest method* accounts for the actual number of days that the money is on deposit. Most modern banking institutions have computers that calculate the interest earned by daily compounding or continuous compounding. Banks that pay interest compounded monthly, quarterly, or semiannually will generally use simple interest for any part of an interest period. In this section you will learn to use simple interest for part of a period.

Whenever a transaction takes place during an interest period, it establishes a new balance. Using the daily-interest method, the amount of interest earned between transactions is calculated and then totaled at the end of an interest period.

Example 2

Using the daily-interest method, calculate the interest earned and the quarterly balance for the account in Example 1. Compare this interest to the interest earned using the minimum-balance method.

Solution:
Calculate the interest between each transaction and between the last transaction and the end of the quarter (June 30). Use Banker's Rule.

(1) Principal: $680
   Rate: 5%(4) = 0.05
   Time: 22 days; April 1 to April 23

$$I = Prt$$
$$= \$680 \times 0.05 \times \tfrac{22}{360}$$
$$= \$2.08$$

(2) Principal: $530
   Rate: 5%(4)
   Time: 9 days; April 23 to May 2

$$I = \$530 \times 0.05 \times \tfrac{9}{360}$$
$$= \$.66$$

(3) Principal: $850
   Rate: 0.05
   Time: 31 days; May 2 to June 2

$$I = \$850 \times 0.05 \times \tfrac{31}{360}$$
$$= \$3.66$$

(4) Principal: $1,050
   Rate: 0.05
   Time: 13 days; June 2 to June 15

$$I = \$1,050 \times 0.05 \times \tfrac{13}{360}$$
$$= \$1.90$$

(5) Principal: $800
   Rate: 0.05
   Time: 15 days; June 15 to June 30

$$I = \$800 \times 0.05 \times \tfrac{15}{360}$$
$$= \$1.67$$

Total interest: $2.08 + $.66 + $3.66 + $1.90 + $1.67 = $9.97

New balance as of June 1 = $809.97

The minimum-balance method earned $6.63, so the daily-interest method earned $3.34 more.

Exercises

Compute the balance for each row in the following passbooks.

	Date	Deposit	Withdrawal	Interest	Balance
	Feb. 7	$200.00			$563.85
1.	Feb. 23		$76.00		?
2.	Mar. 2	$240.00			?
3.	Mar. 16		$50.00		?
4.	April 6	$125.50			?

	Date	Deposit	Withdrawal	Interest	Balance
	Oct. 1	$300.00			$937.80
5.	Oct. 15		$150.00		?
6.	Nov. 2	$350.00			?
7.	Nov. 12	$75.00			?
8.	Dec. 3	$315.00			?
9.	Dec. 13		$400.00		?
10.	Jan. 1			$13.66	?

Use the minimum-balance method to find the interest earned on the following accounts. The transactions for one quarter are shown.

11. Rate of interest: $5\frac{1}{4}\%$ compounded quarterly

Date	Balance
April 1	$698.40
April 17	$528.00
May 3	$978.00
May 13	$778.00
June 1	$1,128.00

12. Rate of interest: $6\frac{1}{2}\%$ compounded quarterly

Date	Balance
July 2	$2,462.35
July 21	$2,122.35
Aug. 1	$2,722.35
Aug. 5	$2,472.35
Sept. 9	$2,941.63
Sept. 24	$2,876.63

Find the interest for the daily-interest time periods shown below. Use the Banker's Rule.

No. of Days	Annual Rate of Interest	Principal
13. 12	4.5%	$726.40
14. 23	5.75%	$538.12
15. 18	6%	$1,365
16. 26	5.5%	$952.66
17. 47	6.25%	$1,921.30

18. Use the daily-interest method to find the interest and new balance on the account shown below. Use the Banker's Rule. The rate of interest is 5%(4).

Date	Deposit	Withdrawal	Interest	Balance
7-1	$540.00			$1,260.00
7-15		$125.00		$1,135.00
8-3	$200.00			$1,335.00
8-9		$82.00		$1,253.00
9-2	$416.50			$1,699.50
9-20		$620.00		$1,049.50
10-1			?	?

Savings Programs

A savings program can be distinguished from a savings account by the regularity of its deposits and by the available tax advantages. The most common savings programs are those that save for retirement. *Individual Retirement Accounts* (IRAs) may be established by an individual at a qualified savings institution. The United States government allows you to save up to $2,000 per year and defer the payment of taxes until retirement. Retired persons generally have lower income and more personal deductions; so taxes would be less on the IRA money saved during the working years. Self-employed people may have a tax-deferred program called a *Keogh plan,* and many businesses have company retirement programs that involve payments by the employee and matching funds contributed by the company. People who save for major purchases, such as cars and homes, can save systematically by having payroll deductions deposited into credit unions or by having automatic transfers from their checking account to their savings account. Of course, these programs don't provide the tax savings that retirement accounts afford.

The key ingredient to a savings program is not the amount of each payment but the faithfulness to regular deposits. Faithfulness, steadfastness, and consistency are character traits that you can learn from the Lord. Our God is faithful and unchanging. Read in Psalms 88 and 89 about the Lord's faithfulness. Men apart from God's enabling power are prone to unfaithfulness. Proverbs 20:6 says, "Most men will proclaim every one his own goodness: but a faithful man who can find?"

Each of the savings programs mentioned has the same basic structure—equal deposits of money, spaced at equal periods of time. Anytime you make payments or deposits in this way, it's called an *annuity.* A house payment, as well as a savings program, is an annuity. In the diagram below you will see a representation of a sequence of payments, each of R. The value of the payments, including accrued interest, is labeled as S_n and called the amount, or future value.

S_n
(amount)

$R \quad\quad R \quad\quad R \quad\quad R \quad\quad R \quad\quad\quad\quad R \quad\quad R$

The value of S_n comes from applying compound interest to each payment to get the compound amount at the date of S_n. So S_n is the total (or sum) of all these compound amounts. It would be very time consuming to calculate the amount of every annuity using the separate payments. Thus, a formula has been developed to give the total S_n, using the payment R, the interest rate i per interest period, and the number of payments n:

$$S_n = R\left[\frac{(1 + i)^n - 1}{i}\right]$$

At first, you may think that this formula looks too complicated to use. Actually, though, you won't need to do the calculation of the complex-looking factor next to R because it is listed among the factors in the financial tables. A simpler form is used to identify it and point out the values to look up. We can say $s_{\overline{n}|i} = [\frac{(1+i)^n - 1}{i}]$; so the expression for S_n becomes $S_n = Rs_{\overline{n}|i}$. If you have an exponential calculator, you may want to work out the value of $Rs_{\overline{n}|i}$ yourself. If you use the finance tables, you will find $S_{\overline{n}|i}$ listed under **Amount Saved for $1 per Period.** When you need to find the payment R in the formula, you must solve for R.

$$S_n = Rs_{\overline{n}|i} \qquad \text{Now divide.}$$

$$\frac{S_n}{s_{\overline{n}|i}} = \frac{R s_{\overline{n}|i}}{s_{\overline{n}|i}} \qquad \text{Cancel like factors.}$$

$$\frac{S_n}{s_{\overline{n}|i}} = R \qquad \text{Now write the quotient as a product.}$$

$$S_n(\frac{1}{s_{\overline{n}|i}}) = R \qquad \text{Now put } R \text{ on the left.}$$

$$R = S_n(\frac{1}{s_{\overline{n}|i}})$$

$\frac{1}{s_{\overline{n}|i}}$ is found under the column **Payment to Save $1.**

Example 1

Suppose that a diligent worker deposits $50 per month for 30 years into an IRA program. For this length of time the interest rate would probably change many times, but assume that it remained at 10%(12). How much is in the fund after 30 years?

Solution:

Find the rate: $\quad i = \frac{10\%}{12} = \frac{5}{6}\%$

Find the number of payments: $\quad n = 12 \times 30 = 360$

$$S_n = Rs_{\overline{n}|i} \qquad \text{Now substitute.}$$

$$S_{360} = 50 \times s_{\overline{360}|\frac{5}{6}\%}$$

Now find the $\frac{5}{6}\%$ page in the finance tables. Under **Amount Saved for $1 per Period** $(s_{\overline{n}|i})$ go down to $n = 360$ and get the factor.

$$S_{360} = \$50(2,260.487922)$$

$$= \$113,024.40 \text{ after 30 years}$$

Example 2

Suppose that a man wants to save regularly for his 3-year-old daughter's college education. If the daughter goes to college at 18 years of age, and if the fund will need $30,000, how much per month at 12%(12) will the man need to deposit?

Solution:

Find the rate: $i = \frac{12\%}{12} = 1\%$

Find the number of payments: $n = 12 \times 15 = 180$

$R = s_{\overline{n}|i}\left(\frac{1}{s_{\overline{n}|i}}\right)$

$\qquad = \$30,000\left(\frac{1}{s_{\overline{180}|1\%}}\right)$ Look up factor under **Payment to Save $1.**

$\qquad = \$30,000(0.002001681)$

$\qquad = \$60.05$ per month for 15 years

Not all savings programs are based on monthly payments; quarterly and semiannual payments are other convenient intervals that are used. In this text the frequency of compounding will match the payment interval. If the bank compounds interest quarterly, the payments will be quarterly. Many banks pay interest compounded daily, but this requires financial tables more extensive than this text contains. In the optional section the use of a calculator for annuities will allow you to handle a broader scope of problem. In Examples 3 and 4 you will see how to find the amount of a savings plan when two different interest rates are used.

Example 3

In the city where Mr. Bagwell lives, the banks pay interest at 10%(4) on all automatic-transfer savings programs. How much can Mr. Bagwell save with quarterly deposits of $95 for 5 years?

Solution:

Find i: $\frac{10\%}{4} = 2\frac{1}{2}\%$

Find n: 4 quarters per year $\times$ 5 years $= 20$

Substitute into the formula $S_n = R s_{\overline{n}|i}$

$S_{20} = 95 s_{\overline{20}|2\frac{1}{2}\%}$ Look up the factor.

$\qquad = \$95(25.54465761)$

$\qquad = \$2,426.74$ after 5 years

Example 4

What is the amount of a 10-year savings program of $120 per month if the bank pays 8%(12) for the first 5 years and 10%(12) for the second 5 years?

Solution:

Find (a) the amount of the first 5 years' deposits and use it as a lump sum invested at compounded interest for the last five years. Then find (b) the amount of the second 5 years' deposits and add the two quantities.

(a)
$$S_n = Rs_{\overline{n}|i}$$
$$S_{60} = 120s_{\overline{60}|\frac{2}{3}\%} \qquad i = \frac{8\%}{12} = \frac{2}{3}\%$$
$$= \$120(73.476856)$$
$$= \$8,817.22$$

$$S = P(1 + i)^n \qquad i = \frac{10\%}{12} = \frac{5}{6}\%$$
$$= \$8,817.22(1 + \tfrac{5}{6}\%)60$$
$$= \$8,817.22(1.6453089)$$
$$= \$14,507.05$$

(b)
$$S_n = Rs_{\overline{n}|i}$$
$$S_{60} = \$120s_{\overline{60}|\frac{5}{6}\%}$$
$$= \$120(77.437072)$$
$$= \$9,292.45$$

total: $14,507.05 + $9,292.45 = $23,799.50 after 10 years

Exercises

For each savings program, calculate the amount in the fund after the given time period. Assume that no deposits were missed and that the interest rate was fixed.

	Payment	Interest Rate	Time	Amount
1.	$15	6% (12)	3 years	
2.	$25	7% (12)	30 months	
3.	$45	8% (4)	5 years	
4.	$60	9% (12)	15 months	
5.	$200	10% (12)	20 years	
6.	$100	6% (2)	30 years	
7.	$90	14% (4)	4.5 years	
8.	$75	18% (12)	20 months	

For each savings program, calculate the payment needed to save the given amount in the given time period.

	Amount	Interest Rate	Time	Payment
9.	$20,000	8%(12)	10 years	
10.	$500	6%(4)	2 years	
11.	$1,000,000	15%(12)	30 years	
12.	$6,000	18%(4)	3 years	
13.	$2,500	9%(12)	30 months	
14.	$950	8%(2)	5 years	
15.	$1,280	14%(12)	9 months	
16.	$14,500	10%(12)	8 years	

17. Mary Taylor has $40 per month deposited into her credit-union account, which pays 12%(12). If she has been doing this for $4\frac{1}{2}$ years, how much is in her savings fund?

18. Bill McGrew needs to save $8,200 for a new car in four years. If his credit union pays 15%(12), what deposit should he make each month into the account?

19. When Martin Castil found he could save $18 per month on his insurance programs, he decided to deposit the $18 into his IRA account. If the account pays 15%(12), by how much will it increase his IRA when he retires in 25 years?

20. The retirement plan at Mrs. Barkley's school was paying 6%(12) during her first 15 years there, but the last 15 years it has paid 9%(12). What is the value of her retirement fund if she has always deposited $25 per month and her school has matched those deposits? (Apply $\frac{3}{4}$% per month compound interest to the first 15-year amount.)

Annuities with a Calculator (optional)

As you have read, an annuity is simply a sequence of equal payments spaced at equal time intervals. The amortized loans of Chapter 8 and the savings programs of this chapter are both a type of annuity called an *ordinary annuity*. If you let the payment for a loan or the deposit for a savings program be *R,* the following diagrams illustrate these two situations for an ordinary annuity.

Loan Annuity

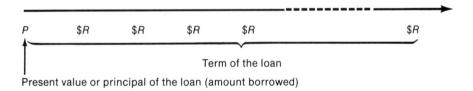

Term of the loan

Present value or principal of the loan (amount borrowed)

Savings Annuity

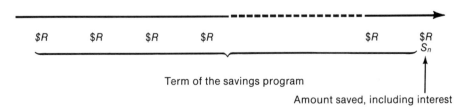

Term of the savings program

Amount saved, including interest

In Chapter 8 you were introduced to the methods of finding loan payments and the amount borrowed with the help of finance tables. A similar formula exists for this type of annuity as was given for savings annuities. The following table summarizes the formulas for the four factors in the finance tables. If you know about geometric sequences, you can derive these formulas yourself.

Finance Table Formulas

Amount Saved for $1/Period	Payment to Save $1	Amount Borrowed for $1 Payment	Payment to Borrow $1
$S_n = R\left[\dfrac{(1+i)^n - 1}{i}\right]$	$R = S_n\left(\dfrac{1}{s\,\overline{n}\rvert_i}\right)$	$P = R\left[\dfrac{1 - (1+i)^{-n}}{i}\right]$	$R = P\left(\dfrac{1}{p\,\overline{n}\rvert_i}\right)$
$= R s\,\overline{n}\rvert_i$		$= R p\,\overline{n}\rvert_i$	

If you have a good calculator with a $\boxed{y^x}$ button, you can do loan and savings problems for just about any interest rate and term within the register capacity of your calculator.

Example 1

Find the amount saved with a $25-per-month IRA account paying $9\frac{3}{4}\%(12)$ for 40 years.

Solution:
Use the first formula (amount saved).

Calculator Steps	Value on Calculator	Portion of Formula
0.0975 $\div$ 12 $=$ STO	0.008125	i (and stored for later)
$+$ 1 $=$	1.008125	$1 + i$
y^x 480 $=$	48.63004504	$(1 + i)^n$ (where $n = 40 \times 12 = 480$)
$-$ 1 $=$	47.63004504	$(1 + i)^n - 1$ (numerator ready)
$\div$ RM $=$	5862.15939	$\dfrac{(1 + i)^n - 1}{i}$ (factor complete)
$\times$ 25 $=$	$146,553.98	$R\left[\dfrac{(1 + i)^n - 1}{i}\right]$ (now have S_n)

Example 2

Find the monthly payment for a $8,500 loan at 13%(12) for 3 years.

Solution:

Use the fourth formula (payment to borrow $1).

Calculator Steps	Value on Calculator	Portion of Formula
0.13 ÷ 12 = STO	0.010833333	i (and stored)
+ 1 =	1.010833333	$1 + i$
y^x 36 +/- =	0.678478401	$(1 + i)^{-n}$ (where $n = 12 \times 3 = 36$)
+/- + 1 =	0.321521599	$1 - (1 + i)^{-n}$ (numerator ready)
÷ RM =	29.67891678	$\left[\dfrac{1 - (1 + i)^{-n}}{i}\right]$ ($P_{\overline{n}\rvert i}$ factor complete)
1/x	0.033693952	$\dfrac{1}{P_{\overline{n}\rvert i}}$ (reciprocal complete)
× 8,500 =	286.3985927	You now have payment R.

Ans.: $286.40 per month

Exercises

Find the amount saved with the payment, rate, and term given for each savings program.

	Payment	Interest Rate	Term	Amount Saved
1.	$12.60	4% (12)	45 years	
2.	$45.00	8.25% (4)	3 years	
3.	$55.00	11.68% (12)	5.5 years	
4.	$115.00	13.5% (12)	11 years	
5.	$5.00	9% (365)	15 years	

Find the payment needed for each savings program to save the amount given.

	Amount	Interest Rate	Term	Payment
6.	$1,000,000	12.5% (12)	35 years	
7.	$8,500	6.5% (12)	4 years	
8.	$25,000	11% (12)	18 years	
9.	$955	5.25% (4)	2.5 years	
10.	$41,900	7.68% (365)	11 years	

Find the required payment for each loan to pay off the given principal.

	Principal	Interest Rate	Term	Payment
11.	$1,500	14.5% (12)	18 months	
12.	$3,600	17.35% (12)	2 years	
13.	$14,800	9.85% (12)	4 years	
14.	$45,000	10.65% (12)	19 years	
15.	$250,000	7.35% (4)	7.5 years	

Find the amount that can be borrowed for each given payment, interest rate, and term.

	Payment	Interest Rate	Term	Amount Borrowed
16.	$25	13.25% (12)	18 months	
17.	$82	11.5% (12)	80 months	
18.	$130	12.86% (12)	48 months	
19.	$295	15.25% (12)	16 years	
20.	$752	10.75% (12)	28 years	

Chapter 9 Review

annuity
blank endorsement
check
checkbook register
compound amount
compound interest
credit union
currency
daily interest
effective interest rate
electronic teller
interest period

IRA
minimum balance
outstanding check
passbook
payee
present value
rate per period
restricted endorsement
savings program
special endorsement
tax-deferred
transaction

Review Exercises

Write out the following dollar amounts as you would on a check.

1. $25.50
2. $185.23
3. $2,456.00
4. $5.82
5. $539.15
6. $10,928.00

Use the finance tables to determine the compound amount and compound interest earned by each of the following accounts.

	Principal	Interest Rate	Term	Amount	Interest
7.	$890	6% (2)	4 years		
8.	$635	5% (4)	2 years		
9.	$1,462	4% (4)	3 years		
10.	$2,335	7% (12)	18 months		
11.	$88	15% (12)	5 years		
12.	$5,800	9% (2)	8 years		
13.	$9,400	10% (12)	7 months		
14.	$115,000	8% (4)	4 years		

Use the formula and your calculator to find the compound amount of each investment.

	Principal	Interest Rate	Term	Amount
15.	$719	8% (365)	6 months	
16.	$850	9.68% (4)	2 years	
17.	$976	5½% (4)	16 years	
18.	$1,500	7.38% (2)	21 years	
19.	$450	14.25% (4)	5 years	
20.	$2,643	10.5% (2)	8 years	

Find the present value (principal) that must be invested to obtain the indicated amount.

	Amount	Interest Rate	Term	Principal
21.	$125,000	8% (12)	30 years	
22.	$45,000	6% (2)	10 years	
23.	$2,500	10% (4)	3 years	
24.	$6,000	12% (12)	5 years	
25.	$852	6% (1)	4 years	

Find the effective-interest rate using the finance tables. The given values are the nominal annual rate.

26. 5%(4) **28.** 18%(4)
27. 2%(2) **29.** 24%(12)

Find the amount in each savings-program fund after the given time period. Assume that no payments are missed and that the interest rate was fixed.

	Payment	Interest Rate	Time	Amount
30.	$28	5% (4)	6 years	
31.	$51	6% (2)	7 years	
32.	$115	8% (12)	2 years	
33.	$300	15% (12)	5 years	
34.	$75	6% (1)	30 years	
35.	$14.50	12% (12)	30 months	

Compute the balance for each row in the following passbook. Then determine the interest earned for the quarter. Use the minimum-balance method. Interest is calculated at $5\frac{1}{2}\%$ compounded quarterly.

36.

Date	Deposit	Withdrawal	Interest	Balance
Jan. 2	$260.00			$960.23
Jan. 10		$50.00		?
Jan. 16	$225.00			?
Feb. 1	$245.00			?
Feb. 15	$200.00			?
Feb. 20		$400.00		?
Mar. 2	$250.00			?
Mar. 8		$275.00		?
Mar. 17	$290.00			?
Mar. 23		$150.00		?
Apr. 1			?	?

Find the interest for the time-periods shown below. Use the daily-interest method, and use a 365-day year.

No. of Days	Annual Rate of Interest	Principal
37. 15	$5\frac{1}{2}\%$	$347.12
38. 24	6%	$626.84
39. 12	$5\frac{3}{4}\%$	$513.36
40. 26	$5\frac{1}{4}\%$	$738.75

Transportation

"Dad, can I borrow the car tonight? I'll buy some gas."

Sooner or later just about every teenager ends up making a similar-sounding request. Borrowing the family car has become practically an American tradition. However, many new drivers have no idea just how *much* this luxury costs. Even without considering the initial cost of paying for a new car, much more than just a few dollars' worth of gasoline per trip are needed to keep a car on the road. Every part on a vehicle—from the tires to the vinyl top—wears down a little bit each time the car is used. It's only a matter of time before any given part wears out and needs replacing.

Furthermore, there are hidden costs for registration, license plates, annual taxes, and insurance, as well as routine maintenance costs for oil, antifreeze, transmission fluid, brake fluid, filters, wax, and windshield cleaner. The actual cost of filling the gas tank is merely one more in a long line of expenses.

If you plan to drive a car, good stewardship of your money requires you to be aware of all the various expenses involved. By knowing about these costs and the alternatives open to you, you'll be able to plan ahead and avoid wasting your dollars.

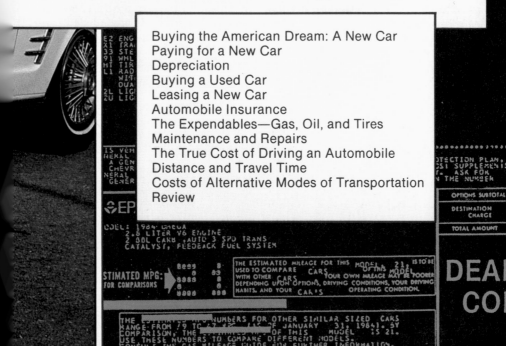

Buying the American Dream: A New Car
Paying for a New Car
Depreciation
Buying a Used Car
Leasing a New Car
Automobile Insurance
The Expendables—Gas, Oil, and Tires
Maintenance and Repairs
The True Cost of Driving an Automobile
Distance and Travel Time
Costs of Alternative Modes of Transportation
Review

Buying the American Dream: A New Car

If you go shopping for a new automobile without giving the decision some serious study, you may regret it. There are a number of factors to weigh besides how the car looks and what the monthly payment is. The first thing a Christian should do before making any consideration is to pray. In the Old Testament Joshua made a serious mistake concerning the Gibeonites because "the men . . . asked not counsel at the mouth of the Lord" (Josh. 9:14). In Psalm 25:12 we learn that the Lord teaches us the way we should choose. Being a good steward of the resources God has given us demands that we make well-thought-out decisions preceded by earnest prayer.

You should make a choice of car size based on your financial ability to operate the vehicle. Larger families will need larger vehicles, and larger cars cost more per mile to operate.

Table 10.1
Suburban-Based Cost of Operating an Automobile

Size	Total Costs in Cents per Mile
Passenger van	39.25
Large	30.62
Intermediate / mini-van	27.84
Compact	23.31
Subcompact	22.71

You should choose which make of car is best for you based on the most quality for the least expenditure. There are several magazines that compare all different makes of automobiles as to quality and cost of repairs. *Consumer Reports* and *Consumer Research* have regular articles about individual automobiles and annual reports about all of the current makes and models. After you have decided about size and have one or two makes in mind, you should visit several dealerships before making any commitment. (Warning: *Every* car dealer will want to be the one who sells you a car. Until you've shopped around, however, you'll never know who is offering you the best deal.)

The new car at the dealership will have a sticker on the left rear window explaining the price. You will see a base price near the top and then a list of options that are on that particular car. Each option will have a cost listed. At the bottom of the sticker you will find the total of all the options and the base price. This is called the *sticker price*. You should find a car you like with just those options you feel are necessary.

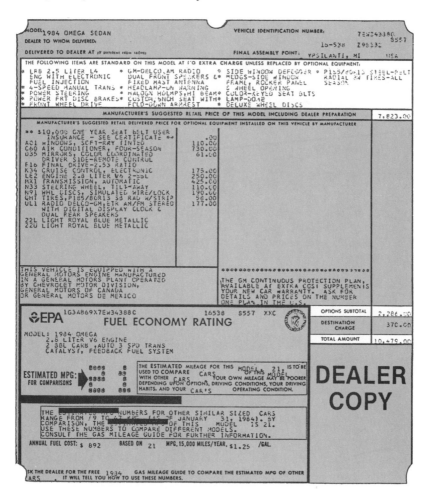

You are now ready to talk to a salesman about the price. First, you must decide if you will accept his offer for trading in your old car or if you can do better selling it yourself. Generally, if your old car is in poor condition or looks bad, trading it in will be the better choice. If you know that your old car is a dependable used car that has been well maintained, you can probably do better selling it yourself. Unless you are buying a model that is in high demand, you can expect to get some discount off the sticker price. This discount is one reason you need to shop at several dealerships.

Your last consideration should be the availability of a factory warranty. Some warranties must be paid for by the purchaser. Others are offered without charge by the manufacturer. If you have studied your car selection in *Consumer Reports*, you will know what kind of repair problems to expect and can make sure you are not buying a product that will cost you hundreds of dollars in repair bills.

Example 1

Mr. Faraday would like to know what size new car he can afford to operate on a $50-per-week budget. He drives 200 miles each week.

Solution: He should calculate the cost per mile and then compare it to values in Table 10.1.

$$\frac{\$50.00}{200 \text{ miles}} = \$.25 \text{ per mile}$$

He can afford a compact or subcompact vehicle.

Example 2

Miss Warner drives 15,000 miles per year in her compact car. How much should she budget per year for automobile costs? how much per week? (From Table 10.1, a compact car costs 23.31 cents per mile to operate.)

Solution: $\dfrac{15,000 \text{ miles}}{\text{year}} \cdot \dfrac{\$0.2331}{\text{mile}} = \$3,496.50 \text{ per year}$

$\phantom{Solution: \dfrac{15,000 \text{ miles}}{\text{year}} \cdot \dfrac{\$0.2331}{\text{mile}} } = \$67.24 \text{ per week}$

Example 3

The sticker price on a new Ford is $11,953. If the dealer allows a 10% discount, what will it cost?

Solution:

$$\$11,953 \cdot 10\% = \$11,953 \cdot 0.10 = \$1,195.30$$

$$\$11,953.00 - \$1,195.30 = \$10,757.70 \quad (\text{new cost})$$

Example 4

If the sales tax for the car in Example 3 is figured at 5%, what is the tax owed on the discounted price?

Solution:

$$\$10,757.70 \cdot 5\% = \$10,757.70 \cdot 0.05 = \$537.89$$

Note: The cents' place was found by rounding $537.885. Some states have a maximum sales tax on automobiles, for example, $300.

Example 5

Rick Lundberger has the following offer from an automobile dealer:

Sticker price: $8,940.00
Discount: 6%
Trade-in allowance: $2,100.00
Sales tax: 4%

Find what the car will cost, including sales tax.

Discount = 6% · $8,940.00 = $536.40
New cost = $8,940.00 − $536.40 = $8,403.60
Trade-in allowance = $2,100.00
Balance owed = $6,303.60
Tax at 4% = $252.14
Drive-away price = $6,555.74

Example 6

If Mr. Lundberger has no trade-in, the dealer will give him an 8% discount. He sold his old car privately for $2,400. Find the drive-away price and net price.

Sticker price = $8,940.00
Discount at 8% = $715.20
New cost = $8,224.80
Sales tax 4% = $328.99
Drive-away price = $8,553.79
Resale of old car = $2,400.00
Net price = $6,153.79

Note: The sales tax was calculated on the sticker price less discount because there was no trade-in. The buyer pays a little more tax by selling his own car, but he can often get more than enough to compensate by selling privately.

Exercises

Find the discount cost and the 5% sales tax for each automobile, given the sticker price and discount rate below.

1. $6,550; 2%
2. $8,590; 4%
3. $9,250; 5%
4. $10,900; 5%
5. $11,755; 8%

6. $12,200; 8%
7. $13,290; 9%
8. $14,460; 9%
9. $15,280; 10%

Find how much should be budgeted for automobile costs, given the weekly mileage and the size of the car. Use Table 10.1 and round to the dollar.

10. 180 mi./week; subcompact
11. 50 mi./week; large
12. 250 mi./week; van
13. 300 mi./week; intermediate
14. 400 mi./week; compact
15. 125 mi./week; subcompact

Find the cost per mile and the largest vehicle choice for the following mileage and budget requirements. Use Table 10.1.

16. $55/week; 250 miles
17. $1,700/year; 4,700 miles
18. $4,650/year; 15,000 miles
19. $125/week; 535 miles
20. $86/week; 275 miles

21. Pastor Hand is considering an automobile with a sticker price of $8,200. He can get a 2% discount and received $1,850 for his trade-in. Find the cost of the vehicle, including 6% sales tax (maximum $500).

22. When Dr. Harris ordered his new car with just the options he wanted, it meant he would not get a discount. The sticker price was $21,500 and his trade-in was quoted at $8,250. Find the drive-away cost of his new car, including 4% sales tax.

23. Bill Musgrove sold his motorcycle for $1,200 and went to look for a small pickup. He found a truck for $5,995 base price. If the dealer requires 20% down, can he buy a vehicle with any options? If he uses the $1,200 for a down payment, find the drive-away cost of the vehicle, including 5% sales tax.

24. Which of the following family cars is the better buy, and what is the savings?
    a. $12,250 sticker price
       6% discount with trade-in
       $2,700 trade-in allowance
       5% sales tax
    b. $12,250 sticker price
       8% discount
       $1,600 trade-in allowance
       6% sales tax ($500 max.)

25. Which dealer is offering the best value for the buyer of an automobile with a sticker price of $9,438.50?

a. 5% discount
$1,800 trade-in allowance
6% sales tax ($500 max.)

b. 8% discount
$1,600 trade-in allowance
6% sales tax ($500 max.)

Project: Select 5 or 6 automobiles, some foreign, some domestic, and research their qualities in *Consumer Reports* or *Consumer Research*. Some areas in which they may be contrasted are federal recalls, repairs, mileage, crash abilities, and used-car value. You may even want to make a preliminary ranking of the cars for each category by using an opinion poll of friends who own those cars.

Paying for a New Car

After you make the calculations for the drive-away cost of a new car, you still have a nagging question to be answered. Where does the money come from to pay this balance? Most people borrow the money. Unless the money is a gift or an inheritance, you must either borrow it or save it. If you save some money from every paycheck, you will also earn interest toward your automobile purchase. However, if you have to borrow money and pay the loan back over a period of time, you will have to *pay* interest, which will greatly increase the cost of buying the car.

You may wonder why people would borrow money when they have to pay so much interest. The answer is basically twofold: either they can't wait because their old car is so bad, or they don't have enough self-discipline to save money. Patience and self-discipline are characteristics of a Spirit-filled life, but being patient and self-disciplined does not necessarily mean that one is Spirit-filled. Some people are born with these traits. For believers who are not, though, the Lord has promised to help them as they yield to His will.

The examples that follow will show you how to contrast the costs associated with paying cash to the costs associated with financing. We will contrast the purchasing of a $10,000 automobile by financing for four years with the cost of starting a savings program four years before the purchase.

Example 1

Paying Cash

Sticker price = $10,000
State tax at 5% = $500
Amount that must be saved = $10,500

Now find the amount that you must put into a savings account each month to save $10,500 over 4 years at an interest rate of 6%(12).

In the finance tables, look under **Payment to Save** and use 48 for the number of payments. Remember, $i = \frac{6\%}{12} = \frac{1}{2}\%$

$$\text{Payment } R = \$10,500 \ (0.018485)$$
$$= \$194.09 \text{ per month}$$

Note: You would probably round up to $195.

If you use $R = 195$ and the *amount saved* column, the savings account you have is $10,549.08 after 4 years.

$$\text{Amount} = \$195 \ (54.09783)$$
$$= \$10,549.076$$

But how much cash did you actually put into the bank?

$$\text{Cash outlay} = 48 \text{ months} \times \frac{\$195}{\text{month}}$$
$$= \$9,360$$

How much interest did you *earn* during the four years?

$$\text{Interest earned} = \text{amount in the account} - \text{cash outlay}$$
$$= \$10,549.08 - \$9,360$$
$$= \$1,189.08$$

Just think, the bank gave you nearly $1,200 to keep your automobile "kitty" with them! Can you think of advantages and disadvantages to the savings plan for buying a car?

Example 2

Financing the Balance

Sticker price = $10,000
State tax at 5% = $500
Basic price = $10,500
Down payment = $2,000   (might be in the form of a trade-in)
$10,500 − $2,000 = $8,500

You must borrow $8,500.

Now you must find the monthly payment for an amortized loan to pay off $8,500 over 4 years at 10%(12). (To *amortize* a loan means to clear the debt in installments.) Notice that the interest rate you pay to borrow will be higher than the rate you are paid to save.

In the finance tables look under **Payment to Borrow** for $i = \frac{10\%}{12} = \frac{5}{6}\%$ and 48 payments.

$$\text{Payment} = \$8,500 \times (0.0253626)$$
$$= \$215.58 \text{ per month}$$

How much money did you actually pay the loan company?

$$\text{Cash outlay} = 48 \text{ months} \times \frac{\$215.58}{\text{month}}$$
$$= \$10,347.84$$

How much interest did you pay the loan company?

$$\text{Interest paid} = \text{cash outlay} - \text{principal borrowed}$$
$$= \$10,347.84 - \$8,500$$
$$= \$1,847.84$$

As you can see, using someone else's money is expensive! Can you think of advantages and disadvantages to financing a car?

Example 3

Let's try to make a larger down payment and see what it saves you in interest charges.

$$\text{Sticker price} = \$10,000$$
$$\text{State tax at } 5\% = \$500$$

$$\text{Basic price} = \$10,500$$
$$\text{Down payment} = \$3,500$$

$$\$10,000 - \$3,500 = \$7,000$$
$$\text{You must borrow } \$7,000.$$

Find the **Payment to Borrow** this $7,000 for 28 months at 10%(12).

$$R = \$7,000 \times (0.0253626)$$
$$= \$177.54$$

$$\text{Total cash outlay} = 48 \text{ months} \times \frac{177.54}{\text{month}}$$
$$= \$8,521.92$$

$$\text{Interest paid} = \$8,521.92 - \$7,000$$
$$= \$1,521.92$$

Paying a $3,500 down payment saved you $325.92 in interest charges.

Exercises

Find the amount saved for the given monthly payment, interest rate, and time.
 1. $25; 8%(12); 3 years
 2. $75; 9%(12); 4 years
 3. $105; 12%(12); 3 years
 4. $175; 7%(12); 4 years
 5. $210; 9%(12); 5 years
 6. $280; 6%(12); 3 years

Find the monthly payments needed to save the following amounts for the given interest rate and time. Round payments up to the cent.

   7. $5,000; 6%(12); 4 years
   8. $8,500; 8%(12); 3 years
   9. $6,500; 9%(12); 3 years
   10. $3,500; 8%(12); 2½ years
   11. $10,800; 7%(12); 4 years
   12. $12,200; 6%(12); 4 years

Find the monthly payments to pay off a loan for the given amount at the given interest rate and time. Round payments up to the cent.

   13. $3,000; 10%(12); 2 years
   14. $5,000; 10%(12); 3 years
   15. $7,500; 12%(12); 3 years
   16. $8,800; 12%(12); 4 years
   17. $9,600; 15%(12); 4 years
   18. $11,300; 15%(12); 5 years

Find how much interest the borrower will pay for each of the loans in problems 13 through 18.

   19. (from exercise 13)
   20. (from exercise 14)
   21. (from exercise 15)
   22. (from exercise 16)
   23. (from exercise 17)
   24. (from exercise 18)

   25. List some advantages and disadvantages of buying a car with cash through a savings program.

   Advantages:
      a. ?
      b. ?
      c. ?

   Disadvantages:
      a. ?
      b. ?
      c. ?

   26. Give some advantages and disadvantages of buying a car by the financing method.

   Advantages:
      a. ?
      b. ?
   Disadvantages:
      a. ?
      b. ?

FOR MR. HOOTER'S NEW CAR, DEPRECIATION SET IN BEFORE HE DROVE IT OFF THE LOT.

Depreciation

So now you have a brand-new automobile. What you may not know is that the day you drove it out of the dealership it decreased in value. This loss in value of a vehicle during any part of its lifetime is called *depreciation*. How much depreciation occurs in a given period of time depends on a number of factors, such as make, mileage, mechanical condition, and body condition. The rate of depreciation is most rapid at the beginning of a vehicle's lifetime and is the single greatest expense of automobile ownership.

Automotive dealerships receive quarterly publications that list the values of all the different makes and models including adjustments for options and differences in mileage. When you trade in a used car at a new-car dealership, the salesman is usually going to offer you the wholesale value of what your car is worth in his NADA book (National Dealers Association). The actual depreciation of an automobile can be determined only by the difference between original value and resale value, but estimates from dealers' books and government publications are fairly accurate. The following table taken from a government publication shows the depreciation of a $10,000 intermediate-size automobile.

Table 10.2
Depreciation Costs for Intermediate-Size Autos

Year 1	Year 2	Year 3	Year 4	Year 5
14,500 miles	13,700 miles	12,500 miles	11,400 miles	10,300 miles
$2,385 16.45¢ per mile	$1,401 10.23¢ per mile	$1,213 9.70¢ per mile	$956 8.39¢ per mile	$900 8.74¢ per mile

Formulas for Finding Depreciation

The average annual depreciation $= \dfrac{\text{accumulated depreciation}}{\text{age of car}}$

The straight-line rate of depreciation $= \dfrac{\text{average annual depreciation}}{\text{original cost}}$

Example 1

Using Table 10.2, find the average annual depreciation for the first 3 years.

$$\text{accumulated depreciation} = \$2,385 + \$1,401 + \$1,213$$
$$= \$4,999$$
$$\text{average annual depreciation} = \frac{\$4,999}{3} = \frac{\$1,666.33}{\text{year}}$$

Example 2

Using Table 10.2, what is the resale or trade-in value of the automobile after 4 years?

$$\text{accumulated depreciation} = \$5,955$$
$$\text{resale value} = \$10,000 - \$5,955 = \$4,045$$

Example 3

Using Table 10.2, find the straight-line rate of depreciation over 4 years.

$$\text{average annual depreciation} = \frac{\$5,955}{4} = \$1,488.75$$
$$\text{rate of depreciation} = \frac{\$1,488.75}{10,000} = 14.89\%$$

Example 4

What is the rate of depreciation for year 3?

$$\text{Value at the beginning of year 3} = \text{Original cost} - 2 \text{ years' depreciation}$$
$$= \$10,000 - (\$2,385 + \$1,401)$$
$$= \$10,000 - \$3,786$$
$$= \$6,214$$

$$\text{rate for year 3} = \frac{\$1,213}{\$6,214} = 19.5\%$$

Exercises

Find the depreciation for the following automobiles, given the original cost and the resale value.

Original	Resale
1. $8,500	$1,800
2. $5,950	$2,250
3. $12,900	$4,500
4. $15,200	$10,800

Find the average annual depreciation for the following automobiles.

Original Cost	Resale Value	Age of Vehicle
5. $6,500	$1,800	4
6. $9,750	$4,350	5
7. $10,500	$1,700	4
8. $15,900	$10,600	5

Use the following table for problems 9 through 15.

Table 10.3

**Depreciation Costs
for $8,800 Compact Sedan**

Year 1	Year 2	Year 3	Year 4	Year 5
14,500 miles	13,700 miles	12,500 miles	11,400 miles	10,300 miles
$1,595 11.0¢ per mile	$1,105 8.07¢ per mile	$1,005 8.04¢ per mile	$805 7.06¢ per mile	$689 6.69¢ per mile

9. What is the total depreciation for the first 3 years?

10. What is the resale value of the automobile after 3 years?

11. What is the average annual depreciation for the first 3 years?

12. What is the straight-line rate of depreciation for the first 3 years?

13. What is the rate of depreciation for year 4?

14. What is the average annual depreciation for the first 4 years?

15. What is the value of the automobile after $3\frac{1}{2}$ years?

16. How many miles does the automobile have after 5 years?

17. Carol Peroni can get $2,500 for her compact car as a trade-in. Five years ago she bought it new for $8,500. What is the average annual depreciation and the rate of depreciation on her car?

18. Charles Barrett wants to estimate the resale value in 4 years of a new $6,900 subcompact. He knows the average annual depreciation is $1,050. What should the car sell for in 4 years?

19. What did Mike Jurgensen pay for his compact car 5 years ago if it has a resale value of $2,150 today? Use the table for problems 9 through 15.

20. When the dealer offered Ben Aitama $2,700 for his 4-year-old, intermediate-sized car, he went somewhere else with his business. Can you explain what Ben knew? Use Table 10.2.

Buying a Used Car

You will probably buy several cars during your lifetime. Your first car will most likely be a used car. Finding and deciding upon a good used car requires you to do your "homework." As with a new car, you should pray for the Lord to direct you and keep you from making a mistake. The potential for getting a bad deal is far greater when buying used cars. After you have done what is expected by way of careful study and checking, it will be exciting to see the Lord's faithful leading and blessing of your efforts.

The next step you should take is to study *Consumer Reports* magazine and find out which automobiles are good buys and which ones to avoid. You will find that some makes of four-cylinder engines last only 60,000-80,000 miles before they need an overhaul. Others will go 120,000-150,000 miles before "dying." *Consumer Reports* also has a *Guide to Used Cars* that can be purchased.

When you have found a good prospect in your price range, the next step is to find out what *repairs* it needs as is. Just about every used car will need some repairs; so don't let that discourage you. If you are buying from a private individual, ask him for maintenance and repair records and ask him what he knows needs repair or service. (Of course, a dishonest seller won't tell you the complete truth, but if you forget to ask, an otherwise honest one may not think

to tell you either.) If you are buying from a dealer, you will see a *buyer's guide* displayed on the car window. The *Federal Trade Commission* (FTC) requires that information about warranties and possible defects be stated on the buyer's guide. A brochure about used-car buying can be obtained from the FTC, Washington, D.C., 20580. Most dealers will allow you to take the car to a mechanic for inspection. If you are getting close to choosing a particular car, it may be well worth the expense of the mechanic's time to know what the car needs. This mechanic can also give you some good estimates about what it will cost to make the repairs. You may even find that he will refund the diagnostic fee if you let him do the repair work.

Remember, you are looking for the overall quality and dependability of the vehicle. You should figure the *actual* cost as the asking price plus the cost for repairs. Many people have found that buying and repairing a vehicle with reasonably low mileage and a good reputation has been better for them than buying untried new cars.

Example 1

Imagine that you are considering purchasing a 2½-year-old, intermediate-sized automobile with 32,550 miles and a price tag of $4,780.00. A mechanic spent 2 hours checking it out and gave you a repair estimate of $523.00. If the mechanic charged $22 per hour and the sales tax is 5%, find out the cost for the automobile.

$$
\begin{aligned}
\text{Price} &= \$4,780 \\
\text{Sales tax at } 5\% &= \quad \$239 \\
\text{Mechanic's checkup} &= \quad \$44 \text{ (2 hr.} \times \$22 \text{ per hr.)} \\
\text{Repair estimate} &= \quad \$523 \\
\text{Net cost} &= \$5,586
\end{aligned}
$$

Example 2

How does the above cost compare to the depreciated value of the automobile? Use Table 10.2.

(Mileages)

Year 1:	14,500		32,550
Year 2:	13,700		−28,200
	28,200	Year 3:	4,350

Note: Depreciation for year 3 = 4,350 × ($0.097/mile)
= 422

Accumulated depreciation: $2,385 (Year 1)
$1,401 (Year 2)
+$422 (Year 3)
$4,208

$10,000
−$4,208
Trade-in or resale value: $ 5,792

So the book value, $5,792, is $206 larger than the net cost. The cost of this vehicle is reasonable.

Example 3

Using the same example, if you have a $2,000 down payment from the sale of your old car, calculate the required monthly payments for a loan on the balance at 12%(12) for 30 months.

$$
\begin{array}{rl}
\text{Cost:} & \$5,586 \\
\text{Money in hand:} & \underline{-2,000} \\
\text{Balance:} & \$3,586
\end{array}
$$

In the finance tables, under $i = \frac{12\%}{12} = 1\%$, find the **Payment to Borrow** under 30 periods.

$$
\begin{aligned}
R &= 3,586 \times (0.0387481) \\
&= \$138.95 \text{ per month}
\end{aligned}
$$

Exercises

Find the total cost of diagnostic work and repairs for each of the following used cars.

Day	Mechanic's Time	Rate per Hour	Estimated Repairs	Total
1.	2.25	18	386	
2.	2.0	24	565	
3.	1.5	22	185	
4.	3.0	20	859	
5.	0.75	22	251	
6.	1.25	18	403	

7. Mr. Willie Wright just bought a 3½-year-old compact car from the Pontiac dealership. He paid $3,850 for the car. It had 48,250 miles and needed new tires and brakes, which totaled $385. If sales tax is 5%, find his net cost for the car.

8. Use Table 10.3 to find out if Mr. Wright paid a reasonable price for the car. Based on accumulated depreciation, what was the value of the car?

9. Cindy Nestberg traded her old car for a late-model used car. The sticker price was $6,250, and she got $2,200 for her trade-in. If state tax is 5%, how much does she have to finance?

10. Find Cindy's monthly payment if she can finance the balance at 10%(12) for 3 years.

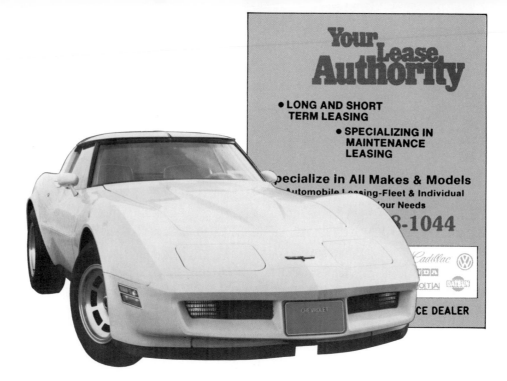

Leasing a New Car

Leasing is a relatively new method of providing an automobile for the American consumer. Most people understand the concept of renting a home or an apartment: someone else owns the things you are renting. When you lease an automobile, you are paying someone for the use of a vehicle he owns. An automobile lease is a rental agreement that you will use the vehicle for 3, 4, or 5 years at an agreed-upon rate per month. The *lessor* (the person who owns the vehicle) will regain possession of the vehicle from the *lessee* at the end of the lease period. At that time the automobile will have depreciated in value to what is called the *residual value*. The lessor can make an accurate estimate of this residual value through special books that are published for that purpose. For someone who owns his own automobile, he would refer to the residual value as trade-in value or resale value. Leases are called *closed-end* if the consumer just turns in the automobile to the dealer at the end of the lease period. Leases are called *open-end* if a price adjustment is required for vehicles above or below the predicted residual value. Competition has generally moved the industry toward closed-end leases, in which there is less risk to the consumer.

There are certain advantages to leasing an automobile. For example, leasing requires no down payment, although a security deposit equal to one month's rent is usually required. For people who need reliable, late-model automobiles, leasing can do the job with fewer headaches. Leasing does have some disadvantages, however. For instance, you have no trade-in when the lease is done. Also, there are always mileage quotes in the terms of the lease. If you exceed the limits of the contract over the period of the lease, you may have to pay 10 to 15 cents per mile for the excess.

Table 10.4
Sample Leasing Rates/Month (Closed-end leases)

Term of Lease	Mileage Limit*	Subcompact	Compact	Mini-van & Intermediate	Large Sedan	Full-size Van
3 years	45,000	131	174	216	259	294
4 years	60,000	123	162	198	234	258
5 years	75,000	118	152	184	216	234
*Excess mileage charged at 8¢ per mile						

Automobile leasing companies calculate their monthly lease rates using the amount of depreciation and the residual value. The leasing process is very similar to a bank loan with similar interest rates and contractual agreements. Table 10.4 gives some typical rates for different lease durations and sizes of automobiles. Actual rates depend on the sticker price of specific cars, their predicted residual value, and interest rates.

Example 1

Using the sample leasing rates in Table 10.4, how much would a customer pay out over the life of the lease for a 4-year contract on a large sedan?

$$\frac{\$234}{\text{month}} \times 48 \text{ months} = \$11,232$$

Example 2

What would the first payment on a 5-year lease contract for a mini-van be if it includes a security deposit?

$$\text{first payment} = \text{monthly payment} + \text{security deposit}$$
$$= \$184 + \$184$$
$$= \$368$$

Example 3

If the lessee of the mini-van in Example 2 put 83,000 miles on the vehicle, how much of his security deposit will he get back at the end of the lease?

$$\text{Excess-mileage charge} = (83,000 - 75,000) \times .08$$
$$= \$8,000 \times 0.08$$
$$= \$640$$

Note: This $640 exceeds the deposit. Customer must pay additional charges.

$$\text{Additional charges} = (\$640 - \$184)$$
$$= \$456$$

Example 4

Every week, Mr. Kesselring puts 200 miles on his car driving to and from work, except during his 2-week vacation. He takes a 6,000-mile vacation trip every other year and a 1,000-mile trip the other years. How much mileage per week does he have for casual driving on a 4-year lease?

work mileage: $(200 \times 50) =$	10,000	miles per year
work mileage $\times 4 =$	40,000	for four years
vacation: $(2 \times 6,000) + (2 \times 1,000) =$	14,000	
total $=$	54,000	miles for four years

The mileage limit $= 60,000$, so $60,000 - 54,000 = 6,000$ for total casual miles.

6,000 miles divided by 4 years $= 1,500$ miles/year
1,500 miles divided by 52 weeks $= 28.8$ miles/week for casual driving

Example 5

If Mrs. Svensen wants to lease an intermediate-sized vehicle and she has $43 per week in her budget, what length lease should she take?

$$\$43/\text{week} \times \frac{52 \text{ weeks}}{\text{year}} = \frac{\$2,236}{\text{year}}$$

$$\frac{\$2,236}{\text{year}} \div \frac{12 \text{ months}}{\text{year}} = \frac{\$2,236}{12} \text{ per month}$$

$$= \$186.33/\text{month}$$

She should take a 5-year lease.

Caution: Don't assume that there are 4 weeks in every month $(4 \times 43 = 172)$. This would mean she doesn't have enough for any intermediate lease.

Note: $\frac{52 \text{ weeks}}{12 \text{ months}} = 4.33$ weeks/month

$$43 \times 4.33 = 186.19$$

Exercises

Find the total amount paid out over the life of each lease.
1. 3-year, compact
2. 4-year, subcompact
3. 5-year, mini-van
4. 3-year, van
5. 4-year, intermediate

Find the initial payment for each of the leases.
6. 4-year, van
7. 3-year, compact
8. 5-year, subcompact
9. 5-year, large sedan

Find the excess-mileage surcharge for each of the leases.
10. full-size van, 5-year lease, 92,000 miles
11. intermediate, 3-year lease, 51,000 miles
12. subcompact, 4-year lease, 63,000 miles
13. compact, 4-year lease, 102,000 miles

Find the net mileage surcharge or security-deposit refund at the end of each lease.
14. subcompact, 3-year lease, 46,500 miles
15. mini-van, 5-year lease, 81,200 miles
16. large sedan, 4-year lease, 63,000 miles
17. van, 3-year lease, 44,800 miles
18. What is the biggest vehicle Tracy Smith can lease for 4 years on a $48 per week budget?
19. What is the biggest vehicle Randy Olsen can lease for 5 years on a $1,500 per year budget?
20. If Brian Cameon leases a compact car on a $2,000-per-year budget, what is the shortest lease he can afford?
21. If Mr. McCoy leases a large sedan on a $50 per week budget, what is the shortest lease he can afford?
22. Candy Manson drives 38 miles into Washington from her home. She makes this trip 5 days a week. She drives another car on weekends and during her 2-week vacation. Find the mileage surcharge on a 3-year lease.

Automobile Insurance

Whether you have purchased a new or used car or have leased a new car, the laws of your state require you to have a minimum amount of insurance. Insurance is protection you buy from a company to pay for losses due to accidents or natural disasters. Each insurance company charges its customers for the amount and type of insurance they want. The money that customers pay is called the *premium*. The amount and type of insurance is called *coverage*. The total of all the premiums that a company receives pays for its operations and employees plus the *claims* made by customers for accidents. The monetary value of all claims in a given geographical area determines the rates that people in that area pay for automobile insurance.

The three general types of insurance coverage are liability, collision, and comprehensive. *Liability* insurance pays for bodily injury and property damage caused by the insured vehicle. The limits of this coverage are stated by giving these numbers. For example, *$15,000/$30,000/$25,000* (abbreviated 15/30/25) means the insurance company will pay for bodily injury up to $15,000 per person, $30,000 per accident, and for property damage up to $25,000. *Collision* insurance pays for damages to the policyholder's own vehicle due to a collision with another object or upset of that vehicle. *Comprehensive* insurance pays for loss or damage to the vehicle of the insured due to causes other than collision or upset. (For instance, it would pay for losses due to theft, fire, wind, and vandalism.) Collision and comprehensive coverage are often sold with *deductibles*. This means the policyholder is responsible for the first $100 or $200 in losses, but the insurance company pays for all losses above that.

Liability insurance is also available for *uninsured* motor-vehicle coverage. This means the insurance company covers bodily injury and property damage losses the policyholder sustains because of a motorist who has no liability insurance. Some states require this insurance, even though motorists also have to have liability insurance.

Use Table 10.5 and the associated footnotes to find the semiannual premiums for automobile insurance.

Table 10.5
Typical Semiannual Premiums for Liability Insurance
Bodily Injury and Property Damage

Limits in Thousands*	Pleasure	Work less than 10 Miles	Work Greater than 10 Miles	Retired
15/30/25	74.2	76.4	78.7	73.5
25/50/25	80.7	83.1	85.6	79.8
50/100/25	89.5	92.2	94.9	88.6
100/300/50	102.4	105.5	108.7	101.4

Property damage limits can be decreased by increments of $5,000 with a 1% reduction in the rate. Property damage limits can be increased up to $100,000 by increments of $25,000 with a 3% increase in the rate.

Table 10.6
Typical Semiannual Premiums for Collision Coverage
Late-Model Vehicles of Different Insurance Rating Groups

Type of Deductible	Subcompact	Compact	Intermediate	Large Sedan
$100 Ded.	66.6	68.8	84.1	111.1
$200 Ded.	48.5	58.3	72.5	97.8

- An 18% surcharge is added to the base liability and collision premium for each driving-record point due to traffic violations.
- Semiannual premiums for liability and collision are doubled for vehicles operated part-time by unmarried, under-25 male drivers. They are quadrupled if he is the full-time driver.
- A 25% discount is given for liability and collision policies written on automobiles with teenage drivers who maintain a B average in school.

Table 10.7
Typical Semiannual Premiums for Comprehensive Coverage
Late-Model Vehicles of Different Insurance Rating Groups

	Subcompact	Compact	Intermediate	Large Sedan
Full Coverage	20.1	23.2	38.6	57.5
$100 Deductible	13.0	15.4	31.6	43.9

Example 1

Find the semiannual premium for a subcompact vehicle used for pleasure with 15/30/10 liability, $200-deductible collision, and full-coverage comprehensive. Its driver is an under-25 male driver who is a B student.

liability 15/30/25:	$74.20
deduction for 15/30/10 (3%):	−$2.23
	$71.97
collision ($200 deductible):	+$48.50
	$120.47
surcharge for young male driver:	+$120.47
	$240.94
good student discount (25%):	−$60.24
	$180.70
comprehensive (full):	+$20.10
total semiannual premium:	$200.80

Example 2

Find the semiannual premium for an intermediate-sized vehicle with 25/50/25 liability, $200-deductible collision, and full-coverage comprehensive. The owner is a retired school teacher.

liability:	$79.80
collision:	$72.50
comprehensive:	+$38.00
total semiannual premium:	$190.30

Example 3

Find the liability-coverage premium for a vehicle whose principle driver is an unmarried male under 25 with 3 driving-record points. The vehicle is used for going to work more than ten miles, and the coverage limits are 50/100/25.

base premium:	$94.90
under 25 male surcharge:	×4
	$379.60
surcharge (driving-record points):	+$204.98
total semiannual premium:	$584.58

This last example illustrates the tremendous price to be paid for irresponsibility. Through records, the insurance companies know which group of drivers causes the greatest amount of loss through insurance claims. They know that unmarried young men under twenty-five and drivers who get traffic tickets cannot be counted on as safe drivers. Therefore, sensible driving habits save you money in more ways than one.

Example 4

Find the semiannual premium for Mrs. Siato's large sedan. She drives her car to work less than 10 miles per day. She wants 100/300/100 liability, $100 deductible collision, and full coverage comprehensive.

basic liability premium for 100/300/50:	$105.50
increase for 50,000 more property damage (6%):	+6.33
	$111.83
$100 deductible collision:	+$111.10
full-coverage comprehensive:	+$57.50
total semiannual premium:	$280.43

Exercises

Calculate the semiannual premiums for liability insurance coverage for each of the limits and use categories.

1. 15/30/20; pleasure
2. 25/50/50; retired
3. 100/300/25; work > 10

4. 15/30/100; work < 10
5. 50/100/75; retired
6. 15/30/5; pleasure

Calculate the semiannual premiums for collision insurance coverage for each of the stated deductibles and surcharges or discounts.

7. $100 deductible, subcompact, under-25 male driver, part-time

8. $200 deductible, large sedan, principal driver has 4 points

9. $200 deductible, compact, teenage single male principal driver with a B average

10. $100 deductible, intermediate

11. $200 deductible, large sedan, principal driver has 1 point

12. $200 deductible, subcompact, teenage female driver with a B average

13. What do you think is the problem with having a liability policy with 15/30/5 limits?

14. If you had $100-deductible comprehensive coverage on an intermediate automobile, how many years would it take to make up for a broken windshield costing $529 by not having full comprehensive?

15. Calculate the semiannual premium for Amy Long's new compact car. She wants 25/50/25 liability, $200 deductible collision, and full comprehensive. She drives the car to work, a distance of less than 10 miles.

16. Calculate the semiannual premium for Robert Wood's large sedan. He wants 25/50/100 liability, $100-deductible collision, and full comprehensive. He had a wreck last year and has 2 points on his driving record. He uses the car for pleasure.

17. How long would one have to pay into a $200-deductible collision policy as opposed to $100 deductible in order to make up for one claim for $1,200 on a compact car?

18. Sally Crocket is calculating her weekly automotive costs. How much does her automobile insurance cost per week if her liability limits are 25/50/15, her collision is $100 deductible, and she has full comprehensive coverage? She puts 110 miles per week on her subcompact car going to and from work Monday through Friday.

19. Todd Moore is trying to convince his dad that they can afford a second car so that Todd can drive to high school and to his grocery-store job after school and Saturdays. Todd can afford only $10 per week for insurance because of his expenses for gas, tithe, and savings for college. If Todd keeps up his B average and they buy just 15/30/25 liability classified as work-use less than 10 miles, can he afford it? How much would it cost?

   If he doesn't keep up the B average, can he afford it? How much would it cost?

20. To help his son understand the foolishness of juvenile behavior while driving an automobile, Mr. Cockran calculated a hypothetical insurance rate. If an intermediate car driven for pleasure has liability limits of 25/50/25, $100-deductible collision, and full comprehensive, what is the normal charge in semiannual premium, and what is the difference in the charge if an unmarried teenage son gets a 4-point ticket for reckless driving in the family car?

Project: Do a study of the automobile insurance on your family car(s). Find the type of coverage, limits and deductibles, surcharges and discounts, and the semiannual premium. Do some comparison shopping at two other insurance companies to compare the cost for the same coverage. If you can find a company that insures only non-drinking drivers, see how their rates compare. Are there other valuable, but not necessarily important, criteria to use in choosing an automobile insurance company? Ask around.

The Expendables—Gas, Oil, and Tires

When people figure the cost of taking a trip, they seldom calculate anything but gasoline costs. This is understandable; the gasoline gauge is very visible. And so is the price on the gasoline pump. However, many other costs like depreciation and insurance are used up in a less visible way. Even tires and oil may not seem to cost much because the expenditure comes in lumps at widely spaced intervals.

Do you know how to calculate gas mileage? Do you know how far your family car will go on one tank of gasoline? How do you figure oil costs for a new car that does not burn oil?

The unit *miles per gallon* (mpg) has an indicated division in the word *per*. If you know how many miles a car traveled and how many gallons it took, simply divide the number of miles by the number of gallons. (In the International System the units would be kilometers per liter.)

Example 1

Find what mileage a car gets for a 532-mile trip that used 15.2 gallons of gasoline.

$$\frac{532 \text{ miles}}{15.2 \text{ gallons}} = 35 \text{ mi./gal.}$$

Example 2

How much gasoline would be required to go 850 miles in a car that gets 26 mi./gal.?

This problem is similar to Example 1, except the unknown is the denominator of the left side.

$$\frac{850 \text{ miles}}{x \text{ gallons}} = 26 \text{ mi./gal.}$$

Remove the units and look at the equation.

$$\frac{850}{x} = 26$$

Solve for x by multiplying each side by x.

$$\not{x} \cdot \frac{850}{\not{x}} = 26 \cdot x$$

$$850 = 26 \cdot x$$

Now divide both sides by 26 to isolate x.

$$\frac{850}{26} = x, \text{ so } x = 32.7 \text{ gallons}$$

Example 3

How far can an automobile go on one 15-gallon tank of gasoline if it gets 27 miles per gallon? (This distance is called the *range* of an automobile.)

$$\frac{x \text{ miles}}{15 \text{ gallons}} = 27 \text{ mi.}/\text{gal.}$$

Remove the units to concentrate on the equation.

$$\frac{x}{15} = 27$$

Solve for x by multiplying each side by 15.

$$15 \cdot \frac{x}{15} = 15 \cdot 27$$

$$x = 405 \text{ miles}$$

(*Note:* You would be wise to buy gas before driving 350 miles. At 350 miles there are only 2 gallons left in the tank.)

Example 4

A compact car gets 30 miles per gallon. If gasoline costs $1.16 per gallon, what is the cost per mile for fuel?

$$\frac{\text{cost}}{\text{mile}} = \frac{\$1.16}{\text{gallon}} \cdot \frac{1 \text{ gallon}}{30 \text{ miles}}$$

$$= \frac{\$1.16}{30}$$

$$= \$0.039 \text{ per mile}$$

Even though new cars do not burn much oil, they need to have the oil and filter changed at regular intervals. The automobile manufacturers give recommendations based on miles between oil changes. Many of them suggest 7,500 miles or 6 months between oil changes. However, you would be wise to cut both of these in half if you want to give your car quality care.

YOU MEAN I WAS SUPPOSED TO PUT OIL IN THIS CAR?!

Example 5

Calculate the oil's cost per mile when the oil and filter on a new car are changed every 4,000 miles. A typical car will need 5 quarts of oil at $1.50 each and an oil filter at $4.50. Labor will be about $10.00 at a typical dealership.

$$
\begin{array}{rl}
5 \times 1.50 = & \$7.50 \\
1 \times 4.50 = & \$4.50 \\
\text{Labor} = & +\$10.00 \\
\hline
& \$22.00
\end{array}
$$

$$
\text{cost per miles} = \frac{\$22.00}{4,000}
$$

$$
= \$.0055 \text{ per mile}
$$

(*Note:* Changing a car's oil is not difficult. After the initial investment of an oil-filter wrench and a plastic drainage pan, you can permanently cut your oil costs in half by having someone demonstrate how to change it yourself.)

The original-equipment tires on a new car can be expected to go about 30,000-35,000 miles. This expense is hidden in the cost of the vehicle. Purchasing the first set of replacement tires presents an interesting decision for the consumer. Is it better to buy a less expensive tire that gets less total mileage or a more expensive tire that gets more total mileage? Which gives the least cost per mile? Tire manufacturers have a warranty based on tread wear. If a tire fails before the warranted lifetime of, say, 40,000 miles, the manufacturer pays the consumer a refund based on the percent of tread wear.

Example 6

If a car with 32,000 miles needs new tires, which of the following gives the least cost per mile?

a. 30,000-mile tire for $50.00 each
   cost for set "a":
   $4 \times \$50 = \$200$
   tax at 5% = $10
   total = $210

   $\frac{\text{cost}}{\text{mile}} = \frac{\$210}{30,000} = \$.007/\text{mile}$

b. 40,000-mile tire for $60.00 each
   cost for set "b":
   $4 \times \$60 = \$240$
   tax at 5% = $12
   total = $252

   $\frac{\text{cost}}{\text{mile}} = \frac{\$252}{40,000} = \$.006/\text{mile}$

Example 7

In Example 6 the owner must also decide how much longer he will keep the car. Find the miles on the vehicle when each set of tires will need replacing again.

a. 32,000 = current mileage
   30,000 = tire mileage
   62,000 = mileage when tires will need replacing

b. 32,000 = current mileage
   40,000 = tire mileage
   72,000 = mileage when tires will need replacing

If he plans to sell the car at 60,000 miles (about 4 years old), this would change the cost per mile on set "a" to the following:

$$\frac{\$210}{28,000} = \$.0075/\text{mile}$$

And the cost of set "b" would change to the following:

$$\frac{\$252}{28,000} = \$.009/\text{mile}$$

In this case, his expected selling date makes set "a" the better buy.

Example 8

How much rebate would a consumer get for a 40,000-mile, $60 tire that failed after 12,000 miles?

Solution:
In practice, tire dealers do not use the mileage to prorate tire use. Instead they use the tread wear. A new tire has $\frac{11}{32}$ of an inch tread thickness. If a tire has $\frac{7}{32}$ of an inch tread thickness left, the consumer has not used 7 of those original 11 32ths. He will get $\frac{7}{11} \cdot (\$60)$, or $38.18 rebate. He has used up $\frac{4}{11} \cdot (\$60)$, or $21.82 of the tire's value.

Exercises

Calculate the mileage for each of the following.

1. 562 miles; 18 gal.
2. 1,492 miles; 77 gal.
3. 486 km; 42 liters
4. 1,156 km; 109 liters
5. 386 miles; 9 gal.
6. 1,066 miles; 75 gal.
7. On their vacation last summer, the Fisher family kept track of the gasoline mileage. The odometer read 35,963 when they left home with a full tank of gasoline. When they filled up at the end of the trip, the odometer read 42,177. Their log book for gasoline purchases showed 296.4 gallons at a total cost of $281.58. What mileage did their car get? What was the average price they paid for gasoline?

8. The Muellers are planning their vacation for next summer. How much should they budget for gasoline if their car gets 26 mpg, the trip will cover about 3,500 miles, and gasoline costs average about $1.15 per gallon? (Round your numbers up because this is an estimate.)

Calculate the amount of gasoline needed for each of the given trip miles and car mileages. Calculate fuel costs if gasoline averages $1.18 per gallon.

9. 800 miles; 18 mpg
10. 1,000 miles; 25 mpg
11. 1,900 km; 12 km/l
12. 563 km; 9.2 km/l
13. 7,359 miles; 20 mpg
14. 238 miles; 43 mpg

Find the maximum range of the following automobiles whose tank capacities and mileages are given.

15. 11 gallons; 42 mpg
16. 15 gallons; 23 mpg
17. 20 gallons; 18 mpg
18. 20 gallons plus 15 gallons reserve; 14 mpg

Calculate the cost for an oil and filter change for each of the following vehicles. Use $1.50 per quart, $4.50 per filter, $10 for labor.

19. 4 quart capacity, 5% sales tax
20. 5 quart capacity, 6% sales tax
21. 6 quart capacity, 4% sales tax

22. Kathleen Ramsey wants to calculate the cost of oil and filters for her automobile, which she plans to keep until it has 64,000 miles. If she changes the oil and filter every 4,000 miles at a cost of $22.75 ($1.50 tax included) and if her car burns one quart of oil every 4,000 miles, what are her oil costs?

23. Which set of tires gives the best cost per mile? Brand A is a 30,000-mile tire for $38.75 each, and Brand B is a 40,000-mile tire for $42.95. Use 5% for sales tax.

24. Pastor Detweiler's car has 28,500 miles and needs a set of tires. If he buys a set designed for 40,000 miles for $62 each plus 4% sales tax and he trades his car at 62,000 miles, what is his total cost and the cost per mile?

25. How much money did Cindy Jamison get for a rebate on her blown tire if she originally paid $69.50 and the tread thickness gauge read $\frac{6}{32}$ of an inch?

Maintenance and Repairs

Another expense of owning an automobile that many people fail to consider is maintenance and repairs. There are people who neglect the maintenance and some repairs because they think that they cannot afford the expense. Actually, however, they do not understand the true cost of owning and operating an automobile. A proper budget for automobile costs must allow for all costs, not just gas and oil. Many high school young people become car owners without being financially capable of the responsibilities involved. To be a good steward of the money invested in an automobile, you must understand the costs of keeping the vehicle in safe operating condition. Good care of a car is also an investment in its future resale value.

Scheduled maintenance, or preventive maintenance, has to do with the regular upkeep and care of an automobile. The car may not stop running if the oil is not changed regularly, but regular oil changes will prevent future damage and maintain a more efficient engine. Good preventive maintenance will help lower the overall cost of repairs, will give the car a longer life expectancy, and will help avoid highway emergencies. Table 10.8 gives some typical scheduled maintenance items along with typical costs.

Table 10.8
Scheduled Maintenance*

Item	Time Interval (mi.)	Cost of Parts	Labor Units at $30 per Unit
1. Oil change & filter	4,000	10.50	0.4
2. Emisson system	15,000	(15.00)**	0.5
3. Cooling system	12,000	5.00	0.5
4. Tune up	12,000	20.00	1.8
5. Lubrication	12,000	—	0.3
6. Air & fuel filters	12,000	9.50	0.25

Time intervals are more conservative than typical manufacturers'. They represent more severe driving conditions.

**The EGR canister would be replaced at 45,000 miles.*

Unscheduled repairs usually disable the vehicle or make it unsafe to operate. They involve systems and parts that wear out but which do so at an unknown point in the life of the car. Table 10.9 shows some typical repairs with labor costs and parts as separate entries. Remember that sales tax applies only to parts.

Table 10.9
Automobile Repair Work (4-Cylinder Compact)

Item	Cost of Parts	Labor Units at $30/Unit
1. Rear shock absorbers (2)	30.00	0.8
2. Front struts (2)	130.00	1.9
3. Brake linings (4)	44.00	3.5
4. Ignition module (1)	125.00	0.6
5. Distributor (1)	35.00	0.7
6. Starter (1)	45.00	0.6
7. Muffler (1)	35.00	1.2
8. Catalytic Converter (1)	45.00	1.0
9. Ball joints (2)	30.00	1.9
10. Water pump (1)	42.00	1.2

Example 1

Calculate the repair bill for replacing the struts, shock absorbers, and a muffler. Use 5% sales tax.

	Parts	Labor
struts (2):	130.00	1.9
shocks (2):	30.00	0.8
muffler (1):	+35.00	+1.2
totals:	195.00	3.9 units at $30 ea. = $117.00
+ tax:	+9.75	
	204.75	

final total = $204.75 (parts + tax) + $117.00 (labor) = $321.75

Example 2

If Mr. Peck schedules a tune-up every 10,000 miles and keeps his car for 65,000 miles, find his cost per mile for this maintenance item. Use a 6% sales tax.

$\frac{6,500}{10,000} = 6.5$, or 6 complete tune-ups during the period of ownership

	Parts	Labor Units
cost for each:	20.00	1.8
tax for each:	+1.20	×30
totals:	21.20 +	54.00 = $75.20 per tune-up

total cost during period of ownership = $75.20 × 6 = $451.20

$$\frac{\text{cost}}{\text{mile}} = \frac{\$451.20}{65,000} = \$0.007/\text{mile}$$

Example 3

Buddy Smith put a new water pump on his old pickup. He saved the labor costs and got a 12% discount on the part. How much did he save?

$$\$42.00 \text{ (part)} \times 12\% = \quad 5.04$$
$$1.2 \text{ (labor)} \times \$30 = \quad +36.00$$
$$\text{savings} = \quad 41.04 \text{ (excluding tax)}$$
$$5\% \text{ (tax)} \times 5.04 = \quad +.25$$
$$\text{total savings} = \quad \$41.29 \text{ (including tax)}$$

Exercises

Calculate the total repair cost for each of the items in Table 10.9 with a 5% sales tax.

1. rear shocks
2. front struts
3. brake linings
4. ignition module
5. distributor
6. starter
7. muffler
8. catalytic converter
9. ball joints
10. water pump

Calculate the total cost for each maintenance item for an automobile driven 60,000 miles. Include those items that would occur at the end of the period. Use a 5% sales tax.

11. oil change & filter
12. emission system
13. cooling system
14. tune-up
15. lubrication
16. air & fuel filters
17. While the mechanic was servicing the cooling system on Brad Lanier's car, he found that the water pump was also bad. How much did the service and repairs cost Brad with a 6% sales tax?

The True Cost of Driving an Automobile

You have learned about and calculated several factors associated with owning and operating an automobile. It should be apparent that it takes more than gasoline to keep an automobile on the road. The various costs can be divided into two categories: costs of ownership and costs of operation.

Costs of Ownership
Depreciation
Insurance
Finance charges (forgone interest*)
Fees, plates, taxes

Costs of Operation
Gas, oil, and tires
Maintenance and repairs
Parking and toll fees

(*When a car is purchased with cash, the money is taken out of the bank; so the potential interest that would have been earned from that money is lost. This lost interest is called *forgone interest*. Forgone interest is ultimately much less than finance charges, however.)

In order to calculate the true cost of driving an automobile, all of the above costs need to be taken into account. It is best to express this total as cost per mile, cost per year, or cost per day rather than one lump sum. The cost of fees, plates, taxes, parking, and tolls varies greatly from state to state and even from one town to another. This text uses some typical values that might occur in a large metropolitan area.

Example 1

Find the cost per mile for an intermediate-sized automobile driven 54,000 miles in 4 years.

Data:
Original cost = $10,000 (cash purchase; savings were at 6%[12])
Mileage = 21 mpg
Gasoline = $1.15 per gallon
Insurance = 25/50/25 liability work < 10, $200-deductible collision, full comprehensive
Tires = one replacement set, 30,000-mile quality; $50 each
Repairs = $650
Maintenance = as scheduled in Table 10.8
Registration and title fees = $25 one time
License plates and taxes = $138 per year
Parking = $25 per month

Solution:

Cost of Ownership

depreciation (Table 10.2):

$$\left.\begin{array}{c} 2,385 \\ 1,401 \\ 1,213 \\ 956 \end{array}\right\} \quad 52,100 \text{ miles}$$

$$\underline{\quad 166} \qquad 1,900 \text{ miles (at } 8.74\cent/\text{mi.)}$$
$$\$6,121$$

insurance (Tables 10.5-10.7):

$$\begin{array}{ll} 83.10 & \text{liability} \\ 72.50 & \text{collision} \\ \underline{38.60} & \text{comprehensive} \\ \$194.20 & \text{per 6 months} \end{array}$$

4-yr. total: $\$194.20 \times 8 =$ $1,553.60

finance charges (forgone interest)

$\$10,000 \times 6\%(12) =$ $2,704.89 ($i = \frac{1}{2}\%$; $n = 12 \times 4 = 48$)

registration and titles fees = $25.00

license plates and taxes (138×4) = $552.00

total = $10,956.49

Cost of Operation

gas: $\frac{54,000}{21 \text{ mpg}} = 2,571.4$ gal.

2,571.4 gal. $\times$ 1.15/gal. =   2,957.11

oil: $\frac{54,000}{4,000} \approx 13$ changes

$$\begin{array}{lr} 13 \text{ (changes)} \times 23.03 = & 299.39 \\ \text{tires: } 4 \times 50 + 5\% \text{ tax} = & 210.00 \end{array}$$

maintenance: (3 times for emission, 4 times for cooling system, tune-up, lubrication, air & fuel

$$\begin{array}{lr} \text{filters)} = & 547.65 \\ \text{repairs} = & 650.00 \\ \text{parking (\$20} \times \text{48)} = & \underline{960.00} \\ \text{total} = & \$5,623.65 \end{array}$$

total of ownership *and* operation = $16,580.64

$$\frac{\text{cost}}{\text{mile}} = \frac{16,580.64}{54,000} = \$0.307 \text{ per mile}$$

Example 2

Find the cost per mile for a compact-size automobile driven 46,000 miles in 4 years.

Data:

  Original cost = $8,800 (20% down payment, financed at 12%(12) for 4 years)
  Mileage = 26 mpg
  Gasoline = $1.15 per gallon
  Insurance = 15/30/50 liability (pleasure), $100-deductible collision; $100-deductible comprehensive
  Tires = one replacement set, 40,000-mile quality, $55 each
  Repairs = brakes (4), water pump, struts, shocks, muffler
  Maintenance = as scheduled in Table 10.8
  Registration and title fees = $20 one time
  License plates and taxes = $95 per year
  Parking and tolls = $15 per month

Solution:

Cost of Ownership

depreciation (Use Table 10.3.):

1,595.00 ⎫	
1,105.00 ⎬	40,700
1,005.00 ⎭	
374.18	5,300 at 7.06¢ per mile
$4,079.18	

insurance (Tables 10.5-10.7):

76.43	liability
68.80	collision
15.40	comprehensive
$160.63	per 6 months

4-yr. total ($160.63 × 8) = $1,285.04

finance charges: (payment = $7,040 × (0.0263338) = $185.39)

total paid out ($185.39 × 48) =	8,898.72
less principal:	−7,040.00
	$1,858.72

forgone interest on $1,760 at 6%(12) =	$476.06
registration and title fees =	$20.00
license plates and taxes (4 × $95) =	$380.00

cost of ownership total = $8,099.00

Cost of Operation

gas: $\frac{46,000}{26 \text{ mpg}} = 1,769.2$ gal.

$$1,769.2 \times 1.15 = \quad \$2,034.58$$

oil: $\frac{46,000}{4,000} \approx 11$ changes

11 × $23.03 per change =	253.33
tires: 4 × $55 + tax at 5% =	231.00
maintenance: 3 times for items 2-6 =	425.94
repairs (itemized):	
brakes =	151.20
water pump =	80.10
struts =	193.50
shocks =	55.50
muffler =	72.75
total repairs =	$553.05

parking and tolls ($15 × 48) =	$720.00
cost of operation total =	$4,217.90

total of ownership *and* operation = $\quad$ $12,316.90

$$\frac{\text{cost}}{\text{mile}} = \frac{\$12,316.90}{46,000} = \$0.268 \text{ per mile}$$

$$\frac{\text{cost}}{\text{mile}} = \frac{\$12,316.90}{4} = \$3,079.23 \text{ per year}$$

$$\frac{\text{cost}}{\text{day}} = \frac{\$3,079.23}{365} = \$8.44 \text{ per day}$$

Exercises

Each group of exercises will be referenced to the data at the beginning. For some costs the value will be given, but for others you will have to do a calculation based upon information from tables in this chapter. Use 5% tax where applicable.

A. Data:
    Vehicle = subcompact driven 50,000 miles in 4 years
    Original cost = $7,000 (paid cash from an account at 6%[12])
    Mileage = 30 mpg
    Gasoline = $1.15 per gallon
    Insurance = 15/30/25 liability (work > 10) $200-deductible collision;
       full comprehensive
    Tires = one replacement set, $37 each
    Repairs = brake linings replaced, struts, ignition module; starter
    Maintenance = as scheduled in Table 10.8
    Registration and title fees = $20 yearly
    License plates and taxes = $75 per year
    Parking and tolls: none

1. Calculate the 4-year depreciation using 20% for year 1, 18% for year 2, 16% for year 3, and 14% for year 4.
2. Calculate the insurance premiums using Tables 10.5-10.7. (Note: The tables give semiannual premiums.)
3. Calculate the forgone interest earnings from taking the money out of the bank.
4. Calculate the total charges for registration and fees over the 4 years.
5. Calculate the total taxes and license-plate costs over the 4 years.
6. Calculate the cost of gasoline.
7. Calculate the cost of oil if it is changed every 4,000 miles and if the car requires 4 quarts for a change and burns 1 quart every 4,000 miles.
8. Calculate the cost of replacement tires.
9. Calculate maintenance costs over 4 years, but don't include oil since it was done in question 7. Use Table 10.8.
10. Calculate the repair costs for just those items listed.
11. Calculate the cost per mile paid by the owner during the time of ownership.
12. Calculate the cost per year and per day to own and operate this vehicle.

B. Data:
    Vehicle = large sedan driven 68,000 miles in 5 years
    Original cost = $12,500 (20% down payment, financed at 9%[12] for 3 years)
    Mileage = 18 mpg
    Gasoline = $1.20 per gallon
    Insurance = 100/300/100 liability (retired with 2 record points), $100-deductible
      collision, full comprehensive
    Tires = one replacement set, 40,000-mile quality
    Repairs = brake linings replaced, shocks (4), ignition module (1),
      starter (2), muffler (2), catalytic converter (1), water pump (1)
    Maintenance = as scheduled in Table 10.8
    Registration and title fees = $26 per year
    License plates and taxes = $115 per year
    Parking and tolls = $5 per month

13. Calculate the 5-year depreciation with a straight-line rate of 15%.

14. Calculate the insurance premiums using Tables 10.5-10.7.

15. Calculate the interest paid in finance charges and the forgone interest on the down payment. Assume a savings account of 6%(12) over 5 years.

16. Calculate the total charges for registration and fees over 5 years.

17. Calculate the total taxes and license-plate costs over 5 years.

18. What were the total costs of ownership over 5 years?

19. Calculate the cost of gasoline.

20. Calculate the cost of replacement tires at $75 each plus taxes.

21. Calculate the maintenance costs over the 5-year time. Be sure to include oil and filter changes.

22. Calculate the repair costs for those items listed.

23. Calculate the 5-year cost of parking and fees.

24. Calculate the total operation costs for 5 years.

25. Calculate the cost per mile for the total costs of ownership and operation of this vehicle for 68,000 miles.

26. Calculate the cost per year and the per day cost to own and operate this vehicle.

Distance and Travel Time

Can you think of some reasons that someone might want to travel by means other than by automobile? Besides recreational vehicles such as bicycles, serious travelers would consider airplanes, buses, or trains the only three alternatives to driving an automobile. The fares for these commercial passenger carriers are constantly changing, so one must get rate quotations within a short time of the travel date. In order to make a true comparison of different modes of transportation, all expenses must be compared. You can't just compare the airfare with the cost of gasoline. Time is an important consideration when making travel plans. Business people who must get to other cities (except those nearby) usually travel by air because time is money in their world.

To make comparisons between modes of transportation, you will need to find distances from maps, calculate time of travel, estimate arrival times, and map out best routes. Many maps have tables along the sides which give distances between major cities. Most road maps have the distance written on the roads, but you still have to add these to get the total for a trip. Figuring travel time requires an average rate of travel and a total distance to be traveled.

Distance = rate × time; now solve for time.

$$\text{time} = \frac{\text{distance}}{\text{rate}}$$

To estimate the time of arrival for a given trip, you will need to know the starting time, time spent traveling, and time-zone crossings. This can be tricky because as you travel toward the west, you gain an hour at each time zone. When traveling east, you lose an hour at each time zone.

Example 1

Anna Petrovna wants to calculate the distance from Atlanta to Washington, D.C., traveling on the interstate system. How far is it?

        Atlanta to Charlotte = 138 + 29 + 77 = 244

        Charlotte to Durham = 85 + 40 = 125

        Durham to D.C. = 69 + 55 + 23 + 109 = 256

        total: 244 + 125 + 256 = 625

        Atlanta to D.C. = 625 miles

Example 2

Anna knows that she can average 50 miles per hour and that she will need 2 one-hour stops for meals and rest. What is her driving time and the total time of her trip?

$$\text{driving time} = \frac{\text{distance}}{\text{rate}} = \frac{625 \text{ miles}}{50 \text{ mph}} = 12.5 \text{ hours}$$

$$+ \text{ time added for stops} = 2.00 \text{ hours}$$
$$= 14.5 \text{ hours} = 14 \text{ hours, } 30 \text{ minutes (total)}$$

Example 3

If Anna leaves Atlanta at 5:30 A.M., what is her estimated time of arrival (E.T.A.) in Washington, D.C.? *Note:* Atlanta and Washington, D.C., are both in the Eastern time zone.

5:30 A.M.*	20:00
+14:30	−12:00 (P.M. starts at noon.)
20:00	8:00 P.M.

Note: Since this trip does not exceed 24 hours, it is still the same day, but we must change the E.T.A to a regular P.M. time since it is after noon.

Example 4

Bob Kramp and two friends are planning to drive straight through from college in Greenville, South Carolina, to summer jobs in Boise, Idaho. They have calculated the distance to be 2,475 miles. If they can average 50 mph, find the total driving time. If they allow 3 hours for various stops, and they leave at 5:30 A.M. on May 26, what is their E.T.A.?

(*Note:* Greenville is in the Eastern time zone, and Boise is in the Mountain time zone.)

$$\text{driving time} = \frac{\text{distance}}{\text{rate}} = \frac{2,475 \text{ miles}}{50 \text{ mph}} = 49.50 \text{ hours}$$

$$\text{time added for stops} = 3.00 \text{ hours}$$
$$= 52.50 \text{ total hours for the trip}$$

To find the E.T.A., you must change the trip time to days, hours, and minutes. Subtract multiples of 24.

$$52.5 = 2(24) + 4.5$$
$$= 2 \text{ days, 4 hours, 30 minutes}$$

Two days means the date is May 28.

5:30 A.M.
+4:30
10:00 A.M. EST
−2:00 time gained from Eastern to Mountain time
8:00 A.M. MST

Bob Kramp and his friends will arrive in Boise, Idaho, on May 28, at 8:00 A.M.

Exercises

Using the map on page 283, find the distances between the given cities.
1. Chicago, Ill.; Memphis, Tenn.
2. Boston, Mass.; Buffalo, N.Y.
3. Louisville, Ky.; Kansas City, Mo.
4. Detroit, Mich.; Knoxville, Tenn.
5. Jacksonville, Fla.; Houston, Tex.
6. Knoxville, Tenn.; New York City, N.Y.

For each given distance and average speed, calculate the driving times.
7. 532 miles; 45 mph
8. 963 km; 88 km/h
9. 2,386 km; 75 km/h
10. 3,046 miles; 53 mph
11. 250 miles; 50 mph
12. 1,155 miles; 55 mph

Find the estimated time of arrival for each trip where the values given are for total trip time, time of departure, beginning time zone, and arrival time zone.
13. 7.3 hr., 8:00 A.M., Eastern, Central
14. 25.8 hr., 7:15 P.M., Eastern, Mountain
15. 61.7 hr., 5:30 A.M., Pacific, Central
16. 92.5 hr., 11:30 A.M., Pacific, Eastern

17. An eastbound airline flight leaves Los Angeles, California, at 12:30 P.M. and arrives in Chicago, Illinois, at 6:36 P.M. What is the flight time?

18. A southbound airplane flight leaves New York City at 6:30 A.M. and arrives in Miami, Florida, at 10:05 P.M. What is the flight time?

19. A westbound airplane flight from Atlanta, Georgia, to Seattle, Washington, takes 7.5 hours of flight time plus 1 hour and 45 minutes in St. Paul, Minnesota. If the flight leaves at 7:05 A.M., what is the E.T.A.?

20. The Carpers plan to travel from San Diego, California, to Washington, D.C., for vacation. If the distance is 2,600 miles and they average 530 miles per day, when will they arrive in Washington, D.C., if they leave San Diego at 7:30 A.M. on June 2? (They begin each day at 7:30 A.M., they average 50 mph, and they allow 2 hours for lunch and stops.)

Costs of Alternative Modes of Transportation

You now have some understanding of how to allow for time differences in planning travel and comparing modes of transportation. Comparison of commercial plane, train, and bus fares must be made by using the other associated costs of travel, such as meals, lodging, and taxi fares. Most people would rather fly because of the time factor required for other modes of travel. Table 10.10 gives a price comparison for airfare and train fare from Atlanta, Georgia, to three other cities.

Table 10.10
Price Comparisons

From Atlanta to . . .	Plane	Amtrak
Washington, D.C.	$ 99.00	$ 99.00
Denver, Colorado	$175.00	$239.00
Los Angeles, California	$225.00	$299.00

You may be surprised to find that the plane fare is the less expensive mode. The competitive fares and speed of travel draw over 80% of the commercial passenger business to the airlines. But keep in mind that if you want to see the countryside or get off the beaten path, you may not want to fly to your destination.

Example 1

What is the cost of weekend airfare if the airline gives a 15% discount off the $256 weekday fare?

$$\text{weekend fare} = \$256 - 15\%(\$256)$$
$$= \$256 - \$38.40$$
$$= \$217.60$$

Example 2

Find the total cost for a family of 5 to fly to another city. The adult fare is $165. The child under 2 is free, the two children, ages 2 and 12, get $\frac{1}{3}$ off the adult fare. *Note:* $\frac{1}{3} \times \$165 = \$55$ discount.

$$2 \text{ adults at } \$165 = \$330$$
$$2 \text{ children at } \$110 = \$220$$
$$\text{total} = \$550$$

Example 3

A businessman knows that the weekend airfare of $93 is 20% lower than the weekday fare. If he goes during the week, what will he have to pay?

$$\text{Let full fare} = x$$
$$x - 20\%x = \$93$$
$$x(1 - 0.20) = \$93$$
$$x(0.8) = \$93$$
$$x = \frac{\$93}{0.8} = \$116.25$$

Exercises

Find the cost of airfare for the following weekend specials. The regular fare and discount are given for each exercise.

1. $186 one way, 15%
2. $285 round trip, 20%
3. $526 round trip, 25%
4. $425 one way standby, 30%
5. $89 one way, 12%
6. $115 round trip, 10%

Find the cost of airfare for each family, given the adult fares and children's discounts.

7. Adult airfare: $432 round trip
   1 child (0-2): free
   2 children (2-12): each $\frac{2}{3}$ of full fare
   2 adults

8. Adult airfare: $186 one-way weekend
   1 child (2-12): 15% discount
   2 adults

9. Adult airfare: $99 one way
   1 child (2-12): $\frac{1}{2}$ price
   2 children (over 12): $\frac{1}{3}$ off
   2 adults

10. Adult airfare: $105 one way
   1 child (0-2): free
   2 children (2-12): $\frac{3}{4}$ full fare
   3 children (over 12): 10% off
   2 adults

11. Jeff Roach knows the weekend airfare to Cleveland is $96, and he knows this is 15% off the weekday fare. What will the airfare be if he decides to go during the week?

12. How much will Sharon Luttrel save on her trip home at Christmas by waiting one day and getting an 18% weekend discount? The regular airfare is $286 round trip.

13. How much can Dr. Hadik save on weekly transportation costs by using the subway? If he parks his car at the suburban station, the fee is $10 per week, and the subway fare is $1.50 one way. If he drives the 14 miles to work, the parking fee is $18 per week, and his car costs $0.233 per mile to operate.

14. The Barretts are planning their vacation to Glacier National Park in Montana. Adult airfare is $630, and the 2 children under 12 get a 25% discount. The flying time is 8 hours with a $1\frac{1}{2}$-hour flight change in St. Paul. If they leave Atlanta at 7:30 A.M., find their E.T.A. and the total cost of their airfare.

15. The McGrew family is going to drive to Glacier Park from South Carolina. They know that the one-way distance is 2,585 miles and that they can drive 450 miles per day, driving 9 hours and allowing 2 hours for midday stops. Motels will average $35 per night, meals will average $40 per day, and their car costs $0.20 per mile to operate. Find their round-trip costs (excluding expenses in Montana) and their E.T.A. if they leave South Carolina at 7:30 A.M. on June 14.

16. Give an advantage and a disadvantage for each mode of transportation in problems 14 and 15.

17. When Kevin and Kristy Jansen go to visit their grandmother in Georgia, they plan to take a train from Los Angeles to Atlanta. The one-way fare is $300 with a 20% discount on the return trip. The trip takes 46 hours, and they leave at 10:00 P.M. on July 10. Find the cost of their round trip and their E.T.A. in Atlanta.

18. Toy salesman Brad Isenbaum flew into Chicago for a 3-day product convention. His airfare was $299 round trip, taxi rides were $16.50, the hotel room was $65 per day, and meals were $35 per day. What were his convention and travel expenses?

19. Mrs. Payne is organizing a chartered bus trip for retired couples. She wants a per-couple cost for taking 16 couples to Middleton Gardens. The bus lease for 2 days is $832, the hotel is $29.50 per couple for the one night, and meals are $18 per day per couple.

Calculate the discount rates (in percentages) for airfares, given the full fare and the special.

20. $99, $69 weekends
21. $230, $210 excursion
22. $129, $100 weekends
23. $465 first class, $405 coach
24. $169, $149 weekends
25. $285, $260 excursion

Chapter 10 Review

buyer's guide
collision
comprehensive
cost of operation
cost of ownership
coverage
deductible
depreciation
drive-away cost
Federal Trade Commission (FTC)
lease

lessee
lessor
liability
maintenance
NADA
premium
resale value
residual value
sticker price
trade-in
warranty

Exercises

Find the drive-away cost for a new automobile, given the sticker price, discount, trade-in allowance, and 5% sales tax.

1. $15,942; 15%; $4,500
2. $8,850; 5%; $1,800
3. $10,500; 10%; $2,350
4. $29,950; 16%; $12,250
5. $6,900; 2%; $1,200
6. $16,200; 12%; $5,600

Use Table 10.1 to find out how much of a monthly budget should go to automobile costs. You are given the automobile size and yearly mileage. Round your final answer up to the next whole dollar.

7. Passenger van; 14,500 miles
8. Mini-van; 12,000 miles
9. Subcompact; 15,500 miles
10. Large sedan; 8,500 miles
11. Intermediate; 10,500 miles
12. Compact; 18,000 miles

Find the amount saved for each monthly payment, interest rate, and time.

13. $150; 6%(12); 3 years
14. $225; 7%(12); 4 years
15. $85; 8%(12); 4 years
16. $100; 9%(12); 5 years
17. $45; 6%(12); 5 years
18. $300; 7%(12); 2 years

Find the monthly payment required to finance the following car loans, given the balance, interest rate, and time. Also find how much interest was paid out over the term of the loan.

19. $4,000; 10%(12), 2 years
20. $8,000; 12%(12), 4 years
21. $10,000; 11%(12), 3 years
22. $6,500; 14%(12), 30 months
23. $2,500; 10%(12), 18 months
24. $7,000; 11%(12), 54 months

Find the average annual depreciation and the straight-line rate of depreciation, given the original cost, the total depreciation, and the number of years.

25. $11,554; $8,150; 5 years
26. $10,540; $3,785; 2 years
27. $8,825; $5,650; 6 years
28. $7,100; $4,825; 8 years
29. $13,800; $7,280; 3 years
30. $13,800; $12,850; 12 years

Find the total amount paid into each automobile lease, given the monthly payment and the length of the contract.

31. $186, 4 years
32. $225, 3 years
33. $289, 4 years
34. $172, 5 years

Calculate the semiannual premium for the following automobiles with the given limits and deductibles. Use Tables 10.5-10.7.

35. 25/50/25 liability, retired, $100-deductible collision and full comprehensive, large sedan
36. 15/30/100 liability, work > 10, under-25 male, part-time driver with B average, no collision or comprehensive
37. 100/300/100 liability, work < 10, $100-deductible collision, full comprehensive, under-25 male, full-time driver with 5 points, compact
38. 50/100/50 liability, pleasure, $200-deductible collision, $100-deductible comprehensive, subcompact

Find the mileage each driver got for a trip with the given distance and amount of gasoline.

39. 435 miles, 26.9 gallons

40. 2,186 km, 145 liters

41. 960 km, 96 liters

42. 840 miles, 35 gallons

43. 1,512 miles, 126 gallons

44. 108 miles, 0.12 gallons

Find the amount of gasoline needed and the estimated trip time for each of the given vehicles.

45. 2,350 miles, 22 mpg, 45 mph

46. 1,552 miles, 36 mpg, 50 mph

47. 832 miles, 18 mpg, 40 mph

48. 555 miles, 21 mpg, 55 mph

Find the estimated time of arrival for each trip, given the distance, average speed, starting time and time zone, and arrival time zone.

49. 485 miles, 40 mph, 4:00 P.M., CST, EST

50. 1,350 miles, 50 mph, 7:30 A.M., CST, PST

51. 3,432 miles, 38 mph, 5:00 A.M., PST, EST

52. 975 miles, 52 mph, 1:30 P.M., EST, EST

53. Sales representative Danny Masters can fly round trip from Atlanta to New York for $225 during the week. He can get a 45% discount for flying weekends, but he will have an extra night of lodging at $52 and 3 meals for $18. Which should he fly, weekdays or weekends? How much would he save?

54. When Rochelle Appleman flies to the racquetball tournament in Dallas, she plans to fly excursion fare, which gives a 52% discount. The regular round-trip fare is $288. What will be the ticket cost?

CHAPTER 11

Purchasing the Necessities: Food and Clothing

"I just can't seem to make ends meet!" How ironic it is that this cry of despair should be heard so often in America, one of the most prosperous nations in the world. However, the lack of money is often not to blame so much as the consumer's lack of control over his money. Buying things is a decision-making process that reflects the attitudes of the buyer. Many Americans are addicted to lifestyles that amount to economic suicide in terms of their weekly budgets.

Perhaps you know of a wife who impulsively charges $100 dresses despite her husband's modest salary. Or maybe you have observed an impoverished man at the supermarket, using food stamps to buy a whole cartful of steaks. Of course, everyone wants to dress well and to eat nutritious meals. Yet good stewardship suggests that we try to eat well and dress nicely at the lowest possible cost—and certainly not beyond our income. The woman who liked to be admired in her designer fashions could learn to make attractive dresses for about $25 apiece, which she probably wouldn't need to charge. The shopper with the food stamps could cook many more nutritious meals without the steaks than he could with them. Sadly, though, the pursuit of the ever-elusive "good life" is a temptation many consumers find too tempting to resist.

Luke 12:15 tells us, "Take heed, and beware of covetousness: for a man's life consisteth not in the abundance of the things which he possesseth." Do these words from Christ mean that you must resign yourself to dowdy clothing and boring meals? Not at all. The truth is that, with a little instruction, you can still enjoy good-quality clothing and meals—at a cost you can afford.

Unit Prices

To buy groceries wisely, you will have to do *comparison shopping*. You will need to compare the prices between different grocery stores by sample shopping and by reading newspaper ads. But you must weigh a number of factors besides prices when choosing where you shop regularly. Comparison shopping extends to choosing between brand names of different products and between package sizes of the same product. Your stewardship principles include not only buying as much as you can for your dollars but the best quality you can as well. Unit pricing gives us an effective way to compare the cost of products in different size packaging. The *unit price* is the cost per ounce, per pound, per liter, etc. You used unit pricing in Chapter 10 when figuring gasoline costs from the price per gallon and the number of gallons. A unit price is actually a rate found by dividing the cost by the quantity. This gives an equivalent fraction whose denominator is one unit.

Example 1

Suppose a 12-oz. package of cheese costs $1.92. Find the cost per ounce and per pound.

$$\frac{\text{cost}}{\text{quantity}} = \frac{\$1.92}{12 \text{ oz.}} \text{ Indicate the division; then divide.}$$

$$\frac{\text{cost}}{\text{quantity}} = \frac{\$1.92}{12 \text{ oz.}} = \frac{\$.16}{1 \text{ oz.}}, \text{ which can be expressed as } \$.16 \text{ per ounce.}$$

To find the cost per pound, recall that 1 lb. = 16 oz.

$$\frac{\$.16}{1 \text{ oz.}} \times \frac{16 \text{ oz.}}{1 \text{ lb.}} \text{ Multiply by a fraction equal to 1 and cancel the common unit, ounces.}$$

$$= \frac{(\$.16)(1 \text{ lb.})}{1 \text{ lb.}} = \frac{\$2.56}{1 \text{ lb.}}, \text{ or } \$2.56 \text{ per pound.}$$

Example 2

Determine which jar of peanut butter is the better buy: a 16-oz. jar for $1.76 or a 12-oz. jar for $1.14.

$$\frac{\text{cost}}{\text{quantity}} = \frac{\$1.76}{16 \text{ oz.}} = \$.11 \text{ per ounce for the larger jar.}$$

$$\frac{\text{cost}}{\text{quantity}} = \frac{\$1.14}{12 \text{ oz.}} = \$.095 \text{ per ounce for the small jar.}$$

The 12-oz. jar is the better buy. As a general rule, however, if you buy a bigger quantity of something, you get a better unit price.

Example 3

Mrs. Cates wants to know the cost per serving for a 4-pound chuck roast that sells for $2.40 per pound and will serve 12 people.

$$\text{total cost} = 4 \text{ lb.} \times \frac{\$2.40}{\text{lb.}} = (4)(2.40) = \$9.60$$

$$\text{cost per serving} = \frac{\text{cost}}{\text{no. servings}} = \frac{\$9.60}{12} = \$.80 \text{ per serving}$$

Example 4

Angela is buying meat for the home economics class's project dinner. She wants a 6-oz. serving per person and knows that cutting off waste and cooking the meat will give an 8% shrinkage to the quantity she buys. How much should she buy to serve 16 people?

Let x be the amount of meat per serving before shrinkage. Then write an equation to state what happens.

meat − shrinkage = serving (known)

$x - 8\%x = 6$ oz.

$x - 0.08x = 6$ oz.

$(1 - 0.08)x = 6$ oz. (Use the distributive law.)

$.92x = 6$ oz.

$$x = \frac{6 \text{ oz.}}{.92}$$

$x = 6.52$ oz. per serving

total ounces of meat $= 16 \times 6.52 = 104.32$ oz.

$$\text{total pounds of meat} = \frac{104.32 \text{ oz.}}{16 \text{ oz./lb.}} = 6.52 \text{ lb.}$$

She would probably buy about 7 lb.

Exercises

Find the unit prices.

1. 24 fl. oz. for $1.07

2. $6\frac{1}{2}$ oz. for $.57

3. $1\frac{1}{4}$ lb. for $.99

4. 2.98 kg for $2.79

5. 3.24 lb. for $3.21

6. 2 liters for $1.09

Use unit prices to determine which container size is the better buy.

7. Soap:
   84 oz. for $3.95
   42 oz. for $2.39

8. Grape Juice:
   64 fl. oz. for $2.69
   24 fl. oz. for $1.07

9. Ham:
   4 lb. for $8.99
   5 lb. for $14.15

10. Tuna Fish:
    12.5 oz. for $1.85
    6.5 oz. for $.57

11. Cookies:
    12 oz. for $1.19
    1 lb. for $1.49

12. Taco Shells:
    126 g for $.99
    189 g for $1.29

Find the cost per serving for each purchase.

13. serving size: 4 oz.
container: 2 lb.
price: $2.85

14. serving size: 8 fl. oz.
container: 1 gallon
price: $2.05

15. serving size: 6 pieces
package: 1 gross
price: $5.76

16. serving size: 250 ml
container: 3 liters
price: $1.56

17. serving size: $\frac{3}{4}$ lb.
container: 25 lb.
price: $16.95

18. serving size: $\frac{1}{4}$ of a melon
price $.80 per melon

19. Mrs. Olsen wants to know the best buy for 100% pure orange juice. Frozen juice costs $1.17 for a 16-fl.-oz. can and is made by adding 3 cans of water to the concentrate. Bottled juice comes in a half-gallon carton for $1.29. Canned orange juice costs $1.13 for a 46-fl.-oz. can. What is the best buy?

20. Cassie Fowler is checking out hamburger prices for the young-people's party. She can buy regular ground beef for $1.10 per lb., but it shrinks 18% during cooking. Extra-lean ground beef costs $1.69 per lb. and shrinks 5% during cooking. If she wants 4-oz. servings of cooked meat, which meat is the better buy?

21. When Mrs. Barry was selecting meat, she saw a package of chops weighing 2.74 lb. that cost $7.10 and contained 9 chops. She saw another package weighing 9.09 lb. that cost $22.63 and contained 25 chops. Find the cost per pound, the cost per chop, and the weight per chop for each size package.

22. Eric Franklin is planning the awards banquet for his soccer team. He has the following menu. Help him get the cost per person for the 16 players attending. Use 5% sales tax.

Menu	Purchase Costs
8-oz. Delmonico steak	$3.80 per pound
10-oz. baked potato	$2.39 for 10 lb. bag
2 dinner rolls	$.95 for a pkg. of 8
6 butter pats	$1.04 for 48 patties
6 oz. sweet peas	$2.79 for a 6 lb. 9 oz. can
16-oz. soft drink	$1.05 for a 2 liter bottle
1 pt. ice cream	$3.25 for a half-gallon

Cutting Costs with Coupons and Specials

What would you think if every time you went to the grocery store the cashier gave you between three and five dollars to help pay for your purchases? This might well be the case if you had presented 9 or 10 product coupons with your grocery order. The value of most grocery coupons is between 15¢ and $1.00, with 25¢ coupons being very common. A typical family spending $50 per week on groceries might expect to redeem 12 coupons worth about $5.00 during the week.

Some *product coupons* or *manufacturer's coupons* are found inside the package with the product. Other coupons are printed on the package or in newspaper inserts. Occasionally manufacturers offer groups of coupons through the mail, but you must be sure that the offer is worth more than the cost of postage. The coupons will have printed on them the value, the product package size, and the expiration date. Most of them will also have some fine-print conditions stating that only one coupon can be redeemed on the same package.

As you collect coupons for your shopping, try to keep only those that apply to products you actually use or expect to use. You should establish a special drawer or file where you keep coupons; otherwise they can become a mess. A pocket wallet or a small accordion file could be used to carry coupons to the grocery store. If the coupons are kept by product name or in alphabetical order, it will be easier to pull those you expect to redeem.

When you get to the check-out counter, you present your coupons to the cashier. The cashier totals all the groceries, subtracts the value of your coupons, and then adds the tax. (Be aware, however, that some stores add tax before subtracting coupon values.) The store gets its money for the coupons by mailing them directly to the manufacturer of each product. When you think of how many different products a store sells, the amount of clerical work with manufacturer's coupons can be substantial.

Many grocery stores offer additional savings to customers through weekly specials. Many of the really low-priced specials will have a limit of perhaps 3 items with a $10.00 purchase. How a store presents its specials in the newspaper and what you find at the store when you go to buy will tell a great deal about the quality of the store. Watch out for stores that advertise a product which is unavailable early the next day and that give only a more expensive alternative. This little piece of trickery is called *bait and switch*. Quality stores will stand by their products and their advertising and will always give the benefit to their customers in any dispute.

GROCERY	SAVE
FAMILY SIZE **ANNE TEA BAGS** 24 CT. PKG. **1**⁵⁹	10ᶜ
SELECTED **LISK DRINKS** 2 28 OZ. BTLS **$1**	18ᶜ
RAISIN NUT BRAN 14 OZ. BOX **1**⁶⁹	10ᶜ
READY CRUST 6 OZ. PKG. **79**¢	18ᵉ

GROCERY	SAVE
WHITE•PRINTS **ZORTHE TISSUE** 4 ROLL PKG. **99**¢	20ᵉ
TRASH CAN LINER 20 CT. PKG. **1**⁴⁹	40ᶜ
BAG TALL **KITCHEN BAGS** 15 CT. PKG. **1**²⁹	30ᶜ
DO **BATHROOM CLEANER** 17 OZ. CAN **1**²⁹	26ᵉ

Example 1

If the cashier rings up $52.40 for groceries and deducts $4.25 in coupons, what is the percent savings and the cost of the groceries with 5% sales tax?

Solution:
Recall: rate $\times$ base = percentage
In this case the unknown is the rate; call it x.

$$(x)(52.40) = 4.25$$
$$x = \frac{4.25}{52.40} = 0.081$$
$$x = 8.1\%$$

Original cost of groceries:	$52.40
value of coupons:	−4.25
new cost:	48.15
tax:	+2.41
total:	$50.56

Example 2

If the household in Example 1 has a $50 weekly budget, how much money do they save per week and per year by using manufacturers' coupons?

Solution:

Remember that the budget value must include sales tax. Assume an average of 8% savings each week. This problem is almost the reverse of Example 1.

Find the before-tax cost of groceries; call it x.

$$x + 5\%x = 50.00 \text{ (budget)}$$
$$x + 0.05x = 50.00$$
$$1.05x = 50.00$$
$$x = \frac{50.00}{1.05} = 47.62$$

Find the before-coupon cost of groceries; call it y.

$$y - 8\%y = 47.62$$
$$y - 0.08y = 47.62$$
$$0.92y = 47.62$$
$$y = \frac{47.62}{0.92} = 51.76 \text{ (value before coupons)}$$

$$\text{Value of coupons per week} = 51.76 - 47.62 = \$4.14$$
$$\text{Yearly savings} = 52 \times 4.14 = \$215.28$$

Example 3

Use the specials shown in the newspaper ads to find how much a shopper will save if he buys the following:

6 lb. pork tenderloins
4 lb. chuck roast
2 packages of tea bags
1 box of Raisin Nut Bran
1 package of trash-can liners
3 packages of tissue

USDA Choice Beef
Boneless Chuck Roast
$**1**29
lb.   SAVE 70¢ lb.

USDA Choice Beef
Boneless Shoulder
. . lb. $**1**59

GROCERY SAVE
WHITE•PRINTS
ZORTHE TISSUE 4 ROLL PKG. **99**¢ 20¢
TRASH CAN LINER 20 CT BAG TALL PKG **1**49 40¢
KITCHEN BAGS 15 CT DO PKG **1**29 30¢
BATHROOM CLEANER 17 OZ CAN **1**29 26¢

SAVE $1.00 lb.
Whole 2 lb. Average Size
Boneless Pork Tenderloins
$**2**99
lb.

GROCERY SAVE
FAMILY SIZE
ANNE TEA BAGS 24 CT PKG **1**59 10¢
SELECTED
LISK DRINKS **2** 28 OZ BTLS $**1** 18¢
RAISIN NUT BRAN 14 OZ BOX **1**69 10¢
READY CRUST 6 OZ PKG **79**¢ 18¢

Solution:
Find the savings for each special; then add them.

pork tenderloins	$6 × 1.00 =		6.00
chuck roast	4 × .70 =		2.80
tea bags	2 × .10 =		.20
Raisin Nut Bran	1 × .10 =		.10
trash-can liners	1 × .40 =		.40
tissue	3 × .20 =		.60
		$10.10	total savings

Example 4

Find the total amount actually paid for the items in Example 3, and find the percent savings. Use 6% sales tax.

Solution:

pork tenderloin	6 × 2.99 =	$17.94
chuck roast	4 × 1.29 =	5.16
tea bags	2 × 1.59 =	3.18
Raisin Nut Bran	1 × 1.69 =	1.69
trash-can liners	1 × 1.49 =	1.49
tissue	3 × 0.99 =	2.97
		32.43 (subtotal)
		+1.95 (tax)
		$34.38 (total paid)

In order to find the percent savings, you need to know what the shopper would have paid without the specials. This value is the base for comparison.

$$
\begin{aligned}
\text{cost paid} &= \$32.43 \\
\text{savings} &= +10.10 \\
\text{cost without specials} &= \$42.53
\end{aligned}
$$

Using the percent equation $r \cdot b = p$, you substitute.

$$r(42.53) = 10.10$$

$$r = \frac{10.10}{42.53} = 0.2374$$

$$\text{savings} = 23.74\%$$

Example 5

A family saves $10 each week by using specials, and their groceries average $55 per week, including 5% tax. What is their percent savings? What is their yearly budget with and without buying specials? What is their annual savings using specials?

Solution:
You must compare the savings to the cost of groceries before the coupons and without tax. The before-tax budget plus the savings gives the amount of groceries that could be purchased using the specials.

Let x be the before-tax value of the budget.

$$
\begin{aligned}
x + 5\%x &= 55 \text{ (budget)} \\
1.05x &= 55 \\
x &= \tfrac{55}{1.05} = \$52.38
\end{aligned}
$$

Cost of groceries before specials $= 52.38 + 10 = \$62.38$

Using the percent equation, $r \cdot b = p$, $r(62.38) = 10.00$, $r = 16\%$

yearly budget with specials $= 52 \cdot 55 = \$2,860$

yearly budget without specials $= 52 \cdot 65.50 = \$3,406$

annual savings $= \$3,406 - \$2,860 = \$546$

Note: If this same family also used coupons, Example 2 would indicate an additional savings of about $215 for a total of $761. (The two budgets are about the same.)

Exercises

Find the actual cost of groceries and the percent savings, given the before-tax cost of groceries and the value of the coupons. Use 4% sales tax.

1. G: $29.84
   C: $5.04
2. G: $97.25
   C: $11.90
3. G: $55.00
   C: $9.50

4. G: $18.00
   C: $1.25
5. G: $62.81
   C: $7.56
6. G: $124.54
   C: $15.25

Given the weekly budget, the percent of the total saved through coupons, and a 5% sales tax, find the full price of the groceries before tax and coupons and the value of the coupons.

7. B: $82
   C: 7%
8. B: $45
   C: 12%
9. B: $56
   C: 9.5%

10. B: $35
   C: 15%
11. B: $60
   C: 8%
12. B: $41
   C: 14%

Use the following advertised specials to find the savings for each grocery list.

MEAT — SAVE

Item	Price	Save
BONELESS N.Y. STRIP STEAKS LB.	4.49	50¢ LB.
FAMILY PACK • CHOPPED STEAK PATTIES LB.	1.69	30¢ LB.
BEEF BOTTOM • BONELESS ROUND STEAKS LB.	1.99	70¢ LB.
3 LBS OR MORE • 100% PURE GROUND CHUCK LB.	1.69	20¢ LB.

MEAT — SAVE

Item	Price	Save
COUNTRY STYLE • FRESH PORK SPARERIBS LB.	1.69	20¢ LB.
LOIN END COMBO PORK LOIN CHOPS LB.	1.89	10¢ LB.
RIB END ROAST BONELESS PORK LOIN LB.	2.69	30¢ LB.
FAMILY PACK • FRESH PORK STEAKS LB.	1.69	30¢ LB.

MEAT — SAVE

Item	Price	Save
FAMILY PACK • FRESH FRYER DRUMSTICKS LB.	99¢	40¢ LB.
FAMILY PACK • FRESH FRYER THIGHS LB.	99¢	40¢ LB.
NECKS • WINGS OR TURKEY DRUMSTICKS LB.	69¢	10¢ LB.
U.S.D.A. GRADE 'A' FRESH TURKEYS LB.	89¢	20¢ LB.

SEAFOOD — SAVE

Item	Price	Save
50 TO 60 COUNT MEDIUM SHRIMP LB.	4.99	$2.00 LB.
ATLANTIC OCEAN FLOUNDER FILLETS LB.	3.99	$2.00 LB.
POND RAISED FRESH CATFISH LB.	2.49	50¢ LB.
50 TO 60 COUNT LARGE SHRIMP LB.	6.99	$2.00 LB.

FLORAL — SAVE

Item	Price	Save
PETITE FRESH BOUQUETS EA.	2.99	EVERY DAY LOW PRICE
TWO STEM ROSE IN BUD VASES EA.	5.99	EVERY DAY LOW PRICE
ASSORTED FOLIAGE PLANTS 4" POT	1.99	EVERY DAY LOW PRICE

PRODUCE — SAVE

Item	Price	Save
FRESH GREEN BEANS LB.	59¢	40¢ LB.
CALIFORNIA RED OR GREEN LEAF LETTUCE LB.	69¢	30¢ LB.
LONG SLENDER GREEN CUCUMBERS	4 FOR $1	33¢ ON 4

PRODUCE — SAVE

Item	Price	Save
RED RIPE CHERRY TOMATOES PT. BSK.	99¢	30¢
SEEDLESS FLORIDA LIMES	6 FOR $1	24¢ ON 6
GOURMET DELIGHT FRESH MANGOES EA.	99¢	EVERY DAY LOW PRICE

PRODUCE — SAVE

Item	Price	Save
DELICIOUS IMPORTED PISTACHIOS LB.	3.89	EVERY DAY LOW PRICE
NEW CROP RED POTATOES LB.	39¢	10¢ LB.
SELECT MEDIUM YELLOW ONIONS 3 LB BAG	99¢	EVERY DAY LOW PRICE

13. 2 lb. steak patties
2.9 lb. fryer drumsticks
5 lb. green beans
5 lb. red potatoes

14. 12.5 lb. turkey
1.5 lb. leaf lettuce
1 pt. cherry tomatoes
3 lb. yellow onions

15. 3 lb. catfish
8 cucumbers
12 limes
10 lb. red potatoes

16. 1.5 lb. N.Y. strip steaks
1.2 lb. leaf lettuce
4 cucumbers
1 pt. cherry tomatoes

17. 4.5 lb. pork spare ribs
2 lb. green beans
4 mangoes
2.1 lb. leaf lettuce

18. 2.3 lb. flounder fillets
1 doz. limes
8 cucumbers

Given the following weekly grocery budgets, the amount saved with coupons, and the amount saved with specials, find the percent savings and the annual savings. Use 5% sales tax.

19. grocery budget: $45
    coupons: $7
    specials: $5
20. grocery budget: $64.00
    coupons: $10.50
    specials: $8.25
21. grocery budget: $52.00
    coupons: $11.25
    specials: $5.35

22. grocery budget: $32.00
    coupons: $6.50
    specials: $4.85
23. grocery budget: $83.00
    coupons: $14.25
    specials: $11.50
24. grocery budget: $125.00
    coupons: $16.50
    specials: $15.25

Cutting Costs Through Quantity and Seasonal Buying

You have probably noticed from the unit prices displayed in grocery stores that buying larger quantities normally gives lower unit prices. Of course, buying a larger quantity of some foodstuff means that you will take much longer to use it up. However, it will mean lower costs per serving, as long as you don't change your eating habits. In this section you will learn ways to buy in volume and ways to preserve and store the larger quantities and low-priced seasonal foods.

Buying a month's supply of some food that is on special and keeping it in the freezer will help extend the savings beyond the immediate sale. For many people, buying the larger economy size of something like canned vegetables is more trouble than the savings are worth. For them, the best value comes from being able to buy many of the smaller cans but at a unit price comparable to the big cans. This desire has led to the formation of *buying cooperatives,* in which fifteen or twenty families combine their buying efforts in order to get wholesale prices. The co-op can buy foods in bulk and then distribute them among its members according to their individual needs. Each member family pays for their purchases on the basis of their part of the whole. For instance, if the co-op bought 10 cases of soup and a family needed $\frac{1}{2}$ case, they would pay

$\frac{1}{20}$ of the total cost of the soup. The savings for co-op buying usually amount to 15 to 20 percent.

Those who buy through co-ops will not generally be able to take advantage of manufacturers' coupons. They will also be more limited in the selection of brand names, unless the cooperative is very large. Volume discounts for canned goods, packaged foods, and bottled items are usually limited to those who can buy wholesale, as with cooperatives. Discounts for fresh fruits and vegetables at farmers' markets and truck farms vary with the quantities purchased but generally offer worthwhile savings. For example, you can buy a whole bushel of apples, oranges, or green beans for very little more than what a 10-lb. sack costs at a grocery store. The bushel of apples will weigh 40 lb. and cost $10 to $12, while 10 lb. of apples at the grocery store will cost $8.00. Many farmers' markets even have retail sections where you can buy any amount desired. Such prices will be better than the produce section of the grocery store, but the best savings will still come from buying by the bushel or box. One of the most economical ways to buy produce is at truck farms or at *you-pick* farms. However, don't forget to consider transportation costs to get to the farm.

By far the lowest prices for fruits and vegetables are those you grow in your own garden. One family was able to pay for a $400 garden tiller with their food savings from the first year. Remember, though, that a vegetable garden does cost something. You have to buy seed (and maybe a tiller), and you have to expend time. To illustrate the potential savings, $6.00 for green bean seeds might yield 2 or 3 bushels of beans. When canned or frozen, this could amount to over 100 quarts of beans worth $75 to $80.

Canning or freezing sizable amounts of fruits and vegetables ranks among the best methods for cutting food expenses. Produce that is abundant during certain parts of the season will be reasonably inexpensive at those times but may be expensive during other seasons.

Even buying half or a quarter of a beef and keeping it in a locker or home freezer will significantly cut meat costs. Keep in mind that the purchase price and operating costs of a freezer must be accounted for in figuring the savings realized by freezing quantities of meat and produce.

As with coupon buying and specials, you can calculate the savings realized from buying in volume and buying in season. Knowing the real value of the family budget can add the interest and motivation necessary to keep up the extra effort that it takes to stock up the pantry and freezer.

Good stewardship of your resources often means that more money for an automobile or housing can be set aside in long-term savings. It can also provide money for gifts to the Lord's work. Many Christians have never experienced the joy of giving to the Lord's work because their finances are so limited by poor stewardship and foolish spending habits.

Home Freezers

Home freezers have become as common as automobiles to the American family. They come in a variety of designs. The upright freezer looks just like a refrigerator, whereas chest freezers look like refrigerators lying on their backs. Each type has its own advantages and disadvantages. On one hand, chest freezers are more efficient because the cold air does not fall out when the door is opened. (Remember, cold air falls because it's heavier.) On the other hand, upright freezers use less floor space and are generally a little more attractive to have sitting around your house.

Refrigerator-freezers come in three styles. The most common type has the refrigerator on the bottom and the freezer on the top. A few companies make models with the freezer on the bottom and the refrigerator on the top because the refrigerator is opened more often. The most expensive models of refrigerator-freezers are side-by-sides, with two vertical doors. The narrower door is usually the freezer since the larger capacity is needed for the refrigerator where objects are moved around more often and are not packed as closely.

Most modern appliances, like freezers, are required to have an energy-consumption certificate. This allows the consumer to determine the cost of operation for various electricity rates. It also provides a means of comparing the particular model to others of about that same capacity. On a new freezer or refrigerator, you will find a yellow tag on the front, giving the energy information.

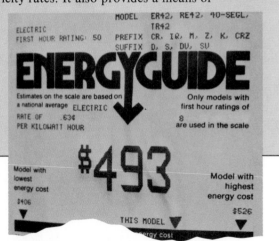

Example 1

Mr. Dunn's family has purchased a 20-ft.^{3} freezer for $950. This model costs $84 per year to operate. If they can save 15% on their $55 weekly grocery budget, what is the pay-back period for their new freezer?

Solution:

$$\text{the savings per week} = 15\%(\$55) = \quad \$8.25$$

$$
\begin{aligned}
\text{food savings per year} = (52)(\$8.25) = &\quad \$429.00 \\
\text{operating costs per year} = &\quad -\$84.00 \\
\text{net savings} = &\quad \$345.00
\end{aligned}
$$

$$\text{pay-back period} = \frac{\text{total cost}}{\text{yearly savings}} = \frac{950}{345} = 2.75 \text{ years} = 2 \text{ years, 9 months}$$

Example 2

When Mr. Jordan was shopping for a refrigerator-freezer, he observed that the unit he liked was expected to cost $78 per year to operate. The energy certificate was based on 6.25 cents/kilowatt hour. How much should he expect to pay if electricity in his area costs 7.75 cents/kWh?

Solution:

$$\frac{\text{cost/kwh}}{\text{cost/kwh}} = \frac{\text{yearly cost}}{\text{yearly cost}} \quad \text{Now substitute.}$$

$$\frac{6.25}{7.75} = \frac{78}{x} \qquad \text{Then solve for } x.$$

$$(6.25)x = (78)(7.75)$$

$$x = \frac{(78)(7.75)}{(6.25)} = \$96.72 \text{ yearly costs}$$

Example 3

How much does a family save per year on meat and vegetables by canning and freezing the following?

		Avg. store price
250 lb. beef at $1.50/lb.		$2.25/lb.
100 qt. beans at $.10/qt.		$.70/qt.
100 pt. corn at $.25/pt.		$.80/pt.
70 qt. peaches at $.35/qt.		$1.09/qt.
50 qt. applesauce at $.30/qt.		$.60/qt.

Solution:

Find the savings for each item by using the quantity and the difference in unit prices.

beef	$250 \times .75/lb. =$	$187.50
beans	$100 \times .60/qt. =$	$60.00
corn	$100 \times .55/pt. =$	$55.00
peaches	$70 \times .74/qt. =$	$51.80
applesauce	$50 \times .30/qt. =$	$15.00
	$=$	$369.30 (total savings per year)

You will notice that the largest savings comes from buying meat in quantity. This means that this family would need a freezer for their meat; consequently the net savings would be $369.30 minus operating costs of $70-$80 per year.

Example 4

A refrigerator-freezer costs $1,050, uses $83 of power per year at the rate of 6.25¢/kWh and will need one major repair during its 15-year life. If you assume that the repairs will cost 10% of the initial price and that the electric rate in the owner's area is 8.2¢/kWh, what is the annual cost of owning and operating this unit?

Solution:

First, find the yearly energy cost, using a proportion.

$$\frac{6.25}{8.2} = \frac{83}{x} \quad \text{Cross-multiply } 6.25x = (83)(8.2)$$

Dividing gives $x = \frac{(83)(8.2)}{6.25} = \$108.90$ per year.

Next, find the annual ownership costs.

$$\frac{\text{total cost}}{\text{year}} = \frac{1,050 + 105}{15} = \frac{1,155}{15} = \$77$$

$$\text{total} = \$108.90 + \$77.00 = \$185.90$$

Exercises

Find the annual freezer-operating costs from the following energy-certificate data.

1. $55/year at 4.75¢/kWh
   electric rate: 7.2¢/kWh

2. 1,246 kWh/year
   electric rate: 6.5¢/kWh

3. 732 kWh/year
   electric rate: 8.2¢/kWh

4. $115/year at 6.85¢/kWh
   electric rate: 4.95¢/kWh

5. $48/year at 5.25¢/kWh
   electric rate: 7.25¢/kWh

6. 108 kWh/month
   electric rate: 5.5¢/kWh

Find the annual cost of owning and operating a refrigerator-freezer with a life expectancy of 18 years, one major repair at 8% of initial cost, and the following cost and energy data.

7. price: $845 *Hotpoint*
   1,500 kWh/year
   rate: 5.7¢/kWh

8. price: $1,525 *General Electric*
   1,350 kWh/year
   rate: 6.25¢/kWh

9. price: $695 *Frigidaire*
   $49/year at 4.75¢/kWh
   rate: 8.2¢/kWh

10. price: $1,050 *Whirlpool*
    $72/year at 7.5¢/kWh
    rate: 4.95¢/kWh

11. price: $755 *Coldspot*
    1,090 kWh/year
    rate: 7.5¢/kWh

12. price: $1,285 *Kelvinator*
    $89/year at 6.25¢/kWh
    rate: 8.25¢/kWh

Find the pay-back period for each refrigerator-freezer in problems 7-12, given the weekly budget and the percent savings through stocking up. Ignore the repair costs and give answers in years.

13. *Hotpoint*
    $58/week
    6%

14. *General Electric*
    $90/week
    12%

15. *Frigidaire*
    $65/week
    10%

16. *Whirlpool*
    $72/week
    14%

17. *Coldspot*
    $88/week
    16%

18. *Kelvinator*
    $112/week
    13%

Calculate the savings realized by purchasing each foodstuff in volume.

19. 40-lb. box apples: $10
    regular: 79¢/lb.

20. 100-lb. sack of flour: $23
    regular: $1.90/5 lb. sack

21. 50 lb. potatoes: $11.50
    regular: $3.90/10 lb. sack

22. 80-count box of oranges: $10.50
    regular: 4 for $1.00

23. 100-count box of peaches: $10.00
    regular: 6 for $1.00

24. 10-lb. sack of pecans: $20
    regular: $1.80/8 oz.

25. The Wood family belongs to a 20-family food cooperative. Find their part of the cost for the following orders. (Use 5% sales tax.)

Item	Woods' Order	Total Purchased	Total Cost Before Tax
soup	$\frac{1}{2}$ case	16 cases	$88.00
flour	25 lb.	500 lb.	$60.00
oatmeal	8 lb.	160 lb.	$24.00
beans	$\frac{2}{3}$ case	20 cases	$72.00

26. Stephen Schnaiter runs a produce stand by the highway near his dad's farm. He buys 40-lb. boxes of produce from his dad. He buys apples for $4, peaches for $5, sweet corn for $6, and tomatoes for $3.50. Each week he can usually sell 3 boxes of each. If Stephen needs to make a $12 profit per box, what should he use for unit prices (per pound)? What is his weekly profit?

27. The Wolfe family planted a garden with the following expenses: tiller, $450; seeds, $32.50; tools, $26.00; seedlings, $5.50; and canning equipment, $100.00. If they were able to reduce their $60-per-week grocery bill by $10, how much did they lose the first year? If their only costs the second year were seeds and seedlings, how much did they save?

28. The corner grocery buys Granny Smith apples for $12 per 40-lb. box. If they sell these apples for 79¢/lb., how much do they make per box?

29. The Guthrie boys eat 3 pounds of peanut butter per week. If they buy it in 1-lb. jars, it costs $2.65 each. Excluding tax, how much could they save per year by purchasing 20-lb. cartons for $33 each?

Project: Research food cooperatives. Find out how they are organized, how to buy from a wholesale supplier, and how much would be saved. To determine savings, make a 20-item grocery list of very basic foodstuffs and a yearly quantity for a typical family of four.

Nutrition

There are few, if any, young people who have not been warned by their parents to cut back on junk food. The name *junk food* implies that as a food something is basically worthless. *Food* means more than a tangible substance that can be eaten. Food value refers to the imparting of nutrients, or *nutrition.* The term *junk food* has come to mean edibles that are either lacking in nutrition or are out of balance in containing too much of one thing, such as sugar.

When people speak of a balanced diet, they are referring to a regular intake of food that provides the correct proportions of and a complete range of the required nutrients. Good nutrition will provide our bodies with calories, fats, proteins, carbohydrates, fatty acids, vitamins, minerals, and roughage. The calorie (actually kilocalorie) is a unit expressing the amount of energy provided by a food and burned by our bodies. All food eventually becomes glucose as the body breaks it down through digestion. When someone refers to a candy bar as *empty calories,* he means there are no other nutrients or vitamins available—just calories. There are many charts and books available that give nutrient information about almost every food imaginable. By using one of these charts, you can determine how much nutrition you get from your regular food intake. You can then compare it to what nutritionists say is a proper diet. It may take a little record keeping and some simple calculations, but you may profit greatly from the study. Most of us find that our diets are out of balance, usually in three areas: too much fat, too much sugar, and consequently too many calories.

Have you ever heard the expression "You are what you eat"? Good health and vitality depend more on diet than on anything else. Young people don't always believe this because it takes time for a poor diet to have its effect on the body. Although many so-called experts would disagree about the details, it's obvious that cancer and cardiovascular disease are diseases of civilization. Well-developed civilizations, past and present, are characterized by sedentary people overeating rich, fatty foods. On the other hand, the Hunza, a people who live in the Himalayas of Northern Pakistan on a very simple vegetable-and-fruit diet, have never recorded a single case of cancer. One writer, commenting in 1970 on the relationship between cancer and diet, suggested that if the entire world ate like the Westerners who consume large amounts of meat, fat, sugar, refined grains, salt, coffee, and alcohol, there would be 11,500,000 new cases of cancer each year. And of these new cases, there would be 2,000,000 in China alone. He also suggested the opposite. Let the rest of the world eat like the rural, inland Chinese, and there would be no new cases of cancer.

The question you may have on your mind right now is "How do I know what nutrients are in the food I eat?" Packaged foods are required to have their contents on the package, listed in order of largest amount to smallest amount. This listing may not give the actual quantities of each nutrient, but it does provide some guidance. What will surprise you is how many packaged foods list some form of sugar as one of the 3 most abundant ingredients. The average American eats about 130 grams of sugar every day. This is almost his weight in sugar every year. Even if you decided not to put any sugar on your food, you would have to shop very carefully to avoid eating large amounts of it. On packaged foods you will find label after label listing such sugars as sucrose, dextrose, fructose, corn syrup, honey, molasses, and brown sugar. You can find the nutrients that occur in unpackaged foods by using tables like those available from the U.S. Department of Agriculture. A portion of such a table is given in the back of this textbook. Only certain foods have been selected from among the many listed.

PHOSPHORUS	2	15
MAGNESIUM	2	6
ZINC	25	30
COPPER	4	6

*WHOLE MILK SUPPLIES AN ADDITIONAL 30 CALORIES, 4 g FAT, AND 15 mg CHOLESTEROL.
**CONTAINS LESS THAN 2% OF THE U.S. RDA OF THIS NUTRIENT.

INGREDIENTS: SUGAR; CORN, WHEAT AND OAT FLOUR; SALT; DRIED APPLES; APPLE JUICE CONCENTRATE; CINNAMON; COLOR ADDED;

VITAMINS AND MINERALS: VITAMIN C (SODIUM ASCORBATE AND ASCORBIC ACID); VITAMIN B_3 (NIACINAMIDE); ZINC (ZINC OXIDE); IRON; BAKING SODA; VITAMIN A (PALMITATE, PROTECTED WITH BHT); VITAMIN B_6 (PYRIDOXINE HYDROCHLORIDE); VITAMIN B_2 (RIBOFLAVIN); VITAMIN B_1 (THIAMIN HYDROCHLORIDE); FOLIC ACID AND VITAMIN D.

CARBOHYDRATE INFORMATION

	CEREAL	WITH SKIM MILK
COMPLEX CARBOHYDRATES	12 g	12 g
SUCROSE & OTHER SUGARS	14 g	20 g
TOTAL CARBOHYDRATES	26 g	32 g

What happens when someone consumes more food calories than his body uses? His body stores the extra food as fat. However, when he increases his level of activity, his body may burn more calories than he consumes as food. In this situation the fat stored in the body supplies the extra energy requirements. Studies have been done which identify the number of calories needed per day for different levels of activity and different temperature conditions. Table 11.1 gives some of this data. You may find it interesting that mountain climbers have to calculate calorie requirements carefully so that they carry enough food but not so much that weight and bulk become a problem.

Table 11.1
Calorie Requirements[1]

Bodily Activity	Kcalories Required per Pound of Weight Each Hour		Typical Duration of Activity in Hours	Total Kcalories per Day for 145-lb. Man
	men	*women*		
sleeping (basal rate)	0.4	0.43	8.0	510
sitting	0.60	0.55	4.7	409
standing with moderate movement	1.00	.85	8.5[2]	1,233
light exercise (walking)	1.68	1.48	1.5	390
moderate exercise or physical labor (bicycling)	2.20	1.85	0.7	223
very active exercise (running, swimming)	4.05	3.70	0.5[3]	411

Footnotes:

[1]The values in this table are a composite from several different sources.

[2]The large amount of standing time indicates a job such as a bank teller's, in which the person stands while at work. A certain amount of movement and some short walks would be included.

[3]Unless the person is in good physical condition, this level of activity would have to occur at several shorter intervals.

Example 1

In 1986 the population of the world reached 5 billion, the population of the United States alone reaching 260 million. Using this ratio and the 1985 cancer death rate for the United States, find the cancer death rate for the world population if it were to have the same diet and lifestyle as those in the United States.

Solution: 1985 U.S. cancer death rate = 4.62/100,000 population

$$\frac{2.6 \times 10^8}{5.0 \times 10^9} = \frac{4.62}{x} \quad \text{Use a proportion.}$$

Solve for x.

$$x = \frac{(4.62)(5 \times 10^9)}{2.6 \times 10^9} = 88.8/100,000, \text{ or } 4,440,000 \text{ deaths per year from cancer}$$

Example 2

How many calories does the following lunch provide? See the nutrition chart.

1 cup Vegetable Beef Stew	235
2 slices whole wheat bread	110
2 pats of margarine	100
8-oz. glass (1 cup) milk	160
2 carrots	40
$\frac{1}{2}$ cup raw peach slices	33
total:	678

Example 3

Miss Ling is a 115-lb. nurse at Memorial Hospital. From the following activity duration times, find how many calories she uses in a typical day. Use Table 11.1. Round off to the nearest whole number.

sleeping	8.5 hours
sitting	5.2 hours
standing	4.0 hours
walking	4.8 hours
physical labor	1.5 hours

Solution:

sleeping:	$8.5 \times 0.43 \times 115 = 420$
sitting:	$5.2 \times 0.55 \times 115 = 329$
standing:	$4.0 \times 0.85 \times 115 = 391$
walking:	$4.8 \times 1.48 \times 115 = 817$
physical labor:	$1.5 \times 1.85 \times 115 = 319$
total:	2,276

Example 4

Find the total calories and total grams of protein, fat, and carbohydrates for the following meal: 6-oz. sirloin steak (lean and fat), 1 cup mashed potatoes with butter and milk, 1 ear sweet corn, $\frac{1}{2}$ cup green beans, 2 plain rolls, 2 pats of butter, and 1 piece of chocolate cake with $\frac{1}{2}$ cup of ice milk. Water was the only beverage.

Item	Calories	Protein	Fat	Carbohydrate
steak	660	40	54	0
potatoes	185	4	8	24
corn	70	3	1	16
beans	15	1	—	4
rolls	230	6	4	40
butter	100	—	12	—
cake	445	5	20	67
ice milk	143	5	5	21
totals:	1,848	64	104	172

Example 5

Find the total calories, protein, fat, and carbohydrates for the following meal: 6-oz. baked shad (fish), 2 slices of cracked wheat bread, $\frac{1}{2}$ cup cooked broccoli, $\frac{1}{4}$ cup grated carrots (raw), $\frac{1}{2}$ cup collard greens (raw), $\frac{1}{4}$ cup mung bean sprouts, $\frac{1}{4}$ cup soybean sprouts, $\frac{1}{4}$ tomato, $\frac{1}{4}$ cantaloupe.

Item	Calories	Protein	Fat	Carbohydrate
shad	340	40	20	0
bread	120	4	2	24
broccoli	20	2.5	—	3.5
carrots	11	—	—	3
greens	27.5	—	—	—
mung sprouts	7.5	1	—	1.5
soybean sprouts	10	1.5	0.5	1
tomato	9	0.5	—	2
cantaloupe	30	0.5	—	7
totals:	575	50	22.5	42

If you study these two meals, you will see some significant differences. The meal in example 4 is a typical Western-civilization supper. The meal in example 5 is an equivalent to that eaten in an undeveloped country, where most of the food is uncooked fruits and vegetables and whole-grain breads. These "uncivilized diets" contain very little meat, except fish and poultry, and most of the fat comes through dairy products from cows or goats. The following exercises contain some questions about Examples 4 and 5 which should help you focus on the distinctions between these two meals.

Exercises

Find the number of calories available in each meal.

1. Breakfast:
   2 soft-boiled eggs
   2 pc. toast (white bread)
   1 cup orange juice
   2 pats margarine

2. Breakfast:
   $\frac{2}{3}$ cup (1 oz.) Bran Flakes (40%)
   $\frac{1}{2}$ cup skim milk
   $\frac{1}{2}$ grapefruit (pink)
   1 pc. toast (white bread)
   1 pat margarine

3. Breakfast:
   4 pancakes (Buckwheat)
   $\frac{1}{4}$ cup (4 tablespoons) syrup
   $\frac{1}{2}$ cup prune juice
   1 orange

4. Breakfast:
   1 cup corn grits (enriched)
   3 pats butter
   3 biscuits
   2 scrambled eggs
   6 slices crisp bacon
   1 cup apple juice
   2 cups coffee (with 2 tablespoons sugar)

5. Lunch:
   1 cup cottage cheese (uncreamed)
   $\frac{1}{2}$ cup sliced peaches (fresh)
   tuna sandwich:
     3 oz. tuna
     1 large lettuce leaf
     2 slices whole wheat bread (toasted)
   1 8-oz. glass cola

6. Lunch:
   3 (6.3-oz.) fried chicken drumsticks
   1 baked potato
   3 pats margarine
   $\frac{1}{2}$ cup diced carrots (cooked)
   2 slices whole wheat bread
   2 glasses water
   1 slice apple pie

7. Lunch:
   2 sandwiches:
       4 slices whole wheat bread
       2 tablespoons mayonnaise
       4 oz. sliced boiled ham
       4 oz. cheddar cheese
       2 large lettuce leaves
   1 cup tomato soup
   2 large dill pickles
   1 medium apple

8. Supper:
   5 oz. roast beef (lean)
   6 spears green asparagus
   $\frac{1}{2}$ cup cauliflower
   $\frac{1}{2}$ cup mashed potatoes (butter + milk)
   2 rolls (plain, enriched)
   2 pats margarine

9. Supper:
   3 oz. roasted ham
   2 stalks raw celery
   6 slices raw cucumber
   1 cup dandelion greens (cooked)
   $\frac{1}{2}$ cup green peas (cooked)
   1 ear sweet corn (cooked)
   1 slice Boston brown bread
   $\frac{1}{2}$ cup strawberries (no sugar)

Find the number of calories expended on each activity or series of activities. Use Table 11.1.

10. Lisa Parker, 110 lb.
    walking to and from school at 4 mph
    distance one way is 1.75 miles

11. Bobby Peck, 155 lb.
    bike riding for 3 hours

12. Laurie Hay, 130 lb.
    standing at work from 8:00 to 5:00 with 3 breaks during which she sits for a total of 80 minutes

13. John Dunn, 150 lb.
    shoveling snow for $3\frac{1}{2}$ hours with one sitting-down break for 20 minutes

14. David Bell, 138 lb.
    running 6.2 mile race
    running at 6.5 minutes per mile

15. Robby Greenwald, 132 lb.
    7-mile hike one way at 5 mph (moderate exercise)
    1 hour of sitting
    8 hours of sleep
    7 miles back with 1 hour of sitting

Use Examples 4 and 5 for questions 16 through 21.

16. Which meal would be best for a person whose work involves sitting at a desk all day?

17. Which meal is best for a woman who does $\frac{1}{2}$ hour of light exercise a day but is otherwise sedentary? Explain.

18. Which do you see as the biggest nutritional difference between steak and shad?

19. What do you see as a deficiency in the Example 5 meal?

20. What do you see as a deficiency in the Example 4 meal?

21. What 3 items would you change in the Example 4 meal to lower the calories and fat?

22. Jill Foote is a diabetic; she has to start limiting her calorie intake so as to expend more calories daily than she consumes. If she sleeps 8 hours, sits in school 6 hours, stands with moderate movement 4 hours, participates in cheerleading (very active exercise) for 2 hours, and sits resting all other hours, find the number of calories she can consume to keep her diabetes under control. (Assume a weight of 120 lb.)

23. Jill decided to lose 1 pound per week for 5 weeks and needs to reduce her intake of calories accordingly. How many calories can she consume daily, based on her activity level found in problem 22? *Note:* You must expend 3,500 calories to lose 1 lb.

24. Plan meals for 1 day that include all 4 food groups and will meet Jill's required calorie-intake requirement for losing 1 lb. per week.

25. Todd Menz is a 180-lb. high school senior who participates in soccer, basketball, baseball, and track. He exercises at a very active rate for 3 hours a day. How many extra calories should he consume to compensate for that burn-off?

26. List ways in which you can alter your food intake to assure better nutrition.

Markup and Pricing for Clothing

Did you ever wonder how much the store paid for the suit you just bought on sale for $155? Maybe you've also wondered how the merchant could take 25% off and still make money. What if the clothing store marks up their prices 25% over cost, then has a 25%-off sale? Do they make money, break even, or lose money?

Clothing stores and other retailers buy their clothes (inventory) from wholesale stores or factories. They *mark up* this cost by a certain percent in order to pay for *overhead* (expenses) and to achieve a *profit*. The price that you see is called the *retail* price. If all the clothing that a retailer puts in his store sells, there is no need for specials and sales. On the realistic side, however, the retailer can expect some of the clothing that he buys never to sell or to sell only way below his cost. For this reason the markup rate must be large enough to assure a profit by the sale of only part of the goods. On the other hand, it must be low enough to be competitive with other stores selling similar products.

Principles for Making Buying Decisions

1. Do you really need the item? Why do you need it?
2. Is this item worth the cost you must pay for it?
3. Could you buy an equal product for less money?
4. Would you be able to wait and save your money until later?
5. Are you buying this item to impress someone or to make yourself look important?
6. Are you buying this item to feed a bad habit?
7. Does this item fall outside the scope of your budget?

Example 1

Mr. Zachary uses a 35% markup rate on all his men's clothing lines. If he pays $15.50 apiece for slacks, what retail price should they sell for?

Solution:

$$\begin{aligned} \text{retail price} &= \text{cost} + 35\% \,(\text{cost}) \\ &= 15.50 + (0.35)(15.50) \\ &= 15.50 + 5.43 \\ &= \$20.93 \end{aligned}$$

Remarks:
1. Mr. Zachary may consider selling them at $19.95 because it seems much less expensive even though it is only 98 cents less.
2. The calculation can be made easier on your calculator by using the distributive law at step 2.

$$\begin{aligned} \text{retail price} &= 15.50 + (0.35)(15.50) \\ &= 15.50\,[1 + 0.35] \\ &= 15.50(1.35) \text{ Start here with calculator.} \\ &= \$20.93 \text{ (rounded up to nearest cent)} \end{aligned}$$

Example 2

Mary can buy clothes at the boutique where she works for only 5% over cost. She wants to get a dress that retails for $39.95. If the company uses a 28% markup rate, what is Mary's cost for the dress, including 5% sales tax?

Solution:
Since Mary doesn't have the store's cost at hand, that must be found first.

Recall that retail price = cost + 28% of cost. Let the unknown cost be x and substitute in the known retail price.

$$39.95 = x + 0.28x$$

Now solve for x, using the distributive law first.

$$39.95 = (1 + 0.28)x$$
$$39.95 = 1.28x$$

$$\frac{39.95}{1.28} = x$$

Therefore, the store's cost = $31.21.

$$\begin{aligned} \text{Mary's cost} &= \text{store cost} + 5\% \\ &= 31.21 + 5\%(31.21) \\ &= 31.21 + (0.05)(31.21) \\ &= (1.05)(31.21) \text{ using the distributive law again} \\ &= \$32.77 \\ +5\% \text{ sales tax:} &\quad \underline{\$\ 1.64} \\ \text{total:} &\quad \$34.41 \end{aligned}$$

Remarks: Why couldn't you just add 10% to the store's cost to get Mary's 5% charge plus the 5% tax? Notice: ($31.21)($1.10) = $34.33, which is smaller by 8 cents. The sales tax applies to the *total* selling price, including the 5% charge that Mary pays.

Example 3

Mr. Robbins wants to find the break-even point for sales for 200 sport coats. The coats cost him $17,290. He uses a markup of 25%, which he knows allows 10% for overhead and 15% for profit.

Solution:

The break-even point means he has sold enough coats so that he has recovered his cost of $17,290 and 10% for overhead, or $1,729.

Income needed for break-even point = $17,290 + $1,729 = $19,019

The cost of each coat = $\frac{\$17,290}{200}$ = $86.45

$$\text{Retail price} = \text{cost} + 25\%(\text{cost}) = 86.45 + 25\% \, (86.45)$$
$$= (1.25)(86.45)$$
$$= \$108.06$$

Now how many coats at this price equal $19,019?

$$\frac{19,019}{108.06} = 176 \text{ coats that must be sold to break even}$$

Remarks:
1. If Mr. Robbins cannot sell the remaining 24 coats $(200 - 176 = 24)$ at $108.06, he will not make 15% profit.
2. The likelihood of his selling every coat at full price is slight. It would be better to charge more initially and then sell as many as he can at a reduced price than to leave many unsold.

Example 4

Let's help Mr. Robbins sell his sports coats and not have to cut into his 15% profit margin. Since he can advertise from the 10% overhead and since a new shipment will draw eager buyers, let's price the coats at $129.95 and find the break-even point.

$$\frac{19,019}{129.95} = 146.36, \text{ or } 147 \text{ coats to break even}$$

Now let's have a half-price sale and hope that at least 40 of the remaining 53 sell $(200 - 147 = 53)$. Here's why:

$$129.95 \times 50\% = \$64.98 \text{ new price}$$

$$\text{profit} = 15\%(17,290) = \$2,593.50 \text{ profit he wants to make in dollars}$$

$$\frac{\text{amount of profit he wants to make}}{\text{cost per coat}} = \text{number of coats he must sell}$$

$$\frac{\$2,593.50}{\$64.98} = 39.9, \text{ or } 40 \text{ coats needed to sell}$$

At this point Mr. Robbins has 13 coats left. He has made $2,593.50 for profit and $1,729 for overhead. On Monday he advertises sports coats for $15 each and sells 8 for another $120 profit. The other 5 coats he sends to a charity for a tax credit.

What is his profit margin now?

$$\frac{\text{profit}}{\text{cost}} = \frac{2,593.50 + 120}{17,290} = 15.7\% \quad \text{Not a bad profit!}$$

Exercises

Find the retail price and the actual markup, given each wholesale cost and markup rate.
1. wholesale: $25.45
   markup rate: 18%
2. wholesale: $89.00
   markup rate: 27%
3. wholesale: $129.50
   markup rate: 35%
4. wholesale: $5.45
   markup rate: 59%
5. wholesale: $15.25
   markup rate: 31%
6. wholesale: $21,480
   markup rate: 16%

Find the markup and the markup rate, given the wholesale and retail costs.
7. wholesale: $11.20
   retail: $18.95
8. wholesale: $21.43
   retail: $29.99
9. wholesale: $55.00
   retail: $95.00
10. wholesale: $100
    retail: $200
11. wholesale: $49.50
    retail: $89.99
12. wholesale: $12,486.52
    retail: $16,983.86

Find the wholesale price, given the retail price and the markup rate.

13. retail: $19.95
markup rate: 38%

14. retail: $124.99
markup rate: 28%

15. retail: $9,253
markup rate: 18%

16. retail: $519.95
markup rate: 24%

17. retail: $89.99
markup rate: 24%

18. retail: $3.99
markup rate: 62%

Find the break-even point for sales of the following:

19. item: deck shoes
quantity: 500 pairs
wholesale: $16.45 each
overhead: 12.5%
profit: 16.5%

20. item: silk ties
quantity: 288
wholesale: $2,376 total
overhead: 10%
profit: 14%

21. item: 3-piece suits
quantity: 150
wholesale: $152 each
overhead: 14%
profit: 20%

22. item: wool skirts
quantity: 275
wholesale: $22.50 each
overhead: 12%
profit: 18%

23. item: blouses
quantity: 325
wholesale: $2,648.75 total
overhead: 10%
profit: 26%

24. item: dresses
quantity: 500
wholesale: $39.50 each
overhead: 12%
profit: 34%

25. Danny Blumenfeld is working up some prices for a shipment of 144 sweaters that cost $2,592 total. His store has an overhead rate of 14%, and he wants to break even at 100 sweaters. If his profit margin is 18% and he allows for 6 no-sellers, find the initial price and his lowest sale price.

26. Using 3 prices, Mr. Robbins sold 500 ties that cost him $2,500. He sold 150 at $10, 147 at $8.50, and all but 50 at a special sale price. If he maintained his overhead and profit margin as in Example 3 and broke even at 297 ties, what did he use for the last sale price? How did this price compare to his cost per tie?

27. In your own words, explain how a merchant can sell clothes below cost and still make a profit.

28. Mr. Robbins has 5 leather coats that he purchased for a total of $1,000.00. He had them priced at $250 for over a month but none sold. If he sells them at a 5%-off sale, what will happen to his profit margin? Use the overhead figure given in Example 3.

Uncover the Best Buys of
The Season and Save!
25% OFF
with this coupon
All our summer styles, plus selected
fall fashions. Included are dress
and casual wear by famous designers.
LARSON LORD & CO.

Sales and Discounts

In the last section you learned about clothing prices from the perspective of the sellers, focusing on how they establish prices and recover inventory costs. You saw that sales were an important technique in getting a merchant beyond the break-even point so that he makes a profit. For really large, nationwide companies, specials are used to increase volume; because their inventories are so large and so easily replenished, getting rid of the "last few" is not the same concept. They usually deal in small tail-end pieces of inventory only when items are being discontinued.

It is a fact of the market place that clothing sales primarily benefit people with somewhat uncommon sizes because there are fewer shoppers looking for odd sizes. However, don't give up on sales just because you are occasionally frustrated. Some stores will be better for you than others, and certain styles that tend to be conservative may not be popular but may meet your needs nicely. Whether the Lord puts you in a place of limited resources or whether you are just holding down expenses through good stewardship, you can have a good time shopping around as you stretch your "clothes dollar."

Popular clothes—what does that mean in your life? Have you become a victim of peer pressure, buying trendy, expensive clothes so that the popular crowd will accept you? Have you ever said something like, "I wouldn't be caught dead wearing clothes from that place"? If so, you have become a victim of pride. Furthermore, your dollars are ripe for picking by the sellers of designer clothes.

Examine this issue from two perspectives. First, if you observe objectively, among the so-called popular, sharp dressers among young people, you will often find an individual or two from wealthy homes. Price is no concern to them. The people they gather as followers, however, are often stretched financially to keep up with the styles. In fact, most of them could not keep up were it not for the sacrifices of parents. Often the entire earnings from a young person's part-time job will go to purchase expensive clothes. Nothing goes to the Lord's work, and nothing goes into savings. Then the resulting poor habits of stewardship plague that person for the rest of his life.

The second perspective lies with the clothes and their sellers. If the merchandisers can develop a catchy name and logo that becomes popular, they can capture the loyalty of the consumers, causing the laws of price competition to fail. The consumer no longer perceives the price as a basis for decisions. Why should a miniature emblem on the front of a sweater make it double in price? Only because the customer perceives it to be worth twice as much. Or suppose a seamstress makes two identical skirts. In one she places an unknown label and in the other, a label from a currently popular designer. Some young women would apparently prefer death to wearing a skirt they thought came from an outlet store; yet they would be willing to give a month's wages for the other simply because of the label. In fact, disreputable clothiers have taken advantage of Americans' slavish adoration for brand names by sewing imitation designer labels onto inexpensive clothing and selling it to retailers at exorbitant prices. Of course, there is good quality clothing and there is junk, but the presence or lack of a specific fashion designer's name is not the sole determiner of quality.

There are a few principles to keep in mind for saving with specials and sales:

1. If you don't need it, it's not a bargain.
2. Get there early, while the selection is good.
3. Beware of no-return policies.
4. Learn how to wait for the sales—especially after Christmas.
5. If it doesn't fit, don't buy it. Alterations can "eat up" everything you saved.

Sometimes you can buy clothes at an especially low price through going-out-of-business sales or other temporary bargains. By taking advantage of these low prices, you can save yourself money by buying next year's clothing today.

Example 1

Fonda can get a 20% discount at the ladies' shop where she works. If something is already on sale, she receives only a 10% discount on the sale price. What did she pay for the following three purchases, including 4% sales tax?

Solution:

Item One was not on sale, so her price

$$= \$21.99 - 20\%(21.99)$$
$$= (1 - 0.20)(21.99)$$
$$= (0.8)(21.99)$$
$$= \textbf{\$17.59}$$

Item Two is $\frac{1}{3}$ off, making the sale price $= \$14.99 - \frac{1}{3}(14.99)$
$$= (1 - \tfrac{1}{3})(14.99)$$
$$= (\tfrac{2}{3})(14.99)$$
$$= \$9.99$$

So Fonda's price for Item Two $= \$9.99 - 10\%(9.99)$
$$= (1 - 0.10)(9.99)$$
$$= (0.9)(9.99)$$
$$= \mathbf{\$8.99}$$

Item Three is 15% off, making the sale price $= \$39.99 - 15\%(39.99)$
$$= (1 - 0.15)(39.99)$$
$$= (0.85)(39.99)$$
$$= \$33.99$$

So her price for Item Three $= \$33.99 - 10\%(33.99)$
$$= (1 - 0.10)(33.99)$$
$$= (0.9)(33.99)$$
$$= \mathbf{\$30.59}$$

total of her 3 items: $\$17.59 + \$8.99 + \$30.59 =$ $\$57.17$
tax (4%) $=$ $\underline{\$2.29}$
total: $\mathbf{\$59.46}$

Example 2

Schaeffers' Shoe Store had a 25%-off sale last week, and this week the ad says you can get an additional 15% off if you bring in an old pair of shoes, regardless of their condition. How much discount do you get this week?

Solution:

This is an often-misunderstood principle. Some people add the rates, but the 15% is to be applied only to the sale cost rather than the original cost.

First let x be the original retail price; then find the first sale price.

Sale price $= x - 25\%x$
$$= (1 - 0.25)x \quad \text{(using the distributive law)}$$
$$= 0.75x$$

Since $0.75x$ is the sale price from last week, find the new sale price for this week.

New sale price $= (0.75x) - 15\%(0.75x)$
$$= (1 - 0.15)(0.75x) \quad \text{(using the distributive law)}$$
$$= (0.85)(0.75x)$$
$$= 0.638x$$
$$= 63.8\%x$$

If the new sale price is 63.8% of the original retail price, then the discount is 36.2%. (Subtract from 100%.)

Exercises

Find the sale price for each item, given the retail price and the discount.

1. retail: $9.99
   discount: $\frac{1}{3}$ off

2. retail: $19.95
   discount: 15%

3. retail: $25.00
   discount: $\frac{1}{4}$ off

4. retail: $59.99
   discount: 20%

5. retail: $119.95
   discount: 10%

6. retail: $199.99
   discount: $\frac{1}{2}$ price

Find the original retail price, given the discount and the sale price.

7. 15% off, now $29.50

8. 25% off, now $51.25

9. $\frac{1}{3}$ off, now $66

10. 20% off, now $42

Find the total percent of discount for the following purchases if an additional 10% senior-citizen's discount is given on the sale price.

11. was: $29.95
    sale price: $24.95

12. retail: $88.50
    discount: 15%

13. retail: $15.88
    discount: $\frac{1}{4}$ off

14. was: $65.95
    sale price: $49.95

15. retail: $30.00
    discount: 30% off

16. retail: $2,952.00
    discount: $\frac{1}{3}$ off

Find the amount and percent of the additional discount in each case, given the retail price, the first discount, and the new sale price.

17. retail: $84.95
    discount: 25% off
    now: $54.16

18. retail: $24.95
    discount: $\frac{1}{3}$ off
    now: $14.65

19. retail: $139.99
    discount: 15% off
    now: $71.39

20. retail: $555.55
    discount: 20% off
    now: $333.33

21. When the Millstone Men's Shop went out of business, they started out with a $\frac{1}{3}$-off sale. A week or two later they advertised 50% off the sale price of every item in the store. Last week they had a sign advertising 60% off any price from any previous sale. What is the discount percent if you bought something during this latest sale?

Catalog Buying

About a hundred years ago in the United States, people relied heavily on catalog buying. In those days catalogs were affectionately called "wish books." In this age the only advantage catalogs can offer is a better price. Unless you live in a rural area, you can find almost anything that's available in a catalog in a local store.

How can catalog companies offer lower prices? Most of them have low overhead costs and rely on volume sales. Low overhead comes from having a large warehouse facility instead of showrooms and display areas. Warehouses are relatively inexpensive compared to retail stores. The work force in terms of sales and stock people can be much smaller in a warehouse, and warehouse inventory work can be easily merchandised. In effect, the catalog company often gives the ordinary consumer a price that is close to wholesale. Besides the lower prices due to volume and low overhead, people who buy from an out-of-state company don't have to pay sales tax. Finally, the descriptions of clothes in a catalog often give far more information than the clerk in a store or the labels in the store clothes.

There are some disadvantages to catalog buying, however. In the first place, you may not have to pay sales tax, but you will pay for postage and handling. Depending on the item's price, its weight, and the shipping distance, the postage may be even more than sales tax. Second, many people balk at buying clothes via catalogs because they can't be sure that they will like what they receive: the fit, the color, and the quality of a garment cannot be determined by a photograph of it on a model. And of course, if you don't have the time to wait for the arrival of a mail-order item, that will be a serious disadvantage. Finally, if the company is out of something, you will receive a *back order* notice, stating that your order will be sent when their supplies are replenished. With some companies, it can be a long wait.

But you *can* save money with catalog buying, in spite of certain disadvantages. Many companies guarantee your complete satisfaction and will pay the return postage. After you have shopped around and know your local prices, you might want to try making a "wish book" purchase yourself.

Table 11.2
Typical Postage and Handling Rates

Amount of order	UPS — Parcel Post	Federal Express
$0.00-$25.00	$2.95	$10.00
$25.01-$50.00	$4.25	$12.00
$50.01-$100.00	$4.95	$13.00
$100.01-$150.01	$5.50	$13.50
Over $150.00	$6.00	$14.00

Example 1

Mrs. Cuthrell is comparing retail-store costs to catalog prices. She will have to pay postage and handling (P & H) with a catalog order but no sales tax. She isn't in a hurry; so United Parcel Service (UPS) or Parcel Post (PP) will be used instead of Federal Express (FE).

The retail price for her purchases would be $34.50, plus 5% sales tax. She can buy equal value for $28.95 in a catalog. Which is her best buy?

Solution:

The retail cost will be $34.50 + $1.73 (tax) = $36.23.

The catalog cost will be $28.95 + $4.25 (P & H from Table 11.2) = $33.20. (best)

Notes:
1. If Mrs. Cuthrell had needed the items within 48 hours and had chosen Federal Express, the P & H would have been $12.00, making a total of $40.95. (Being in a hurry costs more.)
2. Well-run catalog companies usually process an order within 2 days and use the 2-to-4 day service of UPS and Parcel Post. This means that you can call in an order and receive it in the same week.

Example 2

Jack Steele has decided to order some work clothes from the Wear Guard catalog. Four shirts, 4 pairs of pants, 2 pairs of gloves, 6 pairs of socks, 1 pair of shoes, and 1 coat will cost $237.38 plus P & H (UPS). Locally, this order would be $296.95 plus 5% sales tax. Find his savings and the percent discount he gets below retail.

Solution:
$$\text{retail cost} = \$296.95 + 14.85 \text{ (tax)} = \$311.80$$
$$\text{catalog cost} = \$237.38 + \$6.00 \text{ P \& H} = \$243.38$$
$$\text{savings} = \$68.42$$

Recall the percent equation and note that we need the rate.
$$\text{rate} \times \text{base} = \text{percentage}$$
$$(\text{rate}) \times 311.80 = 68.42$$
$$\text{rate} = \frac{68.42}{311.80}$$

$$\text{rate} = 0.219 = 21.9\% \text{ discount}$$

Example 3

Could we help Mr. Steele (Example 2) figure the cost of charging part of his purchase? He would like to pay about $50 per month. His charge card requires interest at $1\frac{1}{2}\%$ per month on the unpaid balance.

Solution:

When his statement arrives, it will have listed $243.38 for his work clothes. If he pays $50 before the close date, that will leave $193.38 unpaid balance. Since he wants to pay about $50, it will take 4 payments to clear the debt. In the finance tables under $i = 1\frac{1}{2}\%$ find the factor for the payment for a loan of $1.00.

$$
\begin{aligned}
\text{payment} &= \text{factor} \times \$193.38 \\
&= (0.259445)(\$193.38) \\
&= \$50.17
\end{aligned}
$$

Mr. Steele can make 4 payments of $50.17 to pay off the $193.38.

$$
\begin{aligned}
\text{total paid in} = 4 \times \$50.17 = &\quad \$200.68 \\
\text{amount financed} = &\quad \underline{\$193.38} \\
\text{interest} = &\quad \$7.30
\end{aligned}
$$

total cost of the work clothes goes to $243.38 + $7.30 = $250.68

Check his discount below retail again:

$$
\begin{array}{r}
\$311.80 \\
-250.68 \\
\hline
\$61.12 \text{ savings}
\end{array}
$$

$$
\begin{aligned}
\text{rate} \times \text{base} &= \text{percentage} \\
\text{rate} \times \$311.80 &= \$61.12 \\
\text{rate} &= \frac{61.12}{311.80} = 0.196 = 19.6\% \text{ discount}
\end{aligned}
$$

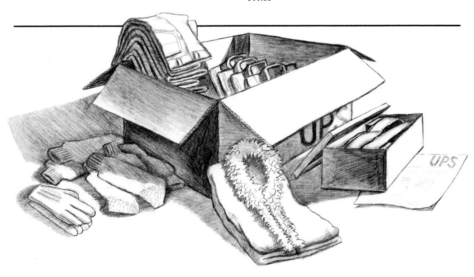

Example 4

The following catalog order for clothing uses the catalog page from the teacher's manual. Use this example as a guide while doing exercises 7-12.

CATALOG ORDER FORM
☐ Sure-Gro Seeds
☐ Health is Wealth Vitamins
☒ Perfect Fit Clothing

Print below only if name or address at right is incorrect, or missing. Is this an address change?
☐ Yes   ☒ No

First Name	Initial	Last Name

Name Jane   R   Doe

Street
Address _____ Rt. 9 Box 281

City Helena State MT ZIP _____

Daytime
Phone _____

DELIVER TO: Ship to another address? Give directions below:

Name _____

Street
Address _____ Rt. _____ Box _____

City _____ State _____ ZIP _____

Page #	STOCK NO.	Color	Size	Quan-tity	DESCRIPTION	-Price Each-	TOTAL PRICE
23	G99 B 0021	WHITE	M	2	MEN'S OXFORD CLOTH SHIRT	$12.99	25.98
23	R510-4674 E	NAVY	31-32	2	MEN'S CORDUROY SLACKS	23.00	46.00
23	R273-1347 D	80 GRAY	13	1	WOMEN'S CORDUROY SKIRT	18.00	18.00
23	R280-8806 D	15 CREAM	10	1	WOMEN'S BLOUSE	17.00	17.00
23	R-261-7751 D	02 ROSE	9/10	1	WOMEN'S QUILTED COAT	89.00	89.00

Payment Method:

☒ Check or money order enclosed

Charge my: ☐ Visa ☐ MasterCard ☐ American Express

Write Credit Card Account Number in boxes below:

Amount for Goods	195.98
SC Residents 5% sales Tax	
Standard Delivery Charge	6.00
Federal Express Delivery Charge	
Credits or Previous Balance	
TOTAL	201.98

_____   _____
Signature   Expiration Date

Exercises

In each question determine the savings, if any, and the percent discount below retail for the catalog purchases.

1. retail: $199.99
  sales tax: 4%
  catalog: $149.99
  P & H: FE

2. retail: $25.99
  sales tax: 6%
  catalog: $19.99
  P & H: UPS

3. retail: $145.99
  sales tax: 5%
  catalog: $119.99
  P & H: Parcel Post

4. retail: $12.99
  sales tax: 5%
  catalog: $9.99
  P & H: UPS

5. retail: $78.99
  sales tax: 4%
  catalog: $69.99
  P & H: FE

6. retail: $33.00
  sales tax: 5%
  catalog: $28.00
  P & H: Parcel Post

Using a copy of the order form and catalog pages provided from the teacher's manual, make out a catalog order for each question. Be sure to fill in each piece of required information, extend the unit prices, total the order, figure postage and handling, and get the remittance amount.

7. Vitamin C-300, 400 tablets
  Vitamin E Complex, 200 I.U. 100 capsules
  Multiple-Minerals, 100 tablets
  Fiber-Bran, 500 tablets

8. tomatoes, 2 pkt.
  potatoes, 9 lb.
  peppers, 2 pkt.
  peas, 5 lb.
  corn, 2 lb.
  beans, 2 lb.

9. two men's turtleneck shirts, size L, burgundy
  one pair men's cabin slippers, size 12
  one women's robe, size M, magenta
  one pair women's scuffs, size 7

10. Calcium, 250 tablets
  B-Complex, 300 tablets
  Vitamin A & D, 200 capsules
  Multiple Vitamins, 360 tablets
  Fiber-Bran, 1,000 tablets

11. marigolds, 1 pkt. yellow, 1 pkt. orange
  geraniums, 1 pkt. cherry, 2 pkt. scarlet
  carnations, 1 pkt.
  shrub rose, 3 plants
  pampas grass, 2 plants

12. two women's pullovers: size 5 in leather gray, size M in medium blue
  one men's sweatshirt, size XL, navy/green
  one men's sweatpants, size M, navy/green
  one pair men's leather walkers, size 12D
  two women's corduroy skirts, size 7 in black, size 11 in gray

Calculate the actual monthly payment for each charged order, given the total, down payment, approximate payment size or number of payments, and the interest rate per month. Use the finance tables.

13. order: $285.25
    down payment: $55
    payment size: about $45
    rate/month: 1.75%

14. order: $423.95
    down payment: $100
    no. of payments: 6
    rate/month: 2.0%

15. order: $185.50
    down payment: $25
    payment size: about $25
    rate/month: 1.5%

16. order: $361.18
    down payment: $60
    no. of payments: 5
    rate/month: 1.0%

17. Mr. Hassem called in this order to the Perfect Fit Clothing Company: 1 men's charcoal-colored wool mountain parka, size L; 2 white oxford-cloth shirts, size M; 1 pair leather walkers, size 12M. He paid 20% when the charge-card statement arrived and the balance in 3 equal monthly payments. Find the total cost of his order, including UPS postage. Find the initial payment and the 3 monthly payments if the interest rate is 18%(12). What did he pay for interest charges?

18. Use a copy of the catalog order form and make out an order for the following items from the Sure-Gro Seed Catalog: 4 lb. of green beans, 5 lb. of English peas, 9 lb. of white potatoes, $\frac{1}{8}$ oz. of tomato seed, 4 begonia bulbs, 2 pkt. of rose geranium seed, and 1 pkt. gold marigold seed. (Use UPS delivery and tax if within the state.)

Making Your Own Clothes ————

Have you ever wondered who makes those adorable clothes you see in the stores? It may surprise you that ordinary working people sitting at sewing machines produce all the clothes you see in stores. Of course, they must get the job by possessing a certain degree of skill and knowledge about sewing. Some of them, through talent and practice, become extremely skilled and produce nearly flawless products. Since they are human beings, however, they do make their share of mistakes. Flawed clothing that is still acceptable to the consumer is sold in outlet stores under the title of *seconds*.

Although far more women than men sew clothing, the profession is open to both. Women who sew for a living are called *seamstresses,* while the men are called *tailors*. With very little training, lots of practice, and the desire to learn, you can learn to sew good quality clothing for yourself and your family. You will need a good sewing machine and a few incidentals like scissors, pins, needles, and measuring tape. Of course, each garment will require a pattern, fabric, and notions such as buttons, zippers, thread, and interfacing.

Example 1

Mrs. Brooks is making a dress to wear at her daughter's wedding. Find the total cost of materials using the quantities from the pattern and the unit prices. Use 5% sales tax.

Solution:

1 pattern at $5.75	5.75
$2\frac{1}{2}$ yd. linen at $5.99/yd.	14.98
$\frac{1}{2}$ yd. interfacing at $1.39/yd.	.70
1 20" zipper at $.85 each	.85
1 card buttons at $.85 each	.85
1 large spool thread at $1.15 each	1.15
subtotal:	24.28
5% tax:	1.20
total:	$25.48

Note: Although it would be difficult to compare this dress to one from a retail store, the price range may be $90 up to $150, depending on the store.

Example 2

Adrienne is trying to decide whether to buy a wool skirt on sale for $22.99 or to make one like it at home. All she needs is the fabric and a pattern. The pattern costs $3.75 and requires $1\frac{5}{8}$ yards of 60"-wide fabric. In 60" material, a wool blend costs $8.00/yd., and a 100% wool flannel costs $12.99/yd. Determine the cost of each option and help her decide.

Solution:

The wool blend skirt:

1 pattern =	$ 3.75
$1\frac{5}{8}$ yd. at $8.00/yd. =	$13.00
subtotal =	$16.75
5% tax =	$ 0.84
total =	$17.59

The 100% wool skirt:

1 pattern =	$ 3.75
$1\frac{5}{8}$ yd. at $12.99/yd. =	$21.11
subtotal =	$24.86
5% tax =	1.24
total =	$26.10

Remarks:
1. The wool skirt at the store sale will cost Adrienne $24.14, tax included. She can save $6.55 by making the wool-blend skirt. The 100% wool flannel would cost more than the store garment.
2. Her final decision should be based on a comparison between the material in the store skirt and the wool blend proposed for the less expensive home-made skirt.
3. If she makes the wool-blend skirt, her percent savings will be . . .

$$\frac{\$6.55}{\$24.14} = 0.27 = 27\%$$

Example 3

Mrs. Matthews makes half of the clothes for her two girls. Her records show that she saves 35% over retail prices. The family budget allows $350 per year per girl. How much would she spend per year for her two girls if she did not sew their clothes?

Solution:

Ignore taxes and just suppose that they are part of the cost. The total cost for both girls is $700; so the 50% (half) that can be attributed to Mrs. Matthew's sewing efforts is $350. Since she saves 35% over retail, the $350 represents 65% of the retail-store cost.

$$\text{Recall: rate} \times \text{base} = \text{percentage}$$
$$65\%(x) = \$350$$
$$0.65x = 350$$
$$x = \frac{350}{0.65} = \$538.46 \text{ retail value}$$

$350 + $538.46 = $888.46 per year for clothes for her girls

Note: $888.46 − $700 = a yearly savings of $188.46

Exercises

Find the cost of the fabric yardage for each pattern and the given unit prices.

1. men's shirt:
   3¼ yd. of 45″ fabric
   cotton/polyester $3.99/yd.

2. women's blouse:
   2 yd. of 45″ fabric
   88% cotton $8.99/yd.

3. men's vest:
   shell 1⅜ yd. of 45″ fabric
   lining 1⅜ yd. of 45″ fabric
   cotton corduroy shell $3.99/yd. (45″)
   75% polyester lining $2.49/yd. (45″)

4. women's skirt:
   1½ yd. of 60″ fabric
   1½ yd. of 45″ lining
   linen skirt fabric (60″) $5.99/yd.
   cotton/polyester lining (45″) $2.49/yd.

5. men's pants:
   2¾ yd. of corduroy at $3.99/yd.

6. women's dress:
   3⅜ yd. of 45″ fabric
   polyester blend (45″) at $4.99/yd.

Find the savings realized by making family clothes, given the budget, the percent of clothes made, and the percent of savings over retail.

7. budget: $800
   25% homemade
   30% savings

8. budget: $500
   35% homemade
   50% savings

9. budget: $380
   50% homemade
   35% savings

10. budget: $725
    28% homemade
    22% savings

11. budget: $565
    62% homemade
    20% savings

12. budget: $1,200
    40% homemade
    32% savings

Using the price list below and the data in each problem about materials and retail costs, contrast the cost of purchased clothing to self-made clothes. Give the amount of savings, if any, by using home-manufactured clothes. Use 5% sales tax.

Materials and Prices

60" wool blend $7.99/yd.
60" polyester sports cloth $3.99/yd.
60" cotton denim $4.99/yd.
45" cotton/polyester blend $3.99/yd.
45" 100% cotton muslin $2.29/yd.
45" cotton corduroy $3.99/yd.
buttons—6 at $.75/card
buttons—3 at $.80/card

zipper—7" $.60
zipper—22" $1.00
thread $1.15/large spool
ladies' 3-pc. suit pattern $5.75
ladies' skirt pattern $3.75
men's shirt pattern $4.25
men's pants pattern $4.75
pocket liners $4.50/4 count

13. ladies' 3-pc. suit, retail: $83
    1 pattern
    3½ yd. wool blend
    1½ yd. polyester sports cloth
    1 7" zipper
    1 card of 6 buttons
    2 spools thread

14. ladies' skirt, retail: $19.95
    1 pattern
    1⅛ yd. cotton denim
    1 7" zipper

15. men's shirt, retail: $15.95
    1 pattern
    3¼ yd. cotton/polyester blend
    2 cards of 6 buttons

16. men's pants, retail: $25.00
    1 pattern
    2¾ yd. cotton corduroy
    1 7" zipper
    1 set of pocket liners

Chapter 11 Review ———————————————

back order
bait and switch
break-even point
buying cooperatives
calories
comparison shopping
energy certificate
inventory
markup

nutrition
overhead
pay-back period
product coupon
profit
seamstress
seconds
tailor
unit pricing

Review Exercises

Using unit prices, determine which container is the better buy.

1. potatoes:
15 lb. for $3.00
5 lb. for $1.15

2. bread:
1.5-lb. loaf for $.95
2-lb. loaf for $1.10

3. chicken:
3.25 lb. for $3.22
5.5 lb. for $6.55

4. cookies:
12 oz. for $1.35
16 oz. for $2.40

5. peanut butter:
40 oz. for $3.69
12 oz. for $1.27

6. pinto beans:
2 lb. for $.79
5 lb. for $1.89

Find the cost per serving for each purchase.

7. serving size: $2\frac{1}{2}$ oz.
container: 40 oz.
price: $3.69

8. serving size: 4 oz.
container: $1\frac{3}{4}$ lbs.
price: $2.75

9. serving size: 200 ml
container: 2 liter
price: $1.05

10. serving size: $\frac{1}{16}$ of a melon
price: $2.72 per melon

Find the final cost of groceries, tax included, and the percent savings for the given original cost of the groceries and the given value of the coupons. Use 6% for sales tax.

11. groceries: $58.20
coupons: $7.15

12. groceries: $115.85
coupons: $9.85

13. groceries: $38.41
coupons: $5.20

14. groceries: $41.15
coupons: $6.80

Given the weekly budget, the percent presented in coupons, and a sales tax of 4%, find the values of the groceries before tax and coupons, and the dollar value of the coupons.

15. budget: $38
coupons: 3%

16. budget: $42
coupons 4%

17. budget: $55
coupons: $6\frac{1}{2}$%

18. budget: $68
coupons: 5%

Find the annual cost of owning and operating a refrigerator-freezer with a life expectancy of 20 years, one major repair at 7% of purchase price, and the given energy data.

19. price: $925
    1,645 kWh per year
    rate: 6.3¢ per kWh

21. price: $1,420
    $83 per year @ 6.5¢ per kWh
    rate: 7.4¢ per kWh

20. price: $1,175
    1,440 kWh per year
    rate: 5.9¢ per kWh

22. price: $829
    $72 per year @ 6.25¢ per kWh
    rate: 8.1¢ per kWh

23. Find the payback period for the unit in problem 21 if it helps a family save 11% on a weekly budget of $75.

Find the number of calories available in each meal.

24. breakfast:
    1 cup orange juice, canned, unsweetened
    1 cup oatmeal with 0.5 cup skim milk and
    1 T. sugar
    1 slice whole-wheat toast (no butter)

25. lunch:
    1 bologna sandwich:
       2 slices white bread
       1 T. mayonnaise
    12-oz. glass of regular cola
    10 french fries—deep fat

26. supper:
    0.5 cup frozen green peas (cooked)
    0.5 cup mashed potatoes (butter and
    milk)
    2 dinner rolls (plain, enriched)
    6 oz. beef liver, fried

Find the number of calories expended on each activity or series of activities. Use Table 11.2.

27. Reinhardt Heintz, 160 lb.
    7 hours of carpentry labor

28. Mark Champlain, 112 lb.
    6 hours of typing
    1 hour of standing
    1 hour of walking

29. Stan Matthia, 125 lb.
    8 hours of sleep
    12 hours of walking
    4 hours of sitting

30. Rose Mary Miller, 105 lb.
    45 minutes of swimming
    2.5 hours of bicycling
    1.25 hours of walking
    30 minutes of sitting

Find the markup and the retail price for each given wholesale cost and markup rate.

31. wholesale: $18.50
  markup rate: 15%

32. wholesale: $520.00
  markup rate: 75%

33. wholesale: $65.00
  markup rate: 8%

34. wholesale: $115.50
  markup rate: 25%

Find the wholesale cost for each retail price and markup rate.

35. retail: $29.95
  markup rate: 15%

36. retail: $41.50
  markup rate: 104%

37. retail: $1,585
  markup rate: 22%

38. retail: $8,950
  markup rate: 3%

Find the total percent of discount for the following purchases if an additional 15% senior citizen's discount is also given on the sale price.

39. was: $50.00
  sale price: $42.50

40. retail: $195.95
  sale: 25% off

41. was: $118.00
  sale price: $90.00

42. retail: $19.95
  sale: 20% off

Determine the savings, if any, and the percent discount below retail for each catalog order. Assume that there is no sales tax on these catalog orders.

43. retail: $56.80
  tax: 5%
  catalog: $41.00
  P & H: UPS

44. retail: $255.00
  tax: 6%
  catalog: $200
  P & H: F. E.

45. retail: $82.45
  tax: 4%
  catalog: $75.50
  P & H: Par. Post.

Find the savings realized by making family clothes, given the budget, percent of clothes made, and the percent of savings over retail.

46. budget: $490
  30% homemade
  25% savings

47. budget: $1,000
  50% homemade
  32% savings

48. budget: $825
  25% homemade
  18% savings

49. Vince Petrona has a china and pottery shop in the West Towne Mall. He recently purchased 1,000 stoneware settings for $20,000. If his business requires 15% for overhead and he wants 20% profit, what is his break-even point?

50. When the Wilderness Outfitters Shop went out of business, they began with a 20%-off sale. Two weeks later they advertised 60% off every item in the store. Last week the sign in the window said 70% off any price for any previous sale. What is the discount percent below the original price for an item purchased during this latest sale?

Housing

The decisions you make about housing should demand even greater care than those concerning the purchase of an automobile. After all, you might be committing yourself to a contract in which you promise to pay a lending institution a certain amount of money every month for 25 or 30 years. And even if you decide to rent, there are factors to be weighed and details to be examined before you make the decision of what or where to rent. But all such decisions must follow the path of prayer and the Lord's guidance. When you seek the Lord's wisdom for decision-making, there comes a certain peace that He will open and close the doors of opportunity as He desires.

The *location* of a home to buy or rent may be one of the very first factors to evaluate. First, the type of neighborhood should be one that is improving rather than decaying so that your investment in a home will not depreciate. Second, the *price* of the house or the *cost* of renting will also have to be within your financial means. You cannot expect to live in an area that is very nice but where the costs are way over your head. You may have to lower your level of expectation somewhat. Also, the location of the housing in proximity to your church and work will be a definite financial benefit. To illustrate this truth, imagine a man who buys a house 10 miles farther from his work than another possible house. If he drives to and from work 5 days a week, this man's choice will make him drive 100 miles farther each week. If you allow one week per year sick leave and two weeks' vacation, he drives to work 49 weeks per year. This makes 4,900 extra miles per year. Now if you take an approximate per-mile cost of 23 cents (see Chapter 10), the man pays $1,127 per year more. Lastly, if he owns the home for 30 years and keeps driving to the same job, it will cost him $33,810 extra during those thirty years. That is a lot to pay for a decision that may have been made with almost no forethought! Learn now the ways to avoid such unnecessary costs.

Renting or Leasing
Buying a Home—Mortgages
Down Payment and Monthly Payment
Interest Paid on a Mortgage
Outstanding Balance and Owner's Equity
Building a House
Review

Renting or Leasing

Most people have to start out renting a house, apartment, or mobile home until they can save enough money for a down payment on a house. Most *unfurnished* rental housing comes with kitchen appliances and no other furniture, whereas *furnished* housing has everything but dishes and linens. Of course, unfurnished housing is normally the less expensive of the two, provided the size and number of bedrooms is equal.

How much should you be willing to pay for housing? The rule of thumb says to pay no more than one-fourth of your monthly salary, or about one week of pay. It would be wise to base that amount on your take-home salary. What are some other costs associated with renting? Most *landlords*—owners of rental housing—require one month's rent paid in advance plus a *security deposit* equal to one month's rent. (This deposit is his insurance that he will be reimbursed if you damage the property.) So to rent a house for $425 per month, you will have to pay $850 up front. You will also have to arrange for telephone, power, and water to be supplied to the house you are going to rent. The utility companies may require a deposit and connection fee. They will especially want a deposit if you have never been their customer before. Typically, the deposit for power and telephone service is about $50 to $100. *Tenants* are the people doing the renting. In unfurnished apartments or houses they are encouraged to buy insurance on their belongings, since the landlord will have insurance only on the building.

Some people who rent out apartments and houses require the tenant to sign a *lease.* This is a written contract between the landlord and the tenant that they both sign. The lease states in writing the conditions under which the property is rented. Among other things, it states the amount of rent, length of occupancy, renewability, payment due date, amount of security deposit, conditions resulting in forfeiture of deposit, acceptance of pets and children, terminating procedures, and whether alterations are allowed.

Example 1

How much monthly rent can a couple afford for an apartment if their combined yearly incomes are $34,200?

Solution:
First find their combined monthly income.

$$\frac{34,200}{12} = \$2,850 \text{ per month}$$

Using the "one-fourth of income principle," we get . . .

$$\frac{2,850}{4} = \$712.50 \text{ per month}$$

Example 2

How much will it cost up front for a couple to move into an apartment that rents for $385 per month? They will need one month's rent for security deposit, $80 for power deposit, $30 for telephone deposit, and $25 for water deposit.

Solution:

rent:	$385
deposit:	$385
power deposit:	$ 80
telephone deposit:	$ 30
water deposit:	$ 25
	$905 up-front cost

Remarks:
1. Many utilities charge a deposit equal to one-half the typical monthly service.
2. When a customer has made a satisfactory payment record for 18 to 24 months, most utilities will refund his deposit with interest.
3. If a customer within a given service area of a public utility changes location by moving to new housing, the utility generally will not require a deposit unless the customer has a poor payment record.

Example 3

Suppose that the couple in Example 2 have maintained a satisfactory utility-payment record for 24 months. How much money will they get back from their utility deposits if the companies pay 6%(12)?

Solution:
They have $135 in principal $(80 + 30 + 25)$, which has been invested at $i = \frac{6}{12} = \frac{1}{2}\%$ for $n = 24$.

$$\begin{aligned} \text{Amount} &= \text{principal } x \cdot (1 + i)^n \\ &= \$135(1.005)^{24} \\ &= \$135(1.127160) \\ &= \$152.17 \end{aligned}$$

Note: Use the finance table for the factor $(1 + i)^n$. It will be under the compound amount column.

Example 4

If the couple in Example 1 finds an apartment for $400 per month and saves the rest of their housing budget, how long will it take them to save $10,000 for a down payment on a house? Assume that they can earn 8%(12).

Solution:

First find the amount available to save.

$$\$712.50 - \$400 = \$312.50 \text{ available}$$

$$\text{Amount saved} = \text{payment} \cdot \text{factor}$$

$$\$10,000 = \$312.50(x)$$

Notice that we know the payment and the amount; so by dividing we obtain the value of the amount-saved factor from the finance tables.

$$x = \frac{10,000}{312.50} = 32.0$$

Ordinarily we would look up the factor to find the amount saved (or the payment). This time we need the number of periods; so we look under $i = \frac{8\%}{12} = \frac{2}{3}\%$ and find a factor that just exceeds 32.0. The table will look like this:

.6 %	n	Amount of $1 at Comp. Int.	Amount Saved for $1/Period	Payment to Save $1
	26	1.1885785659	28.2867848782	0.0353521973
	27	1.1965024230	29.4753634440	0.0339266385
	28	1.2044791058	30.6718658670	0.0326031681
	29	1.2125089665	31.8763449728	0.0313712253
SEMIANNUALLY →	30	1.2205923596	→ 33.0888539392	0.0302216572
If compounded	31	1.2287296420	34.3094462988	0.0291464919
semiannually,	32	1.2369211729	35.5381759408	0.0281387543
nominal annual rate is	33	1.2451673141	36.7750971138	0.0271923143
	34	1.2534684295	38.0202644279	0.0263017634
$1^1/_3\%$	35	1.2618248857	39.2737328574	0.0254623110

Thirty payments, in this case 30 months, will be required. This is $2\frac{1}{2}$ years.

Note: They will actually have ($312.5)(33.088853) = $10,340.27.

Remarks:
1. In the section entitled "Down Payment and Monthly Payment" you will find out how big a house they can buy with this down payment.
2. This savings project will take considerable self-discipline. Along the way, there will be many temptations to spend the money on other supposedly important things.

Exercises

Find the monthly rent that could be paid based on the "one-fourth of income" principle. Round to the nearest dollar.

1. Yearly income: $24,500

2. Weekly income: $380

3. Semimonthly income: $860

4. Yearly income: $38,400

5. Weekly income: $280

6. Semimonthly income: $580

Find the up-front cost of occupying each rental property.

7. Rent: $325 per month
Deposit: $\frac{1}{2}$ month's rent
Power: $\frac{1}{24}$ of annual cost of $780
Water: $\frac{1}{2}$ quarterly charge of $48

8. Rent: $625 per month
Deposit: one month's rent
Utilities: former qualified customer

9. Rent: $125 per week
Deposit: 2 weeks' rent
Utilities: 1 week's rent

10. Rent: $415 per month
Deposit: $\frac{1}{20}$ the annual rent
Power: $80
Telephone: $35
Water: $15

11. Rent: $800 per month
Deposit: $\frac{1}{20}$ the annual cost
Power: $100
Telephone: former customer
Water: $18

12. Rent: $89 per week
Deposit: 3 weeks' rent
Power: $50
Water: $20
Gas: $15

Find the amount of each refunded security deposit, given the original amount deposited, the number of months left with the utility, and the interest rate.

13. Deposit: $85
Term: 18 months
Rate: 4%(4)

14. Deposit: $215
Term: 24 months
Rate: 6%(12)

15. Deposit: $110
Term: 20 months
Rate: 5%(12)

16. Deposit: $50
Term: 36 months
Rate: 6%(4)

17. Deposit: $290
Term: 15 months
Rate: 7%(12)

18. Deposit: $64
Term: 21 months
Rate: 8%(4)

19. The McGregor family has an annual income of $26,500. They rent a mobile home for $275 per month. Using the one-fourth of income principle, find how much they can save per month for a down payment of $12,800 on a house. Also find how long it will take them if their money is invested at 6%(12).

20. The Scheiderer family has an annual income of $45,888. They are renting a farmhouse for $585 per month. Using the one-fourth of income principle, find how much they can save per month and how long it will take to save $20,000. Assume an interest rate of 10%(12).

Buying a Home—Mortgages

When you have enough money saved for a down payment and when you have spent time in prayer for guidance, it's time to ask yourself a few practical questions:

1. Is the location economical and appreciating?
2. Does the home meet my needs for space and personal preferences?
3. Can I afford the purchase price in terms of down payments and monthly payment?
4. If the home needs repair, has the price been lowered to compensate?
5. Does the price of the home compare favorably with others of similar size in the neighborhood?
6. Does the debt that I incur with the purchase of the home still leave my total indebtedness under 2.5 times my annual income?

When you have finally arrived at favorable answers to the questions above, you're ready to arrange for a home loan, called a mortgage. With a *mortgage* you will be paying interest to a bank for the use of their money to pay whatever part of the purchase price your down payment does not cover. Some mortgages have *fixed* rates of interest throughout their 20-to-30-year life; whatever rate it starts at will remain. On the other hand, *adjustable-rate mortgages (ARM)* change rates every year or two according to a process related to current prime-interest rates. ARM mortgages are more common during times of inflation, when interest rates are climbing rapidly.

Most people are unprepared for the *closing costs* associated with a mortgage. Some of the costs are charged by the lending institution, while others come from legal and technical requirements. These charges are called closing costs because several of them are paid at the time of the legal transfer of the property—called the *closing date*. The table below gives a list of closing costs, including some typical amounts charged. Several of the terms are defined in the notes below the table.

Table 12.1
Sample Mortgage Closing Costs

I. *Costs payable to the lending institution:*

points (average $3\frac{1}{2}$) .... 3.5% of the loan value

title insurance .... $15 + $3.50 per $1,000 loan value

origination fee .... 1.5% of loan (up to $29,999),
                                      1% of loan ($30,000—$60,000),
                                      or 0.5% of loan (over $60,000)

TRETS fee $50

II. *Costs payable to others:*

property survey $150

appraisal (value of home) $200

credit report (credit rating of
     borrower) $50

attorney fee .... 1% of the loan value

document stamps .... $1.00 per $1,000 loan value

recording of deed and mortgage ..... $0.35 per $1,000 loan value

mortgage insurance .... $2.50 per $1,000 loan value

termite inspection $75

Remarks:

1. *Points* is a term used by the lender to state how much of a discount charge he will subtract from the face value of the loan. One point equals one percent. If the lender charges 2 points on a $10,000 loan, he would subtract 2%($200) and give the borrower $9,800. The $200 becomes a prepaid interest charge because the borrower will still have to pay back $10,000.
2. *Origination fee* is the lender's charge to originate, or create, the loan, including all paperwork and documentation.
3. *TRETS fee* stands for Transatlantic Real Estate Tax Service and is sometimes abbreviated to *RETS*. It ensures that the taxes on the property get paid during the period of the loan.

Example 1

Find the costs charged by a lending institution for a $45,000 home loan. Use Table 12.1.

Solution:

$3\frac{1}{2}$ points means we take $3\frac{1}{2}\%$ of $45,000:

$$(0.035)(\$45,000) = \$1,575$$

1% origination fee means we take 1% of $45,000:

$$(0.01)(\$45,000) = \$450$$

Title insurance is $15 + 3.50 \times 45 = \$172.50$.

The TRETS fee is $50.

Total of four charges is $2,247.50.

Notice this charge as a percentage of the loan.

$$\text{rate} \times \text{base} = \text{percentage}$$
$$\text{rate} \times (45,000) = \$2,247.50$$
$$\text{rate} = \frac{2,247.50}{45,000} = 0.0499 = 4.99\%$$

Example 2

Find the closing costs, not payable to the lender, for a $45,000 loan.

Solution:

Since only four of those costs require a calculation, we do them first and then add in the others.

$$\begin{aligned}
\text{attorney fee} &= 1\% \times \text{loan value}\\
&= (0.01)(45,000)\\
&= \mathbf{\$450}
\end{aligned}$$

$$\begin{aligned}
\text{document stamps} &= \$1.00 \times \text{loan value in thousands}\\
&= (1.00)(45)\\
&= \mathbf{\$45}
\end{aligned}$$

$$\begin{aligned}
\text{recording deed} &= 0.35 \times 45\\
&= \mathbf{\$15.75}
\end{aligned}$$

$$\begin{aligned}
\text{mortgage insurance} &= 2.50 \times 45\\
&= \mathbf{\$112.50}
\end{aligned}$$

total all the charges:

survey:	$150.00
appraisal:	$200.00
credit report:	$ 50.00
attorney fee:	$450.00
documentation stamps:	$ 45.00
recording:	$ 15.75
mortgage:	$112.50
termite:	$ 75.00
total of charges:	**$1,098.25**

Note: The total closing costs for the $45,000 loan would be . . .

$$\$2,247.50 + \$1,098.25 = \$3,345.75$$

As a percent of the loan value, this is found as . . .

$$\text{rate} = \frac{\$3,345.75}{\$45,000} = 0.074 = 7.4\%$$

Example 3

The Carper family has an annual income of $28,000. If they already owe $4,500 for an automobile, how much could they borrow for a home?

Solution:

$$
\begin{aligned}
\text{maximum indebtedness} &= \quad 2.5 \times \text{annual salary} \\
&= \quad 2.5 \times 28,000 \\
&= \quad \$70,000 \\
\text{less outstanding loans:} &\quad \underline{-\$4,500} \\
\text{maximum home loan} &= \quad \$65,500
\end{aligned}
$$

Remarks:

If you compare the monthly payment for a $65,500 loan to the principle of housing costs at one-fourth the income, you will usually find the one-fourth rule to be more conservative. The latter rule gives an acceptable payment of about $583 per month with a $28,000 income. But the $65,500 loan would require over $700 per month.

Example 4

If Mr. Carper gets a loan at City Bank, they will charge points, and he will receive $63,207.50. How many points is City Bank charging?

Solution:

The discount is $65,500 - \$63,207.50 = \$2,297.50$. Find what percent of the loan this represents.

$$
\begin{aligned}
\text{rate} \times \text{base} &= \quad \text{percentage} \\
\text{rate} \times (\$65,500) &= \quad \$2,292.50 \\
\text{rate} &= \quad \frac{\$2,292.50}{65,500} = 0.035 = 3.5\%
\end{aligned}
$$

Since each percent is a point, the charge is $3\frac{1}{2}$ points.

Exercises

Find the points discount for each loan given.

1. loan: $32,000

    points: $1\frac{1}{2}$

2. loan: $62,000

    points: 3

3. loan: $81,000

    points: $2\frac{1}{2}$

4. loan: $25,000

    points: $5\frac{1}{2}$

5. loan: $57,000

    points: $3\frac{1}{4}$

6. loan: $72,500

    points: $1\frac{3}{4}$

Find the points charged for each loan, given the loan value and the proceeds. (*Proceeds* is the money the borrower actually receives after the discount is removed.)

7. loan: $36,000

    proceeds: $34,920

8. loan: $58,500

    proceeds: $57,622.50

9. loan: $93,500

    proceeds: $89,292.50

10. loan: $22,000

    proceeds: $21,670

11. loan: $67,500

    proceeds: $63,956.25

12. loan: $84,600

    proceeds: $81,427.50

Using Table 12.1, find all the closing costs for the following loans. If a different value is to be used for any of the charges stated in Table 12.1, it will be stated with the loan value.

13. loan: $30,000

    points: $2\frac{1}{4}$

    attorney: $1\frac{1}{2}\%$

14. loan: $64,500

    points: $3\frac{3}{4}$

    attorney: 2%

15. loan: $81,600

    points: $1\frac{3}{4}$

    attorney: $1\frac{1}{4}\%$

16. Find what percent of the loan value the closing costs in problems 13-15 represent.

Find the maximum indebtedness for each family, given their income.

17. income: $15,900/year

18. income: $285/week

19. income: $1,350/month

20. income: $33,500/year

21. income: $560/week

22. income: $2,520/month

23. Mike Matthews is hoping to buy a home soon. He has $11,500 saved for a down payment and other costs. He knows that putting $10,000 down will leave a $40,000 loan. Find his closing costs if the points are $3\frac{1}{4}$ and the attorney's fee is $1\frac{1}{2}\%$ of loan value. How much more money will he need to save in order to pay the closing costs?

24. A home is advertised for $69,500 with a required down payment of 20%. What size of an annual income would a buyer need to purchase this home? How much money is needed for the down payment? How much money would be needed for closing costs if the lender charges $4\frac{1}{2}$ points? How long would it take to save the down payment and closing costs at $275 per month receiving 8%(12)?

Down Payment and Monthly Payment

Now that you understand how closing costs are determined, it's time to examine down payments and monthly payments. What determines the size of a down payment? The company that is responsible for the loan if the borrower defaults determines the amount of down payment required. A *conventional* loan belongs to a commercial bank; they usually require 20% down. An *FHA* loan is backed by the Federal Housing Administration, which often allows as low as 3% to 5% down payments. A *VA* loan, backed by the Veterans' Administration, is available only to United States military veterans and often requires no down payment on a small loan.

The amount of a loan that a borrower must get from a bank, called the *principal,* begins to accrue interest the very next day. At the end of one month, the borrower's first payment will pay off the interest for that month and a portion of the principal. The amount that goes toward interest is very large when the loan begins. For example, a $45,000 loan at 12%(12) would accrue 1% of $45,000, or $450, during the first month. Of course, the payment must be larger than this, or the principal will never decrease, and the loan will exist forever. To keep the monthly payment from being too large, most home loans are for 20 to 30 years. In the following examples, you will see how to calculate down payments and monthly payments. You will also see how changing the length of the loan, called the *term* of the loan, will affect the size of the payment and the amount of principal decreased with each payment.

Example 1

Using a conventional loan that requires 25% down, how much money must be provided for the down payment on an $84,500 house?

Solution:

Find 25% of the cost of the house.

$$25\%(\$84,500) = (0.25)(\$84,500) = \$21,125$$

Note: The most you could borrow with a conventional loan for this house is $84,500 − $21,125 = $63,375.

Example 2

Find the monthly payment for a 30-year loan to buy the house in Example 1. The interest rate is 14%(12).

Solution:

You are looking for the *payment to borrow* $63,375 at $i = \frac{14\%}{12} = 1\frac{1}{6}\%$.

Also, 30 years times $\frac{12 \text{ months}}{\text{year}} = 360$ payments.

payment $R = \$63,375 \times$ (factor)   Find the factor under 360 where $i = 1\frac{1}{6}\%$.
     $= (\$63,375)(0.011848718)$
     $= \$750.92$ (rounded from $750.9124722)

Note: You round *up* to the nearest cent if any nonzero number occurs in the third place to the right of the decimal. This method of rounding is only used for mortgage payments.

Example 3

In Example 2, how much of the first monthly payment goes to principal and how much to interest?

Solution:

Since $i = 1\frac{1}{6}\%$ per month, find the interest that accrues the first month.

Note: $1\frac{1}{6}\% \approx 0.0116666667$

$$(1\frac{1}{6}\%)(\$63,375) = \$739.38 \text{ to interest}$$

Now take the difference between payment and interest.

$$\$750.92 - \$739.38 = \$11.54 \text{ to principal}$$

Note: Now you can also find the new balance after the first payment is made.

$$\$63,375.00 - \$11.54 = \$63,363.46 \text{ (new balance)}$$

Example 4

Do Example 2 for a 25-year loan and see how the payment changes. Also do Example 3 for the new payment.

Solution:

$i = 1\frac{1}{6}\%$ (unchanged), but $n = 12 \times 25 = 300$ payments

$$
\begin{aligned}
\text{payment} \quad &= \$63,375 \times \text{payment to borrow factor} \\
&= (\$63,375)(0.01203761) \\
&= \$762.89 \text{ (about \$12 more per month)}
\end{aligned}
$$

The same amount still goes to interest for the first period; that is $739.38.

$$
\begin{aligned}
\text{The amount to principal} \quad &= \$762.89 - \$739.38 \\
&= \$23.51
\end{aligned}
$$

Remark: In the next section you will see how $12 more per month paid toward the principal will affect the total interest paid over the life of the loan.

Many banks provide a computer-generated *amortization schedule* for their customers. As you should remember, to "amortize" means to pay back a loan through installments that periodically decrease the outstanding principal (or debt). Below is a portion of an amortization schedule for the loan in Examples 1 and 2.

Sample Amortization Schedule

Payment No.	Payment	Interest Paid	Principal Paid	Loan Balance
0				$63,375.00
1	$750.92	$739.38	$11.54	$63,363.46
2	$750.92	$739.24	$11.68	$63,351.78
3	$750.92	$739.10	$11.82	$63,339.96
4	$750.92	$738.97	$11.95	$63,328.01
5				
6				

Exercises

Find the down payment for each home listed by price with the percent down required.

1. price: $32,500
   down: 5% VA

2. price: $54,900
   down: 20% Conventional

3. price: $69,900
   down: 3% FHA

4. price: $38,200
   down: 4% VA

5. price: $60,000
   down: 20% Conventional

6. price: $91,000
   down: 8% FHA

Find the monthly payment for each loan, given the principal, the interest rate, and the term of the loan.

7. principle: $31,000
   rate: 9%(12)
   term: 30 years

8. principle: $43,900
   rate: 12%(12)
   term: 25 years

9. principle: $68,000
   rate: 14%(12)
   term: 20 years

10. principle: $36,000
    rate: 15%(12)
    term: 20 years

11. principle: $48,000
    rate: 16%(12)
    term: 25 years

12. principle: $84,000
    rate: 14%(12)
    term: 30 years

13. For problems 7-12, find how much of the first payment goes to principal and how much to interest.

14. Find the payment for problem 7, using a term of 25 years.

15. Find the payment for problem 7, using a term of 20 years.

16. Find the payment for problem 12, using a term of 25 years.

17. Find the payment for problem 12, using a term of 15 years.

18. For what reason would a borrower want to have a longer term on a loan?

19. For what reasons would a borrower want to have a shorter term on a loan? Give two.

20. Complete lines 5 and 6 of the amortization schedule on page 353.

21. Mr. Hendrickson makes $18,000 per year and wants to buy a house. Use the one-fourth monthly income rule to get the payment he could afford. Use the 2.5 times annual income rule and 12%(12) to get his maximum debit limit and expected payment over 30 years.

22. Find out how much Mr. Hendrickson in problem 12 could borrow at 12%(12) for a 30-year loan if he uses the one-fourth of income rule. (Hint: Use Example 2, but remember that the unknown is different.)

23. The Van Camps can afford a monthly housing payment of $825. Use the one-fourth of income rule to get their annual income. How much could they borrow at 15%(12) for 20 years with a monthly payment of $825?

24. Find all the costs involved with buying an $87,500 home, including a 20% down payment, closing costs, and monthly payment. Use an interest rate of 15%(12) for 25 years and 1.75 points.

Interest Paid on a Mortgage

In the last section you saw that using a shorter term for a loan applied more of the payment toward principal. This would mean a faster reduction of the loan balance and, consequently, less interest charged for each succeeding month. You should expect that a shorter-term loan will mean much less interest paid out over the life of the loan. What may surprise you, however, is just how much interest is actually paid on a home mortgage.

Example 1

How much interest does a home owner pay over the life of a $30,000 loan financed at 12%(12) over 25 years?

Solution:
Find the payment: $i = \frac{12\%}{12} = 1\%$; $n = 25 \times 12 = 300$

$$\begin{aligned} \text{payment } R \quad &= \$30,000 \times \text{payment to finance \$1 factor} \\ &= (\$30,000)(0.010532241) \\ &= \$315.97 \text{ per month} \end{aligned}$$

Now multiply this monthly payment times 300 to get the total amount paid out on the loan.

$$\begin{aligned} \text{total paid} = 300 \times \$315.97 = \quad &\$94,791.00 \\ \text{principal paid off} = \quad &\underline{-\$30,000.00} \\ \text{total interest paid} = \quad &\$64,791.00 \end{aligned}$$

Remark: The interest was more than double the original loan principal.

Example 2

How much interest does the home owner in Example 1 pay over the life of the loan if the term is 20 years? How much interest does the home owner save with the shorter term?

Solution:

Find the new payment: $i = 1\%$, but $n = 20 \times 12 = 240$

$$
\begin{aligned}
\text{payment } R &= \$30,000 \times \text{payment to finance \$1 factor} \\
&= (\$30,000)(0.011010861) \\
&= \$330.33 \text{ per month}
\end{aligned}
$$

$$
\begin{aligned}
\text{total paid} = \$330.33 \times 240 &= \$79,279.20 \\
\text{principal paid off} &= \underline{-\$30,000.00} \\
\text{total interest paid} &= \$49,279.20
\end{aligned}
$$

$$
\begin{aligned}
\text{savings with interest} &= \$64,791.00 \\
&= \underline{-\$49,279.20} \\
\text{savings} &= \$15,511.80
\end{aligned}
$$

Remark: For just $14.36 per month extra, the home owner saved $15,511.80 in interest charges. Certainly, if there were any way to put the extra $14.36 into the family budget, it would be a wise decision.

Exercises

Calculate the amount of interest paid over the life of each loan.

1. loan: $24,000
   rate: 10%(12)
   term: 15 years

2. loan: $35,600
   rate: 9%(12)
   term: 20 years

3. loan: $49,900
   rate: 12%(12)
   term: 25 years

4. loan: $18,900
   rate: 15%(12)
   term: 10 years

5. loan: $57,400
   rate: 14%(12)
   term: 25 years

6. loan: $84,250
   rate: 10%(12)
   term: 30 years

7. Find the interest paid for the loan in problem 1 if the term is changed to 10 years. Also find the savings in interest.

8. Find the interest paid for the loan in problem 5 if the term is changed to 20 years. Also find the savings in interest.

9. Find the interest paid for the loan in problem 6 if the term is changed to 20 years. Also find the savings in interest.

10. Find the interest paid for the loan in problem 2 if the rate is changed to 12%(12). How much more is paid?

11. Find the interest paid for the loan in problem 3 if the interest rate is changed to 10%(12). How much is saved?

Outstanding Balance and Owner's Equity

It may come as a surprise to you, but most people never pay off their home loans. This fact doesn't imply that they all *default* (fail to pay) but that they sell the home before the term of the loan is up. If a home owner plans to sell his house, he will need to know his equity. *Owner's equity* means that part of the home's value that belongs to the owner. It consists of the down payment, the reduction in the loan principal, and the increase in value since the purchase. Anyone who sells a house wants to be sure his selling price will return his owner's equity.

Two of the numbers that make up the equity are quite easy to find. First, the down payment will be known from the original price. Second, the increase in value comes from the difference in original value and current value. Of course, the property could have decreased in value, especially if it were located in a decaying neighborhood or an area blighted by economic failure. The reduction in loan principal requires you to calculate the *outstanding balance* (or loan balance). The difference between the loan balance and the original loan will be the reduction in principal. The following examples may present some surprises about how slowly the principal reduces on long-term loans. You saw in the last section how a shorter term saved interest. It will also be true that the shorter term will speed up the growth of the owner's equity.

To better understand outstanding balance, look at the following figure illustrating a 25-year loan.

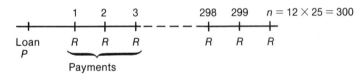

You can see that the original loan (principal) will be paid off by 300 payments. Now look at a portion of the above line needed to get the outstanding balance after 5 years (60 payments).

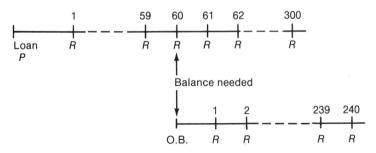

Rewrite the last part of the loan just like a new loan with 240 payments.

Use the original payment and the new term (240) to get the outstanding balance at payment 60.

Example 1

Find the outstanding loan balance after 5 years for a 25-year loan of $25,000 if the interest rate is 15%(12).

Solution:

Find the payment, where $i = \frac{15\%}{12} = 1\frac{1}{4}\%$, $n = 300$

$$\begin{aligned}
\text{Payment } R \quad &= \$25,000 \times \text{payment to borrow factor} \\
&= (\$25,000)(0.012808306) \\
&= \$320.21 \text{ per month}
\end{aligned}$$

Now find the amount borrowed for $n = 240 = 300 - 60$.

$$\begin{aligned}
\text{Amount} \quad &= (\$320.21)(\text{amount borrowed factor}) \\
&= (\$320.21)(75.94227758) \\
&= \$24,317.48 \quad \text{(outstanding balance after 5 years)}
\end{aligned}$$

This gives the reduction in principal: $25,000 − $24,317.48 = $682.52.

Remarks:
1. You can find out how much interest was paid during the first 5 years by getting the total paid less the reduction in principal.

$$\text{total paid} = \quad 60 \times \$320.21$$

$$\begin{aligned}
&= \quad \$19,212.60 \\
\text{reduction in principal} &= \quad \underline{-\$\quad 682.52} \\
\text{interest} &= \quad \$18,530.08
\end{aligned}$$

2. The total interest for this loan can be compared to the first 5 years of interest:

$$\text{total paid (25 years)} = \quad 300 \times \$320.21$$

$$\begin{aligned}
\text{total paid} &= \quad \$96,063.00 \\
\text{principal} &= \quad \underline{-\$25,000.00} \\
\text{interest} &= \quad \$71,063.00
\end{aligned}
\qquad \frac{18,530.08}{71,063} = 26\%$$

Thus, the $18,529.08 paid in the first 5 years is 26% of the total interest.

Study the following balances and reduction in principal for blocks of 5 years:

10 years: Balance = $22,878.89   Reduction = $2,121.11
15 years: Balance = $19,847.53   Reduction = $5,152.48
20 years: Balance = $13,459.90   Reduction = $11,540.10

Example 2

Find the owner's equity at 5 years if the original price of the house were $31,250 and the value has increased 12%.

$$\begin{array}{rr}
\text{down payment} = \$31,250 - \$25,000 = & \$6,250.00 \\
\text{increase in value } 12\%(31,250) = & \$3,750.00 \\
\text{reduction of loan principal} = & +\$\ \ \ 682.52 \\
\text{total} = & \$10,682.52
\end{array}$$

Example 3

There is one other quick way for a home owner to find the outstanding balance on his mortgage. He can use the amortization schedule that is available from the lending institution. Find the outstanding balance for the following loan at the end of 9 years.

Solution:

Find the number of the payment: $9 \times 12 = 108$

Find this value in the left column and read across to the extreme right column for the balance.

Payment No.	Payment	Interest Paid	Principal Paid	Loan Balance
107	$750.92	$536.36	$214.56	$45,759.10
108	$750.92	$533.86	$217.06	$45,542.04
109	$750.92	$531.32	$219.60	$45,322.44
110	$750.92	$528.76	$222.16	$45,100.28

The outstanding balance after 9 years is $45,542.04.

Exercises

Find the outstanding balance at the given year for each mortgage given.

1. house A: $83,000
   down payment: 20%
   rate: 12%(12)
   term: 30 years
   Find balance at 5 years.

2. house B: $65,500
   down payment: 5%
   rate: 15%(12)
   term: 25 years
   Find balance at 5 years.

3. house C: $41,500
   down payment: 3%
   rate: 9%(12)
   term: 20 years
   Find balance at 10 years.

4. house D: $110,000
   down payment: 20%
   rate: 14%(12)
   term: 30 years
   Find balance at 15 years.

5. house E: $52,900
   down payment: 5%
   rate: 10%(12)
   term: 25 years
   Find balance at 20 years.

6. house F: $73,450
   down payment: 3%
   rate: 12%(12)
   term: 20 years
   Find balance at 15 years.

Find (1) the reduction in the loan principal and (2) the owner's equity for houses A through F. The change in value is given as appreciation.

7. house A, appreciated: 5%
8. house B, appreciated: 8%
9. house C, appreciated: 27%

10. house D, appreciated: 24%
11. house E, appreciated: 36%
12. house F, appreciated: 31%

Find the amount of interest paid on each mortgage for houses A through F.

13. house A
14. house B
15. house C

16. house D
17. house E
18. house F

19. Find the outstanding balance and interest paid for house A at 5 years if the term of the original loan is 20 years. Compare your answers to the answers for questions 1 and 13 as a percent reduction over those answers.

20. Find the outstanding balance and interest paid for house C at 10 years if the term of the original loan is 25 years. Compare your answers to the answers for questions 3 and 15 as the percent increase over those answers.

21. Looking at the outstanding balances and reduction in principal for Example 1, what conclusions can you draw?

Building a House

After living in a house or an apartment for a few years, some families find the idea of building a house attractive. And just as you can have clothes tailor-made to fit perfectly, you can have a house tailor-made to fit the space and design needs of your family. Having your own house built lets you decide what features are important enough to include and which frills to exclude. Most decisions to build eventually come down to the cost. Depending on how much work the home owners do themselves, the same amount of house can be purchased at a lower price or possibly more house for the same price. Anyone who will work hard and get advice can substantially lower building costs by tackling part of the work themselves. To understand how this labor helps in being a good steward, consider a savings of just $3,000 in labor on the price of the house. This will means $38 savings on the monthly payment for a 25-year, 15%(12), loan. This saves $8,500 in interest paid over the 25-year term.

The very first step in building a house is to find a building site, called a *lot*. As was the case for renting an apartment or buying a house, the location of a lot can have long-term economic advantages or disadvantages. Lots vary greatly in price with rural sites costing as low as $5,000 and exclusive areas costing up to $35,000 or $40,000. Most people will probably pay around $15,000 for a half-acre lot. Knowing the location of the lot and any local building restrictions, the home owner then decides on a house plan.

House plans, in conceptional form, are available from many companies. These show the artist's view of the exterior and a simplified plan of the floor layout. A detailed set of plans, called *blueprints,* must be purchased to actually build the house. Blueprints may cost from $50 to $250. Custom blueprints are usually the most expensive, but they will always be exactly what the owner wants. Blueprints are drawn to scale so that the physical relationships are all the same, just smaller. Most house-plan blueprints are drawn so that $\frac{1}{4}$ inch on the drawing equals 1 foot on the actual house. If you measure the dimensions on the drawing with a ruler, you can convert that "scaled dimension" to full-size dimensions.

Example 1

The driveway on a house plan measures $3\frac{3}{4}''$. How wide is the driveway if the scale is $\frac{1}{4}'' = 1'$?

Solution:

Change $3\frac{3}{4}''$ to fourths.

$$3\frac{3}{4}'' = \frac{15}{4}'' = 15(\frac{1}{4}'')$$

Since each $\frac{1}{4}''$ is one foot, the driveway is 15' wide.

Example 2

John is making a scale drawing of a house. If he wants to draw the living room, which is 13 ft. by 18 ft., what are the scaled dimensions for $\frac{1}{4}'' = 1'$?

Solution:

13 ft. is $13(\frac{1}{4}'') = \frac{13}{4}'' = 3\frac{1}{4}''$

18 ft. is $18(\frac{1}{4}'') = 4\frac{1}{2}''$

The dimensions are $3\frac{1}{4}''$ by $4\frac{1}{2}''$.

This can also be written $3\frac{1}{4}'' \times 4\frac{1}{2}''$.

Example 3

On the following scale drawing, find the number of square yards of carpet for the living room and den.

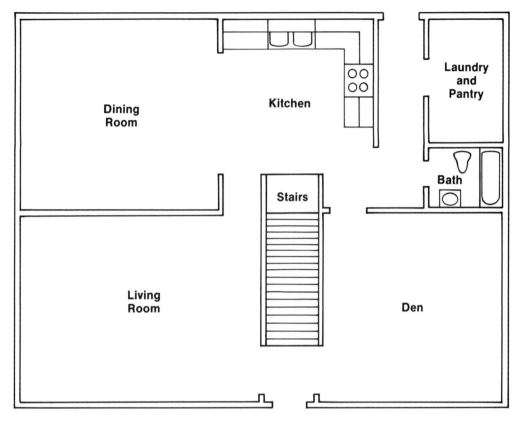

Solution:

There are several steps necessary to find this number:

1. Measure the rooms in inches, getting lengths and widths.
2. Change the scaled dimensions to feet.
3. Calculate the areas in square feet.
4. Change square feet to square yards.

Living Room: scaled dimensions: $1\frac{15}{16}'' \times 2\frac{9}{16}''$

Since there is $\frac{1}{8}$ inch for each foot, divide by $\frac{1}{8}$ to find how many "one-eighths" are in each dimension.

$$1\frac{15}{16} \div \frac{1}{8} = \frac{31}{16} \div \frac{1}{8} = \frac{31}{16} \times \frac{8}{1} = \frac{31}{2} = 15\frac{1}{2} \text{ ft.}$$

$$2\frac{9}{16} \div \frac{1}{8} = \frac{41}{16} \div \frac{1}{8} = \frac{41}{16} \times \frac{8}{1} = \frac{41}{2} = 20\frac{1}{2} \text{ ft.}$$

$$\text{Area} = 15\frac{1}{2}' \times 20\frac{1}{2}' = 317\frac{3}{4} \text{ ft.}^2$$

Since there are 9 ft.^{2} in one yd.^{2}, you get . . .

$$\text{Area} = 317\frac{3}{4} \div 9 = 35.3 \text{ yd.}^2$$

Dining Room: scaled dimensions: $2'' \times 2\frac{1}{8}''$

$$2 \div \frac{1}{8} = 2 \times 8 = 16 \text{ ft.}$$

$$2\frac{1}{8} \div \frac{1}{8} = \frac{17}{8} \div \frac{1}{8} = \frac{17}{8} \times \frac{8}{1} = 17 \text{ ft.}$$

$$\text{Area} = 16 \times 17 = 272 \text{ ft.}^2$$
$$= 272 \div 9 = 30.2 \text{ yd.}^2$$

Summary:

living room:	35.3 yd.^{2}
dining room:	+30.2 yd.^{2}
total:	65.5 yd.^{2}

Example 4

The Franklins are considering buying one of two building lots. The first one is $192' \times 145'$, and the other is $100' \times 300'$. What is the acreage in each lot?

Solution:

A good conversion between acres and property dimension is . . .

$$640 \text{ acres} = 1 \text{ sq. mile.}$$
$$= 5{,}280' \times 5{,}280'$$
$$= 27{,}878{,}400 \text{ ft.}^2$$

Divide by 640:
$$\frac{27{,}878{,}400 \text{ ft.}^2}{640}$$
$$1 \text{ acre} = 43{,}560 \text{ ft.}^2$$

The first lot's area $= 192' \times 145'$
$= 27{,}840 \text{ ft.}^2$ (Divide by 43,560.)
$= 0.639 \text{ acre}$

The second lot's area $= 100' \times 300'$
$= 30{,}000 \text{ ft.}^2$ (Divide by 43,560.)
$= 0.689 \text{ acre}$

Remark: The lots have close to the same acreage, but the first is more "square." A lot that is $208'$ by $208'$ is about one acre because $208' \times 208' = 43{,}264 \text{ ft.}^2$

Example 5

Mr. O'Conner is calculating the cost of shingles for his new house. His roof area is 2,400 ft.^{2}. Shingles cost $45 per 100 ft.^{2}, and labor is $11 per 100 ft.^{2}. Find the cost.

Solution:

Materials: $\dfrac{\$45}{100 \text{ ft.}^2} \times 2,400 \text{ ft.}^2 = \dfrac{(45)(2,400)}{(100)} = \$1,080$

Labor: $\dfrac{\$11}{100 \text{ ft.}^2} \times 2,400 \text{ ft.}^2 = \dfrac{(11)(2,400)}{(100)} = \$264$

$$\text{total} = \$1,080 + \$264 = \$1,344$$

Exercises

Convert the following scale drawing dimensions into feet and inches, given the measurement and the drawing scale.

1. measurement: $5\frac{3}{4}''$
   scale: $\frac{1}{4}'' = 1'$

2. measurement: $3\frac{3}{8}''$
   scale: $\frac{1}{4}'' = 1'$

3. measurement: $6\frac{5}{16}''$
   scale: $\frac{1}{4}'' = 1'$

4. measurement: $2\frac{3}{8}''$
   scale: $\frac{1}{8}'' = 1'$

5. measurement: $1\frac{15}{16}''$
   scale: $\frac{1}{8}'' = 1'$

6. measurement: $4\frac{3}{8}''$
   scale: $\frac{3}{16}'' = 1'$

Convert the following dimensions in feet and inches into scale-drawing dimensions for the given scale.

7. dimensions: $14'\ 6''$
   scale: $\frac{1}{4}'' = 1'$

8. dimensions: $5' \times 9'$
   scale: $\frac{1}{4}'' = 1'$

9. dimensions: $12'\ 3''$
   scale: $\frac{1}{4}'' = 1'$

10. dimensions: $8'\ 6'' \times 12'\ 0''$
    scale: $\frac{1}{8}'' = 1'$

11. dimensions: $9' \times 14'$
    scale: $\frac{1}{8}'' = 1'$

12. dimensions: $21'\ 4''$
    scale: $\frac{3}{16}'' = 1'$

Using the house blueprint on page 367, calculate the following materials.

13. Vinyl flooring for bathroom

14. Number of $9'' \times 9''$ floor tiles needed for kitchen and utility room

15. Carpet for living room

16. Carpet for each bedroom

17. Rolls of wallpaper for the master bedroom when one roll measures $2' \times 48'$. How many rolls are needed? (Ignore windows and doors.)

18. Square feet of vinyl siding (allowing $3' \times 6'$ for each window and door, except $9' \times 7'$ for each garage door)

Find the size in acres of each building lot whose dimensions are given below.

19. 135′ × 169.2′

20. 208.71′ × 208.71′

21. 153.25′ × 161.35′

22. 172′ × 290.3′

23. Calculate the number of cubic yards of concrete needed for a driveway that is 9 feet wide, 150 feet long, and 4 inches thick.

Questions 24 through 30 refer to the house plans given in this chapter. Use the dimensions given on the scale drawing for room measurements.

24. Find the cost of installing vinyl flooring in the bathrooms if materials are $3.80 per ft.² and labor is $1.50 per ft.².

25. Find the cost of installing 9″ × 9″ tiles in the kitchen and utility room if materials cost $25 per box of 45. (No partial boxes are sold.) Installation costs $.20 per tile.

26. Find the cost of vinyl siding if it costs $48 per 100 ft.², with 15% added to the cost for trim and specials. Installation costs $40 per 100 ft.².

27. How many doors are in this house? Get a cost estimate based on the following prices: interior doors cost $55 each, bi-fold doors $60 each, exterior doors $135 each, and garage doors $315 each.

28. If ceiling paint covers 300 ft.² per gallon, how many gallons are needed to paint all the ceilings, including the garage and utility room? Round to the next whole gallon.

29. If wall paint covers 400 ft.² per gallon per coat, how many gallons are needed to paint all the walls in this house with one coat? Do not differentiate colors, and ignore windows and doors. This will allow for closets without calculating them. Include the 2 walls (each 10 feet long) in the hallway in your calculation.

30. Find the cost of windows if they are $135 each.

Country Squire

1,088 sq. ft. heated
576 sq. ft. garage

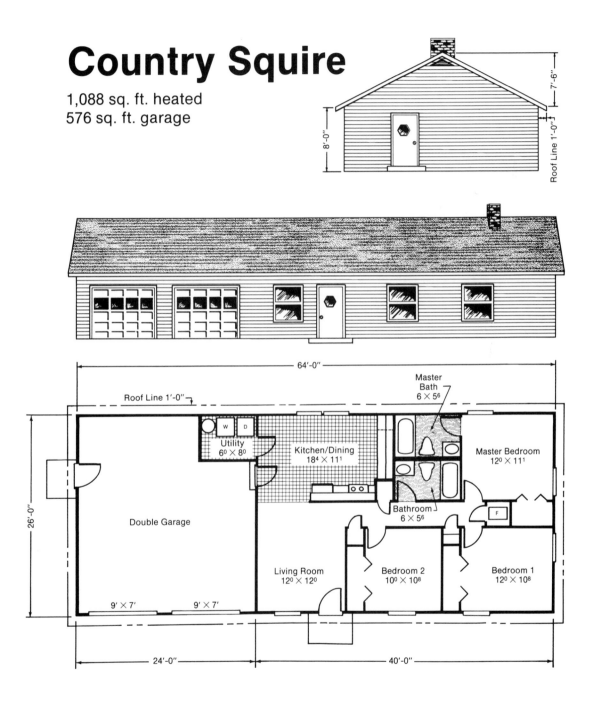

Chapter 12 Review ———

adjustable-rate mortgage	mortgage
amortization schedule	origination fee
blueprint	outstanding balance
closing costs	owner's equity
conventional loan	points
FHA loan	scale drawing
fixed-rate mortgage	tenant
furnished	TRETS fee
landlord	unfurnished
lease	VA loan
lot	

Review Exercises

Find the monthly rent that could be paid based on the one-fourth of income principle. Round to the nearest dollar.

1. yearly income: $29,400

2. semimonthly income: $725

3. weekly income: $420

4. yearly income: $18,900

Find the up-front cost of occupying each rental property.

5. rent: $480 per month
deposit: one month's rent
power: $\frac{1}{2}$ the monthly average of an $840 annual charge
water: $\frac{1}{2}$ the quarterly charge of $58

6. rent: $210 per week
deposit: $\frac{1}{20}$ the annual rent
power: $100
water: $\frac{1}{4}$ the annual charge of $260
telephone: $70

Find the points discount for each loan given.

7. loan: $45,000
points: 4

8. loan: $28,000
points: $2\frac{1}{2}$

9. loan: $70,000
points: $1\frac{7}{8}$

10. loan: $23,560
points: $3\frac{1}{4}$

Find the points being charged for each loan, given the loan value and the proceeds.

11. loan: $75,000
proceeds: $74,062.50

12. loan: $81,200
proceeds: $76,734

13. loan: $28,420
proceeds: $27,212.15

14. loan: $32,000
proceeds: $31,120.00

Find the down payment for each home listed by price with the percent down required.

15. price: $34,900
    down: 15%

17. price: $75,000
    down: 25%

16. price: $55,800
    down: 20%

18. price: $112,000
    down: 22%

Find the monthly payment for each loan, given the principal, interest rate, and term.

19. principal: $24,000
    rate: 7%(12)
    term: 10 years

21. principal: $52,000
    rate: 10%(12)
    term: 20 years

20. principal: $40,000
    rate: 9%(12)
    term: 15 years

22. principal: $84,000
    rate: 14%(12)
    term: 30 years

Find the payment and the amount of interest paid over the life of each loan.

23. loan A: $35,000
    rate: 14%(12)
    term: 10 years

25. loan C: $57,000
    rate: 10%(12)
    term: 20 years

24. loan B: $46,000
    rate: 12%(12)
    term: 15 years

26. loan D: $64,000
    rate: 9%(12)
    term: 30 years

Find the outstanding balance at the given year for each mortgage for loans A through D in problems 23 through 26.

27. loan A
    balance at 5 years

29. loan C
    balance at 15 years

28. loan B
    balance at 10 years

30. loan D
    balance at 25 years

Find the amount of interest paid on each mortgage to the date of the balance found in problems 27 through 30.

31. loan A

33. loan C

32. loan B

34. loan D

Convert the following scale-drawing dimensions into feet and inches.

35. measurement: $3\frac{1}{4}'' \times 4\frac{1}{16}''$
    scale: $\frac{1}{8}'' = 1'\text{-}0''$

37. measurement: $6\frac{3}{8}''$
    scale: $\frac{1}{2}'' = 1'\text{-}0''$

36. measurement: $5\frac{1}{8}'' \times 7\frac{3}{8}''$
    scale: $\frac{1}{4}'' = 1'\text{-}0''$

38. measurement: $2\frac{1}{4}'' \times 3\frac{5}{8}''$
    scale: $\frac{3}{8}'' = 1'\text{-}0''$

Convert the following dimensions in feet and inches into scale-drawing dimensions for the given scale.

39. dimensions: $9'\text{-}6'' \times 11'\text{-}3''$
    scale: $\frac{1}{4}'' = 1'\text{-}0''$

41. dimensions: $4'\text{-}3'' \times 7'\text{-}6''$
    scale: $\frac{1}{2}'' = 1'\text{-}0''$

40. dimensions: $8' \times 10'$
    scale: $\frac{1}{8}'' = 1'\text{-}0''$

42. dimensions: $19'\text{-}4''$
    scale: $\frac{3}{16}'' = 1'\text{-}0''$

Find the size in acres of each building lot whose dimensions are given.

43. $109' \times 216'$

45. $180' \times 193'$

44. $129.5' \times 301.8'$

46. $115.75' \times 263.3'$

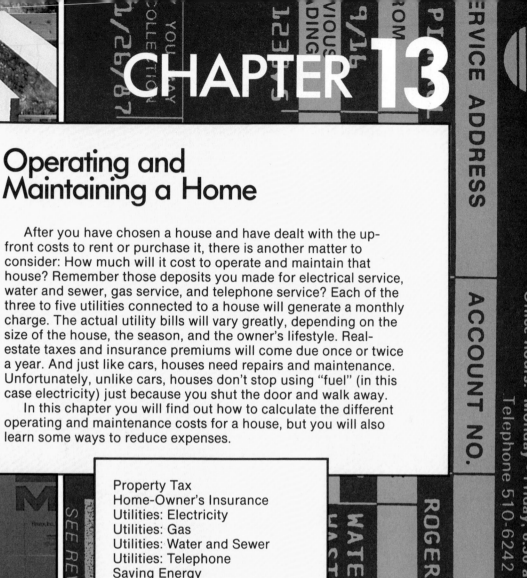

CHAPTER 13

Operating and Maintaining a Home

After you have chosen a house and have dealt with the up-front costs to rent or purchase it, there is another matter to consider: How much will it cost to operate and maintain that house? Remember those deposits you made for electrical service, water and sewer, gas service, and telephone service? Each of the three to five utilities connected to a house will generate a monthly charge. The actual utility bills will vary greatly, depending on the size of the house, the season, and the owner's lifestyle. Real-estate taxes and insurance premiums will come due once or twice a year. And just like cars, houses need repairs and maintenance. Unfortunately, unlike cars, houses don't stop using "fuel" (in this case electricity) just because you shut the door and walk away.

In this chapter you will find out how to calculate the different operating and maintenance costs for a house, but you will also learn some ways to reduce expenses.

Property Tax
Home-Owner's Insurance
Utilities: Electricity
Utilities: Gas
Utilities: Water and Sewer
Utilities: Telephone
Saving Energy
House Repairs and Maintenance
Home Improvements
Review

Property Tax

Municipal and county governments generate most of their revenue by real estate and personal property taxes. For all property in its jurisdiction, the local government's tax officials establish a value, called the *assessed valuation,* or simply *assessed value.* This assessed value is usually lower than the market value. The determination of assessed value for property is often a complicated and sometimes controversial subject. It also varies greatly from community to community. By setting a *tax rate* per unit of assessed value, the government establishes each property owner's tax *liability* (how much he must pay) for a given year.

Several common ways of expressing tax rate are the *cost per $100* of assessed valuation or the *mils per $1* of assessed valuation. A *mil* is one tenth of a cent, or one thousandth of a dollar, expressed as $.001. (For example, 352.5 mils = $0.3525.)

Example 1

Find the tax liability for a house with a market value of $82,000 assessed at 52% at a tax rate of $2.50 per $100.

Solution:
First find the assessed valuation (AV).

$$
\begin{aligned}
AV &= 52\%(\$82,000) \\
&= (0.52)(\$82,000) \\
&= \$42,640
\end{aligned}
$$

Next, multiply the AV times the tax rate. Remember that $2.50 per $100 means $2.50 *divided by* $100.

$$
\begin{aligned}
\text{tax liability} &= \tfrac{\$2.50}{100} \times 42,640 \\
\\
&= \$1,066 \text{ per year}
\end{aligned}
$$

Example 2

Find the tax liability for a $55,000 house in a county with the following tax structure.

Property is assessed at 4% of market value with the following distribution:

Bonds	14.0 mils
County Government	27.6 mils
Schools	83.2 mils
Special Service	76.4 mils
Sanitation	29.3 mils

Solution:
First find the total millage: 230.5 mils. Then find the assessed value:

$$4\%(\$55,000) = \$2,200$$

Recall that 230.5 mils = $0.2305 per each dollar of assessed value.

$$\text{tax liability} = (0.2305)(\$2,200)$$
$$= \$507.10$$

Exercises

Calculate the tax liability for each property, given the assessed value and the tax rate.

	Assessed Value	Tax Rate
1.	$34,500	$1.862 per $100
2.	$12,840	$86.35 per $1,000
3.	$1,980	$185.23 mils per $1
4.	$52,500	$17.3 per $1,000
5.	$41,600	$1.245 per $100
6.	$3,250	$2.85 per $100
7.	$1,440	$287.35 mils per $1
8.	$104,000	$22.94 per $1,000
9.	$152,000	$35.20 per $1,000
10.	$5,500	$123.56 mils per $1

11. Mr. Weiss is contemplating the purchase of an apartment building for $159,000. Find what the real-estate tax will be if rental property is assessed at 6% and the tax rate is 185.7 mils per $1 of assessed value.

12. Mrs. Hess noticed an article in the newspaper, giving the new millage figures for property in her county. Find her obligation if her house is worth $52,000 and is assessed at 4% with the following new millage rates:

Schools	91.4 mils
County Government	34.2 mils
Improvement Bonds	11.9 mils
Special Service District	73.3 mils
Sanitation	20.5 mils
Library Expansion	8.7 mils

13. Frank Hammond's tax notice states that the assessed value of his home is $39,000 and that his real-estate tax obligation is $592.80. What is the tax rate per $100, and how many mils is it?

14. Mrs. Commoros received her real-estate tax notice, stating her obligation to be $396.50. She knows that her county has recently established a tax rate of 206.2 mils. What is the assessed value of her home?

Project: Call or write to your local city or county tax office and find out about tax assessment and tax rates in your area.

Budgeting

People never seem to have enough of two things—time and money. One exciting thing about being a Christian is that you will live forever and enjoy treasures in heaven that can never be taken away. So you don't need to worry about your earthly wealth and time; you can give both to the Lord to use as He pleases. God then expects you to put your mind and energy into advancing His kingdom (Matt. 6:19-34). Unlike the world, you can be content with only food and clothes as long as your life is being invested for eternal rewards.

Life on earth is too short to waste one minute or one dollar; as I Corinthians 10:31 says, "Whether therefore ye eat, or drink, or whatsoever ye do, do all to the glory of God." And when you die, God will ask you to give an account of everything you have done. *Budgeting* (planning the use of time and money) is one of the best tools to monitor your lifestyle and spending.

The first step in budgeting is to set short-term and long-term goals. You must realize that some goals, such as a consistent prayer life or a new home, take a long time to reach; however, the only goals worth accomplishing are those that the Lord has set for you. So good budgeting begins with prayer and a study of the Bible to discover God's thoughts on the matter. God reveals clearly that riches and activity have no value in themselves (Prov. 23:4; Luke 10:39-42); they are simply a means to an end—giving to God's work, sharing with the needy, and encouraging the saints.

Once you resolve how you will spend your time, you will need to write a formal budget of your daily hours. But you need to know a little bit about yourself—your strengths and weaknesses—before you take this step. First, figure out what time of the day your mind and body are at their best, and plan to do the more demanding tasks then. Next, keep a record of your activities for a few weeks before planning your new lifestyle. In this way you can then write a tentative schedule and try it for a few weeks. If it is reasonable, keep it.

Activities that people try to save time for include sports, studies, chores, reading, visitation, Bible study, prayer,

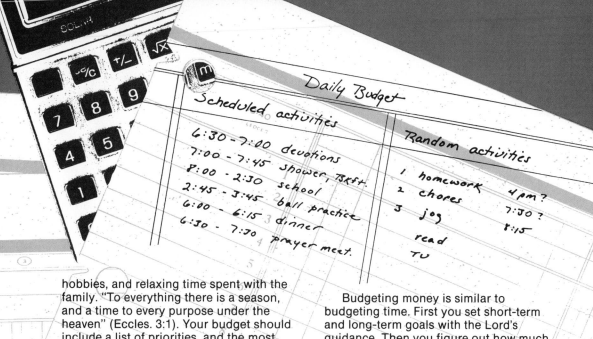

Daily Budget

Scheduled activities

6:30 - 7:00 devotions
7:00 - 7:45 shower, Bkft.
8:00 - 2:30 school
2:45 - 3:45 ball practice
6:00 - 6:15 dinner
6:30 - 7:30 prayer meet.

Random activities

1 homework   4pm?
2 chores
3 jog   7:30?
                  8:15
read
TV

hobbies, and relaxing time spent with the family. "To everything there is a season, and a time to every purpose under the heaven" (Eccles. 3:1). Your budget should include a list of priorities, and the most important activities should be done first. When you give God His time first, He will help you find time for the other things. When you do your hard jobs first, you can enjoy the games later without guilt; and the prospect of fun ahead encourages you to finish the unpleasant tasks more quickly.

Many people keep a daily budget or a weekly budget. Each of these budgets keeps track of scheduled activities on one side and unscheduled activities on the other side. The unscheduled activities should be listed according to priority, and the top two or three should be scheduled for a specific time. Priorities should be ranked in this order: urgent and important, important but not urgent, unimportant but urgent, and miscellaneous tasks. When unexpected delays occur, focus attention on the top priorities so that they get done even if the more trivial matters don't.

Budgeting money is similar to budgeting time. First you set short-term and long-term goals with the Lord's guidance. Then you figure out how much you have to spend each month after you take out taxes and company deductions (for insurance, pensions, and so forth). Next you might record your income and expenses in detail for two or three months. From this record-keeping, you can decide what you have to spend and how you want to change your spending habits.

Your first priority with money, as with time, is to dedicate it to the Lord. Proverbs 3:9 says, "Honour the Lord with thy substance, and with the firstfruits of all thine increase." So before you begin figuring your bills, debts, taxes, or anything else, God expects you to set aside a tithe, or tenth, for Him. This money is not yours to spend.

Since the rest of your money is also the Lord's (Ps. 24:1), you need to ask Him how He wants you to spend it. Short-term goals might include furniture, clothes, gifts, and vacations. Long-term goals might include a new home, a car, a computer, and the college education of your children. Expenses such as utilities, car maintenance, and house upkeep vary from month to month, so it is wise to total the year's expenses, divide the total into twelve equal parts, and save anything extra in a savings account for later.

Weekly Budget

Scheduled activities

practice
practice
prayer meet.
practice
visitation
practice

Random activities

1 chores
  wash car - change oil
  clean gutters
  trim shrubs
2 buy birtday gift
3 help ax

Figure B lists the average percentage of an income spent for each category after taxes, tithes, and offerings. Budgets can have any number of formats, and they range from multi-page, detailed accounts to a few lines on a single piece of paper. You need to design one that meets your specific needs. Detailed budgets are advisable when you start a family, when you change jobs or houses, and when you have numerous investments or expenses. Most budgets are written for one year.

Your final budget should be written neatly on durable paper and stored in a place where you can find it. Many people have a filing cabinet or drawer where they keep their handwritten budgets in a folder. Others buy specially printed books, called *ledgers,* which have budget outlines already made. A third popular record-keeper is the personal computer; new computer programs help you organize, analyze, and graph your finances with ease.

Once you write a budget, stick to it. You will be tempted to change it when money gets tight, but refrain from doing so if at all possible. Instead, you should build flexibility into your budget because you never know what emergency could arise (for example, a doctor's visit or car repair). Some categories, like medical and automotive expenses, should have an amount set aside for miscellaneous expenses. If you do not use the full amount for that month, you can build up a savings account for later.

Nevertheless, your budget is not your boss; the Lord is. So review your budget regularly to see if you can save in some areas or spend money more wisely in other areas. A budget does not safeguard you from the unexpected: you could lose a job, be evicted from your apartment, have a car accident, become ill, get robbed, or have a fire. You, like Job, could manage your house well but still suffer such things. Therefore a budget is never a substitute for praying and doing God's will. Give to His service when the Lord directs, not when it "fits into the budget"; trust Him, not your own labor, to supply your needs.

Good budgeting has many benefits. By differentiating between needs and wants, you can keep your bills paid, your credit good, and your life as productive as possible. You gain more control of your life and prevent waste of a single minute or dollar. Budgets encourage patience as you work toward long-term goals. Your detailed records reveal your exact needs so that you can pray specifically. In addition, your financial records are helpful at tax time. If carried out properly, budgets can be a valuable tool in living an abundant, fulfilling life for God.

Fig. B

Category		Average % of Net Income	Typical Monthly Budget
Income			
	Net Pay		1400 00
	Interest		25
	Dividends		75
	Previous Balance		—
	Other		—
	Total		1500 00
Expenses	Tithe/Offerings	12%	180 00
	Housing:	(34%)	(510) 00
	Rent-Mortgage	16	240
	Util/Telephone		

Home-Owner's Insurance

If your house has a mortgage on it, the lender will require you to carry home-owner's insurance. The value of the insurance policy will have to be equal to or greater than the loan principal. Of course, even if you owned the home debt free, it would be wise to have such a large investment adequately insured against loss by fire, storm, flood, etc. An insurance *policy* is a contract between the home owner, called the *insured,* and the insurance company, called the *insurer.* Under this contract the insured pays the insurer an agreed-on sum of money, called the *premium,* for financial guarantees to pay for the loss of some property due to specified causes.

Home-owner's insurance is divided into two categories: property damage and liability. *Property-damage* coverage pays for the dwelling and all personal effects, and *liability* coverage pays for personal damage to others, including medical payments. The insurance policy will explicitly state everything that is covered by the policy, as well as any specific non-insured items (for example, the cracking or settling of a foundation).

The premiums that a home owner pays to insure his property are usually quoted as cost per $100 or $1,000 of coverage. Premiums are usually annual rates. They are subject to a number of adjustments, depending on such factors as location, type of house, and type of heating system.

The following insurance-premium chart gives some premium costs for typical home-owner's insurance. The property damage limits of 50,000/30,000 state that the policy insures the dwelling for $50,000 and the contents for $30,000. Likewise, the liability limits of 100,000/2,000 mean the insurance policy pays up to $100,000 for personal liability damages and $2,000 per person for medical payments.

Table 13.1
HMS Insurance Company
Annual Home-Owners' Policy Premiums

	Property-Damage Premiums/$1,000	
	Dwelling	*Personal Property—Contents*
$250 deductible	$1.20	$1.05
$500 deductible	$1.05	$0.90

Adjustments:
1. For dwelling above 2,000 ft.^{2}, add $.15 per 100 ft.^{2} for property damage.
2. For rural dwellings outside of fire districts, add 50% to property damage.
3. For dwellings heated by wood-burning stoves, add 15% to the base price for property damage.

Liability Premiums/$1,000

Personal-Property Damage	Medical Payments per Person
$1.30	$5.10

Example 1

Calculate the annual home-owner's insurance premium for a 2,800 ft.^{2} house with limits 65,000/40,000, $250 deductible, property damage and 100,000/5,000 liability. The house has a wood-burning stove.

Solution:

Use Table 13.1 to find the premiums and adjustments.

(1) Property—dwelling:

adjustment for ft.^{2} = $\frac{0.15}{100} \times 800 = \$1.20$

adjustment for the stove = $1.20 \times (15\%) = \$.18$

giving a premium rate of: 1.20   (base)
1.20   (adjustment for ft.^{2})
0.18   (adjustment for stove)
2.58

premium = $\frac{2.58}{1,000} \times 65,000 = \textbf{\$167.70}$

(2) The contents premium will also need a 15% adjustment for the stove.

$$1.05 \times 15\% = \$.16$$

giving a premium rate of: 1.05   (base)
1.20   (adjustment for ft.^{2})
0.16   (adjustment for stove)
2.41

premium = $\frac{2.41}{1,000} \times 40,000 = \textbf{\$96.40}$

(3) Liability—property: $\frac{1.30}{1,000} \times 100,000 = \textbf{\$130.00}$

(4) Liability—medical: $\frac{5.10}{1,000} \times 5,000 = \textbf{\$25.50}$

Now total the 4 parts: $167.70
$ 96.40
$130.00
$ 25.50

Home-owner's premium =   **$419.60 per year**

Example 2

Calculate the annual home-owner's insurance premium on a rural dwelling with limits 45,000/20,000, $250 deductible, property damage, and 50,000/1,000 liability.

Solution:

Use Table 13.1 to find the premiums and adjustments. An adjustment to the property-damage premiums is necessary because of the rural location.

(1) dwelling

$$\text{premium rate} = \$1.20 + 50\%(1.20)$$
$$= \$1.20 + \$.60$$
$$= \$1.80 \text{ per } \$1,000$$
$$\text{premium} = \frac{\$1.80}{1,000} \times 45,000 = \textbf{\$81.00}$$

(2) contents

$$\text{premium rate} = \$1.05 + 50\%(1.05)$$
$$= \$1.05 + \$.53$$
$$= \$.158$$
$$\text{premium} = \frac{1.58}{1,000} \times 20,000 = \textbf{\$31.60}$$

(3) liability—property

$$\text{premium} = \frac{1.30}{1,000} \times 50,000 = \textbf{\$65.00}$$

(4) liability—medical

$$\text{premium} = \frac{5.10}{1,000} \times 1,000 = \textbf{\$5.10}$$

Now total the 4 parts:

$81.00
$31.60
$65.00
$ 5.10

Home-owner's premium = **$182.70 per year**

Exercises

Calculate the annual home-owner's liability-insurance premiums for each set of limits given. Use Table 13.1.

1. 50,000/1,000
2. 100,000/5,000

3. 150,000/10,000
4. 75,000/3,000

Calculate the annual home-owner's property-damage premiums for each set of limits given. Use Table 13.1. Unless conditions are given, assume no adjustments.

5. 35,000/18,000
$250 deductible

6. 42,000/20,000
$250 deductible

7. 50,000/35,000
$500 deductible
rural dwelling

8. 75,000/52,000
$500 deductible
2,500 ft.^{2}

9. 24,000/10,000
$250 deductible
wood-burning stove

10. 35,000/12,000
$250 deductible
rural dwelling

11. 48,000/25,000
$250 deductible

12. 95,000/60,000
$500 deductible
3,200 ft.^{2}
rural dwelling, wood-burning stove

Calculate the total annual home-owner's insurance premiums for the following liability limits and the property-damage premiums from problems 5-12.

13. house 5: 25,000/1,000
14. house 6: 40,000/1,000
15. house 7: 100,000/3,000
16. house 8: 150,000/5,000

17. house 9: 25,000/1,000
18. house 10: 45,000/2,000
19. house 11: 75,000/3,000
20. house 12: 200,000/10,000

21. Mr. and Mrs. Potter want to set up a 6%(12) savings account into which they can make monthly payments to save for their yearly tax liability and insurance premium. Their house is valued at $55,000 and assessed at 4% with a tax rate of 287.3 mils per $1 of assessed value. They carry 60,000/30,000, $250 deductible, property damage; 100,000/3,000 liability; and their house has 2,400 ft.^{2} and a wood-burning stove. Find their tax liability, insurance premium, and monthly deposit to save for these obligations.

22. Mary Lopez is comparing the cost of home-owner's insurance premiums for her house. Her current limits are $250 deductible 50,000/30,000 property damage and 100,000/5,000 liability. She can buy a policy from the DMZ Insurance Company, which offers property-damage coverage at 15% lower than the HMS Company but their liability coverage is 15% higher. Should she switch to DMZ? Justify your answer.

Utilities: Electricity

Have you ever heard someone say something like, "I wonder what our power bill will be this month. We've run our air conditioner almost constantly"? Such statements are common. Actually, though, there really need not be so much guesswork involved in determing how much you'll need to pay. Any home owner can determine his monthly utility bills from two pieces of information—the meter reading and the rate schedule.

The electric meter on a house measures energy consumption in units called *kilowatt-hours* (kWh). One kilowatt is 1,000 watts of electric current. One kilowatt-hour is the same as 1,000 watts of electric energy consumed in one hour. As the current going into your house passes through the meter, you will see that it makes a little flat disk spin in proportion to the rate of consumption. If your house has many power-consuming appliances turned on, the disk will spin very fast. This disk makes a set of dials rotate very much like the odometer on an automobile. The dials shown here are in multiples of ten with the largest number on the left and the smallest on the right.

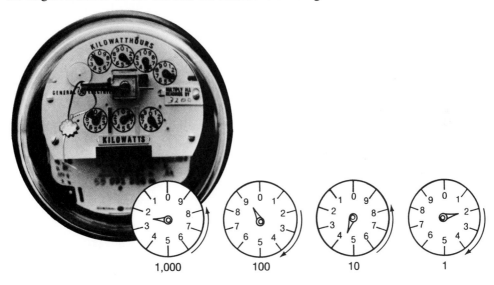

| 1,000 | 100 | 10 | 1 |

The reading in this illustration is 2,942 kWh. If you note carefully the rotation of each dial, you will see that the reading is actually the last number each arrow passed. To establish energy consumption, the power company takes the difference in the meter reading about 30 days apart. For instance, suppose that after 30 days the above meter read 3,767. The energy consumption for that time would be 3,767 − 2,942 = 825 kWh.

Each power company has a rate schedule that it uses to establish charges for power consumption. Table 13.2 shows a typical electric company's rate schedule.

	Table 13.2
	Southern Power Company
	Residential Rate Schedule
0 to 100 kWh	$15.00 (minimum charge)
Next 300 kWh	9.5¢ per kWh
Next 300 kWh	7.0¢ per kWh
Over 700 kWh	6.0¢ per kWh

Example

On May 22 the power meter at a house read 32,095. On June 23 it read 32,920. Find the power consumption, the monthly charges, and the cost per day. Use Table 13.2.

Solution:

The power consumption equals the present reading minus previous reading.

$$32,920 - 32,095 = 825 \text{ kWh}$$

Note that 825 can be divided to match Table 13.2:

$$825 = 100 + 300 + 300 + 125$$

Using a table form, we get . . .

Usage Increments	Cumulative Totals	Cost		Cumulative Totals
100 kWh	100	$15.00		$15.00
300 kWh	400	$28.50		$43.50
300 kWh	700	$21.00		$64.50
125 kWh	825	$ 7.50		$72.00 ◀(monthly charge)

To get the number of days, use the serial table:

$$
\begin{array}{r}
174 \quad \text{(June 23)} \\
\underline{-142} \quad \text{(May 22)} \\
32 \text{ days total}
\end{array}
$$

$$\text{cost per day} = \frac{\$72}{32} = \$2.25$$

Exercises

Read each electric-power meter and record it as a 4-digit numeral.

1.

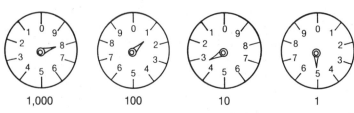

    1,000   100   10   1

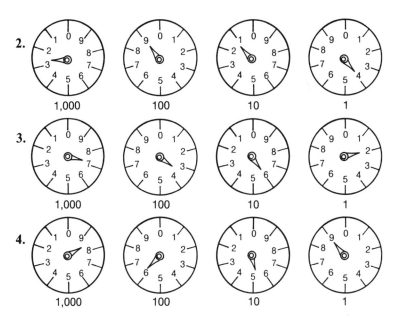

2. 1,000   100   10   1

3. 1,000   100   10   1

4. 1,000   100   10   1

Using the Southern Power Company rate schedule (Table 13.2), calculate the power usage in kWh and the monthly charges.

Account Name	Meter Readings (kWh)		Dates	
	Previous	*Present*	*From*	*To*
5. Mogen	2526	4363	June 23	July 23
6. Washer	1204	1800	Oct. 8	Nov. 9
7. Brezin	2531	3383	Mar. 17	Apr. 16
8. Le Barron	8407	9608	Aug. 3	Sept. 6
9. Battaglia	1249	2252	May 24	June 20
10. Araki	9816	0288	Sept. 13	Oct. 13

Find the number of days of usage from problems 5-10 and the cost per day for each customer. Be sure to account for the exact number of days.

11. Mogen
12. Washer
13. Brezin

14. Le Barron
15. Battaglia
16. Araki

17. Mrs. Brown knows that her electric-power consumption was 755 kWh last month. If her power bill is $56.63, what is the average cost per kWh that her power company charges?

18. Mr. and Mrs. Simons received a power bill for $163.81 for the month of July. If their electric company charges an average of 6.9¢ per kWh, how many kWhs did they consume during July?

Utilities: Gas

In many areas of the United States, consumers have natural gas piped into their houses. Because gas is a popular fuel, those areas that don't have piping distribution use storage tanks and have liquefied petroleum gas (LP gas or Propane) delivered by tank trucks. Gas consumption is measured in cubic feet by a flow meter. A rotating disk like a propeller on the inside of the meter turns dials that record the number of cubic feet of gas passing through the meter.

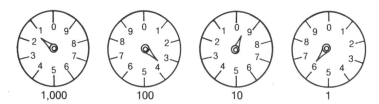

Here the gas meter reads 1,396 hundred cubic feet. (Hundreds of cubic feet is also abbreviated as CCF.) For every complete rotation of a dial, the dial immediately left of it will move one number. This is how we write our decimal-system numbers. The odometer on a car also works this way.

The gas company determines the charges for gas consumption by converting each one hundred cubic feet into an equivalent number of *therms*. The conversion is made by multiplying by a heat factor. This number, obtained experimentally, gives the basic energy content of a given mixture of natural gas. The gas companies change this number regularly to reflect the changing nature of the gas they sell. The Upstate Natural Gas Company has the following rate schedule for year-round residential customers.

Table 13.3
Upstate Natural Gas Company Rate Schedule

Customer	Service Fee	Cost Per Therm	Heat Factor*
Residential year-round customer	3.00	0.44506	1.041/100 ft.³
Winter-heat-only customer	3.00	0.47895	1.041/100 ft³

*The heat factor varies from month to month but ranges from 1.035 to 1.045.

Example

Find the monthly charge for a year-round customer who uses 2,300 cubic feet of natural gas between March 3 and April 3.

Solution: To find the number of therms, multiply the cubic feet of gas used by the heat factor to get therms.

$$2{,}300 \text{ ft.}^3 \times \frac{1.041}{100 \text{ ft.}^3} = 23.943 \text{ therms}$$

The billing computers will round this figure to 24 therms. Now multiply 24 therms by the rate.

$$24 \text{ therms} \times \frac{\$0.44506}{\text{therm}} = \quad \$10.68$$

Add the service fee: $\underline{\$\ 3.00}$

$\$13.68$ = monthly charge

Exercises

Read each gas meter and record it as a four-digit number expressing hundreds of cubic feet (CCF) of natural gas.

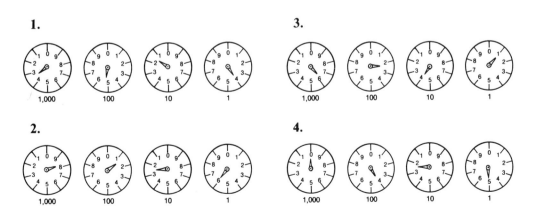

1.

3.

2.

4.

Use Table 13.3 to calculate the natural-gas consumption and the monthly charges. Account numbers with −01 are year-round, and those with −02 are heat only.

Account Number	Meter Readings (CCF)		Dates of Service	
	Previous	*Present*	*From*	*To*
5. 1492-01	4323	4352	Mar. 11	Apr. 10
6. 1066-01	5904	5922	June 19	July 19
7. 1776-02	6752	6806	Nov. 18	Dec. 19
8. 1940-01	1837	1859	Sept. 27	Oct. 24
9. 0721-02	9944	0025	Dec. 3	Jan. 4
10. 0520-02	2181	2294	Jan. 24	Feb. 26

Find the number of days of usage from problems 5-10 and the cost per day for each account.

11. 1492 − 01
12. 1066 − 01
13. 1776 − 02
14. 1940 − 01
15. 0721 − 02
16. 0520 − 02

Utilities: Water and Sewer

The water meter for a typical residential customer can be found underground in the front yard near the street. There is a metal access lid that can be removed to view the dial part of the meter. Depending on the locale, a water meter measures in either gallons or in cubic feet. The sewer-use charge is also derived from the water usage. This makes sense if you remember that the water that you use in your sinks, tubs, and toilets goes out the drain into the sewer system. A small percentage of the water may be used for lawns and gardens, but this is significant only during the summer months. You will notice that the water-meter dial pictured below looks very much like your family car's speedometer/odometer. The register tells the present meter reading.

The meter shown here has had 3,715,421 gallons pass through it.

Dial measures 10 gallons each revolution of the pointer.

Note: Units are read on the dial as the number last passed by the pointer.

Register

The meter reader would write 3,715.4, since charges are by thousands of gallons.

The water company in most communities bills its customers only once each quarter (3 months). By staggering the billing dates so that every month about one-third of its customers receive notices, the company can maintain a steady income and low meter-reading costs. Water and sewer charges are usually based on a unit cost per 1,000 gallons used per quarter. Table 13.4 gives a typical rate schedule for residential water and sewer use.

Table 13.4
Carolina Water and Sewer
Quarterly Residential Rate Schedule/1,000 Gallons

I. WATER

Gallons Used	Inside City	Outside City
First 8,000	0.90	1.35 (*min. allowance)
Next 32,000	0.85	1.25
Next 80,000	0.55	0.85
Next 420,000	0.45	0.75

II. SEWER

Gallons Used	All Customers
First 8,000	0.85 (*min. allowance)
Above 8,000	0.75

A minimum is charged just as if the customer had used 8,000 gallons.

Example

Find the quarterly water and sewer charges for a customer who lives outside the city and who uses 31,380 gallons in a quarter. Use Table 13.4.

Solution:

$$8{,}000 \text{ gal.} \times \frac{1.35}{1{,}000} = \quad \$10.80$$

$$23{,}380 \text{ gal.} \times \frac{1.25}{1{,}000} = \quad +\$29.23$$

$$\text{cost of water} = \quad \$40.03$$

$$8{,}000 \text{ gal.} \times \frac{0.85}{1{,}000} = \quad \$\ 6.80$$

$$23{,}380 \text{ gal.} \times \frac{0.75}{1{,}000} = \quad +\$17.54$$

$$\text{cost of sewer} = \quad \$24.34$$

Exercises

Use Table 13.4 to calculate the quarterly water use and the quarterly water and sewer charges. Account numbers ending with —01 are inside the city, and account numbers ending with —02 are outside the city.

Account Number	Meter Readings		Dates of Service	
	Previous	*Present*	*From*	*To*
1. 1492-01	03715.4	03736.6	Mar. 6	June 4
2. 1066-01	41233.0	41289.1	May 3	Aug. 4
3. 1776-02	11211.8	11333.1	July 7	Oct. 7
4. 1940-01	00579.2	00586.7	Jan. 12	Apr. 13
5. 0721-02	08566.3	08581.7	Feb. 3	May 4
6. 0520-02	145782.1	145814.5	Aug. 16	Nov. 20
7. 1987-01	84522.6	84563.8	Oct. 22	Jan. 18
8. 1984-02	42030.5	42092.2	June 14	Sept. 11

Find the number of days of service and the cost per day for each account for each utility.

9. 1492 − 01
10. 1066 − 01
11. 1776 − 02
12. 1940 − 02
13. 0721 − 02
14. 0520 − 02
15. 1987 − 01
16. 1984 − 02

17. People in the United States typically use 100 gallons of water per capita per day. Using Table 13.4, find the quarterly water and sewer charges for a family of four that lives in the city. Use 90 days as the duration of one quarter.

Utilities: Telephone

Telephone service in the United States is now divided into *local* service and *long-distance* service. Two different telephone companies will provide you with these two services. The local company will usually have available *limited-service* plans and *unlimited-service* plans. Unlimited-service customers are charged a flat fee plus any local toll calls and special phone features. Limited-service customers are charged a lower monthly rate but can make only about 40 calls without extra charges. Another type of limited service is called *local measured service*. With this system, a lower base rate is used, but all calls are measured for time and distance just like long-distance calls.

The long-distance carrier that you choose will charge on the basis of time and distance, both of which are measured by computerized metering systems.

Your telephone bill will also contain taxes and an interstate telephone access fee (ITAF) (about $2.00), plus charges for any special features such as touch-tone and call waiting. Table 13.5 gives a typical rate schedule for local-service calling.

Table 13.5
The Phone Bell Company Residential Rate Schedule

Type of Service	Basic Rate and Restrictions		Measured-Service Rate		
		Distance	First Min.	Addnl. Min.
Flat-rate Unlimited	$17.40* any number of calls		N.A.	N.A.
Limited Service	$13.50* 40 calls before additional charges	city	0.05	0.01
		sub.	0.08	0.03
Measured Service	$12.95* includes up to $7.00 in calls before additional charges	city	0.05	0.01
		sub.	0.08	0.03
Touch-tone	$1.00			
Call Waiting	$3.00	Both for $4.50		
Call Forwarding	$2.00			

Plus $2.00 non-taxable FCC interstate toll access fee

Example 1

Calculate the local telephone-service charges for a measured-service plan with touch-tone. The customer made 25 ten-minute city calls and 8 ten-minute suburban calls. The federal tax rate is 3%, and the state tax rate is 5%.

Solution:
Find the cost of the measured-service calls first.

$$\begin{array}{rl} \text{City call } (0.05)(1) + (0.01)(9) = & \text{\$.14 per call} \\ \times \text{25 city calls:} & \underline{\times 25} \\ & \$3.50 \end{array}$$

$$\begin{array}{rl} \text{Suburban calls } (0.08)(1) + (0.03)(9) = & \text{\$.35 per call} \\ \times \text{8 suburban calls:} & \underline{\times 8} \\ & \$2.80 \end{array}$$

total of calls $3.50 + $2.80 = $6.30

This does not exceed the $7.00 call limit.

$$\begin{array}{rll} \text{Therefore, charges} = & \$12.95 & \text{(base rate)} \\ & \$.39 & \text{(federal tax)} \\ & \$.65 & \text{(state tax)} \\ & \underline{\$2.00} & \text{(ITAF)} \\ & \$15.99 \end{array}$$

The following long-distance service schedule can be used to calculate the cost of calls before you even pick up the telephone. Remember, there will be a 3% federal excise tax but no state tax.

Table 13.6

Long Distance Pricing Schedule

Mileage	Day Rate		Evening		Night/Weekend	
	1st Min.	Addnl. Min.	1st Min.	Addnl. Min.	1st Min.	Addnl. Min.
1-10	0.1930	0.1782	0.1368	0.1069	0.0912	0.0713
11-22	0.2466	0.2313	0.1656	0.1421	0.1104	0.0948
23-55	0.3246	0.2772	0.2140	0.1663	0.1428	0.1109
56-70	0.3510	0.3267	0.2140	0.1960	0.1440	0.1307
71-124	0.3510	0.3267	0.2140	0.1960	0.1440	0.1307
125-292	0.3618	0.3465	0.2149	0.2079	0.1449	0.1386
293-430	0.4400	0.3647	0.2149	0.2140	0.1449	0.1435
431-925	0.4698	0.3740	0.2861	0.2257	0.1906	0.1505
926-1910	0.4920	0.3854	0.3129	0.2317	0.2090	0.1544
1911-3000	0.5330	0.4158	0.3465	0.2495	0.2106	0.1663
3001-4250	0.6035	0.4455	0.3560	0.2673	0.2478	0.1782
4251-5750	0.6212	0.4653	0.3759	0.2792	0.2573	0.1861

Rate Application Periods

	Mon.	Tues.	Wed.	Thurs.	Fri.	Sat.	Sun.
8:00 A.M.-5:00 P.M.							
5:00 P.M.-11:00 P.M.							
11:00 P.M.-8:00 A.M.							

☐ Weekday Rate   ▨ Evening Rate   ▨ Night and Weekend Rate

Example 2

Find the cost of calling home after 5:00 on Sunday afternoon. Suppose that the distance is 1,055 miles and that you plan to talk 30 minutes.

Solution:

Go down the mileage column on Table 13.6 to the interval that contains 1,055 miles. It will be 926-1,910. Under rate application, you will notice that Sunday afternoons are classified as *evening* calls.

Under "Evening," you will see 0.3129 for the first minute and 0.2317 for each additional minutes.

$$
\begin{aligned}
\text{cost} &= (1)(\$.3129) + (29)(\$.2317) + 3\% \text{ tax} \\
&= \$7.03 + 3\%(7.03) \\
&= \$7.03 + \$.21 \\
&= \$7.24
\end{aligned}
$$

Example 3

Determine the savings by making the call in Example 2 during the *night/ weekend* period.

Solution:

$$\text{new cost} = (1)(\$.2090) + (29)(\$.1544) + 3\% \text{ tax}$$
$$= \$4.69 + 3\%(4.69)$$
$$= \$4.69 + \$.14$$
$$= \$4.83$$
$$\text{savings} = \$7.24 - \$4.83$$
$$= \$2.41$$

Exercises

Use Table 13.6 to calculate the monthly local-service charges from the given information. Include federal and state tax.

1. flat rate with touch-tone, call waiting, and call forwarding

2. limited service with touch-tone
   5 calls over the 40 limit:
   city: three 5-minute calls
   sub: two 15-minute calls

3. measured service with touch-tone and call waiting
   city: eighteen 5-minute calls, four 10-minute calls
   sub: twelve 10-minute calls, two 20-minute calls

4. measured service
   city: thirty 5-minute calls, two 60-minute calls
   sub: three 10-minute calls, seven 20-minute calls

5. limited service with 40 limit, touch-tone, call waiting, and call forwarding
   36 calls

Use Table 13.6 to calculate the cost of each long-distance call from the given information.

6. 15 minutes
   285 miles, day

7. 18 minutes
   853 miles, evening

8. 24 minutes
   2,516 miles, night/weekend

9. 7 minutes
   3,560 miles, day

10. 12 minutes
    93 miles, evening

11. 1 hour, 6 minutes
    530 miles, night/weekend

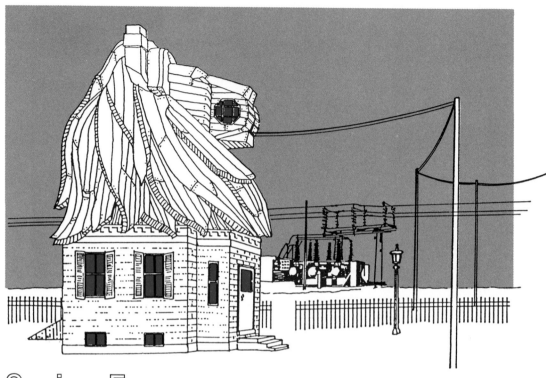

Saving Energy

Your house is like a big wood-and-brick lion with an appetite for energy. Of course, some houses have a bigger appetite than others; some are downright gluttonous. The energy requirements of fuel and electricity increase tremendously when the house is energy inefficient and when its occupants are wasteful. Both problems, however, can be solved by the home owner. He can make the house energy efficient by installing storm doors and windows, providing attic ventilation, insulating, caulking, and weather-stripping. People who have studied ways to save energy claim that making a house energy efficient will save as much as one-third on heating and air-conditioning costs. Some power companies even give the customer a lower power rate for a certified, energy-efficient structure.

The energy wasted by the occupants of a house results from their lifestyle and daily habits. It takes a serious family commitment and the formation of new habits to create an energy-efficient lifestyle. Energy is always wasted in small amounts that at the time seem insignificant. Over a period of time those little losses add up. For example, if each member of a family of four wastes 10 cents of energy a day, they will be throwing away $146 per year, or $2,190 in 15 years. In a metropolitan area that has an average of 25,000 such households, the yearly waste is $3,650,000. Clearly, the stewardship of money and resources takes a daily commitment. The principle of a consistent commitment is clearly stated in the Scriptures: "Moreover it is required in stewards, that a man be found *faithful*" (I Cor. 4:2).

What action can you take to conserve energy? First, minimize the amount of energy needed to heat and cool your home. Raise your air-conditioning thermostat to around 78° in the summer; this is still a fairly comfortable (and much cheaper) temperature to maintain. Next, lower the heating thermostat to 68°; this way your furnace or heat pump won't have to work so hard trying to achieve a higher temperature in winter. Also, take advantage of natural sunlight to help heat your home during cool weather; open draperies and blinds on sunny days and close them at night. And, of course, remember to keep the fireplace damper and the outside doors of the house closed. Every draft costs you money.

Other ways to save energy include conserving the electricity needed to operate your household appliances. For instance, if no one is watching the television or listening to the radio, turn them off. Likewise, turn off lights and other appliances when leaving a room, and limit the amount of time that the refrigerator/freezer doors are open. Furthermore, don't make your water heater work harder than necessary; limit the temperature setting to about 140° and put extra insulation around the water heater to avoid heat loss.

Once you start thinking about energy efficiency, you will find many other ways to save money at home. Booklets from power companies can help you as you develop an energy-efficient lifestyle. Planning ways to limit your energy consumption now will save you thousands of dollars over the course of your life.

Example 1

The Romero family pays $60 per month for electricity except during the three summer months when they use air conditioning. During those months their electric bill is about $132 per month. If making their house energy efficient saves one-third on air-conditioning costs, how much will they save during one summer?

Solution:
the cost of air conditioning:

$$\$132 - \$60 = \$72$$

energy-efficiency savings:

$$\frac{1}{3} \times \$72 = \$24 \text{ savings/month}$$
$$\$24 \times 3 \text{ months} = \$72 \text{ saved in one summer}$$

Remarks:
1. If the Romeros also saved this amount during four months of heating, they would save $168 per year.
2. To add storm windows, storm doors, attic ventilation, insulation, and caulk could cost between $850 and $900. This means that the payback period is about $\frac{850}{168}$, or 5 years.

Besides making your home energy efficient and your lifestyle less wasteful, the use of energy-efficient appliances can help lower power bills. The Energy Efficiency Ratio (EER) tells which appliances have good potential to save your money. An EER below 7 is poor, between 7 and 9 is good, and 10 or more is excellent. The next time you are in an appliance store, look for the EER on the products. By looking at the use of electric power shown in Table 13.7, you can quickly identify those appliances that contribute most to your power costs.

Table 13.7
Appliance Power Usage

	Average Wattage	Est. kWh Used per Month		Average Wattage	Est. kWh Used per Month
Food Preparation			**Heat and Cooling**		
Blender	386	1.3	3-Ton Central Air Conditioner	3,200	770
Broiler	1,436	8.3			
Carving Knife	92	0.7	10-kW Electric Furnace	10,000	2400
Coffee Maker	894	8.8			
Deep Fryer	1,448	6.9	3-Ton Heat Pump	3,360	800
Egg Cooker	516	1.2	**Health and Beauty**		
Frypan	1,196	15.5	Germicidal Lamp	20	11.8
Hot Plate	1,257	7.5	Infrared Heat Lamp	250	1.1
Mixer	127	1.1	Hair Dryer	381	1.2
			Shaver	14	0.2
* Microwave Oven	1,450	15.8	Sun Lamp	279	1.3
* Range/Oven	12,200	97.9	Toothbrush	7	0.1
Range/Self-Cleaning Oven	12,200	100.4	Heating Pad	65	0.8
			Home Entertainment		
Roaster	1,333	17.1	Radio	71	7.2
Sandwich Grill	1,161	2.8	Radio/Record Player	109	9.1
* Toaster	1,146	3.3	B/W Tube TV	160	29.2
Waffle Iron	1,116	1.8	B/W Solid-State TV	55	10.0
Food Preservation			Color Tube TV	300	55.0
15 ft.³ Freezer	341	99.6	* Color Solid-State TV	200	36.7
15 ft.³ Frost-Free Freezer	440	146.8	**Housewares**		
			Clock	2	1.4
12 ft.³ Refrigerator	241	60.7	Floor Polisher	305	1.3
12 ft.³ Frost-Free Refrigerator	321	101.4	Sewing Machine	75	0.9
			Vacuum Cleaner	630	3.8
14 ft.³ Refrig./ Freezer	326	94.8	* Dishwasher	1,201	30.3
			Trash Compactor	400	4.2
* 14 ft.³ Frost-Free Refrig./Freezer	615	152.4	Waste Disposer	445	2.5
Laundry				Average Wattage	Est. kWh Used Per Year
Clothes Dryer	4,856	82.8	**Seasonal Comfort**		
Hand Iron	1,008	12.0	**Conditioning**		
Automatic Washing Machine	512	8.6	Air Cleaner	50	216
			Electric Blanket	177	147
Non-automatic Washing Machine	286	6.3	Dehumidifier	257	377
			Attic Fan	370	291
* Water Heater	4,474	400.9	Circulating Fan	88	43
Water Pump	450	18.8	Rollaway Fan	171	138
Heat and Cooling			Window Fan	200	170
7,500 BTU Window Air Conditioner	2,200	530	Portable Heater	1,322	176
			Humidifier	177	163

Example 2

Find the monthly cost of operating the following appliances with an average power cost of 7.5 cents per kWh: microwave oven, standard range oven, toaster, 14 ft.³ frost-free refrigerator/freezer, electric water heater, solid-state color TV, and a dishwasher.

Solution:

Get the estimated kWh used per month.

microwave:	15.8
range/oven:	97.9
toaster:	3.3
refrigerator/freezer:	152.4
water heater:	400.9
TV:	36.7
dishwasher:	30.3
	737.3 kWh

$$\text{cost} = 737.3 \text{ kWh} \times \frac{\$.075}{\text{kWh}} = \$55.30$$

Example 3

Using Table 13.7, find how many hours per 30-day month and per day the three appliances using the most power are operated.

Solution:

Change kWh to watt-hours.

$$\text{range/oven: } 97.9 \times 1,000 = 97,900 \text{ watt-hours}$$

Look up the wattage rating: 12,200 watts.

Divide the watt-hours by watts to get hours per month.

$$\frac{97,900}{12,200} = 8.02 \text{ hours/month}$$

$$\frac{8.02}{30} = 0.2673 \text{ hours/day}$$

$$= 16 \text{ minutes/day}$$

$$\text{refrigerator/freezer: } \frac{152.4 \times 1,000}{615} = 247.8 \text{ hours/month}$$
$$= 8.26 \text{ hours/day}$$

$$\text{water heater: } \frac{400.9 \times 1,000}{4,474} = 89.6 \text{ hours/month}$$
$$= 2.99 = 3 \text{ hours/day}$$

Example 4

If the water heater in Example 3 is given additional blanket insulation and the water temperature is reduced, the operating time per day can be lowered to 2 hours. How much does this save per 30-day month and per year with power at 7.5 cents per kWh?

Solution:

$$2 \text{ hours per day} \times 30 \text{ days} = 60 \text{ hours per month}$$
$$60 \text{ hours} \times 4{,}474 \text{ watts} = 268{,}440 \text{ watt-hours/month}$$
$$= 268.44 \text{ kWh/month}$$

The savings in power consumption is the difference between the old and new usages.

$$\text{power savings} = 400.9 - 268.4$$
$$= 132.5 \text{ kWh}$$
$$\text{cost savings} = (\$.075)(132.5)$$
$$= \$9.94/\text{month}$$
$$= \$119.28/\text{year}$$

Example 5

Find the power consumption and monthly cost of operating an electric furnace. The furnace rating is 6.6 kilowatts, and it runs 15 minutes out of every hour.

Solution:

Find the furnace's operating time.

$$15 \text{ min.} \times 24 = 360 \text{ minutes/day} = 6 \text{ hours/day}$$

Next find the power consumption.

$$6 \text{ hr.} \times 6.6 \text{ kilowatts} = 39.6 \text{ kWh/day} = 1{,}188 \text{ kWh/30-day month}$$

At 7.5 cents per kWh, the cost is given by . . .

$$\text{cost} = (\$.075)(1{,}188)$$
$$= \$89.10/\text{month}$$

Example 6

Find the monthly savings for replacing a 3-ton heat pump with an EER of 8.0 with a new heat pump with an EER of 9.2. Assume that power costs 7.2 cents per kWh.

Solution:

Since the more efficient appliance has a higher EER, the proportion will be inverse.

$$\frac{\text{New EER}}{\text{Old EER}} = \frac{\text{Old kWh}}{\text{New kWh}} \quad \text{Now substitute.}$$

$$\frac{9.2}{8.0} = \frac{800}{x}, \text{ so } x = \frac{(800)(8.0)}{9.2} = 695.65 \text{ new kWh}$$

$$\text{power savings} = 800 - 695.65 = 104.35 \text{ kWh}$$
$$\text{dollar savings} = 104.35 \times \$.072 = \$7.51 \text{ per month}$$

Exercises

Find how much time the following appliances are normally operating per month and per day according to Table 13.7.
1. microwave oven
2. clothes dryer
3. 12 ft.^{3} frost-free refrigerator
4. automatic washing machine

Find the monthly savings for each energy-efficiency improvement shown. Assume that all the appliances in Table 13.7 have an EER of 8.0 and that electric power costs 8.1 cents/kWh.

5. New 14 ft.^{3} frost-free refrigerator/freezer with 9.1 EER.

6. new water heater with 8.9 EER

7. insulation blanket for water heater: 20% savings

8. insulation for attic: 20% savings on heat; furnace rating: 7,700 watts, runs 18 minutes each hour

9. Use microwave for all oven cooking instead of range oven.

10. Install central air conditioning instead of two 7,500 BTU window units.

Find the monthly cost at 8.0 cents per kWh to operate the following appliances. Assume each EER on Table 13.7 to be 8.0.

11. microwave oven, EER = 9.2

12. clothes dryer, EER = 7.0

13. heat pump, EER = 9.3

14. automatic washing machine, EER = 7.8

15. 15 ft.^{3} freezer, EER = 9.5

16. electric furnace, EER = 6.0

17. Carl Jorgensen plans to get his house certified as an energy-efficient structure. He pays an average of $80 per month now, but the power company will give him a new rate 20% lower than his present rate, and the energy-efficiency work will save 25% over his former costs. What will his new monthly power bill cost?

18. If Mr. Jorgensen (problem 17) pays $735 for the proposed energy improvements, what is the payback period?

House Repairs and Maintenance

The repair work around a home is much like that of the family car—some of it you can do, but other things are best left to the professionals. In recent years hardware stores and building-supplies stores have begun to stock and sell many lines of products just for the *do-it-yourself (DIY)* consumer. Those same stores sell manuals that give the home owner some basic information on such subjects as plumbing, electrical work, concrete and masonry, and vinyl sidings. Several national magazines are devoted to the DIY consumers, and other magazines have helpful features every month.

Table 13.8
Home Repairs and Maintenance

A. *Structure*	C. *Electrical*
plaster—drywall	circuit-breaker panel
siding and trim	wiring
roofing and shingles	switches
gutters and downspouts	receptacles
windows and doors	light fixtures
B. *Mechanical*	D. *Piping/Plumbing*
furnace or heat pump	water pipes
air conditioner	water valves
water heater	drainpipes
fans	sewers
built-in dishwasher	toilets
garbage disposal	bathtub/shower
	sink

Which of the house repairs would the DIY consumer be able to manage? The answer depends on the individual. Many people are both skilled repairmen and home owners. Others believe they have little aptitude for repairing things. However, with a little advice and some diligence, there are a few repair jobs that any home owner can tackle. The objective, of course, is to save money and be a good steward of your resources, but DIY work can bring other benefits as well. One benefit that most people experience is a real sense of satisfaction with the completion of the job as well as the quality of the job. Also, being a successful DIY home owner can provide opportunities to minister to other people by sharing your "expertise." If you want to share your faith in Christ with an unsaved neighbor, help him save $200 or $300 on a repair job, and you will often see him express a new attitude and a willingness to listen. By going out of your way to help, you have earned the right to be heard.

The following three examples illustrate the savings that the home owner can realize by doing his own maintenance and repairs. As a rule, the typical home owner can expect annual repairs and maintenance done by outside forces to average between one and two percent of the value of the home. For instance, a well-maintained $60,000 home can require between $800 and $1,200 each year for maintenance and repairs. (The original quality of workmanship and materials dictates the high or low end of this range of costs.) You will notice that materials cost considerably less when the home owner buys them. Most service and repair people buy their supplies at wholesale rates, but they charge the customers retail value plus overhead and profit, in addition to the hourly labor costs. Many times these people don't make a profit from the labor costs, and their profit on the parts and materials is what keeps their business going.

Example 1

Mr. Chon needs to paint his house. He has 3 options:
  a. do the painting himself on Saturdays
  b. have a painting contractor do it
  c. have vinyl siding put on the house

He knows that the house will need two coats of paint, plus scraping and spot priming. His house is 36 ft. by 50 ft.

Solution:
To price option (a), he needs to get the quantities and cost for materials and equipment. (You can assume he already has ladders.)

$$\text{perimeter of the house} = 2(36 \text{ ft.}) + 2(50 \text{ ft.})$$
$$= 72 \text{ ft.} + 100 \text{ ft.}$$
$$= 172 \text{ ft.}$$

$$\text{area of the outside} = 8 \text{ ft.} \times 172 \text{ ft.}$$
$$= 1,376 \text{ ft.}^2 \text{ (ignore windows)}$$

One gallon covers 400 ft.^{2} per coat or 200 ft.^{2} per 2 coats.

gallons needed for 2 coats $= \frac{1,376}{200} = 6.88$ gallons; therefore 7 whole gallons

Allow two gallons for painting trim.
Allow one more gallon of primer.
Allow four paint brushes and two scrapers.
Cost of option (a):

10 gallons at $15.00 each =	$150
4 brushes at $5.00 each =	$ 20
2 scrapers at $4.00 each =	$ 8
total =	$178

To price option (b), omit the paint brushes and scrapers.
Cost of option (b):

10 gallons at $18.75 =	$187.50
48 hours at $16.00* =	$768.00
total =	$955.50

This typical rate includes wages, taxes, insurance, overhead, and profit.

To price option (c), you need the square feet of siding plus the trim and special-fitting pieces.

Cost of option (c):
  Materials cost:

  siding: 1,376 ft.$^2 \times \frac{\$70}{100 \text{ ft.}^2} =$ $963.20

  trim/special: 20% (of siding cost) = $192.64
  Labor cost:

  1,376 ft.$^2 \times \frac{\$35}{100 \text{ ft.}^2} =$ $481.60
  total = $1,637.44

Remarks:
  1. It is obvious that the DIY approach to this job is the least expensive.
  2. It is not obvious whether option (b) or option (c) is less expensive. Paint has a life expectancy of about 10 to 15 years, whereas vinyl siding would easily last 30 years. If you consider that 2 paint jobs would last 30 years, then you are comparing $1,911 (2 × $955.50) to $1,637.44. (Don't forget, however, that in 15 years it will cost more to paint the house due to inflation.) Vinyl is definitely better, however, if the home owner can afford the extra $682 initial investment.
  3. If the home owner chooses vinyl, he should be sure that the color is one he can live with for a long time.

Example 2

When a pipe broke during the winter, Willie Thompson decided to repair it himself. He had to replace a six-foot section of $\frac{1}{2}$-inch copper pipe and a valve. He used flexible polybutylene pipe. How much did he save by not calling a plumber? Use 5% for the sales tax.

Solution:

Materials

6′ PB pipe (had to buy 10 ft.) =	$ 3.00
1 copper/PB connector =	$ 2.50
1 PB 90° elbow =	$ 2.50
1 PB to threaded copper fitting =	$ 2.00
1 globe valve =	$ 5.00
1 crimping tool =	$15.00
subtotal =	$30.00
5% tax =	$ 1.50
total =	$31.50

To see what a plumber's charges would be, leave out the crimping tool, add 15% for overhead and profit to the materials, and add $1\frac{1}{2}$ hours of labor at $22 per hour.

materials =	$30.00
less crimping tool:	–$15.00
	$15.00
tax =	$ .75
	$15.75
15% overhead/profit =	$ 2.36
total materials =	$18.11
labor: 1.5 hours at $22/hour =	$33.00
total =	$51.11

savings = $51.11 − $31.50 = $19.61

Example 3

When the light switch in Sally Campbell's bedroom broke, she called an electrician who said it would cost $25 for his service call. She decided to fix it herself. She bought the part and a book at the hardware store. How much did she save? Use 5% sales tax.

Solution:

Materials

1 light switch =	$1.75
1 screwdriver =	$2.00
1 how-to book =	$5.50
subtotal =	$9.25
tax =	$ .46
total =	$9.71

savings = $25 − $9.71 = $16.29

Remarks:
1. On little jobs, most electricians can't charge a reasonable price and still make a profit, so they often quote high prices to discourage the customer.
2. How much will it cost Sally the next time a light switch breaks? Just $1.75 + tax for the switch.

Exercises

Calculate the exterior wall area and the amount of paint in gallons for a one-coat coverage of each house given. Allow 380 ft.^{2} per gallon, and assume that the walls all have an 8-foot vertical dimension. (Hint: L-shaped houses are created from two rectangular shapes. However, the area where the two rectangles meet isn't to be painted. It's an interior wall.)

1. house A, rectangular
   32′ × 48′

2. house B, rectangular
   42′ × 54′

3. house C, rectangular
   46′ × 60′

4. house D, L-shaped
   from 2 rectangles 32′ × 32′ and
   32′ × 56′

5. house E, L-shaped
   from 2 rectangles 42′ × 30′ and
   30′ × 60′

6. house F, T-shaped
   from 2 rectangles 40′ × 60′ and
   30′ × 30′

Calculate the commercial-labor costs for painting each house. Use a painting rate of 65 ft.^{2} per hour and $16 per hour for labor.

7. house A, 1 coat
8. house B, 1 coat
9. house C, 2 coats

10. house D, 1 coat
11. house E, 1 coat
12. house F, 2 coats

Calculate the total cost of materials, including 5% sales tax, for each materials list and unit prices.

13. *Electrical:*

	Unit
25′ wire	$ .20/ft.
1 switch box	$ 1.50
1 switch and cover plate	$ 1.75
1 light fixture	$15.00
4 wire nuts	$ .10 each

15. *Paint:*

	Unit
5 gallons paint	$15 each
2 paint brushes	$ 5 each
1 paint roller (comes with pan)	$ 6
2 spare rollers	$ 2 each

14. *Plumbing:*

	Unit
10′ of 1.5″ PVC plastic pipe	$ .35/ft.
2 90° PVC elbows	$ .80 each
1 coupling	$ .70
1 can PVC solvent	$3.00

16. *Water heater:*

	Unit
1 40-gallon water heater	$180.00
1 pressure-relief valve	$ 8.50
2 shut-off valves	$ 2.75 each
2 couplings	$ 1.15 each

17. Jack Knapp did a cost estimate for a deck on the back of his house. Use his materials list and the prices from the local builder to see what the before-tax estimate showed.

Quantity	Materials	Unit Prices
31	2 × 4—8 ft. treated	$2.75
12	2 × 4—10 ft. treated	$3.05
7	2 × 8—10 ft. treated	$4.80
2	2 × 8—8 ft. treated	$4.25
5 lb.	16d galvanized nails	$.85/lb.
5 lb.	10d galvanized nails	$.75/lb.
6 pkg.	sand/cement mix	$4.25/pkg.

18. How much can Amanda Allen save by painting the exterior of her house herself instead of contracting it out? The house is L-shaped: 18′ × 30′ and 32′ × 40′. She plans to use paint that needs only one coat. Use the labor data for problems 7-12.

Home Improvements ────────────

There isn't always a clear distinction between home repairs and home improvements. Repairs are done on items that have deteriorated or broken and that inhibit household functions. Improvements are performed to beautify, improve efficiency, and expand household functions. Improvements tend to raise the value of the house and property, whereas repairs are needed to help the property hold its value. For instance, replacing a water heater would be a repair, but installing a larger, more efficient water heater makes it a repair *and* an improvement. Adding a second bathroom improves the value and function of a house.

The decision to invest money in a home improvement often hinges on two factors: "How much will it cost?" and "Will the value of the house increase by the same amount?" For example, if a new bathroom costs $2,000, but the value of the house only goes from $50,000 to $51,000, then it isn't a wise investment. If viewed as a long-term investment, however, inflation would eventually make the improvement worthwhile.

To determine the cost of a home improvement, the biggest task will be to determine quantities of materials. Once those are established, you will be ready for a trip to the local building-supply company to compare prices and shop for bargains. In this section you will primarily learn about figuring quantities, since you have already had considerable practice totaling lists of materials.

Example 1

How many bundles of insulation will you need for the ceiling of a house that is 42 ft. by 54 ft.? The rafters of the house run across the short dimension and are 16″ apart. A strip of insulation 15″ wide will fit between each one and will run across the width of the house. (Ceiling insulation comes in bundles containing 48.96 ft.²)

Solution:
Since some measurements are in inches and some in feet, you first need to change the 54 feet to inches.

$$54 \text{ ft.} \times \frac{12 \text{ in.}}{\text{ft.}} = 648 \text{ inches}$$

Now find how many 16″ sections are in this length. This will tell you how many strips you'll need.

$$\frac{648 \text{ in.}}{16 \text{ in.}} = 40.5 \text{ strips}$$

You can split one piece in two to finish the half strip.

The total length of insulation will be the width of the house times the number of strips.

$$\begin{aligned} \text{length} &= 40.5 \times 42 \\ &= 1{,}701 \text{ ft. of 15-in.-wide insulation} \end{aligned}$$

Now you have to convert this amount to square feet to find how many bundles you'll need.

$$15 \text{ in.} \div 12 \text{ in.} = 1.25 \text{ ft.}$$
$$\text{So, } 1.25 \times 1{,}701 = 2{,}126.25 \text{ ft.}^2$$

To find the number of bundles, divide the total area by the area per bundle.

$$\frac{2{,}126.25}{48.96} = 43.4 \text{ bundles}$$

You will have to buy 44 bundles.

Example 2

How much wallpaper will be required to cover all four walls of a bedroom that is 12 ft. × 14 ft.? Wallpaper comes in rolls that contain 36 ft.^{2}; however, if the paper requires a pattern match, only 30 ft.^{2} are used for calculating the number of rolls.

Solution:
Even though the room may have a couple of windows and doors, wallpaper is not figured closely enough to consider them. Also recall that most walls are 8 ft. high.

$$\begin{aligned} \text{perimeter of room} &= 2(12 \text{ ft.}) + 2(14 \text{ ft.}) \\ &= 24 \text{ ft.} + 28 \text{ ft.} \\ &= 52 \text{ ft.} \end{aligned}$$

$$\begin{aligned} \text{area of the walls} &= 52 \text{ ft.} \times 8 \text{ ft.} \\ &= 416 \text{ ft.}^2 \end{aligned}$$

$$\text{So the number of rolls} = \frac{416}{30} = 13.9 \text{ (14 rolls total)}$$

Example 3

Find the materials needed to install a chain-link fence around the back yard of the property shown. Fences generally have a post every ten feet. Corner posts and end posts are special sizes, so they are figured separately.

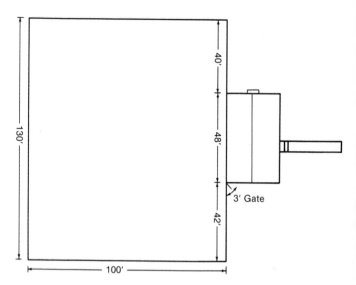

3' Gate

Solution:

$$\text{length of fencing} = 2(100 \text{ ft.}) + 130 \text{ ft.} + 40 \text{ ft.} + (42 \text{ ft.} - 3 \text{ ft.})$$
$$= 200 \text{ ft.} + 130 \text{ ft.} + 40 \text{ ft.} + 39 \text{ ft.}$$
$$= 409 \text{ ft.}$$

Number of end and corner posts: 4 at the corners, one on each side of the house, and one at the opposite end of the gate.

$$= 4 + 2 + 1$$
$$= 7 \text{ special posts}$$

Number of intermediate posts:

$\frac{100 \text{ ft.}}{10 \text{ ft.}} = 10$ spaces, which requires 11 posts, two of which are corner posts

Therefore, each 100-ft. side takes 9 intermediate posts.

$\frac{130 \text{ ft.}}{10 \text{ ft.}} = 13$ spaces, requiring 14 posts, two of which are corner posts

Therefore, the 130-ft. side takes 12 intermediate posts.

$\frac{40}{10} = 4$ spaces; therefore, 3 intermediate posts

$\frac{42 - 3}{10} = \frac{39}{10} = 3.9$, or 4 spaces and 3 intermediate posts

Now get the total:

$$9 + 9 + 12 + 3 + 3 = 36 \text{ intermediate posts}$$

the final materials list: 409 ft. fencing
7 special posts
36 intermediate posts
1 3-ft.-wide gate

Example 4

Find the amount of concrete needed in cubic yards for a driveway 60 ft. long, 9 ft. wide, and 4 in. thick.

Solution:
Using all the dimensions in feet, get the volume in cubic feet.

$$\text{volume} = 60 \text{ ft.} \times 9 \text{ ft.} \times \tfrac{4}{12} \text{ ft.}$$
$$= 180 \text{ ft.}^3$$

There are 27 cubic ft. in a cubic yard, so convert ft.^{3} to yd.^{3} by dividing by the number of cubic feet in a cubic yard.

$$\tfrac{180}{27} = 6\tfrac{2}{3} \text{ yd.}^3$$

Exercises

Find the required ceiling insulation for each house. Assume that the rafters are spaced across the short dimension at 16". Give your answer as linear feet and as a whole number of bundles, where each bundle of $6\tfrac{1}{4}$"-thick-by-15"-wide ceiling insulation contains 48.96 ft.^{2}.

   1. house A, rectangular 32' × 48'

   2. house B, rectangular 42' × 54'

   3. house C, rectangular 46' × 60'

   4. house D, L-shaped from 2 rectangles
      32' × 32' and 32' × 56'

   5. house E, L-shaped from 2 rectangles
      42' × 30' and 30' × 60'

   6. house F, T-shaped from 2 rectangles
      40' × 60' and 30' × 30'

Find the number of rolls of wallpaper required to paper each given room. Give your answer as a whole number of rolls.

   7. rectangular room, 11' × 14', all walls,
      pattern to match

   8. rectangular room, 12' × 18', omit one
      small wall, no pattern to match

   9. rectangular room, 10' × 12', omit one
      large wall, pattern to match

   10. L-shaped room from two rectangles,
      12' × 12' and 12' × 8', no pattern

   11. L-shaped room from two rectangles,
      14' × 16' and 10' × 10', pattern to match

   12. L-shaped room from two rectangles,
      12' × 18' and 12' × 18', small wall on each
      leg omitted, no pattern to match

Find the amount of fencing and posts for each yard.

13. rectangular lot 150′ by 200′, chain-link fence around perimeter, 1 10-foot gate adjacent to a corner

14. rectangular area 80′ by 120′, perimeter farm fence, wooden posts at 10′, no specials at corners, 1 10′-galvanized farm gate

Find the amount of concrete in cubic yards for each project.

15. driveway 10′ by 75′, 5″ thick

16. driveway 8′ × 38′, 4″ thick

17. patio, 12′ by 18′, 4″ thick

18. garage floor, 24′ × 30′, 5″ thick, with 6″-wide band at perimeter that is 15″ thick

19. Mrs. Moser wants her husband to build a patio in the shape of a half-circle. She wants it to have a flat side (diameter) of 16 ft. How much concrete will Mr. Moser need if the patio slab is to be 4″ thick?

20. Bill Johnson is figuring materials for a new, treated-wood deck behind his house. From his plan, figure the lumber that he will need. (Use 4 inches for the width of a 2 × 4 board. This allows a half-inch space between them since they are actually only $3\frac{1}{2}$″ wide.)

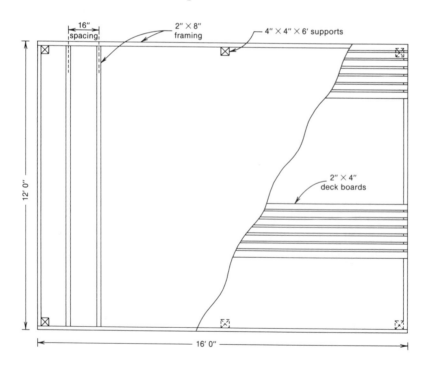

Chapter 13 Review ══════════════════

assessed valuation (assessed value)
do-it-yourself (DIY)
energy-efficiency rating (EER)
home improvement
home-owner's liability
home-owner's property damage
home repair
kilowatt-hours (kWh)
mils
therms

Review Exercises

Find the tax liability for each property.

Assessed Value	Tax Rate
1. $59,800	$1.525 per $100
2. $7,000	147.4 mils
3. $85,250	$13.52 per $1,000
4. $96,000	$3.21 per $100
5. $4,370	224.1 mils

Find the annual home-owner's liability-insurance premium. Use Table 13.1.
  6. 25,000/5,000
  7. 35,000/3,000
  8. 65,000/10,000
  9. 125,000/15,000

Find the annual home-owner's property damage premiums for the given limits. Unless conditions are given, assume no adjustments.

10. 45,000/10,000
    $250 deductible

11. 55,000/25,000
    $250 deductible
    rural dwelling

12. 70,000/30,000
    $500 deductible
    2,800 ft.^{2}

13. 105,000/40,000
    $500 deductible
    3,200 ft.^{2}, rural dwelling

Using the power-company rate schedule in Table 13.2, calculate the power usage in kWh and the monthly charges.

Meter Readings (kWh)	
Previous	*Present*
14. 8,156	9843
15. 1,484	2436
16. 9,722	0534
17. 4,825	5405

Use Table 13.3 to calculate the natural-gas consumption and monthly charges.

Meter Readings (CCF)		
Previous	*Present*	*Type*
18. 1858	1899	year-round
19. 6358	6410	heat
20. 8115	8199	heat
21. 9483	9580	year-round
22. 9951	0024	heat

Use Table 13.4 to calculate the quarterly water and sewer charges.

Account Location	Meter Readings		Quarterly Charges	
	Previous	*Present*	*Water*	*Sewer*
23. city	11623.4	11639.0		
24. city	34721.5	34740.7		
25. rural	78592.1	78615.9		
26. rural	26765.8	26799.5		
27. city	94235.3	94278.6		

Use Tables 13.5 and 13.6 to find the monthly cost of each service or the per-call cost for long distance. Allow for federal tax at 3% and state tax at 5%.

28. Limited service with touch-tone
   6 calls at 5 minutes each/city
   4 calls at 10 minutes each/sub.

29. Measured service with touch-tone and
      call forward
   23 calls at 5 minutes each/city
   11 calls at 8 minutes each/sub.

30. 14 minutes, long distance
   962 miles, evening

31. Flat rate with touch-tone and call waiting

32. Measured service with touch-tone
   45 calls at 4 minutes each/city
   31 calls at 6 minutes each/sub.

33. 22 minutes, long distance
   753 miles, night/weekend

Find the monthly (30 days) and daily operating times for each appliance. Use Table 13.7.

34. 15 ft.^{3} freezer

35. 3-ton central air (used only 4 months)

36. toaster

37. 10-kW electric furnace (used 6 months)

Find the monthly cost to operate the following appliances at a power rate of 7.5 cents/kWh. Assume each EER in Table 13.7 to be 8.0.

38. solid-state color TV
EER $= 6.5$

39. dishwasher
EER $= 8.5$

40. dehumidifier
EER $= 9.1$

41. 12 ft.^{3} frost-free refrigerator
EER $= 7.6$

Calculate the cost of labor and materials to paint each house exterior. Use a coverage rate of 380 ft.^{2} per gallon and $10/gallon, a painting rate of 65 ft.^{2} per hour, and $16 per hour for labor.

42. rectangular house 38′ × 52′, 1 coat

43. L-shaped house 36′ × 32′, 32′ × 45′, 2 coats

44. rectangular house 44′ × 65′, 1 coat

45. L-shaped house 30′ × 40′, 30′ × 60′, 1 coat

46. How many rolls of wallpaper are required to paper a room 14′ × 18′ with a pattern to match?

47. How much insulation is needed for the ceiling of a house 30′ × 45′? Use the data from the exercises on page 409.

48. How many cubic yards of concrete are needed for a garage floor 28′ × 24′ that is 4″ thick and has an 8″-wide band around the perimeter that is 18″ thick?

49. How much fencing and how many posts are needed for a yard that is 50′ × 30′ and has one 10′-wide gate?

50. Kurt Sigmon received his real-estate tax notice showing an obligation of $683.50. If his county has a tax rate of 321.25 mils, what is the assessed value of his property?

CHAPTER 4

Life and Health Insurance

You have learned that automobile insurance and home-owner's insurance protect a person from unforeseen losses to those large investments. Similarly, life insurance protects a family from the loss of income should the wage earner of that family die unexpectedly. Among Christians, there are differences of opinion about the need for life insurance. Some believers contend that buying such insurance shows a lack of trust in the Lord. Others argue that to not have life insurance could violate I Timothy 5:8: "But if any provide not for his own, and specially for those of his own house, he hath denied the faith, and is worse than an infidel." Regardless of your convictions or preferences, the Bible does teach that we are to make preparation for future events. As Proverbs 27:12 says, "A prudent man foreseeth the evil, and hideth himself." And I Chronicles 22:5 records that King David "prepared abundantly before his death" for the building of the temple. In the same way, life insurance should be an abundant preparation by a wage earner to adequately meet the family needs in case of death.

During the last thirty years, medical costs have risen so drastically that the average wage earner cannot afford to be hospitalized without help from medical insurance. A typical four-week hospital stay for major surgery may cost $15,000 to $20,000, which would completely bankrupt the average family. To protect families from this possible disaster, major medical insurance policies are purchased by companies or individuals. These policies usually pay for all or part of the medical costs above a certain level, such as $1,000 or $2,000.

Since there are many different kinds of life and health insurance policies, you would be wise to learn about them now, before you actually purchase a policy.

Life Insurance
Term Insurance
Whole-Life Insurance
Insurance Combined with Investments
Health Insurance
Social Security System

Life Insurance

How can life-insurance companies afford to pay large sums of money to the family of a policyholder when he dies? Of course, the policyholder paid the insurance company a yearly fee called the *premium,* but quite often that fee was paid for only a few years. For example, if the insured person paid an annual premium of $200 for 5 years on a $10,000 policy, then he paid only $1,000, but his *beneficiary* (the person he named to receive the money) receives ten times that amount: $10,000.

The insurance company bases its premiums on at least three significant factors. The first is the statistical prediction of how many policyholders of a certain age will die during the next year and succeeding years. The second is the expenses the company must pay to do business. These expenses include their employees, buildings, equipment, and operating costs. The third factor is how much the company can earn by investing the policyholder's premiums in stocks, bonds, and other securities. This investment of premiums helps to hold down the cost of life insurance. Without it, very few people could afford a life-insurance policy.

We must remember that the statistical prediction of how many people die before a certain age has nothing to do with individuals. God alone holds the appointment of life and death. Because these companies have kept records about large groups of people, they can predict the number of deaths in certain groups by each age. The basic tool used by the insurance underwriters is the Commissioner's Standard Ordinary Mortality Table (or CSO). The CSO table starts with a group of 10,000,000 people living and at age zero. There is a column (l_x) giving the number of people living at age x. There is another column (d_x) giving the number of people expected to die before reaching age x + 1. Yet another column (q_x) gives the prediction, or probability, of a person at age x dying within a year. Note that $q_x = \frac{d_x}{l_x}$. Some tables multiply q_x by 1,000 to give the death rate per 1,000.

Table 14.1
1958 Commissioner's Standard Ordinary Mortality Table

Age Male	l_x Number Living	d_x Number Dying	q_x Death Rate per 1,000	Expectancy, Years	% Living to 65	Age	l_x Number Living	d_x Number Dying	q_x Death Rate per 1,000	Expectancy, Years	% Living to 65
0	10,000,000	70,800	7.08	68.30	68.01	50	8,762,306	72,902	8.32	23.63	77.61
1	9,929,200	17,475	1.76	67.78	68.49	51	8,689,404	79,160	9.11	22.82	78.26
2	9,911,725	15,066	1.52	66.90	68.61	52	8,610,244	85,758	9.96	22.03	78.98
3	9,896,659	14,449	1.46	66.00	68.72	53	8,524,486	92,832	10.89	21.25	79.78
4	9,882,210	13,835	1.40	65.10	68.82	54	8,431,654	100,337	11.90	20.47	80.65
5	9,868,375	13,322	1.35	64.19	68.91	55	8,331,317	108,307	13.00	19.71	81.63
6	9,885,053	12,812	1.30	63.27	69.01	56	8,223,010	116,849	14.21	18.97	82.70
7	9,842,241	12,401	1.26	62.35	69.10	57	8,106,161	125,970	15.54	18.23	83.89
8	9,829,840	12,091	1.23	61.43	69.18	58	7,980,191	135,663	17.00	17.51	85.22
9	9,817,749	11,879	1.21	60.51	69.27	59	7,844,528	145,830	18.59	16.81	86.69
10	9,805,870	11,865	1.21	59.58	69.35	60	7,698,698	156,592	20.34	16.12	88.33
11	9,794,005	12,047	1.23	58.65	69.44	61	7,542,106	167,736	22.24	15.44	90.17
12	9,781,958	12,325	1.26	57.72	69.52	62	7,374,370	179,271	24.31	14.78	92.22
13	9,769,633	12,896	1.32	56.80	69.61	63	7,195,099	191,174	26.57	14.14	94.52
14	9,756,737	13,562	1.39	55.87	69.70	64	7,003,925	203,394	29.04	13.51	97.10
15	9,743,175	14,225	1.46	54.95	69.80	65	6,800,531	215,917	31.75	12.90	100.00
16	9,728,950	14,983	1.54	54.03	69.90	66	6,584,614	228,749	34.74	12.31	....
17	9,713,967	15,737	1.62	53.11	70.01	67	6,355,865	241,777	38.04	11.73	....
18	9,698,230	16,390	1.69	52.19	70.12	68	6,114,088	254,835	41.68	11.17	....
19	9,681,840	16,846	1.74	51.28	70.24	69	5,859,253	267,241	45.61	10.64	....
20	9,664,994	17,300	1.79	50.37	70.36	70	5,592,012	278,426	49.79	10.12	....
21	9,647,694	17,655	1.83	49.46	70.49	71	5,313,586	287,731	54.15	9.63	....
22	9,630,039	17,912	1.86	48.55	70.62	72	5,025,855	294,766	58.65	9.15	....
23	9,612,127	18,167	1.89	47.64	70.75	73	4,731,089	299,289	63.26	8.69	....
24	9,593,960	18,324	1.91	46.73	70.88	74	4,431,800	301,894	68.12	8.24	....
25	9,575,636	18,481	1.93	45.82	71.02	75	4,129,906	303,011	73.37	7.81	....
26	9,557,155	18,732	1.96	44.90	71.16	76	3,826,895	303,014	79.18	7.39	....
27	9,538,423	18,981	1.99	43.99	71.30	77	3,523,881	301,997	85.70	6.98	....
28	9,519,442	19,324	2.03	43.08	71.44	78	3,221,884	299,829	93.06	6.59	....
29	9,500,118	19,760	2.08	42.16	71.58	79	2,922,055	295,683	101.19	6.21	....
30	9,480,358	20,193	2.13	41.25	71.73	80	2,626,372	288,848	109.98	5.85	....
31	9,460,165	20,718	2.19	40.34	71.89	81	2,337,524	278,983	119.35	5.51	....
32	9,439,447	21,239	2.25	39.43	72.04	82	2,058,541	265,902	129.17	5.19	....
33	9,418,208	21,850	2.32	38.51	72.21	83	1,792,639	249,858	139.38	4.89	....
34	9,396,358	22,551	2.40	37.60	72.37	84	1,542,781	231,433	150.01	4.60	....
35	9,373,807	23,528	2.51	36.69	72.55	85	1,311,348	211,311	161.14	4.32	....
36	9,350,279	24,685	2.64	35.78	72.73	86	1,100,037	190,108	172.82	4.06	....
37	9,325,594	26,112	2.80	34.88	72.92	87	909,929	168,455	185.13	3.80	....
38	9,299,482	27,991	3.01	33.97	73.13	88	741,474	146,997	198.25	3.55	....
39	9,271,491	30,132	3.25	33.07	73.35	89	594,477	126,303	212.46	3.31	....
40	9,241,359	32,622	3.53	32.18	73.59	90	468,174	106,809	228.14	3.06	....
41	9,208,737	35,362	3.84	31.29	73.85	91	361,365	88,813	245.77	2.82	....
42	9,173,375	38,253	4.17	30.41	74.13	92	272,552	72,480	265.93	2.58	....
43	9,135,122	41,382	4.53	29.54	74.44	93	200,072	57,881	289.30	2.33	....
44	9,093,740	44,741	4.92	28.67	74.78	94	142,191	45,026	316.66	2.07	....
45	9,048,999	48,412	5.35	27.81	75.15	95	97,165	34,128	351.24	1.80	....
46	9,000,587	52,473	5.83	26.95	75.56	96	63,037	25,250	400.56	1.51	....
47	8,948,114	56,910	6.36	26.11	76.00	97	37,787	18,456	488.42	1.18	....
48	8,891,204	61,794	6.95	25.27	76.49	98	19,331	12,916	688.15	.83	....
49	8,829,410	67,104	7.60	24.45	77.02	99	6,415	6,415	1,000.00	.50	....

Note: Values for females 15 and up are the same as for males 3 years younger.
(From *Life Insurance Fact Book,* American Counsel of Life Insurance. Used by permission.)

Several examples are given to show how the numbers from the table can be used to answer certain questions related to life insurance. Although the subject of death may be unpleasant, it's a sobering reality that should keep us near the Lord. As the Scriptures tell us, death is a consequence of sin, and our sin nature can be given life only through the redeeming work of Christ.

Example 1

What is the probability that a child will die within its first year of life?

Solution:

$$\text{Probability} = \frac{\text{number dying}}{\text{number living}} = \frac{d_0}{l_0} = \frac{70,800}{10,000,000} = 0.00708$$

$$= 0.708\%, \text{ or about 7 out of each 1,000}$$

Example 2

What is the probability that an 18-year-old man will live to age 50? How about an 18-year-old woman?

Solution:

$$\text{Probability} = \frac{\text{number of men living at age 50}}{\text{number of men living at age 18}} = \frac{l_{50}}{l_{18}} = \frac{8,762,306}{9,698,230}$$

$$= 0.903, \text{ or } 90.3\%$$

In other words, out of 1,000 men living at age 18, 903 will still be living at age 50.

$$\text{Probability} = \frac{\text{number of women living at age 50}}{\text{number of women living at age 18}} = \frac{l_{50}}{l_{18}} = \frac{8,948,114}{9,743,175}$$

$$= 0.918, \text{ or } 91.8\%$$

So of 1,000 women living at age 18, 918 will be living at age 50.

Example 3

What is the probability that an 18-year-old man will die before reaching age 50?

Solution:

$$\text{Probability} = \frac{\text{number dying between 18 and 50}}{\text{number living at age 18}} = \frac{l_{18} - l_{50}}{l_{18}}$$

$$= \frac{926,924}{9,698,230}$$

$$= 0.096, \text{ or } 9.6\%$$

Notes:
1. This answer should agree with the number out of 1,000 that are living (see Example 2). $96 + 903 = 999$. The answer is off by one person due to rounding.
2. These examples don't tell how the insurance companies use the CSO table in making up premium rates, but they do show the value of mortality statistics in predicting how many policy benefits they will have to pay in a given time period.

How much life insurance should you purchase? Recall that life insurance has one basic function—to replace the economic loss to a family when the wage-earner dies. The death benefits of a policy should pay for immediate expenses and then provide an income by investment. The immediate expenses include all outstanding debts and mortgages. The monthly income needed depends on the size of the family and the earning power of the surviving spouse. The following example illustrates the calculation for the amount of life insurance needed. It does not, however, address the problem of whether the family can afford to pay the premiums.

Example 4

What amount of death benefits should the wage-earner provide for a family of four having a $35,000 mortgage and $6,000 in miscellaneous car and funeral costs? Assume that money can be invested at 10%(12) and that the family will receive $1,000 per month for 25 years above the other spouse's income.

Solution:
$$\text{immediate costs} = \$35,000 + \$6,000 = \$41,000$$

Imagine that the family lends the remaining insurance benefit to a bank, which makes a $1,000 monthly payment to the family. (This is a good way to think about how investments pay the investor.) Use the finance tables.

$$
\begin{aligned}
\text{investment} \quad &= 1,000 \times \text{amount borrowed factor at } i = \tfrac{5}{6}\% \\
&\quad \text{with } 25 \times 12 = 300 \text{ payments} \\
&= 1,000(110.0472301) \\
&= \$110,047
\end{aligned}
$$

$$\text{total face value of policy} = \$110,047 + \$41,000 = \$151,047$$

Remarks:
1. Since insurance policies are purchased in amounts that are multiples of $1,000, this wage-earner should buy a $151,000 policy. In actual practice, large policies come in increments of $10,000 or $25,000.
2. Many insurance brokers suggest carrying life insurance that equals up to 6 times the wage-earner's annual salary. If you divide the $151,000 by 6, the income level of this family was $25,000 per year. Later you will see the cost of this much insurance.

Exercises

Use the CSO Mortality Table to find the following:

1. l_{25} men
2. l_{55} men
3. d_{20} men
4. l_{30} women
5. l_{58} women

6. d_{25} women
7. q_{25} men
8. q_{85} women
9. q_{60} men

Use the CSO Mortality table to find the number of individuals living to the given age from a group of 1,000 18-year-olds.

10. men to age 25
11. women to age 80
12. men to age 20
13. men to age 35
14. women to age 20

15. women to age 55
16. men to age 40
17. men to age 60
18. women to age 32

Use the CSO Mortality Table to find the number of 20-year-olds, from a group of 1,000, who will die before reaching the given age.

19. men, age 30
20. men, age 42
21. women, age 29

22. women, age 39
23. men, age 85
24. women, age 90

Find the amount of death-benefit life insurance the wage-earner should carry for each of these situations. When only the salary is given, use the "times 6" principle.

25. salary: $1,850 per month
26. salary: $31,800 per year

27. salary: $18,500 per year
28. salary: $1,050 per month

29. home mortgage: $22,000
funeral and miscellaneous:
    $5,000
monthly income: $800
(20 years; 9%[12])

30. home mortgage: $65,000
education trust: $14,000
monthly income: $2,000
(30 years; 9%[12])

31. funeral and miscellaneous:
    $10,000
monthly income: $1,200
(15 years; 8%[12])

32. home mortgage: $35,000
miscellaneous: $5,000
quarterly income: $5,000
(15 years; 8%[4])

Term Insurance

There are three basic types of life insurance—term insurance, whole-life insurance, and endowment insurance. Term insurance provides protection against the loss of income for a specified period of time—usually one, five, ten, or twenty years. Term insurance pays benefits only in case of the death of the insured. In this way it is like car insurance; there are no accumulated cash values. The life insurance that you can buy at an airport before taking a flight is term insurance. Whenever you renew the policy at the end of a term, the cost will increase because you are older and in a higher risk bracket. (Recall the probabilities of death studied with the CSO Mortality Table.)

Insurance companies commonly sell 1-year and 5-year renewable term policies. This means that prices will change every year for 1-year term and will change every 5 years for 5-year term. The "renewable" provision means you don't have to requalify medically each time you renew. Longer term policies are usually sold as decreasing term. This means that the premium remains fixed but the benefits that the policy pays drop each year. This form of insurance is especially for protecting long-term decreasing debt, like a home mortgage.

Term insurance gives the greatest amount of protection for the amount spent until the insured is older. It provides the best buy for home buyers, parents of young children, or those with huge obligations during a fixed period of time. The following listing from one insurance company illustrates how significantly the cost of term insurance increases in the latter years. These costs are for a 5-year, renewable, $100,000 policy.

Age	Cost per Year
25	$130
30	$136
35	$164
40	$227
45	$333
50	$515
55	$848
60	$1,015

From looking at these figures, you can quickly conclude that the insured needs to develop other assets and investments during the younger years. With sufficient investments, by age 50 the insured can eliminate or significantly reduce the insurance costs needed to protect the beneficiary against loss of income. The following typical term-insurance premium table comes from an actual company. (*Note:* The letter *M* stands for $1,000, and premiums are per $1,000.)

Table 14.2
Term Insurance Premiums per $1,000

Age on Last Birthday	Annual Renewable		5-Year Renewable		20-Year Decreasing Term	
	25M to 99M	100M to 250M	25M to 99M	100M to 250M	25M to 99M	100M to 250M
20	2.81	1.97	3.01	2.11	3.22	2.25
21	2.82	1.97	3.02	2.11	3.23	2.26
22	2.84	1.99	3.04	2.13	3.25	2.28
23	2.85	2.00	3.05	2.14	3.27	2.29
24	2.86	2.00	3.05	2.14	3.30	2.31
25	2.87	2.01	3.06	2.14	3.34	2.34
26	2.88	2.02	3.07	2.15	3.39	2.37
27	2.88	2.02	3.07	2.15	3.44	2.41
28	2.91	2.04	3.11	2.18	3.51	2.46
29	2.95	2.07	3.15	2.21	3.58	2.51
30	2.98	2.09	3.18	2.23	3.66	2.56
31	3.02	2.11	3.21	2.25	3.77	2.64
32	3.06	2.14	3.26	2.28	3.94	2.77
33	3.13	2.19	3.33	2.33	4.17	2.92
34	3.21	2.25	3.43	2.40	4.44	3.19
35	3.30	2.31	3.57	2.50	4.74	3.32
36	3.42	2.39	3.77	2.64	5.07	3.55
37	3.55	2.49	3.97	2.78	5.44	3.81
38	3.74	2.62	4.24	2.97	5.84	4.09
39	3.96	2.77	4.48	3.14	6.29	4.40
40	4.21	2.95	4.82	3.37	6.78	4.75
41	4.47	3.13	5.12	3.58	7.31	5.12
42	4.79	3.35	5.50	3.85	7.91	5.54
43	5.13	3.59	5.94	4.16	8.56	5.99
44	5.49	3.84	6.41	4.49	9.27	6.49
45	5.90	4.13	6.90	4.83	10.04	7.03
46	6.37	4.46	7.50	5.25	10.89	7.62
47	6.89	4.83	8.17	5.72	11.82	8.27
48	7.48	5.24	8.99	6.29	12.84	8.99
49	8.12	5.68	9.88	6.92	13.94	9.76
50	8.92	6.24	10.96	7.67	15.14	10.60

Example 1

Find the first annual premium for a $55,000 annual renewable term policy issued at age 26.

Solution:

The $55,000 is the same as 55M, so it falls between 25M and 99M. The rate per M is $2.88.

$$\text{premium} = 55 \times \$2.88 = \$158.40$$

Example 2

Find the annual premium for the first 5 years of a $100,000, 5-year, renewable policy issued at age 35.

Solution:

The cost per $1,000 is $2.50.

$$\text{premium} = 100 \times \$2.50 = \$250 \text{ per year}$$

Remarks:
1. The total cost of the premiums for 5 years is $5 \times \$250 = \$1,250$. If the insured had purchased 5 years' worth of annual renewable term, the cost would be
$$\$231 + \$239 + \$249 + \$262 + \$277 = \$1,258$$
2. You could conclude that sometimes buying 5-year term is a little more economical than one-year term. Of course, there is a wide variation in the cost of insurance from different companies; some will offer less expensive annual term and others will offer less expensive 5-year.

Example 3

Find the amount of 20-year decreasing term that a 30-year-old can buy on a $15-per-month insurance budget.

Solution:
$$\$15 \text{ per month} \times 12 \text{ months} = \$180 \text{ per year}$$

Since rate per $M \times$ policy value in $M = $ cost per year, you can substitute:

$$3.66x = 180$$
$$x = \frac{180}{3.66} = 49.2 \text{ thousand}$$

The insured can buy $49,000 worth of 20-year decreasing term.

Exercises

Use Table 14.2 to find the annual premium for each of the term insurance policies.

	Age	Type	Face Value
1.	21	annual	$25,000
2.	32	annual	$150,000
3.	25	5-year	$50,000
4.	38	5-year	$130,000
5.	28	decreasing	$80,000
6.	25	decreasing	$180,000
7.	35	annual	$90,000
8.	37	5-year	$200,000
9.	26	decreasing	$45,000
10.	40	5-year	$230,000

Use Table 14.2 to find the maximum amount of insurance coverage that each budgeted amount will buy. Round to the nearest thousand.

	Age	Type	Budget
11.	23	annual	$250/year
12.	40	5-year	$600/year
13.	31	decreasing	$450/year
14.	27	decreasing	$18/month
15.	39	5-year	$65/month
16.	29	annual	$25/month

17. The church board wants to find the amount to be budgeted for Pastor Nichols's life insurance. He is 38 years old, earns $30,000 per year, and has a $40,000 home mortgage. His family will need $\frac{1}{2}$ of his salary for 25 years. If money can be invested at 12%(12), find the total insurance requirement and the annual premium for 5-year renewable term.

18. Tom Ratliff is 29 years old and wants a $100,000 term policy. Find his total costs for the first five years if he buys a 5-year policy and if he buys an annual policy.

19. 29-year-old Sara Peterson has a 20-year, $40,000 mortgage on her condominium. She wants a 20-year, decreasing-term policy to protect this property for her beneficiary. What will the annual premium cost?

20. How much life insurance can 34-year-old Judy Hartway buy for $21 per month if . . .
   (a) she buys annual term?
   (b) she buys 5-year term?
   (c) she buys 20-year decreasing term?

Whole-Life Insurance

Whole-life insurance is a form of protection for the financial welfare of a family that can be kept in force at the same fixed premium for as long as the insured lives. When you are younger, whole life (sometimes called *straight life*) costs more than term insurance because it is building a cash reserve (or cash value) that compensates for later years when the insured is a higher risk. Figure 14.1 illustrates how the premiums vary for annual renewable term and whole-life policies taken out at age 20.

Age of Insured Person
Annual Premium for Each $1,000 Face Value
Figure 14.1

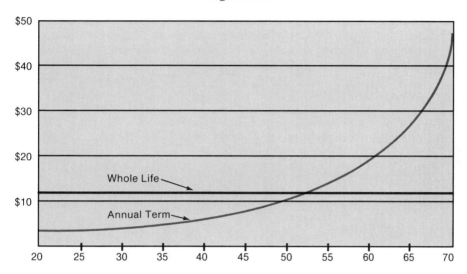

The excess above the cost of *term* insurance is invested at interest so that the fund has a value for insurance benefits during those latter years, when the fixed premium will not pay for the actual cost of insurance. This cash value of the whole-life policy can be used as *collateral* (a guarantee of ability to pay back), or *security,* for a loan from the company, as funds to pay *premiums,* as funds to buy paid-up insurance, or as the *surrender value* of the policy if it is canceled.

Some straight-life policies don't require premiums for the lifetime of the insured. They are called *limited-payment* policies, and they have a fixed number of years over which the premiums are paid. Many companies offer policies that are paid up in 70 years, 30 years, or often at age 65. Limited-payment policies will have higher premiums since they are paid over a shorter time span. This results in a faster accumulation of cash value and thus emphasizes the savings feature of the straight-life policy. Table 14.3 gives typical annual premiums per $1,000 of insurance for whole life and 20-payment life, plus cash values per $1,000 of insurance.

Table 14.3
Annual Premiums per $1,000

Male Age on Last Birthday	Whole Life					20-Payment Life				
	5M to 24M	25M to 100M	Cash value end of year			5M to 24M	25M to 100M	Cash value end of year		
			10	15	20			10	15	20
20	9.64	8.84	75	124	181	14.35	13.75	130	216	319
21	9.94	9.14				14.76	14.16			
22	10.27	9.47				15.18	14.58			
23	10.62	9.83				15.61	15.01			
24	10.98	9.18				16.07	15.47			
25	11.36	10.56	93	152	219	16.54	15.94	153	254	373
26	11.76	10.96				17.04	16.44			
27	12.18	11.38				17.55	16.95			
28	12.63	11.83				18.10	17.50			
29	13.10	12.30				18.65	18.05			
30	13.60	12.80	115	185	262	19.24	18.64	181	296	432
31	14.13	13.33				19.85	19.25			
32	14.68	13.88				20.49	19.89			
33	15.27	14.47				21.15	20.55			
34	15.90	15.10				21.86	21.26			
35	16.56	15.76	140	221	309	22.59	22.00	211	342	496
36	17.26	16.46				23.35	22.75			
37	18.00	17.20				24.15	23.55			
38	18.78	17.98				24.99	24.39			
39	19.60	18.80				25.85	25.25			
40	20.48	19.68	167	261	358	26.75	26.15	242	390	563

Notes:
1. Premiums for females are the same as for males 3 years younger.
2. Policies greater than $100,000 have a 5% discount from the stated rate.

Example 1

Find the annual premium for a 27-year-old male to purchase a $75,000 whole-life policy.

Solution:
The $75,000 falls between 25M and 100M, so the cost per thousand is $11.38

$$\text{premium} = \frac{11.38}{1,000} \times 75,000 = \$853.50 \text{ per year}$$

Example 2

Find the annual premium for a $20,000, 20-payment whole-life policy purchased by a female, age 36.

Solution:
The $20,000 falls between 5M and 25M, and the rate for a female at age 36 would be the same as a male at age 33.

$$\text{premium} = \frac{21.15}{1,000} \times 20,000 = \$423.00 \text{ per year}$$

Example 3

Find the cash value and the total amount paid in premiums for a $38,000 whole-life policy at the end of policy year 15. Assume that the policy was originally issued to a male, age 35.

Solution:

The face value falls between $25,000 and $100,000, so the premium is $15.76 per thousand. Since the policyholder is 35, the cash value is $221 per thousand.

$$\text{premium} = \frac{15.76}{1,000} \times 38,000 = \$598.88$$

$$\text{amount paid in premiums} = 15 \times 598.88 = \$8,983.20$$

$$\text{cash value} = \frac{221}{1,000} \times 38,000 = \$8,398.00$$

Example 4

If Mr. Brooks, age 32, has a life-insurance budget of $225 per year, what is the maximum amount of life insurance he can buy?

Solution:

For whole life the premium $= \frac{\text{rate}}{1,000} \times$ face value. The face value is unknown, so substitute for premium and rate and solve for face value. You won't know whether to use the premium for 5M to 24M or for 25M to 100M until you have divided, so try it for 5M to 24M.

$$225 = 14.68 \times \text{F. V.}$$

$$\frac{225}{14.68} = \frac{14.68}{14.68} \times \text{F. V.}$$

$$15.33 = \text{F. V.}$$

So Mr. Brooks can buy $15,000 of whole life.

For 20-payment life, we get the following:

$$225 = 20.49 \times \text{F. V.}$$

$$\frac{225}{20.49} = \frac{20.49}{20.49} \times \text{F. V.}$$

$$10.98 = \text{F. V.}$$

Mr. Brooks can buy only $10,000 of 20-payment life, but for 39¢ above his budget he can get $11,000.

$$\frac{20.49}{1,000} \times 11,000 = \$225.39$$

Exercises

Use Table 14.3 to find the annual premium for each of the life-insurance policies.

	Age	Sex	Policy	Face Value
1.	20	M	W. L.	$10,000
2.	30	F	W. L.	$25,000
3.	23	M	20-pymt.	$15,000
4.	40	F	20-pymt.	$20,000
5.	24	F	W. L.	$14,000
6.	25	M	W. L.	$35,000
7.	32	M	20-pymt.	$40,000
8.	37	F	20-pymt.	$60,000
9.	40	M	W. L.	$85,000
10.	31	F	W. L.	$75,000

Find the cash value and the total amount paid in premiums for each of the life-insurance policies.

	Age	Sex	Policy	Face Value	Policy Year
11.	30	M	W. L.	$35,000	20
12.	43	F	20-pymt.	$20,000	10
13.	33	F	W. L.	$85,000	15
14.	35	M	W. L.	$90,000	10
15.	28	F	W. L.	$50,000	20

Find the maximum amount of insurance that each budget will buy.

	Age	Sex	Policy	Budget
16.	33	F	20-pymt.	$250/year
17.	25	M	W. L.	$180/year
18.	36	M	W. L.	$40/month
19.	40	M	20-pymt.	$25/month
20.	43	F	W. L.	$600/year

21. Mary Armstrong wants to borrow money from her life-insurance company using her policy's cash value as collateral. The company will lend up to 95% of the cash value. Mary has a $30,000, whole-life policy, which she started at age 28. If she is now 38 and wants the maximum loan, what amount can she borrow?

22. If Mary Armstrong's (see problem 21) insurance company charges 6%(12) for loans and Mary pays her loan off with 24 monthly payments, how much is each monthly payment?

23. Robert Morgan plans to purchase $55,000 of whole-life insurance. If he buys the insurance at age 30, what is the expected cash value of the policy at age 40? How much could he borrow against the cash value at 90% loan collateral?

24. How much could a 25-year-old man save annually on a $24,000, whole-life policy by purchasing a $25,000 policy instead?

Life Insurance Combined with Investments

Endowment life and a new type of insurance called *universal life* are a combination of savings or investments and life insurance. An endowment-life policy offers a specific amount of death benefit for a fixed term, such as 10 or 20 years. If the insured lives to the end of the term, he will receive the face value of the policy as a lump sum or as an income annuity—usually in monthly payments. Technically, you could say endowment life is a limited-payment, whole-life policy with a rapid built-in cash value growth that will provide retirement income.

Universal-life insurance provides the insured the flexibility of making payments to a cash fund that is tied to the money market or other securities, such as stocks and bonds. The insurance company serves as the manager of this fund, and it uses the yearly premiums to pay their fees (called *loading*), buy term insurance for the insured, and invest the rest for the purpose of growth. Universal life is the insurance industry's answer to competitors who advise people to buy term insurance and invest the difference that would go for whole-life, endowment, or limited-payment insurance.

The introduction of the *Individual Retirement Account* (IRA) programs by the United States Congress has made the "buy-term-invest-the-difference" argument attractive. IRA programs allow a person to save up to $2,000 per year in a tax-deferred account with any qualified institution. Waiting to pay the taxes at retirement allows the fund to grow more rapidly, and it reduces the taxes because of the larger number of exemptions allowed for retired people.

There are advantages and disadvantages with each of the insurance-savings programs. Most policyholders are looking for a program that provides the most insurance and the most savings for their money. (Many people, though, don't have enough income to afford adequate insurance coverage and savings for retirement. To compensate for this situation, companies often provide retirement programs for their employees.) The advantage of term insurance plus an IRA is lower cost, but many people don't have the self-discipline to use their money this way. Endowment life, universal life, and whole life provide the consumer with a leveled payment of premiums and the care of professional management. But anyone who doesn't qualify for a tax-deferred IRA program may also have to pay taxes on the capital gains of a universal-life policy. Furthermore, tax-deferment laws are always subject to change by the United States Congress.

The following example will help you make a financial comparison of the different insurance-savings programs.

Table 14.4
Insurance Policies with Savings

				Standard Values			Age	20-year Endowment Annual Premium/M
				Cash Value Accumulations Based on Various Interest Rates				
		Loading & Expense	Current Term Ins.	Guar.	Curr.			
End Year	Cumulative Premiums	Charges This Year	Charges This Year	@ 4.5%	@ 10%	8%		
							20	42.25
							21	42.28
							22	42.32
							23	42.37
							24	42.42
1	2,000	551	371	977	1227	1199	**25**	**42.48**
2	4,000	181	395	2317	2932	2844	26	42.55
3	6,000	181	442	3669	4756	4570	27	42.62
4	8,000	181	466	5020	6738	6410	28	42.69
5	10,000	181	514	6371	8867	8347	29	42.79
6	12,000	181	562	7710	11159	10390	30	42.84
7	14,000	181	597	9022	13643	12558	31	42.94
8	16,000	181	657	10309	16312	14838	32	43.03
9	18,000	181	705	11555	19198	17251	33	43.15
10	20,000	181	753	12760	22322	19806	34	43.27
11	22,000	181	812	13909	25695	22504	**35**	**43.40**
12	24,000	181	896	14975	29318	25331	36	43.55
13	26,000	181	967	15954	33228	28309	37	43.71
14	28,000	181	1051	16830	37442	31438	38	43.90
15	30,000	181	1134	17587	41988	34730	39	44.09
16	32,000	181	1241	18195	46876	38174	40	44.29
17	34,000	181	1360	18634	52128	41769	41	44.50
18	36,000	181	1503	18885	57754	45503	42	44.73
19	38,000	181	1658	18915	63780	49374	43	44.98
20	40,000	181	1813	18689	70246	53393	44	45.25
							45	**45.50**
							46	46.47
							47	47.49
							48	48.24
							49	49.06
							50	49.95

Universal Life-Cash Values
Standard Issue - Increasing Death Benefit
Male Age 45 - $2,000 Annual Premium - $100,000 Initial Amount

Example 1

If a 45-year-old man wants to budget $2,000 per year for 20 years in an insurance-savings program, what program will give him the best retirement fund at age 65? Use the data from Table 14.4.

Solution:
 (a) Endowment life:

$$\frac{\$2,000 \text{ per year}}{\$45.5 \text{ per } \$1,000} = \$44,000 \text{ (rounded) face value}$$

After 20 years (age 65) the insured will receive $44,000, which is the face value of the policy. He will have paid 20 × $2,000 (i.e., $40,000) into the fund.

 (b) Universal life:

$$\frac{\$2,000 \text{ per year}}{\$20.00 \text{ per } \$1,000} = \$100,000 \text{ face value}$$

After 20 years the insured will still have paid $40,000 but will receive $53,393. (This assumes a constant 8% return on investments.)

 (c) Term plus IRA:

The simplest calculation for this program occurs if the man buys $100,000 face value 20-year decreasing term insurance. From Table 14.2 you will find the premium as $7.03 per $1,000 or $703 per year for 20 years. From the annual $2,000 budget, $1,297 ($2,000 − $703) will go into the IRA account. To find the *amount saved* after 20 years at 8%, use the finance table.

$$\text{amount saved} = \$1,297 \times (45.7619643)$$
$$= \$59,353.27$$

Remarks:
 1. The decreasing term insurance will have a death benefit of about $5,000 smaller each year. This means that at the end of 10 years there will be $50,000 of insurance and about $18,000 in the IRA account.
 2. The use of annual renewable term would allow the insured to keep $100,000 of term insurance and accumulate just about the same amount in the IRA account. This calculation is large and tedious because every year the premium and the savings are different. Each savings payment would have to be carried forward by compound interest to the 20-year date.

Example 2

If a couple plans for their son's college education by purchasing a $30,000 endowment policy, what is the annual cost if the insured is age 23?

Solution:

The premium at 23 years is $42.37 per thousand.

$$\text{annual cost} = \frac{\$42.37}{1,000} \times 30,000 = \$1,271.10 \text{ per year}$$

Example 3

At the rate of 8%, how long does it take before the cash value of a $100,000 universal-life policy issued at age 45 exceeds the accumulated premiums? This is the *break-even point*.

Solution:

Using Table 14.4, go down the cumulative-premium column and the cash-value column (8%) and find the year at which the cash value first exceeds the cumulative premiums.

at year 11: $22,000, $22,504

Remark:

Notice that there is no break-even point at 4.5%.

Example 4

How much of the annual premium for year 7 of the $100,000 universal-life policy goes toward the savings portion of the program?

Solution:

Add the *loading* and *current term insurance;* then subtract from $2,000.

$$\$181 + \$595 = 778$$
$$\text{savings portion} = \$2,000 - \$778 = \$1,222$$

Remark:

1. Notice that the portion going to savings for year 20 is very small.

$$\$181 + \$1,813 = \$1,994$$
$$\text{savings portion} = \$2,000 - \$1,994 = \$6$$

2. If the insured had reduced the death-benefit term insurance for the later years by an amount equal to the cash value accumulations, then a much greater cash value could have been accumulated.

Example 5

How much money would accumulate at $2,000 per year for 20 years at 8%? How much greater is this value than the actual cash value of a universal-life policy as shown in Table 14.3? What does this difference represent?

Solution:

Use the finance tables to find the *amount saved* factor as 8% and $n = 20$.

$$
\begin{aligned}
\text{amount saved} &= \quad \$2,000 \times (45.761964) \\
&= \quad \$91,523.93 \\
\text{cash value:} &\ -\$53,393.00 \\
\text{difference} &= \quad \$38,130.93
\end{aligned}
$$

This difference went to the insurance company to buy term insurance and pay loading.

Exercises

Use Table 14.4 to find the amount of 20-year endowment insurance that can be purchased for each budget. Round to nearest thousand.

Age	Annual Budget
1. 20	$635
2. 50	$2,800
3. 41	$1,335
4. 34	$4,000
5. 35	$1,100
6. 26	$2,600
7. 30	$1,500
8. 45	$3,458
9. 28	$1,710
10. 38	$880

Use Table 14.4 to find the accumulated cash value for each year and interest rate for the universal-life policy.

End Year	Percent
11. 6	4.5%
12. 9	8%
13. 13	10%
14. 16	8%
15. 18	4.5%

Use Table 14.4 to find the portion of each premium that goes to savings for the $100,000 universal-life policy.

End Year

16. 5
17. 8
18. 12
19. 15
20. 17

Use Table 14.4 to find the annual cost for each 20-year endowment policy. Round to the nearest dollar.

	Age	Face Value
21.	46	$25,000
22.	40	$35,000
23.	27	$45,000
24.	32	$60,000
25.	24	$80,000

26. If Doug Stambaugh buys a $100,000 universal-life policy at age 45, what is the break-even point on his investment for a 10% interest rate?

27. Paul Velino, age 30, needs $150,000 in life insurance. He wants to buy term and invest the difference. By paying $1.00 per month extra, he can make the term insurance payments monthly, and he plans to save the difference in an IRA account paying 9%(12).

(a) Using Table 14.3, find the annual premium for 150M whole life.

(b) What is the monthly premium for 150M whole life?

(c) Using Table 14.2, find the annual premium for 150M, 20-year decreasing term.

(d) What is the monthly charge for 150M, 20-year decreasing term?

(e) How much is available to invest monthly at 9%(12) in an IRA account?

(f) At 20 years, what would be the cash value of the whole-life policy?

(g) At 20 years, what is the amount saved in the IRA account?

(h) If the decreasing term lowers $\frac{1}{20}$ each year, how much insurance does Paul have during the twentieth year?

(i) What is the total of Paul's IRA and his term insurance during the twentieth year?

(j) What would the total of insurance and cash value be if Paul had purchased whole life?

28. Repeat problem 27, but use 150M annual renewable term instead of the fixed-payment decreasing term. Use a table with 20 entries to answer questions (c), (e), (g), and (i). Use annual payments instead of months, and use 9%(1) for the investment rate.

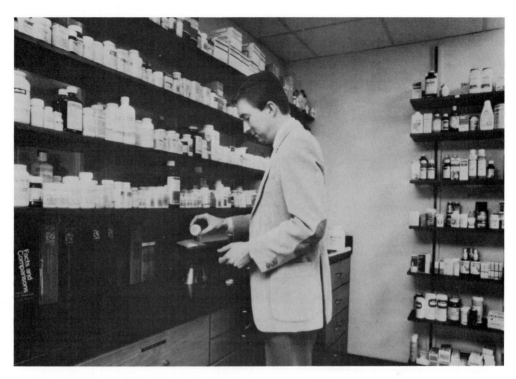

Health Insurance

Health insurance provides financial resources to meet the cost of medical care and loss of income due to sickness or injury. The type of insurance that pays for loss of income is called *disability-income* coverage. This type of coverage may pay for short-term disability, long-term disability, or both.

There are three types of payment programs available—private and group insurance, social security, and worker's compensation. Worker's-compensation laws provide benefits for injuries or disease arising from one's employment. Of course, one very difficult factor in the collection of disability benefits is the definition of the word *disability*. Some policies define it as inability to perform any kind of gainful employment, while others identify it as the inability to perform the specific task of one's education, training, and present skills.

The second type of health-insurance coverage, medical expense, pays for hospital care, doctors, and medical supplies for the insured and his dependents. Medical expenses can be covered in one of two ways: on a *service basis* or on an *indemnity basis*. Medical plans, such as Blue Cross-Blue Shield, provide service benefits to the insured at member hospitals. As long as the services are within the guidelines of the insurance program, the insured pays no extra, regardless of what the hospital would have charged a non-member. Indemnity-basis plans provide cash reimbursement for medical expenses.

Medical-expense benefits are also categorized as *basic* coverage or as *major medical coverage*. Basic coverage pays for hospital room and board, laboratory fees, x-rays, drugs, and medical equipment. Some basic programs pay for certain surgical benefits and out-patient care. Basic programs often have a $100 deductible and somewhat low upper limits of $2,000 or $3,000. Major medical coverage protects the insured against catastrophic medical expenses associated with traumatic accidents and complicated surgery. These insurance programs have high upper limits, some to $1,000,000. They usually have a deductible of up to $1,000 and a *coinsurance* provision. After the deductible is satisfied, the insured pays about 20% of the covered expenses, and the insurer pays the other 80%. There are comprehensive medical-insurance programs that combine the basic program with a major-medical program. This keeps the deductible portion lower and helps pay the coinsurance provision up to the limits of the basic coverage.

Retired persons have the federal Medicare program, which includes hospital insurance and supplemental medical insurance. This insurance program is part of Social Security and requires the insured to pay premiums. The coverage is similar to a comprehensive major-medical program.

The following medical-expense insurance programs are to be used for the examples and exercises to calculate covered expenses. Since you have worked numerous problems in calculating the premiums for life insurance, this section will deal only with payments made to the insured for medical expenses. Premiums for health insurance would be determined like those for life insurance.

Table 14.5
Medical Expense Insurance Coverage

Plan A: *Basic*
$100 deductible
$5,000 maximum limit
$120 per day hospital room—maximum
$1,000 surgical procedure—maximum

Plan B: *Major-Medical*
$500 deductible
$250,000 maximum limit
$140 per day hospital room—maximum
80/20 coinsurance

Plan C: *Comprehensive*
$50 deductible
$500,000 maximum limit
$130 per day hospital room—maximum
80/20 coinsurance above $10,000

Example 1

Below is the hospital statement resulting from Rachel Catawba's automobile accident. Find the dollar amount of the bill that Rachel must pay personally. Her place of employment carries Plan B medical insurance.

```
                    FARRINGTON MEMORIAL HOSPITAL
Rachel M. Catawba
Box 100
Airesville, TX

                              Unit Cost        Extension
22 days room and board          $165            $3,630
surgical supplies and
   radiology                                    $5,850
surgeon fee                                     $2,500
anesthesiology                                  $  900

                              Total:           $12,880
```

Solution:
Find the amount that the insurance company will pay; then subtract from
$12,880.

$$
\begin{aligned}
\text{Room } (22 \times \$140) &= \quad \$3,080 \\
\text{supplies, radiology} &= \quad \$5,850 \\
\text{surgeon} &= \quad \$2,500 \\
\text{anesthesiology} &= \quad \underline{\$\ \ 900} \\
&\qquad \$12,330 \\
\text{less deductible:} &\quad \underline{-\$\ \ \ 500} \\
&\qquad \$11,830 \\
80\% \text{ coverage:} &\quad \underline{\times 0.80} \\
\text{amount paid by insurance company} &= \quad \$\ 9,464
\end{aligned}
$$

covered expenses

amount paid by Rachel = $12,880 − $9,464 = $3,416

Example 2

Find what it will cost Rob Garrett for his surgery. Below is a list of his
expenses. His insurance is Plan A.

$$
\begin{aligned}
\text{private room } (\$200/\text{day for 10 days}) &= \quad \$2,000 \\
\text{operating room and anesthesia} &= \quad \$1,150 \\
\text{surgeon} &= \quad \$3,000 \\
\text{supplies, medicine, lab work} &= \quad \$1,500
\end{aligned}
$$

Solution:
Amount covered by insurance:

room and board (10 × $120) =	$1,200	
operating room and anesthesia =	$1,150	covered expenses
surgeon =	$1,000	
supplies =	$1,500	
	$4,850	
less deductible:	–$ 100	
amount paid by insurance company =	$4,750	(within maximum of $5,000)

Cost of the hospital stay:

room and board (10 × $200) =	$2,000
operating room =	$1,150
surgeon =	$3,000
supplies =	$1,500
total =	$7,650

amount to be paid by Rob Garrett = $7,650 – $4,750 = $2,900

Example 3

Here is an excerpt from Alex Pushkov's hospital bill. Find the cost to Alex under insurance Plan C.

semi-private room ($125/day for 63 days)	$7,875
radiology	$ 500
emergency room	$ 250
medical supplies, medicine, equipment	$5,750
doctor's fee ($35/day for 58 days)	$2,030
physical therapy ($25/visit × 42 visits)	$1,050
total	$17,455

Solution:

Find what the insurer pays:	$17,455	
less deductible:	–$ 50	
	$17,405	
maximum without coinsurance:	–$10,000	paid by insurance
	$ 7,405	
Coinsurance pays 80% of the balance:	×.80	
	$ 5,924	

total paid by insurance = $15,924

total paid by Alex Pushkov = $17,455 – $15,924 = $1,531

Exercises

For each problem, find the amount of the medical expenses paid by the insurance company and by the insured.

	Plan	Cost of Room	No. Days	Surgeon	Medical Supplies	Paid by Ins. Co.	Paid by Insured
1.	A	$140	7	$1,500	$1,750		
2.	B	$135	24	$5,000	$3,490		
3.	C	$165	16	none	$1,850		
4.	B	$225	18	$7,500	$5,650		
5.	C	$145	11	$3,800	$2,100		
6.	A	$130	6	$950	$850		
7.	C	$130	36	$9,450	$7,500		
8.	B	$180	4	$1,500	$480		
9.	A	$155	21	$2,500	$2,340		
10.	B	$150	15	$3,150	$3,100		

11. When Clint McMahon had bypass surgery, he was insured under Plan B. He spent 20 days in a private room that cost $180 per day. The surgeon's fee was $7,500, and the other expenses for supplies, medicine, and x-rays cost $6,500. What percent of the medical expenses did he have to pay?

12. The university where Professor Maria Landei teaches carries Plan C health insurance for all the faculty and their dependents. Her daughter was hospitalized for 12 days. Her room was $150 per day, the doctor's fee was $35 per day, the medical supplies and equipment were $1,600, and x-rays were $800. Find Dr. Landei's share of the medical costs.

13. Five members of the Caldwell family were hospitalized following an automobile accident. Mr. Caldwell's employer provides Plan C health insurance, and his automobile insurance pays $10,000 for bodily injury for each person with a maximum of $30,000 per accident. Find what medical expenses the Caldwells will be responsible for and how the two insurance companies split the other expenses.

Combined expenses of the family's medical care:
semi-private room (96 days at $155/day)	?
physicians and surgeons	$11,500
x-rays and laboratory work	$ 2,200
medical supplies	$ 8,490
physical therapy	$ 4,200
emergency room and ambulance	$ 2,300

14. Terri Simpson carries Plan A health insurance. Her recent hospital stay cost $200 per day for 12 days. The physician's fee was $1,800, the medical supplies and x-rays were $2,800, the physical therapy costs were $800, and miscellaneous costs came to $520. Find her share of the medical expenses, and find the payment if she finances the costs at 12%(12) for 18 months.

Social Security System ———————————

The Federal Social Security Act of 1936 had as its purpose the formation of an endowment, or trust, from which benefits could be paid to retired persons who had paid their fair share into the fund during their working years. In principle, it should have followed closely the results of a cash value, whole-life or endowment policy. In practice, however, the fund has been overdrawn to meet benefit payments it was never intended for. The purpose as stated by the writer says that benefits were to be within the means of society, were to be limited enough to keep people from becoming dependent on the state, and were to be based on the needs of lower-income citizens.

In its present state, Social Security taxes the working citizens to pay benefits to any eligible recipients. This makes it more a welfare system than an insurance program. (In a *welfare system,* the government supplies economic aid to all the poor rather than returning money originally paid by workers.) In Chapter 7 you studied about the Federal Insurance Contributions Act (FICA) withholding from wages. The percent of wages withheld and the maximum value of withholding for FICA is scheduled to increase as inflation increases. This flexibility allows benefits to retired and disabled persons to receive inflation-compensating increases. Besides retirement benefits, Social Security provides medical insurance (Medicare), disability benefits, and death and survival payments.

This section will focus on retirement benefits. Many young people may not think that retirement is an interesting topic, but what you have studied about life insurance should prove otherwise. The time to prepare for retirement is when you are young because the costs are much less than if you wait. Likewise, the time to prepare for heaven is now when you are young. You have a lifetime to serve the Lord and to lay up treasures in heaven. A man who is old may never find the Lord, and if he does, he has little of his life left to give in service.

Anyone who has worked 40 quarters (10 years) and paid FICA taxes is eligible for full retirement benefits. The retirement benefit one receives is called the *Primary Insurance Amount* (PIA). The calculation of a retired person's PIA relates to his *average indexed monthly earnings* (AIME). Average monthly earnings is just an average value of the income the employee earned during the working years. The word *indexed* means that the average has been adjusted to compensate for inflation. Anyone can find out his credited earnings by writing to the Social Security office. An example of indexed earnings is shown in Table 14.6.

Table 14.6		
	Actual Earnings	**Indexed Earnings (1982)**
1958	$4,000	$15,825
1968	$7,400	$19,302
1978	$17,000	$23,402

When it's time for you to retire, the government will index your average monthly income to the year in which you turned 60. This AIME will be used to calculate your monthly benefits. Table 14.7 shows some projected monthly benefits given in 1981 dollars.

Table 14.7
Monthly Benefit for Workers Retiring at 65

Year of Retirement	Low Earnings	Average Earnings	Maximum Earnings
1983	$314.70	$471.60	$604.30
1984	$300.80	$451.60	$583.10
1985	$297.80	$445.70	$578.60
1986	$300.00	$450.40	$588.70
1987	$302.30	$454.70	$597.70
1988	$306.80	$461.70	$611.80
1989	$311.30	$468.70	$625.00
1990	$315.30	$475.50	$637.80
1995	$336.10	$507.00	$698.90
2000	$359.90	$544.70	$779.60
2005	$384.10	$585.20	$867.20
2010	$409.40	$628.70	$958.50

The formula to calculate the benefits (PIA) is adjusted each year to allow for inflation. The formula for those who reached age 65 in 1987 is given below.

Table 14.8

AIME[1]	PIA [2] Calculation
up to $267	90% of AIME
$267 − $1,612	$240.30 + 32% of amount above $267.00
$1,612 or more	$670.70 + 15% of amount above $1,612.00

[1] Average Indexed Monthly Income
[2] Primary Insurance Amount (retirement benefit)

The PIA must be adjusted for those who retire early, between 62 and 65, and for those who retire later, between 65 and 70.

PIA Adjustments

Before 65: deduct 20% of PIA at 62
deduct 10% of PIA at 63.5
Use 0.56% per month for other ages less than 65.

After 65: Increase PIA by 3% per year up to a maximum of 15%. Use 0.25% per month for other ages between years.

Example 1

Find the retirement benefits for a worker whose average indexed monthly earnings were $1,438 and who retires at 65.

Solution:
Since 1,438 falls between 267 and 1,612 on Table 14.8 . . .

$$
\begin{aligned}
\text{PIA} &= 240.30 + 32\% \text{ of } (1,428 - 267) \\
&= 240.30 + 0.32(1,171) \\
&= 240.30 + 374.72 \\
&= \$615.02 \text{ per month}
\end{aligned}
$$

Example 2

Jocelyn Duvanelle plans to retire at 62. She has AIME of $1,280. Find her retirement benefits.

Solution:
First find her benefits for age 65 retirement.

$$
\begin{aligned}
\text{PIA} &= 240.30 + 32\% \text{ of } (1,280 - 267) \\
&= 240.30 + 0.37(1,013) \\
&= 240.30 + 324.16 \\
&= 564.46
\end{aligned}
$$

$$
\begin{aligned}
\text{reduced benefits} &= 546.46 - 20\%(564.46) \\
&= 564.46 - 112.89 \\
&= \$451.57
\end{aligned}
$$

Remark: It is faster to take 80%(564.46) than to subtract 20% from it.

$$
\begin{aligned}
\text{reduced benefit} &= 80\%(564.46) \\
&= 0.80(564.46) \\
&= \$451.57
\end{aligned}
$$

Example 3

When José Sangarins reached the age of 63 years and 2 months, a precarious work situation forced him to retire. If his AIME was $1,825, what are his retirement benefits?

Solution:
First find his benefits at age 65 from Table 14.8.

$$
\begin{aligned}
\text{PIA} &= 670.70 + 15\% \, (1,825 - 1,612) \\
&= 670.70 + 0.15 \, (213.00) \\
&= 670.70 + 31.95 \\
&= \$702.65
\end{aligned}
$$

To find the percent reduction in benefits, calculate the number of months between his retirement age and age 65.

$$\begin{array}{r} 65 \text{ years, } 0 \text{ months} \\ -63 \text{ years, } 2 \text{ months} \\ \hline \end{array}$$

Because 2 is larger than 0, you must rewrite the first number:

$$\begin{array}{r} 64 \text{ years, } 12 \text{ months} \\ -63 \text{ years, } 2 \text{ months} \\ \hline 1 \text{ year, } 10 \text{ months, or } 12 + 10 = 22 \text{ months} \end{array}$$

$$\begin{aligned} \% \text{ reduction} \ &= 0.56\%(22) \\ &= 12.32\% \end{aligned}$$

$$\begin{aligned} \text{adjusted PIA} \ &= 702.65 - 12.32\%(702.65) \\ &= 702.65 - 0.1232(702.65) \\ &= 702.65 - 86.57 \\ &= \$616.08 \end{aligned}$$

Example 4

Find the retirement benefits for Mrs. Munger; she has worked until age 68 years and 3 months and now plans to retire. Her AIME was $945.

Solution:

First find the age 65 benefits from Table 14.8.

$$\begin{aligned} \text{PIA} \ &= 240.30 + 32\%(945 - 267) \\ &= 240.30 + 0.32(678) \\ &= 240.30 + 216.96 \\ &= \$457.26 \end{aligned}$$

The percent increase in her benefits will be 3% per year for 3 years and 0.25% for each of 3 months.

$$\begin{aligned} \text{percent increase} \ &= 3(3\%) + 3(0.25\%) \\ &= 9\% + 0.75\% \\ &= 9.75\% \end{aligned}$$

$$\begin{aligned} \text{adjusted PIA} \ &= 457.26 + 9.75\%(457.26) \\ &= 457.26 + 0.0975(457.26) \\ &= 457.26 + 44.58 \\ &= \$501.84 \end{aligned}$$

Exercises

Find the retirement benefits for each given age and AIME. Use Table 14.8.

Age at Retirement	AIME
1. 65 years	580
2. 62 years	920
3. 70 years	1,150
4. 62 years, 8 months	1,280
5. 67 years, 4 months	1,450
6. 63 years, 3 months	1,600
7. 66 years, 5 months	1,840
8. 68 years, 9 months	1,900
9. 64 years, 1 month	2,000
10. 69 years, 4 months	2,200

11. How much in total benefits will Cassandra Elliott have earned by age 65 if she retires at 62 and has an AIME of $1,385?

12. When Sammy Linn retires at age 65, he will receive social-security benefits on an AIME of $2,350 and payments from a $100,000, 20-year, universal-life policy. His policy earned at 10%, and he will use it for 20 years of income invested at 12%(12). Find his social-security benefits and his income from the value of the universal-life policy. What is the total anticipated monthly income? Use Tables 14.4 and 14.8, as well as the finance tables in the back of the book.

13. When Doctor Aldridge decided to retire at age 68 years and 4 months, he found that his average indexed monthly earnings were $2,250. What is his monthly social-security benefit?

14. Contrast the benefits from social-security insurance for two people the same age who retire with an AIME of $1,820 when one opts for 62 and the other waits till 65. Make a table of their yearly accumulated benefits, and find out at what age the later retiree finally catches the other in total benefits received. To simplify calculations, don't change their original benefit amount to compensate for inflation.

Chapter 14 Review

average indexed monthly earnings (AIME)
basic coverage
beneficiary
benefits
break-even point
cash value
coinsurance
collateral
deductible
disability income
endowment insurance
face value
indemnity basis
individual retirement account (IRA)
limited-payment insurance
loading
major-medical coverage
Medicare
mortality table
policyholder
premium
primary insurance amount (PIA)
security
service basis
surrender value
term insurance
universal-life insurance
welfare system
whole-life insurance
worker's compensation

Use the CSO Mortality Table to find the number of persons from a group of 1,000
22-year-olds living to the given age.

1. women to age 75
2. men to age 33
3. men to age 48
4. women to age 52
5. men to age 78

6. women to age 43
7. women to age 34
8. men to age 83
9. men to age 59
10. women to age 27

Using Table 14.2, find the annual premium for each term-insurance policy.

11. age 27, annual, $25,000
12. age 34, annual, $125,000
13. age 40, 5-year, $75,000

14. age 47, decreasing, $110,000
15. age 31, 5-year, $20,000
16. age 50, decreasing, $50,000

Using Table 14.2, find the maximum amount of term-insurance coverage available
with each given budget.

17. 27, annual, $500 per year
18. 34, 5-year, $290 per year
19. 40, decreasing, $680 per year
20. 44, annual, $32 per month

Using Table 14.3, find the annual premium for each insurance policy and give the
cash value at the given year.

	Age	Sex	Policy	Face Value	Policy Year
21.	23	F	20-pymt.	$10,000	10
22.	25	M	W. L.	$25,000	15
23.	30	M	20-pymt.	$35,000	20
24.	35	M	W. L.	$75,000	10
25.	38	F	W. L.	$100,000	15

Using Table 14.3, find the maximum amount of insurance each budget will buy. Round to the nearest thousand.

	Age	Sex	Policy	Budget
26.	30	M	20-pymt.	$420/yr.
27.	28	F	W. L.	$190/yr.
28.	34	F	20-pymt.	$48/mo.
29.	38	F	W. L.	$24/mo.
30.	37	M	W. L.	$550/yr.

Using Table 14.4, find the maximum amount of 20-year endowment insurance that can be purchased for each budget. Round to the nearest thousand.

	Age	Annual Budget
31.	21	$500
32.	28	$850
33.	32	$1,200
34.	43	$1,800
35.	50	$3,200

Using Table 14.4, find the portion of each premium that goes to the savings portion of a $100,000 universal-life policy.

End Year

36. 7
37. 10
38. 13
39. 16
40. 18

Using Table 14.3, find the amount of the medical expenses paid by the insurance company and by the insured.

	Plan	Cost of Room	No. Days	Surgeon	Medical Supplies	Paid by Ins. Co.	Paid by Insured
41.	A	$145	8	$1,580	$2,200		
42.	B	$162	12	$950	$1,800		
43.	C	$180	14	$2,500	$2,900		
44.	B	$155	21	$3,500	$2,000		
45.	C	$140	25	$4,800	$6,200		

Using Table 14.8, find the social-security retirement benefit for each individual, given his age and AIME.

	Age at Retirement	AIME	Retirement Benefit
46.	66 years, 2 months	$785	
47.	68 years, 11 months	$1,215	
48.	62 years, 3 months	$1,560	
49.	64 years, 4 months	$1,800	
50.	65 years	$2,125	

Photo Credits

Appendix

Measurement References

Customary Measurements

Length
12 inches (in.) = 1 foot (ft.)

36 inches = 1 yard (yd.)

3 feet = 1 yard

$5\frac{1}{2}$ yd. = 1 rod (rd.)

320 rods = 1 mile (mi.)

5,280 feet = 1 mile

Mass
16 ounces (oz.) = 1 pound (lb.)

2,000 pounds = 1 ton (T.)

Capacity

Dry
2 pints (pt.) = 1 quart (qt.)

8 quarts = 1 peck (pk.)

4 pecks = 1 bushel (bu.)

Liquid
8 ounces (oz.) = 1 cup (c.)

2 cups = 1 pint (pt.)

2 pints = 1 quart (qt.)

4 quarts = 1 gallon (gal.)

Approximate Conversions to S.I.

Length
Larger to Smaller

1 in. ≈ 2.54 cm

1 mi. ≈ 1.61 km

Mass
Larger to Smaller

1 oz. ≈ 28.33 g

1 lb. ≈ 0.45 kg

Capacity
Larger to Smaller

1 oz. ≈ 2.96 cl

1 gal. ≈ 3.79 l

Formulas

Perimeter of a rectangle: $P = (2 \times length) + (2 \times width)$

Circumference of a circle: $C = diameter \times \pi$ (where $\pi = 3.14$)

Area of a rectangular region: $A = base \times height$

Area of a square region: $A = base^2$

Area of a triangular region: $A = \frac{1}{2}base \times height$

Volume of a rectangular box: $V = length \times width \times height$

Volume of a cube: $V = side^3$

Serial Table

The Number of Each Day of the Year

Procedure for leap years: Count the number of every day after February 28 as one greater than that given in the table. (*Note:* 1984 was a leap year.)

Day of Month	Jan.	Feb.	Mar.	Apr.	May	June	July	Aug.	Sept.	Oct.	Nov.	Dec.	Day of Month
1	1	32	60	91	121	152	182	213	244	274	305	335	1
2	2	33	61	92	122	153	183	214	245	275	306	336	2
3	3	34	62	93	123	154	184	215	246	276	307	337	3
4	4	35	63	94	124	155	185	216	247	277	308	338	4
5	5	36	64	95	125	156	186	217	248	278	309	339	5
6	6	37	65	96	126	157	187	218	249	279	310	340	6
7	7	38	66	97	127	158	188	219	250	280	311	341	7
8	8	39	67	98	128	159	189	220	251	281	312	342	8
9	9	40	68	99	129	160	190	221	252	282	313	343	9
10	10	41	69	100	130	161	191	222	253	283	314	344	10
11	11	42	70	101	131	162	192	223	254	284	315	345	11
12	12	43	71	102	132	163	193	224	255	285	316	346	12
13	13	44	72	103	133	164	194	225	256	286	317	347	13
14	14	45	73	104	134	165	195	226	257	287	318	348	14
15	15	46	74	105	135	166	196	227	258	288	319	349	15
16	16	47	75	106	136	167	197	228	259	289	320	350	16
17	17	48	76	107	137	168	198	229	260	290	321	351	17
18	18	49	77	108	138	169	199	230	261	291	322	352	18
19	19	50	78	109	139	170	200	231	262	292	323	353	19
20	20	51	79	110	140	171	201	232	263	293	324	354	20
21	21	52	80	111	141	172	202	233	264	294	325	355	21
22	22	53	81	112	142	173	203	234	265	295	326	356	22
23	23	54	82	113	143	174	204	235	266	296	327	357	23
24	24	55	83	114	144	175	205	236	267	297	328	358	24
25	25	56	84	115	145	176	206	237	268	298	329	359	25
26	26	57	85	116	146	177	207	238	269	299	330	360	26
27	27	58	86	117	147	178	208	239	270	300	331	361	27
28	28	59	87	118	148	179	209	240	271	301	332	362	28
29	29		88	119	149	180	210	241	272	302	333	363	29
30	30		89	120	150	181	211	242	273	303	334	364	30
31	31		90		151		212	243		304		365	31

Nutritive Values of Foods

Food, Approximate Measure, and Weight (in Grams)	grams	Food Energy (Calories)	Pro-tein (gm)	Fat (total lipid) (gm)	Fatty Acids Satu-rated (Total) (gm)	Unsaturated Oleic (gm)	Lino-leic (gm)	Carbo-hy-drate (gm)
Milk:								
whole (3.5% fat)	1 cup 244	160	9	9	5	3	trace	12
nonfat (skim)	1 cup 246	90	9	trace	...	...	...	13
dry, nonfat, instant	1 cup 70	250	25	trace	...	...	...	36
Cheese:								
Cheddar or American:								
ungrated	1-inch cube 17	70	4	5	3	2	trace	trace
grated	1 cup 112	445	28	36	20	12	1	2
	1 tablespoon 7	30	2	2	1	1	trace	trace
Cheese foods, Cheddar	1 ounce 28	90	6	7	4	2	trace	2
Cottage cheese:								
creamed	1 cup 225	240	31	9	5	3	trace	7
	1 ounce 28	30	4	1	1	trace	trace	1
uncreamed	1 cup 225	195	38	1	trace	trace	trace	6
	1 ounce 28	25	5	trace	...	...	...	1
Ice cream, plain	8 ounces 142	295	6	18	10	6	1	29
Ice milk	1 cup 187	285	9	10	6	3	trace	42
Eggs:								
boiled	2 eggs 100	160	13	12	4	5	1	1
scrambled	1 egg 64	110	7	8	3	3	trace	1
Bacon	2 slices 16	100	5	8	3	4	1	1
Hamburger:								
lean	3 ounces 85	185	23	10	5	4	trace	0
Roast beef:								
lean and fat	3 ounces 85	165	25	7	3	3	trace	0
Beef steak, broiled:								
lean and fat	3 ounces 85	330	20	27	13	12	1	0
Beef, canned:								
Corned beef	3 ounces 85	185	22	10	5	4	trace	0
Beef and vegetable stew	1 cup 235	210	15	10	5	4	trace	15
Chicken:								
flesh and skin only	2.7 ounces 76	155	25	5	1	2	1	1
Drumstick, fried								
with bone	2.1 ounces 59	90	12	4	1	2	1	trace
Ham:								
light cure, roasted	3 ounces 85	245	18	19	7	8	2	0
boiled, sliced	2 ounces 57	135	11	10	4	4	1	0
Bologna, slice	8 slices 227	690	27	62	...	...	...	2
Fish and shellfish:								
Ocean perch, breaded	3 ounces 85	195	16	11	...	...	...	6
Salmon, canned	3 ounces 85	120	17	5	1	1	trace	0
Shad, baked	3 ounces 85	170	20	10	...	...	...	0
Tuna, canned in oil	3 ounces 85	170	24	7	...	...	...	0
Beans:								
Lima, cooked	1 cup 192	260	16	1	...	...	...	48
Peanut butter	1 tablespoon 16	95	4	8	2	4	2	3
Asparagus								
canned spears, green	6 spears 96	20	2	trace	...	...	...	3

Food, Approximate Measure, and Weight (in Grams)			Food Energy	Pro-tein	Fat (total lipid)	Fatty Acids			Carbo-hy-drate
						Satu-rated (Total)	Unsaturated		
							Oleic	Lino-leic	
		grams	(Calo-ries)	(gm)	(gm)	(gm)	(gm)	(gm)	(gm)
Snap beans, green									
cooked	1 cup 125		30	2	trace	...	...	...	7
Broccoli spears	1 cup 150		40	5	trace	...	...	...	7
Carrots, raw:									
whole	1 carrot 50		20	1	trace	...	...	...	5
grated	1 cup 110		45	1	trace	...	...	...	11
cooked	1 cup 145		45	1	trace	...	...	...	10
Cauliflower	1 cup 120		25	3	trace	...	...	...	5
Celery, raw	1 stalk 40		5	trace	trace	...	...	...	2
Corn:									
cooked, ear	1 ear 140		70	3	1	...	...	...	16
canned	1 cup 256		170	5	2	...	...	...	40
Cucumbers, raw, pared:									
whole	1 cucumber 207		30	1	trace	...	...	...	7
sliced	6 slices 50		5	trace	trace	...	...	...	2
Dandelion greens,									
cooked	1 cup 180		60	4	1	...	...	...	12
Lettuce, raw:									
Iceberg	1 head 454		60	4	trace	...	...	...	13
Looseleaf	2 leaves 50		10	1	trace	...	...	...	2
Peas, green:									
cooked	1 cup 160		115	9	1	...	...	...	19
Potatoes:									
baked	1 potato 99		90	3	trace	...	...	...	21
boiled, peeled	1 potato 122		80	2	trace	...	...	...	18
French-fried	10 pieces 57		155	2	7	2	2	4	20
mashed:									
milk added	1 cup 195		125	4	1	...	...	...	25
milk, butter added	1 cup 195		185	4	8	4	3	trace	24
Spinach, cooked	1 cup 180		40	5	1	...	...	...	6
Sprouts, raw:									
Mung bean	1 cup 90		30	3	trace	...	...	...	6
Soybean	1 cup 107		40	6	2	...	...	...	4
Tomatoes, raw	1 tomato 150		35	2	trace	...	...	...	7
Tomato juice	1 cup 242		45	2	trace	...	...	...	10
Apples, raw	1 apple 150		70	trace	trace	...	...	...	18
Apple juice	1 cup 249		120	trace	trace	...	...	...	30
Pink grapefruit	½ grapefruit 285		60	1	trace	...	...	...	15
Grapefruit juice,									
unsweetened	1 cup 247		100	1	trace	...	...	...	24
Oranges, navel	1 orange 180		60	2	trace	...	...	...	16
Orange juice:									
unsweetened	1 cup 249		120	2	trace	...	...	...	28
frozen concentrate:									
6-ounce can	1 can 210		330	5	trace	...	...	...	80
diluted	1 cup 248		110	2	trace	...	...	...	27
Peaches:									
whole	1 peach 114		35	1	trace	...	...	...	10
sliced	1 cup 168		65	1	trace	...	...	...	16
Prune juice	1 cup 256		200	1	trace	...	...	...	49
Strawberries, raw	1 cup 149		55	1	1	...	...	...	13

Food, Approximate Measure, and Weight (in Grams)		grams	Food Energy (Calories)	Protein (gm)	Fat (total lipid) (gm)	Saturated (Total) (gm)	Unsaturated Oleic (gm)	Unsaturated Lino-leic (gm)	Carbo-hy-drate (gm)
Biscuits	1 biscuit 38		140	3	6	2	3	1	17
Bran flakes	1 ounce 28		85	3	1	...	...	...	23
Breads:									
Boston brown	1 slice 48		100	3	1	...	...	...	22
cracked-wheat	1 slice 23		60	2	1	...	...	...	12
white	1 slice 23		65	2	1	trace	trace	trace	12
whole-wheat	1 slice 23		55	2	1	trace	trace	trace	11
(toasted)	1 slice 19		55	2	1	trace	trace	trace	11
Corn grits, cooked:									
enriched	1 cup 242		120	3	trace	...	...	...	27
unenriched	1 cup 242		120	3	trace	...	...	...	27
Pancakes:									
wheat	1 cake 27		60	2	2	trace	1	trace	9
buckwheat	1 cake 27		55	2	2	1	1	trace	6
Pies:									
apple	1 piece 135		345	3	15	4	9	1	51
Rolls, plain	1 roll 38		115	3	2	trace	1	trace	20
Butter:									
2 sticks	1 cup 227		1,625	1	184	101	61	6	1
⅛ stick	1 tablespoon 14		100	trace	11	6	4	trace	trace
pat or square	1 pat 7		50	trace	6	3	2	trace	trace
Margarine:									
2 sticks	1 cup 227		1,635	1	184	37	105	33	1
⅛ sticks	1 tablespoon 14		100	trace	11	2	6	2	trace
pat or square	1 pat 7		50	trace	6	1	3	1	trace
Mayonnaise	1 tablespoon 15		110	trace	12	2	3	6	trace
Syrup	1 tablespoon 20		60	0	0	...	...	...	15
Sugar, granulated	1 cup 200		770	0	0	...	...	...	199
	1 tablespoon 12		45	0	0	...	...	...	12
Beverages, carbonated:									
cola type	1 cup 240		95	0	0	...	...	...	24
Pickles:									
large dill	1 pickle 135		15	1	trace	...	...	...	3
Soup, canned:									
tomato	1 cup 245		90	2	2	trace	1	1	16

Finance Tables

	n	Amount of $1 at Comp. Int.	Amount Saved for $1/Period	Payment to Save $1
Rate	1	1.0050000000	1.0000000000	1.0000000000
	2	1.0100250000	2.0050000000	0.4987531172
.5%	3	1.0150751250	3.0150250000	0.3316722084
	4	1.0201505006	4.0301001250	0.2481327930
	5	1.0252512531	5.0502506256	0.1980099750
	6	1.0303775094	6.0755018788	0.1645954556
	7	1.0355293969	7.1058793881	0.1407285355
	8	1.0407070439	8.1414087851	0.1228288649
	9	1.0459105791	9.1821158290	0.1089073606
	10	1.0511401320	10.2280264082	0.0977705727
	11	1.0563958327	11.2791665402	0.0886590331
	12	1.0616778119	12.3355623729	0.0810664297
	13	1.0669862009	13.3972401848	0.0746422387
	14	1.0723211319	14.4642263857	0.0691360860
	15	1.0776827376	15.5365475176	0.0643643640
	16	1.0830711513	16.6142302552	0.0601893669
	17	1.0884865070	17.6973014065	0.0565057902
	18	1.0939289396	18.7857879135	0.0532317305
	19	1.0993985843	19.8797168531	0.0503025273
ANNUALLY	20	1.1048955772	20.9791154373	0.0476664520
If compounded	21	1.1104200551	22.0840110145	0.0452816293
annually,	22	1.1159721553	23.1944310696	0.0431137973
nominal annual rate is	23	1.1215520161	24.3104032250	0.0411346530
	24	1.1271597762	25.4319552411	0.0393206103
1/2%	25	1.1327955751	26.5591150173	0.0376518570
	26	1.1384595530	27.6919105924	0.0361116289
	27	1.1441518507	28.8303701453	0.0346856456
	28	1.1498726100	29.9745219961	0.0333616663
	29	1.1556219730	31.1243946060	0.0321291390
SEMIANNUALLY	30	1.1614000829	32.2800165791	0.0309789184
If compounded	31	1.1672070833	33.4414166620	0.0299030394
semiannually,	32	1.1730431187	34.6086237453	0.0288945324
nominal annual rate is	33	1.1789083343	35.7816668640	0.0279472727
	34	1.1848028760	36.9605751983	0.0270558560
1%	35	1.1907268904	38.1453780743	0.0262154958
	36	1.1966805248	39.3361049647	0.0254219375
	37	1.2026639274	40.5327854895	0.0246713861
	38	1.2086772471	41.7354494170	0.0239604464
	39	1.2147206333	42.9441266640	0.0232860714
QUARTERLY	40	1.2207942365	44.1588472974	0.0226455186
If compounded	41	1.2268982077	45.3796415338	0.0220363133
quarterly,	42	1.2330326987	46.6065397415	0.0214562163
nominal annual rate is	43	1.2391978622	47.8395724402	0.0209031969
	44	1.2453938515	49.0787703024	0.0203754086
2%	45	1.2516208208	50.3241641539	0.0198711696
	46	1.2578789249	51.5757849747	0.0193889439
	47	1.2641683195	52.8336638996	0.0189273264
	48	1.2704891611	54.0978322191	0.0184850290
	49	1.2768416069	55.3683213802	0.0180608690
MONTHLY	50	1.2832258149	56.6451629871	0.0176537580
If compounded	51	1.2896419440	57.9283888020	0.0172626931
monthly,	52	1.2960901537	59.2180307460	0.0168867486
nominal annual rate is	53	1.3025706045	60.5141208997	0.0165250686
	54	1.3090834575	61.8166915042	0.0161768606
6%	55	1.3156288748	63.1257749618	0.0158413897
	56	1.3222070192	64.4414038366	0.0155179735
	57	1.3288180543	65.7636108558	0.0152059777
	58	1.3354621446	67.0924289100	0.0149048114
	59	1.3421394553	68.4278910546	0.0146139240
	60	1.3488501525	69.7700305099	0.0143328015
	120	1.8193967340	163.8793468065	0.0061020502
	180	2.4540935622	290.8187124494	0.0034385683
	240	3.3102044758	462.0408951615	0.0021643106
	300	4.4649698122	692.9939624324	0.0014430140
	360	6.0225752123	1004.5150424526	0.0009955053
	420	8.1235514938	1424.7102987601	0.0007018971
	480	10.9574536717	1991.4907343310	0.0005021364
n		$(1+i)^n$	$s_{\overline{n}|}$	$\dfrac{1}{s_{\overline{n}|}}$

456

Pres. Value of $1 at Comp. Int.	Amount Borrowed for $1 Payment	Payment to Borrow $1	n
0.9950248756	0.9950248756	1.0050000000	1
0.9900745031	1.9850993787	0.5037531172	2
0.9851487593	2.9702481380	0.3366722084	3
0.9802475217	3.9504956597	0.2531327930	3
0.9753706684	4.9258663281	0.2030099750	5
0.9705180780	5.8963844061	0.1695954556	6
0.9656896298	6.8620740359	0.1457285355	7
0.9608852038	7.8229592397	0.1278288649	8
0.9561046804	8.7790639201	0.1139073606	9
0.9513479407	9.7304118608	0.1027705727	10
0.9466148664	10.6770267272	0.0936590331	11
0.9419053397	11.6189320668	0.0860664297	12
0.9372192434	12.5561513103	0.0796422387	13
0.9325564611	13.4887077714	0.0741360860	14
0.9279168768	14.4166246482	0.0693643640	15
0.9233003749	15.3399250231	0.0651893669	16
0.9187068407	16.2586318637	0.0615057902	17
0.9141361599	17.1727680236	0.0582317305	18
0.9095882188	18.0823562424	0.0553025273	19
0.9050629043	18.9874191467	0.0526664520	20
0.9005601037	19.8879792504	0.0502816293	21
0.8960797052	20.7840589556	0.0481137973	22
0.8916215972	21.6756805529	0.0461346530	23
0.8871856689	22.5628662218	0.0443206103	24
0.8827718098	23.4456380316	0.0426518570	25
0.8783799103	24.3240179419	0.0411116289	26
0.8740098610	25.1980278029	0.0396856456	27
0.8696615532	26.0676893561	0.0383616663	28
0.8653348788	26.9330242349	0.0371291390	29
0.8610297302	27.7940539651	0.0359789184	30
0.8567460002	28.6507999653	0.0349030394	31
0.8524835823	29.5032835475	0.0338945324	32
0.8482423704	30.3515259179	0.0329472727	33
0.8440222591	31.1955481771	0.0320558560	34
0.8398231434	32.0353713205	0.0312154958	35
0.8356449188	32.8710162393	0.0304219375	36
0.8314874814	33.7025037207	0.0296713861	37
0.8273507278	34.5298544484	0.0289604464	38
0.8232345550	35.3530890034	0.0282860714	39
0.8191388607	36.1722278641	0.0276455186	40
0.8150635430	36.9872914070	0.0270363133	41
0.8110085005	37.7982999075	0.0264562163	42
0.8069736323	38.6052735398	0.0259031969	43
0.8029588381	39.4082323779	0.0253754086	44
0.7989640180	40.2071963959	0.0248711696	45
0.7949890727	41.0021854686	0.0243889439	46
0.7910339031	41.7932193717	0.0239273264	47
0.7870984111	42.5803177828	0.0234850290	48
0.7831824986	43.3635002814	0.0230608690	49
0.7792860683	44.1427863497	0.0226537580	50
0.7754090231	44.9181953728	0.0222626931	51
0.7715512668	45.6897466396	0.0218867486	52
0.7677127033	46.4574593429	0.0215250686	53
0.7638932371	47.2213525800	0.0211768606	54
0.7600927732	47.9814453532	0.0208413897	55
0.7563112171	48.7377565704	0.0205179735	56
0.7525484748	49.4903050451	0.0202059777	57
0.7488044525	50.2391094977	0.0199048114	58
0.7450790572	50.9841885549	0.0196139240	59
0.7413721962	51.7255607511	0.0193328015	60
0.5496327334	90.0734533272	0.0111020502	120
0.4074824267	118.5035146676	0.0084385683	180
0.3020961416	139.5807716829	0.0071643106	240
0.2239656800	155.2068640072	0.0064430140	300
0.1660419280	166.7916143923	0.0059955053	360
0.1230988689	175.3802262283	0.0057018971	420
0.0912620788	181.7475842478	0.0055021364	480
$\dfrac{1}{(1+i)^n}$	$p\,\overline{n|}$	$\dfrac{1}{p\,\overline{n|}}$	n

Rate

.5%

ANNUALLY

If compounded
annually,
nominal annual rate is

$1/2\%$

SEMIANNUALLY

If compounded
semiannually,
nominal annual rate is

1%

QUARTERLY

If compounded
quarterly,
nominal annual rate is

2%

MONTHLY

If compounded
monthly,
nominal annual rate is

6%

	n	Amount of $1 at Comp. Int.	Amount Saved for $1/Period	Payment to Save $1

Rate

.583%

	n	$(1+i)^n$	$s\,\overline{n|}$	$\dfrac{1}{s\,\overline{n|}}$
	1	1.0058333333	1.0000000000	1.0000000000
	2	1.0117006944	2.0058333333	0.4985459078
	3	1.0176022818	3.0175340278	0.3313964286
	4	1.0235382951	4.0351363096	0.2478231027
	5	1.0295089352	5.0586746047	0.1976802380
	6	1.0355144040	6.0881835399	0.1642526040
	7	1.0415549047	7.1236979439	0.1403765303
	8	1.0476306416	8.1652528486	0.1224701817
	9	1.0537418204	9.2128834902	0.1085436499
	10	1.0598886476	10.2666253106	0.0974029898
	11	1.0660713314	11.3265139582	0.0882884181
	12	1.0722900809	12.3925852896	0.0806934128
	13	1.0785451063	13.4648753705	0.0742673046
	14	1.0848366194	14.5434204768	0.0687596155
	15	1.0911648331	15.6282570963	0.0639866617
	16	1.0975299613	16.7194219293	0.0598106803
	17	1.1039322194	17.8169518906	0.0561263232
	18	1.1103718240	18.9208841100	0.0528516529
	19	1.1168489929	20.0312559339	0.0499219821
ANNUALLY	20	1.1233639454	21.1481049269	0.0472855607
If compounded ***annually***,	21	1.1299169018	22.2714688723	0.0449004960
nominal annual rate is	22	1.1365080837	23.4013857740	0.0427325121
	23	1.1431377142	24.5378938577	0.0407532939
$^7/_{12}\%$	24	1.1498060175	25.6810315719	0.0389392458
	25	1.1565132193	26.8308375894	0.0372705472
	26	1.1632595464	27.9873508087	0.0357304272
	27	1.1700452271	29.1506103550	0.0343045990
	28	1.1768704909	30.3206555821	0.0329808172
	29	1.1837355688	31.4975260730	0.0317485252
SEMIANNUALLY	30	1.1906406929	32.6812616418	0.0305985739
If compounded ***semiannually***,	31	1.1975860970	33.8719023347	0.0295229949
nominal annual rate is	32	1.2045720159	35.0694884316	0.0285148157
	33	1.2115986859	36.2740604475	0.0275679091
$1^1/_6\%$	34	1.2186663449	37.4856591334	0.0266768685
	35	1.2257752320	38.7043254784	0.0258369055
	36	1.2329255875	39.9301007103	0.0250437635
	37	1.2401176534	41.1630262978	0.0242936463
	38	1.2473516730	42.4031439512	0.0235831570
	39	1.2546278911	43.6504956243	0.0229092473
QUARTERLY	40	1.2619465538	44.9051235154	0.0222691738
If compounded ***quarterly***,	41	1.2693079087	46.1670700692	0.0216604606
nominal annual rate is	42	1.2767122049	47.4363779780	0.0210808675
	43	1.2841596927	48.7130901829	0.0205283630
$2^1/_2\%$	44	1.2916506243	49.9972498756	0.0200011001
	45	1.2991852529	51.2889004999	0.0194973959
	46	1.3067638336	52.5880857528	0.0190157140
	47	1.3143866226	53.8948495863	0.0185546487
	48	1.3220538779	55.2092362089	0.0181129113
	49	1.3297658588	56.5312900868	0.0176893186
MONTHLY	50	1.3375228263	57.8610559456	0.0172827817
If compounded ***monthly***,	51	1.3453250428	59.1985787720	0.0168922974
nominal annual rate is	52	1.3531727723	60.5439038148	0.0165169396
	53	1.3610662801	61.8970765871	0.0161558519
7%	54	1.3690058334	63.2581428672	0.0158082415
	55	1.3769917008	64.6271487006	0.0154733733
	56	1.3850241523	66.0041404013	0.0151505647
	57	1.3931034599	67.3891645537	0.0148391808
	58	1.4012298967	68.7822680136	0.0145386308
	59	1.4094037378	70.1834979103	0.0142483636
	60	1.4176252596	71.5929016481	0.0139678652
	120	2.0096613767	173.0848074335	0.0057775146
	180	2.8489467309	316.9622967213	0.0031549494
	240	4.0387388490	520.9266598255	0.0019196560
	300	5.7254182093	810.0716930231	0.0012344586
	360	8.1164974754	1219.9709957759	0.0008196916
	420	11.5061518407	1801.0546012565	0.0005552303
	480	16.3114114903	2624.8133983334	0.0003809795

n	$(1+i)^n$	$s\,\overline{n|}$	$\dfrac{1}{s\,\overline{n|}}$

Pres. Value of $1 at Comp. Int.	Amount Borrowed for $1 Payment	Payment to Borrow $1	*n*
0.9942004971	0.9942004971	1.0058333333	1
0.9884346284	1.9826351255	0.5043792411	2
0.9827021989	2.9653373245	0.3372297619	3
0.9770030147	3.9423403392	0.2536564360	4
0.9713368829	4.9136772220	0.2035135714	5
0.9657036118	5.8793808338	0.1700859373	6
0.9601030109	6.8394838447	0.1462098636	7
0.9545348907	7.7940187355	0.1283035150	8
0.9489990628	8.7430177983	0.1143769832	9
0.9434953400	9.6865131383	0.1032363231	10
0.9380235361	10.6245366744	0.09412175141	11
0.9325834658	11.5571201402	0.08652674611	12
0.9271749453	12.4842950856	0.08010063791	13
0.9217977916	13.4060928771	0.0745929488	14
0.9164518226	14.3225446997	0.0698199950	15
0.9111368576	15.2336815573	0.0656440136	16
0.9058527167	16.1395342740	0.0619596565	17
0.9005992213	17.0401334953	0.0586849863	18
0.8953761935	17.9355096888	0.0557553154	19
0.8901834567	18.8256931454	0.0531188941	20
0.8850208351	19.7107139805	0.0507338294	21
0.8798881542	20.5906021348	0.0485658454	22
0.8747852403	21.4653873751	0.0465866272	23
0.8697119208	22.3350992958	0.0447725791	24
0.8646680240	23.1997673198	0.0431038806	25
0.8596533793	24.0594206991	0.0415637605	26
0.8546678170	24.9140885161	0.0401379324	27
0.8497111685	25.7637996846	0.0388141506	28
0.8447832661	26.6085829507	0.0375818585	29
0.8398839431	27.4484668938	0.0364319072	30
0.8350130338	28.2834799276	0.0353563282	31
0.8301703732	29.1136503008	0.0343481491	32
0.8253557978	29.9390060986	0.0334012424	33
0.8205691444	30.7595752430	0.0325102019	34
0.8158102513	31.5753854943	0.0316702388	35
0.8110789574	32.3864644516	0.0308770969	36
0.8063751026	33.1928395542	0.0301269796	37
0.8016985279	33.9945380821	0.0294164903	38
0.7970490749	34.7915871570	0.0287425807	39
0.7924265865	35.5840137435	0.0281025071	40
0.7878309062	36.3718446497	0.0274937939	41
0.7832618786	37.1551065283	0.0269142009	42
0.7787193490	37.9338258773	0.0263616964	43
0.7742031639	38.7080290413	0.0258344334	44
0.7697131704	39.4777422117	0.0253307293	45
0.7652492167	40.2429914284	0.0248490474	46
0.7608111516	41.0038025800	0.0243879820	47
0.7563988251	41.7602014051	0.0239462447	48
0.7520120880	42.5122134931	0.0235226519	49
0.7476507917	43.2598642848	0.0231161151	50
0.7433147887	44.0031790735	0.0227256308	51
0.7390039325	44.7421830060	0.0223502729	52
0.7347180770	45.4769010830	0.0219891852	53
0.7304570774	46.2073581604	0.0216415748	54
0.7262207895	46.9335789498	0.0213067067	55
0.7220090699	47.6555880197	0.0209838980	56
0.7178217762	48.3734097959	0.0206725142	57
0.7136587667	49.0870685626	0.0203719641	58
0.7095199006	49.7965884633	0.0200816970	59
0.7054050379	50.5019935012	0.0198011985	60
0.4975962675	86.1263541414	0.0116108479	120
0.3510069139	111.2559576093	0.0089882827	180
0.2476020454	128.9825064963	0.0077529894	240
0.1746597302	141.4869033859	0.0070677920	300
0.1232058536	150.3075679478	0.0066530250	360
0.0869100299	156.5297091675	0.0063885636	420
0.0613067729	160.9188389305	0.0062143128	480
$\dfrac{1}{(1+i)^n}$	$p\,\overline{n|}$	$\dfrac{1}{p\,\overline{n|}}$	*n*

Rate

.58$\overline{3}$%

ANNUALLY
If compounded
annually,
nominal annual rate is

$^7/_{12}$%

SEMIANNUALLY
If compounded
semiannually,
nominal annual rate is

$1^1/_6$%

QUARTERLY
If compounded
quarterly,
nominal annual rate is

$2^1/_2$%

MONTHLY
If compounded
monthly,
nominal annual rate is

7%

n	Amount of $1 at Comp. Int.	Amount Saved for $1/Period	Payment to Save $1
1	1.0066666667	1.0000000000	1.0000000000
2	1.0133777778	2.0066666667	0.4983388704
3	1.0201336296	3.0200444444	0.3311209548
4	1.0269345205	4.0401780741	0.2475138426
5	1.0337807506	5.0671125946	0.1973510518
6	1.0406726223	6.1008933452	0.1639104215
7	1.0476104398	7.1415659675	0.1400253116
8	1.0545945094	8.1891764073	0.1221124018
9	1.0616251394	9.2437709167	0.1081809587
10	1.0687026404	10.3053960561	0.0970365423
11	1.0758273246	11.3740986965	0.0879190542
12	1.0829995068	12.4499260211	0.0803217624
13	1.0902195035	13.5329255279	0.0738938523
14	1.0974876335	14.6231450315	0.0683847420
15	1.1048042178	15.7206326650	0.0636106715
16	1.1121695792	16.8254368828	0.0594338208
17	1.1195840431	17.9376064620	0.0557487980
18	1.1270479367	19.0571905051	0.0524736319
19	1.1345615896	20.1842384418	0.0495436081
20	1.1421253335	21.3188000314	0.0469069553
21	1.1497395024	22.4609253649	0.0445217632
22	1.1574044324	23.6106648673	0.0423537417
23	1.1651204620	24.7680692998	0.0403745640
24	1.1728879317	25.9331897618	0.0385606248
25	1.1807071846	27.1060776935	0.0368920952
26	1.1885785659	28.2867848782	0.0353521973
27	1.1965024230	29.4753634440	0.0339266385
28	1.2044791058	30.6718658670	0.0326031681
29	1.2125089665	31.8763449728	0.0313712253
30	1.2205923596	33.0888539392	0.0302216572
31	1.2287296420	34.3094462988	0.0291464919
32	1.2369211729	35.5381759408	0.0281387543
33	1.2451673141	36.7750971138	0.0271923143
34	1.2534684295	38.0202644279	0.0263017634
35	1.2618248857	39.2737328574	0.0254623110
36	1.2702370516	40.5355577431	0.0246696988
37	1.2787052986	41.8057947947	0.0239201289
38	1.2872300006	43.0845000933	0.0232102032
39	1.2958115340	44.3717300940	0.0225368720
40	1.3044502775	45.6675416279	0.0218973907
41	1.3131466127	46.9719919055	0.0212892824
42	1.3219009235	48.2851385182	0.0207103061
43	1.3307135963	49.6070394416	0.0201584294
44	1.3395850203	50.9377530379	0.0196318043
45	1.3485155871	52.2773380581	0.0191287475
46	1.3575056910	53.6258536452	0.0186477218
47	1.3665557289	54.9833593362	0.0181873209
48	1.3756661004	56.3499150651	0.0177462557
49	1.3848372078	57.7255811655	0.0173233423
50	1.3940694558	59.1104183733	0.0169174915
51	1.4033632522	60.5044878291	0.0165276996
52	1.4127190072	61.9078510813	0.0161530401
53	1.4221371339	63.3205700885	0.0157926563
54	1.4316180481	64.7427072224	0.0154457551
55	1.4411621685	66.1743252706	0.0151116010
56	1.4507699163	67.6154874390	0.0147895111
57	1.4604417157	69.0662573553	0.0144788503
58	1.4701779938	70.5266990710	0.0141790274
59	1.4799791804	71.9968770648	0.0138894913
60	1.4898457083	73.4768562452	0.0136097276
120	2.2196402345	182.9460351817	0.0054660928
180	3.3069214774	346.0382216115	0.0028898542
240	4.9268027708	589.0204156215	0.0016977340
300	7.3401759637	951.0263945609	0.0010514955
360	10.9357296578	1490.3594486633	0.0006709791
420	16.2925498978	2293.8824846631	0.0004359421
480	24.2733855425	3491.0078313687	0.0002864502
n	$(1 + i)^n$	$s\,\overline{n}|$	$\dfrac{1}{s\,\overline{n}|}$

ANNUALLY

If compounded
annually,
nominal annual rate is
$2/3$%

SEMIANNUALLY

If compounded
semiannually,
nominal annual rate is
$1^1/3$%

QUARTERLY

If compounded
quarterly,
nominal annual rate is
$2^2/3$%

MONTHLY

If compounded
monthly,
nominal annual rate is
8%

Pres. Value of $1 at Comp. Int.	Amount Borrowed for $1 Payment	Payment to Borrow $1	n
0.9933774834	0.9933774834	1.0066666667	1
0.9867988246	1.9801763081	0.5050055371	2
0.9802637331	2.9604400411	0.3377876215	3
0.9737719203	3.9342119614	0.2541805093	4
0.9673230996	4.9015350610	0.2040177184	5
0.9609169864	5.8624520473	0.1705770882	6
0.9545532977	6.8170053450	0.1466919783	7
0.9482317527	7.7652370977	0.1287790685	8
0.9419520722	8.7071891699	0.1148476254	9
0.9357139790	9.6429031489	0.1037032089	10
0.9295171977	10.5724203466	0.0945857209	11
0.9233614547	11.4957818013	0.0869884291	12
0.9172464781	12.4130282794	0.0805605190	13
0.9111719981	13.3242002775	0.0750514087	14
0.9051377465	14.2293380240	0.0702773382	15
0.8991434568	15.1284814808	0.0661004874	16
0.8931888644	16.0216703452	0.0624154647	17
0.8872737063	16.9089440515	0.0591402986	18
0.8813977215	17.7903417730	0.0562102748	19
0.8755606505	18.6659024236	0.0535736220	20
0.8697622356	19.5356646592	0.0511884299	21
0.8640022208	20.3996668800	0.0490204083	22
0.8582803518	21.2579472317	0.0470412307	23
0.8525963759	22.1105436077	0.0452272915	24
0.8469500423	22.9574936500	0.0435587619	25
0.8413411017	23.7988347517	0.0420188640	26
0.8357693063	24.6346040580	0.0405933052	27
0.8302344102	25.4648384682	0.0392698348	28
0.8247361691	26.2895746373	0.0380378920	29
0.8192743402	27.1088489774	0.0368883238	30
0.8138486823	27.9226976597	0.0358131586	31
0.8084589559	28.7311566156	0.0348054209	32
0.8031049231	29.5342615387	0.0338589810	33
0.7977863474	30.3320478861	0.0329684301	34
0.7925029941	31.1245508802	0.0321289777	35
0.7872546299	31.9118055101	0.0313363655	36
0.7820410231	32.6938465333	0.0305867956	37
0.7768619435	33.4707084767	0.0298768698	38
0.7717171624	34.2424256392	0.0292035386	39
0.7666064527	35.0090320919	0.0285640573	40
0.7615295888	35.7705616807	0.0279559491	41
0.7564863465	36.5270480272	0.0273769728	42
0.7514765031	37.2785245303	0.0268250960	43
0.7464998375	38.0250243678	0.0262984710	44
0.7415561300	38.7665804978	0.0257954142	45
0.7366451623	39.5032256601	0.0253143885	46
0.7317667175	40.2349923776	0.0248539876	47
0.7269205803	40.9619129579	0.0244129223	48
0.7221065367	41.6840194946	0.0239900089	49
0.7173243742	42.4013438688	0.0235841582	50
0.7125738817	43.1139177504	0.0231943663	51
0.7078548493	43.8217725998	0.0228197068	52
0.7031670689	44.5249396687	0.0224593230	53
0.6985103333	45.2234500020	0.0221124218	54
0.6938844371	45.9173344391	0.0217782677	55
0.6892891759	46.6066236160	0.0214561777	56
0.6847243469	47.2913479619	0.0211455170	57
0.6801897486	47.9715377105	0.0208456941	58
0.6756851807	48.6472228912	0.0205561580	59
0.6712104444	49.3184333356	0.0202763943	60
0.4505234607	82.4214808934	0.0121327594	120
0.3023960523	104.6405921566	0.0095565208	180
0.2029713887	119.5542917024	0.0083644007	240
0.1362365160	129.5645226026	0.0077181622	300
0.0914433724	136.2834941340	0.0073376457	360
0.0613777467	140.7933380016	0.0071026088	420
0.0411973846	143.8203923084	0.0069531169	480
$\dfrac{1}{(1+i)^n}$	$p_{\overline{n}}$	$\dfrac{1}{p_{\overline{n}}}$	n

Rate

$\overline{.6}\%$

ANNUALLY

If compounded annually,

nominal annual rate is

$^2/_3\%$

SEMIANNUALLY

If compounded semiannually,

nominal annual rate is

$1^1/_3\%$

QUARTERLY

If compounded quarterly,

nominal annual rate is

$2^2/_3\%$

MONTHLY

If compounded monthly,

nominal annual rate is

8%

Rate	n	Amount of $1 at Comp. Int.	Amount Saved for $1/Period	Payment to Save $1
.75%	1	1.0075000000	1.0000000000	1.0000000000
	2	1.0150562500	2.0075000000	0.4981320050
	3	1.0226691719	3.0225562500	0.3308457866
	4	1.0303391907	4.0452254219	0.2472050123
	5	1.0380667346	5.0755646125	0.1970224155
	6	1.0458522351	6.1136313471	0.1635689074
	7	1.0536961269	7.1594835822	0.1396748786
	8	1.0615988478	8.2131797091	0.1217555241
	9	1.0695608392	9.2747785569	0.1078192858
	10	1.0775825455	10.3443393961	0.0966712287
	11	1.0856644146	11.4219219416	0.0875509398
	12	1.0938068977	12.5075863561	0.0799514768
	13	1.1020104494	13.6013932538	0.0735218798
	14	1.1102755278	14.7034037032	0.0680114632
	15	1.1186025942	15.8136792310	0.0632363908
	16	1.1269921137	16.9322818252	0.0590587855
	17	1.1354445545	18.0592739389	0.0553732118
	18	1.1439603887	19.1947184934	0.0520976643
	19	1.1525400916	20.3386788821	0.0491674020
ANNUALLY	20	1.1611841423	21.4912189738	0.0465306319
If compounded ***annually,***	21	1.1698930234	22.6524031161	0.0441454266
	22	1.1786672210	23.8222961394	0.0419774817
nominal annual rate is	23	1.1875072252	25.0009633605	0.0399984587
	24	1.1964135294	26.1884705857	0.0381847423
3/4%	25	1.2053866309	27.3848841151	0.0365164956
	26	1.2144270306	28.5902707459	0.0349769335
	27	1.2235352333	29.8046977765	0.0335517578
	28	1.2327117476	31.0282330099	0.0322287125
	29	1.2419570857	32.2609447574	0.0309972323
SEMIANNUALLY	30	1.2512717638	33.5029018431	0.0298481608
If compounded ***semiannually,***	31	1.2606563021	34.7541736069	0.0287735226
	32	1.2701112243	36.0148299090	0.0277663397
nominal annual rate is	33	1.2796370585	37.2849411333	0.0268204795
	34	1.2892343364	38.5645781918	0.0259305313
1¹/₂%	35	1.2989035940	39.8538125282	0.0250917023
	36	1.3086453709	41.1527161222	0.0242997327
	37	1.3184602112	42.4613614931	0.0235508228
	38	1.3283486628	43.7798217043	0.0228415732
	39	1.3383112778	45.1081703671	0.0221689329
QUARTERLY	40	1.3483486123	46.4464816449	0.0215301561
If compounded ***quarterly,***	41	1.3584612269	47.7948302572	0.0209227650
	42	1.3686496861	49.1532914841	0.0203445175
nominal annual rate is	43	1.3789145588	50.5219411703	0.0197933804
	44	1.3892564180	51.9008557290	0.0192675051
3%	45	1.3996758411	53.2901121470	0.0187652073
	46	1.4101734099	54.6897879881	0.0182849493
	47	1.4207497105	56.0999613980	0.0178253242
	48	1.4314053333	57.5207111085	0.0173850424
	49	1.4421408733	58.9521164418	0.0169629194
MONTHLY	50	1.4529569299	60.3942573151	0.0165578657
If compounded ***monthly,***	51	1.4638541068	61.8472142450	0.0161688770
	52	1.4748330126	63.3110683518	0.0157950265
nominal annual rate is	53	1.4858942602	64.7859013645	0.0154354571
	54	1.4970384672	66.2717956247	0.0150893754
9%	55	1.5082662557	67.7688340919	0.0147560455
	56	1.5195782526	69.2771003476	0.0144347843
	57	1.5309750895	70.7966786002	0.0141249564
	58	1.5424574027	72.3276536897	0.0138259704
	59	1.5540258332	73.8701110924	0.0135372749
	60	1.5656810269	75.4241369255	0.0132583552
	120	2.4513570781	193.5142770833	0.0051675704
	180	3.8380432675	378.4057689972	0.0026426658
	240	6.0091515245	667.8868699297	0.0014972596
	300	9.4084145299	1121.1219373178	0.0008919636
	360	14.7305761230	1830.7434830721	0.0005462262
	420	23.0633835518	2941.7844735684	0.0003399297
	480	36.1099020441	4681.3202725429	0.0002136150
	n	$(1+i)^n$	$s_{\overline{n}|}$	$\dfrac{1}{s_{\overline{n}|}}$

Pres. Value of $1 at Comp. Int.	Amount Borrowed for $1 Payment	Payment to Borrow $1	n
0.9925558313	0.9925558313	1.0075000000	1
0.9851670782	1.9777229094	0.5056320050	2
0.9778333282	2.9555562377	0.3383457866	3
0.9705541719	3.9261104096	0.2547050123	4
0.9633292029	4.8894396125	0.2045224155	5
0.9561580178	5.8455976303	0.1710689074	6
0.9490402162	6.7946378464	0.1471748786	7
0.9419754006	7.7366132471	0.1292555241	8
0.9349631768	8.6715764239	0.1153192858	9
0.9280031532	9.5995795771	0.1041712287	10
0.9210949411	10.5206745182	0.0950509398	11
0.9142381550	11.4349126731	0.0874514768	12
0.9074324119	12.3423450850	0.0810218798	13
0.9006773319	13.2430224169	0.0755114632	14
0.8939725378	14.1369949547	0.0707363908	15
0.8873176554	15.0243126101	0.0665587855	16
0.8807123131	15.9050249232	0.0628732118	17
0.8741561420	16.7791810652	0.0595976643	18
0.8676487762	17.6468298414	0.0566674020	19
0.8611898523	18.5080196937	0.0540306319	20
0.8547790097	19.3627987034	0.0516454266	21
0.8484158905	20.2112145940	0.0494774817	22
0.8421001395	21.0533147335	0.0474984587	23
0.8358314040	21.8891461374	0.0456847423	24
0.8296093340	22.7187554714	0.0440164956	25
0.8234335821	23.5421890535	0.0424769335	26
0.8173038036	24.3594928571	0.0410517578	27
0.8112196562	25.1707125132	0.0397287125	28
0.8051808001	25.9758933134	0.0384972323	29
0.7991868984	26.7750802118	0.0373481608	30
0.7932376163	27.5683178281	0.0362735226	31
0.7873326216	28.3556504497	0.0352663397	32
0.7814715847	29.1371220344	0.0343204795	33
0.7756541784	29.9127762128	0.0334305313	34
0.7698800778	30.6826562907	0.0325917023	35
0.7641489606	31.4468052513	0.0317997327	36
0.7584605068	32.2052657581	0.0310508228	37
0.7528143988	32.9580801569	0.0303415732	38
0.7472103214	33.7052904783	0.0296689329	39
0.7416479617	34.4469384400	0.0290301561	40
0.7361270091	35.1830654492	0.0284227650	41
0.7306471555	35.9137126046	0.0278445175	42
0.7252080948	36.6389206994	0.0272933804	43
0.7198095233	37.3587302227	0.0267675051	44
0.7144511398	38.0731813625	0.0262652073	45
0.7091326449	38.7823140074	0.0257849493	46
0.7038537419	39.4861677493	0.0253253242	47
0.6986141359	40.1847818852	0.0248850424	48
0.6934135344	40.8781954195	0.0244629194	49
0.6882516470	41.5664470665	0.0240578657	50
0.6831281856	42.2495752521	0.0236688770	51
0.6780428641	42.9276181163	0.0232950265	52
0.6729953986	43.6006135149	0.0229354571	53
0.6679855073	44.2685990222	0.0225893754	54
0.6630129105	44.9316119327	0.0222560455	55
0.6580773305	45.5896892633	0.0219347843	56
0.6531784918	46.2428677551	0.0216249564	57
0.6483161209	46.8911838760	0.0213259704	58
0.6434899463	47.5346738224	0.0210372749	59
0.6386996986	48.1733735210	0.0207583552	60
0.4079373050	78.9416926690	0.0126675774	120
0.2605494337	98.5934088351	0.0101426658	180
0.1664128448	111.1449540271	0.0089972596	240
0.1062878338	119.1616221582	0.0083919636	300
0.0678860074	124.2818656772	0.0080462262	360
0.0433587725	127.5521636696	0.0078399297	420
0.0276932349	129.6409020116	0.0077136150	480
$\dfrac{1}{(1+i)^n}$	$p\,\overline{n}|$	$\dfrac{1}{p\,\overline{n}|}$	n

Rate

.75%

ANNUALLY

If compounded **annually,** nominal annual rate is

$3/4\%$

SEMIANNUALLY

If compounded **semiannually,** nominal annual rate is

$1^1/_2\%$

QUARTERLY

If compounded **quarterly,** nominal annual rate is

3%

MONTHLY

If compounded **monthly,** nominal annual rate is

9%

n	Amount of $1 at Comp. Int.	Amount Saved for $1/Period	Payment to Save $1
1	1.0083333333	1.0000000000	1.0000000000
2	1.0167361111	2.0083333333	0.4979253112
3	1.0252089120	3.0250694444	0.3305709235
4	1.0337523196	4.0502783565	0.2468966110
5	1.0423669223	5.0840306761	0.1966943285
6	1.0510533133	6.1263975984	0.1632280609
7	1.0598120909	7.1774509117	0.1393252301
8	1.0686438584	8.2372630027	0.1213995474
9	1.0775492238	9.3059068610	0.1074586298
10	1.0865288007	10.3834560849	0.0963070477
11	1.0955832074	11.4699848856	0.0871840730
12	1.1047130674	12.5655680930	0.0795825539
13	1.1139190097	13.6702811604	0.0731513850
14	1.1232016681	14.7842001701	0.0676397768
15	1.1325616820	15.9074018382	0.0628638171
16	1.1419996960	17.0399635201	0.0586855716
17	1.1515163601	18.1819632161	0.0549995613
18	1.1611123298	19.3334795763	0.0517237467
19	1.1707882659	20.4945919061	0.0487933600
20	1.1805448348	21.6653801720	0.0461565868
21	1.1903827084	22.8459250067	0.0437714822
22	1.2003025643	24.0363077151	0.0416037277
23	1.2103050857	25.2366102794	0.0396249730
24	1.2203909614	26.4469153651	0.0378115930
25	1.2305608861	27.6673063264	0.0361437427
26	1.2408155601	28.8978672125	0.0346046299
27	1.2511556898	30.1386827726	0.0331799504
28	1.2615819872	31.3898384624	0.0318574433
29	1.2720951704	32.6514204496	0.0306265389
30	1.2826959635	33.9235156200	0.0294780768
31	1.2933850965	35.2062115835	0.0284040786
32	1.3041633057	36.4995966800	0.0273975630
33	1.3150313332	37.8037599857	0.0264523952
34	1.3259899277	39.1187913189	0.0255631620
35	1.3370398437	40.4447812465	0.0247250688
36	1.3481818424	41.7818210903	0.0239338539
37	1.3594166911	43.1300029327	0.0231857160
38	1.3707451635	44.4894196238	0.0224772543
39	1.3821680399	45.8601647873	0.0218054166
40	1.3936861069	47.2423328272	0.0211674560
41	1.4053001578	48.6360189341	0.0205608934
42	1.4170109924	50.0413190919	0.0199834860
43	1.4288194174	51.4583300843	0.0194331996
44	1.4407262458	52.8871495017	0.0189081849
45	1.4527322979	54.3278757475	0.0184067569
46	1.4648384004	55.7806080454	0.0179273772
47	1.4770453870	57.2454464458	0.0174686383
48	1.4893540986	58.7224918329	0.0170292501
49	1.5017653828	60.2118459315	0.0166080276
50	1.5142800943	61.7136113142	0.0162038808
51	1.5268990951	63.2278914085	0.0158158050
52	1.5396232542	64.7547905036	0.0154428729
53	1.5524534480	66.2944137578	0.0150842272
54	1.5653905600	67.8468672058	0.0147390741
55	1.5784354814	69.4122577658	0.0144066773
56	1.5915891104	70.9906932472	0.0140863535
57	1.6048523530	72.5822823576	0.0137774670
58	1.6182261226	74.1871347106	0.0134794261
59	1.6317113403	75.8053608332	0.0131916792
60	1.6453089348	77.4370721734	0.0129137114
120	2.7070414909	204.8449789035	0.0048817404
180	4.4539195517	414.4703462078	0.0024127178
240	7.3280736332	759.3688359900	0.0013168831
300	12.0569450235	1326.8334028201	0.0007536741
360	19.8373993733	2260.4879247961	0.0004423824
420	32.6386504317	3796.6380517995	0.0002633909
480	53.7006631743	6324.0795809195	0.0001581258
n	$(1+i)^n$	$s\,\overline{n}$	$\dfrac{1}{s\,\overline{n}}$

ANNUALLY

If compounded annually,

nominal annual rate is

$5/6\%$

SEMIANNUALLY

If compounded semiannually,

nominal annual rate is

$1\,2/3\%$

QUARTERLY

If compounded quarterly,

nominal annual rate is

$3\,1/3\%$

MONTHLY

If compounded monthly,

nominal annual rate is

10%

Pres. Value of $1 at Comp. Int.	Amount Borrowed for $1 Payment	Payment to Borrow $1	n
0.9917355372	0.9917355372	1.0083333333	1
0.9835393757	1.9752749129	0.5062586445	2
0.9754109511	2.9506858640	0.3389042569	3
0.9673497036	3.9180355677	0.2552299444	4
0.9593550780	4.8773906456	0.2050276619	5
0.9514265236	5.8288171692	0.1715613942	6
0.9435634945	6.7723806637	0.1476585635	7
0.9357654491	7.7081461127	0.1297328807	8
0.9280318503	8.6361779630	0.1157919631	9
0.9203621656	9.5565401286	0.1046403810	10
0.9127558667	10.4692959953	0.0955174064	11
0.9052124298	11.3745084251	0.0879158872	12
0.8977313353	12.2722397605	0.0814847183	13
0.8903120681	13.1625518285	0.0759731102	14
0.8829541171	14.0455059457	0.0711971505	15
0.8756569757	14.9211629213	0.0670189050	16
0.8684201411	15.7895830625	0.0633328946	17
0.8612431152	16.6508261777	0.0600570800	18
0.8541254035	17.5049515811	0.0571266933	19
0.8470665159	18.3520180970	0.0544899201	20
0.8400659661	19.1920840631	0.0521048155	21
0.8331232722	20.0252073354	0.0499370610	22
0.8262379559	20.8514452913	0.0479583063	23
0.8194095430	21.6708548343	0.0461449263	24
0.8126375634	22.4834923977	0.0444770760	25
0.8059215504	23.2894139481	0.0429379632	26
0.7992610418	24.0886749898	0.0415132837	27
0.7926555786	24.8813305684	0.0401907767	28
0.7861047060	25.6674352745	0.0389598723	29
0.7796079729	26.4470432474	0.0378114102	30
0.7731649318	27.2202081793	0.0367374119	31
0.7667751390	27.9869833183	0.0357308963	32
0.7604381544	28.7474214727	0.0347857286	33
0.7541535415	29.5015750142	0.0338964953	34
0.7479208677	30.2494958819	0.0330584022	35
0.7417397035	30.9912355853	0.0322671872	36
0.7356096233	31.7268452086	0.0315190494	37
0.7295302049	32.4563754135	0.0308105877	38
0.7235010296	33.1798764431	0.0301387500	39
0.7175216823	33.8973981254	0.0295007893	40
0.7115917510	34.6089898764	0.0288942267	41
0.7057108275	35.3147007039	0.0283168193	42
0.6998785066	36.0145792105	0.0277665329	43
0.6940943867	36.7086735972	0.0272415182	44
0.6883580694	37.3970316666	0.0267400902	45
0.6826691598	38.0797008264	0.0262607105	46
0.6770272659	38.7567280923	0.0258019717	47
0.6714319992	39.4281600915	0.0253625834	48
0.6658829745	40.0940430660	0.0249413609	49
0.6603798094	40.7544228754	0.0245372141	50
0.6549221250	41.4093450003	0.0241491383	51
0.6495095455	42.0588545458	0.0237762062	52
0.6441416980	42.7029962438	0.0234175605	53
0.6388182129	43.3418144566	0.0230724074	54
0.6335387235	43.9753531801	0.0227400107	55
0.6283028663	44.6036560464	0.0224196868	56
0.6231102806	45.2267663270	0.0221108003	57
0.6179606089	45.8447269359	0.0218127594	58
0.6128534964	46.4575804323	0.0215250125	59
0.6077885915	47.0653690238	0.0212470447	60
0.3694069719	75.6711633697	0.0132150737	120
0.2245213431	93.0574388230	0.0107460512	180
0.1364615109	103.6246186917	0.0096502165	240
0.0829397495	110.0472300598	0.0090870075	300
0.0504098335	113.9508199769	0.0087757157	360
0.0306385217	116.3233773942	0.0085967243	420
0.0186217440	117.7653907251	0.0084914591	480
$\dfrac{1}{(1+i)^n}$	$p\,\overline{n}|$	$\dfrac{1}{p\,\overline{n}|}$	n

Rate

$.8\overline{3}\%$

ANNUALLY

If compounded annually, nominal annual rate is

$5/6\%$

SEMIANNUALLY

If compounded semiannually, nominal annual rate is

$1^2/_3\%$

QUARTERLY

If compounded quarterly, nominal annual rate is

$3^1/_3\%$

MONTHLY

If compounded monthly, nominal annual rate is

10%

	n	Amount of $1 at Comp. Int.	Amount Saved for $1/Period	Payment to Save $1
Rate	1	1.0100000000	1.0000000000	1.0000000000
	2	1.0201000000	2.0100000000	0.4975124378
1%	3	1.0303010000	3.0301000000	0.3300221115
	4	1.0406040100	4.0604010000	0.2462810939
	5	1.0510100501	5.1010050100	0.1960397996
	6	1.0615201506	6.1520150601	0.1625483667
	7	1.0721353521	7.2135352107	0.1386282829
	8	1.0828567056	8.2856705628	0.1206902920
	9	1.0936852727	9.3685272684	0.1067403628
	10	1.1046221254	10.4622125411	0.0955820766
	11	1.1156683467	11.5668346665	0.0864540757
	12	1.1268250301	12.6825030132	0.0788487887
	13	1.1380932804	13.8093280433	0.0724148197
	14	1.1494742132	14.9474213238	0.0669011717
	15	1.1609689554	16.0968955370	0.0621237802
	16	1.1725786449	17.2578644924	0.0579445968
	17	1.1843044314	18.4304431373	0.0542580551
	18	1.1961474757	19.6147475687	0.0509820479
ANNUALLY	19	1.2081089504	20.8108950444	0.0480517536
	20	1.2201900399	22.0190039948	0.0454153149
If compounded	21	1.2323919403	23.2391940347	0.0430307522
annually,	22	1.2447158598	24.4715859751	0.0408637185
nominal annual rate is	23	1.2571630183	25.7163018348	0.0388858401
	24	1.2697346485	26.9734648532	0.0370734722
1%	25	1.2824319950	28.2431995017	0.0354067534
	26	1.2952563150	29.5256314967	0.0338688776
	27	1.3082088781	30.8208878117	0.0324455287
	28	1.3212909669	32.1290966898	0.0311244356
	29	1.3345038766	33.4503876567	0.0298950198
SEMIANNUALLY	30	1.3478489153	34.7848915333	0.0287481132
If compounded	31	1.3613274045	36.1327404486	0.0276757309
semiannually,	32	1.3749406785	37.4940678531	0.0266708857
nominal annual rate is	33	1.3886900853	38.8690085316	0.0257274378
	34	1.4025769862	40.2576986170	0.0248399694
2%	35	1.4166027560	41.6602756031	0.0240036818
	36	1.4307687836	43.0768783592	0.0232143098
	37	1.4450764714	44.5076471427	0.0224680491
	38	1.4595272361	45.9527236142	0.0217614958
	39	1.4741225085	47.4122508503	0.0210915951
QUARTERLY	40	1.4888637336	48.8863733588	0.0204555980
If compounded	41	1.5037523709	50.3752370924	0.0198510232
quarterly,	42	1.5187898946	51.8789894633	0.0192756260
nominal annual rate is	43	1.5339777936	53.3977793580	0.0187273705
	44	1.5493175715	54.9317571515	0.0182044058
4%	45	1.5648107472	56.4810747231	0.0177050455
	46	1.5804588547	58.0458854703	0.0172277499
	47	1.5962634432	59.6263443250	0.0167711103
	48	1.6122260777	61.2226077682	0.0163338354
	49	1.6283483385	62.8348338459	0.0159147393
MONTHLY	50	1.6446318218	64.4631821844	0.0155127309
If compounded	51	1.6610781401	66.1078140062	0.0151268048
monthly,	52	1.6776889215	67.7688921463	0.0147560329
nominal annual rate is	53	1.6944658107	69.4465810678	0.0143995570
	54	1.7114104688	71.1410468784	0.0140565826
12%	55	1.7285245735	72.8524573472	0.0137263730
	56	1.7458098192	74.5809819207	0.0134082440
	57	1.7632679174	76.3267917399	0.0131015595
	58	1.7809005966	78.0900596573	0.0128057272
	59	1.7987096025	79.8709602539	0.0125201950
	60	1.8166966986	81.6696698564	0.0122444477
	120	3.3003868946	230.0386894574	0.0043470948
	180	5.9958019754	499.5801975356	0.0020016806
	240	10.8925536539	989.2553653874	0.0010108613
	300	19.7884662619	1878.8466261924	0.0005322414
	360	35.9496413277	3494.9641327685	0.0002861260
	420	65.3095947146	6430.9594714569	0.0001554978
	480	118.6477251025	11764.7725102516	0.0000849995
	n	$(1+i)^n$	$s\,\overline{n}|$	$\dfrac{1}{s\,\overline{n}|}$

Pres. Value of $1 at Comp. Int.	Amount Borrowed for $1 Payment	Payment to Borrow $1	n
0.9900990099	0.9900990099	1.0100000000	1
0.9802960494	1.9703950593	0.5075124378	2
0.9705901479	2.9409852072	0.3400221115	3
0.9609803445	3.9019655517	0.2562810939	4
0.9514656876	4.8534312393	0.2060397996	5
0.9420452353	5.7954764746	0.1725483667	6
0.9327180547	6.7281945293	0.1486282829	7
0.9234832225	7.6516777518	0.1306902920	8
0.9143398242	8.5660175760	0.1167403628	9
0.9052869547	9.4713045307	0.1055820766	10
0.8963237175	10.3676282482	0.0964540757	11
0.8874492253	11.2550774735	0.0888487887	12
0.8786625993	12.1337400728	0.0824148197	13
0.8699629696	13.0037030423	0.0769011717	14
0.8613494748	13.8650525172	0.0721237802	15
0.8528212622	14.7178737794	0.0679445968	16
0.8443774873	15.5622512667	0.0642580551	17
0.8360173142	16.3982685809	0.0609820479	18
0.8277399150	17.2260084959	0.0580517536	19
0.8195444703	18.0455529663	0.0554153149	20
0.8114301687	18.8569831349	0.0530307522	21
0.8033962066	19.6603793415	0.0508637185	22
0.7954417887	20.4558211302	0.0488858401	23
0.7875661274	21.2433872576	0.0470734722	24
0.7797684430	22.0231557006	0.0454067534	25
0.7720479634	22.7952036640	0.0438688776	26
0.7644039241	23.5596075881	0.0424455287	27
0.7568355684	24.3164431565	0.0411244356	28
0.7493421470	25.0657853035	0.0398950198	29
0.7419229178	25.8077082213	0.0387481132	30
0.7345771463	26.5422853676	0.0376757309	31
0.7273041053	27.2695894729	0.0366708857	32
0.7201030745	27.9896925474	0.0357274378	33
0.7129733411	28.7026658885	0.0348399694	34
0.7059141991	29.4085800876	0.0340036818	35
0.6989249496	30.1075050373	0.0332143098	36
0.6920049006	30.7995099379	0.0324680491	37
0.6851533670	31.4846633048	0.0317614958	38
0.6783696702	32.1630329751	0.0310915951	39
0.6716531389	32.8346861140	0.0304555980	40
0.6650031078	33.4996892217	0.0298510232	41
0.6584189186	34.1581081403	0.0292756260	42
0.6518999194	34.8100080597	0.0287273705	43
0.6454454648	35.4554535245	0.0282044058	44
0.6390549156	36.0945084401	0.0277050455	45
0.6327276392	36.7272360793	0.0272277499	46
0.6264630091	37.3536990884	0.0267711103	47
0.6202604051	37.9739594935	0.0263338354	48
0.6141192129	38.5880787064	0.0259147393	49
0.6080388247	39.1961175311	0.0255127309	50
0.6020186383	39.7981361694	0.0251268048	51
0.5960580577	40.3941942271	0.0247560329	52
0.5901564928	40.9843507199	0.0243995570	53
0.5843133592	41.5686640791	0.0240565826	54
0.5785280784	42.1471921576	0.0237263730	55
0.5728000776	42.7199922352	0.0234082440	56
0.5671287898	43.2871210250	0.0231015595	57
0.5615136532	43.8486346782	0.0228057272	58
0.5559541121	44.4045887903	0.0225201950	59
0.5504496159	44.9550384062	0.0222444477	60
0.3029947797	69.7005220314	0.0143470948	120
0.1667833601	83.3216639891	0.0120016806	180
0.0918058365	90.8194163483	0.0110108613	240
0.0505344875	94.9465512548	0.0105322414	300
0.0278166892	97.2183310791	0.0102861260	360
0.0153116859	98.4688314108	0.0101554978	420
0.0084283116	99.1571688381	0.0100849995	480
$\dfrac{1}{(1+i)^n}$	$p\,\overline{n}\rvert$	$\dfrac{1}{p\,\overline{n}\rvert}$	n

Rate

1%

ANNUALLY

If compounded annually,

nominal annual rate is

1%

SEMIANNUALLY

If compounded semiannually,

nominal annual rate is

2%

QUARTERLY

If compounded quarterly,

nominal annual rate is

4%

MONTHLY

If compounded monthly,

nominal annual rate is

12%

n	Amount of $1 at Comp. Int.	Amount Saved for $1/Period	Payment to Save $1
1	1.0116666667	1.0000000000	1.0000000000
2	1.0234694444	2.0116666667	0.4971002486
3	1.0354099213	3.0351361111	0.3294745156
4	1.0474897037	4.0705460324	0.2456672869
5	1.0597104169	5.1180357361	0.1953874595
6	1.0720737051	6.1777461530	0.1618713322
7	1.0845812317	7.2498198582	0.1379344618
8	1.0972346794	8.3344010898	0.1199846263
9	1.1100357506	9.4316357692	0.1060261469
10	1.1229861677	10.5416715199	0.0948616164
11	1.1360876730	11.6646576876	0.0857290481
12	1.1493420292	12.8007453606	0.0781204509
13	1.1627510195	13.9500873898	0.0716841387
14	1.1763164481	15.1128384094	0.0661689071
15	1.1900401400	16.2891548575	0.0613905392
16	1.2039239416	17.4791949975	0.0572108727
17	1.2179697210	18.6831189391	0.0535242538
18	1.2321793677	19.9010886601	0.0502485074
19	1.2465547937	21.1332680278	0.0473187582
20	1.2610979329	22.3798228214	0.0446831062
21	1.2758107421	23.6409207544	0.0422995369
22	1.2906952008	24.9167314965	0.0401336748
23	1.3057533115	26.2074266973	0.0381571228
24	1.3209871001	27.5131800087	0.0363462166
25	1.3363986163	28.8341671088	0.0346810780
26	1.3519899335	30.1705657251	0.0331448873
27	1.3677631494	31.5225556586	0.0317233162
28	1.3837203861	32.8903188079	0.0304040835
29	1.3998637906	34.2740391940	0.0291766020
30	1.4161955348	35.6739029846	0.0280316959
31	1.4327178161	37.0900985194	0.0269613735
32	1.4494328572	38.5228163355	0.0259586420
33	1.4663429072	39.9722491927	0.0250173563
34	1.4834502412	41.4385921000	0.0241320940
35	1.5007571606	42.9220423412	0.0232980526
36	1.5182659942	44.4227995018	0.0225109631
37	1.5359790975	45.9410654960	0.0217670180
38	1.5538988536	47.4770445934	0.0210628106
39	1.5720276735	49.0309434470	0.0203952837
40	1.5903679964	50.6029711206	0.0197616855
41	1.6089222897	52.1933391170	0.0191595329
42	1.6276930497	53.8022614067	0.0185865793
43	1.6466828020	55.4299544564	0.0180407870
44	1.6658941013	57.0766372584	0.0175203034
45	1.6853295325	58.7425313598	0.0170234407
46	1.7049917104	60.4278608923	0.0165486579
47	1.7248832804	62.1328526027	0.0160945451
48	1.7450069186	63.8577358831	0.0156598098
49	1.7653653327	65.6027428017	0.0152432651
50	1.7859612616	67.3681081344	0.0148438189
51	1.8067974763	69.1540693960	0.0144604650
52	1.8278767802	70.9608668723	0.0140922743
53	1.8492020093	72.7887436524	0.0137383880
54	1.8707760327	74.6379456617	0.0133980108
55	1.8926017531	76.5087216944	0.0130704053
56	1.9146821069	78.4013234475	0.0127548867
57	1.9370200648	80.3160055544	0.0124508184
58	1.9596186322	82.2530256192	0.0121576075
59	1.9824808496	84.2126442515	0.0118747013
60	2.0056097928	86.1951251011	0.0116015842
120	4.0224706412	259.0689120993	0.0038599768
180	8.0675065093	605.7862722292	0.0016507472
240	16.1802700590	1301.1660050553	0.0007685414
300	32.4513080812	2695.8264069578	0.0003709438
360	65.0846612783	5492.9709667074	0.0001820508
420	130.5344340237	11102.9514877459	0.0000900661
480	261.8011391815	22354.3833584136	0.0000447340
n	$(1+i)^n$	$s\,\overline{n|}$	$\dfrac{1}{s\,\overline{n|}}$

ANNUALLY

If compounded annually, nominal annual rate is

1¹/₆%

SEMIANNUALLY

If compounded semiannually, nominal annual rate is

2¹/₃%

QUARTERLY

If compounded quarterly, nominal annual rate is

4²/₃%

MONTHLY

If compounded monthly, nominal annual rate is

14%

Pres. Value of $1 at Comp. Int.	Amount Borrowed for $1 Payment	Payment to Borrow $1	n
0.9884678748	0.9884678748	1.0116666667	1
0.9770687395	1.9655366143	0.5087669152	2
0.9658010605	2.9313376748	0.3411411823	3
0.9546633217	3.8860009965	0.2573339536	4
0.9436540248	4.8296550212	0.2070541261	5
0.9327716884	5.7624267096	0.1735379989	6
0.9220148485	6.6844415581	0.1496011284	7
0.9113820578	7.5958236159	0.1316512929	8
0.9008718858	8.4966955017	0.1176928136	9
0.8904829184	9.3871784202	0.1065282831	10
0.8802137579	10.2673921781	0.0973957148	11
0.8700630227	11.1374552007	0.0897871176	12
0.8600293469	11.9974845477	0.0833508054	13
0.8501113808	12.8475959285	0.0778355737	14
0.8403077900	13.6879037185	0.0730572059	15
0.8306172553	14.5185209738	0.0688775394	16
0.8210384731	15.3395594469	0.0651909205	17
0.8115701546	16.1511296015	0.0619151740	18
0.8022110260	16.9533406275	0.0589854249	19
0.7929598280	17.7463004556	0.0563497729	20
0.7838153160	18.5301157716	0.0539662036	21
0.7747762596	19.3048920312	0.0518003415	22
0.7658414428	20.0707334740	0.0498237895	23
0.7570096634	20.8277431374	0.0480128833	24
0.7482797332	21.5760228706	0.0463477447	25
0.7396504776	22.3156733482	0.0448115539	26
0.7311207357	23.0467940839	0.0433899828	27
0.7226893598	23.7694834437	0.0420707502	28
0.7143552156	24.4838386593	0.0408432687	29
0.7061171819	25.1899558412	0.0396983626	30
0.6979741501	25.8879299913	0.0386280402	31
0.6899250248	26.5778550161	0.0376253087	32
0.6819687230	27.2598237391	0.0366840230	33
0.6741041743	27.9339279135	0.0357987607	34
0.6663303206	28.6002582341	0.0349647193	35
0.6586461159	29.2589043500	0.0341776298	36
0.6510505264	29.9099548764	0.0334336847	37
0.6435425303	30.5534974067	0.0327294773	38
0.6361211172	31.1896185239	0.0320619503	39
0.6287852889	31.8184038128	0.0314283522	40
0.6215340582	32.4399378709	0.0308261996	41
0.6143664496	33.0543043205	0.0302532460	42
0.6072814988	33.6615858193	0.0297074536	43
0.6002782525	34.2618640718	0.0291869700	44
0.5933557685	34.8552198403	0.0286901074	45
0.5865131155	35.4417329559	0.0282153246	46
0.5797493728	36.0214823287	0.0277612118	47
0.5730636305	36.5945459592	0.0273264765	48
0.5664549889	37.1610009481	0.0269099318	49
0.5599225591	37.7209235072	0.0265104856	50
0.5534654620	38.2743889692	0.0261271317	51
0.5470828290	38.8214717982	0.0257589410	52
0.5407738013	39.3622455996	0.0254050546	53
0.5345375302	39.8967831297	0.0250646774	54
0.5283731764	40.4251563062	0.0247370719	55
0.5222799108	40.9474362170	0.0244215534	56
0.5162569135	41.4636931304	0.0241174851	57
0.5103033741	41.9739965045	0.0238242742	58
0.5044184917	42.4784149963	0.0235413680	59
0.4986014745	42.9770164708	0.0232682508	60
0.2486034304	64.4054202530	0.0155266435	120
0.1239540370	75.0896539752	0.0133174139	180
0.0618036656	80.4168286631	0.0124352081	240
0.0308153988	83.0729658174	0.0120376104	300
0.0153646033	84.3973197191	0.0118487175	360
0.0076608138	85.0576445272	0.0117567328	420
0.0038196931	85.3868834502	0.0117114006	480
$\frac{1}{(1+i)^n}$	$p\,\overline{n}|$	$\frac{1}{p\,\overline{n}|}$	n

Rate

$1.1\overline{6}\%$

ANNUALLY

If compounded annually,

nominal annual rate is

$1^1/_6\%$

SEMIANNUALLY

If compounded semiannually,

nominal annual rate is

$2^1/_3\%$

QUARTERLY

If compounded quarterly,

nominal annual rate is

$4^2/_3\%$

MONTHLY

If compounded monthly,

nominal annual rate is

14%

	n	Amount of $1 at Comp. Int.	Amount Saved for $1/Period	Payment to Save $1
Rate	1	1.0125000000	1.0000000000	1.0000000000
	2	1.0251562500	2.0125000000	0.4968944099
1.25%	3	1.0379707031	3.0376562500	0.3292011728
	4	1.0509453369	4.0756269531	0.2453610233
	5	1.0640821536	5.1265722900	0.1950621084
	6	1.0773831805	6.1906544437	0.1615338102
	7	1.0908504703	7.2680376242	0.1375887209
	8	1.1044861012	8.3588880945	0.1196331365
	9	1.1182921774	9.4633741957	0.1056705546
	10	1.1322708297	10.5816663731	0.0945030740
	11	1.1464242150	11.7139372028	0.0853683935
	12	1.1607545177	12.8603614178	0.0777583123
	13	1.1752639492	14.0211159356	0.0713209993
	14	1.1899547486	15.1963798848	0.0658051462
	15	1.2048291829	16.3863346333	0.0610264603
	16	1.2198895477	17.5911638162	0.0568467221
	17	1.2351381670	18.8110533639	0.0531602341
	18	1.2505773941	20.0461915310	0.0498847873
	19	1.2662096116	21.2967689251	0.0469554797
ANNUALLY	20	1.2820372317	22.5629785367	0.0443203896
If compounded annually,	21	1.2980626971	23.8450157684	0.0419374854
	22	1.3142884808	25.1430784655	0.0397723772
nominal annual rate is	23	1.3307170868	26.4573669463	0.0377966561
	24	1.3473510504	27.7880840331	0.0359866480
1^1/4%	25	1.3641929385	29.1354350836	0.0343224667
	26	1.3812453503	30.4996280221	0.0327872851
	27	1.3985109172	31.8808733724	0.0313667693
	28	1.4159923036	33.2793842895	0.0300486329
	29	1.4336922074	34.6953765932	0.0288222841
SEMIANNUALLY	30	1.4516133600	36.1290688006	0.0276785434
If compounded semiannually,	31	1.4697585270	37.5806821606	0.0266094159
	32	1.4881305086	39.0504406876	0.0256079056
nominal annual rate is	33	1.5067321400	40.5385711962	0.0246678650
	34	1.5255662917	42.0453033361	0.0237838693
2^1/2%	35	1.5446358703	43.5708696278	0.0229511141
	36	1.5639438187	45.1155054982	0.0221653285
	37	1.5834931165	46.6794493169	0.0214227035
	38	1.6032867804	48.2629424334	0.0207198308
	39	1.6233278652	49.8662292138	0.0200536519
QUARTERLY	40	1.6436194635	51.4895570790	0.0194214139
If compounded quarterly,	41	1.6641647068	53.1331765424	0.0188206327
	42	1.6849667656	54.7973412492	0.0182490606
nominal annual rate is	43	1.7060288502	56.4823080148	0.0177046589
	44	1.7273542108	58.1883368650	0.0171855745
5%	45	1.7489461384	59.9156910758	0.0166901188
	46	1.7708079652	61.6646372143	0.0162167499
	47	1.7929430647	63.4354451795	0.0157640574
	48	1.8153548531	65.2283882442	0.0153307483
	49	1.8380467887	67.0437430973	0.0149156350
MONTHLY	50	1.8610223736	68.8817898860	0.0145176251
If compounded monthly,	51	1.8842851532	70.7428122596	0.0141357117
	52	1.9078387177	72.6270974128	0.0137689655
nominal annual rate is	53	1.9316867016	74.5349361305	0.0134165272
	54	1.9558327854	76.4666228321	0.0130776012
15%	55	1.9802806952	78.4224556175	0.0127514497
	56	2.0050342039	80.4027363127	0.0124373877
	57	2.0300971315	82.4077705166	0.0121347780
	58	2.0554733456	84.4378676481	0.0118430276
	59	2.0811667624	86.4933409937	0.0115615837
	60	2.1071813470	88.5745077561	0.0112899301
	120	4.4402132289	275.2170583151	0.0036334957
	180	9.3563344925	668.5067594005	0.0014958712
	240	19.7154935184	1497.2394814757	0.0006678958
	300	41.5441201880	3243.5296150407	0.0003083061
	360	87.5409951357	6923.2796108539	0.0001444402
	420	184.4647520434	14677.1801634752	0.0000681330
	480	388.7006846759	31016.0547740736	0.0000322414
	n	$(1+i)^n$	$s\,\overline{n}|$	$\dfrac{1}{s\,\overline{n}|}$

Pres. Value of $1 at Comp. Int.	Amount Borrowed for $1 Payment	Payment to Borrow $1	n
0.9876543210	0.9876543210	1.0125000000	1
0.9754610578	1.9631153788	0.5093944099	2
0.9634183287	2.9265337074	0.3417011728	3
0.9515242752	3.8780579826	0.2578610233	4
0.9397770619	4.8178350446	0.2075621084	5
0.9281748760	5.7460099206	0.1740338102	6
0.9167159269	6.6627258475	0.1500887209	7
0.9053984463	7.5681242938	0.1321331365	8
0.8942206877	8.4623449815	0.1181705546	9
0.8831809262	9.3455259077	0.1070030740	10
0.8722774579	10.2178033656	0.0978683935	11
0.8615086004	11.0793119660	0.0902583123	12
0.8508726918	11.9301846578	0.0838209993	13
0.8403680906	12.7705527485	0.0783051462	14
0.8299931759	13.6005459244	0.0735264603	15
0.8197463466	14.4202922710	0.0693467221	16
0.8096260213	15.2299182924	0.0656602341	17
0.7996306384	16.0295489307	0.0623847873	18
0.7897586552	16.8193075859	0.0594554797	19
0.7800085483	17.5993161342	0.0568203896	20
0.7703788132	18.3696949474	0.0544374854	21
0.7608679636	19.1305629110	0.0522723772	22
0.7514745320	19.8820374430	0.0502966561	23
0.7421970686	20.6242345116	0.0484866480	24
0.7330341418	21.3572686534	0.0468224667	25
0.7239843376	22.0812529910	0.0452872851	26
0.7150462594	22.7962992504	0.0438667693	27
0.7062185278	23.5025177782	0.0425486329	28
0.6974997805	24.2000175587	0.0413222841	29
0.6888886721	24.8889062308	0.0401785434	30
0.6803838737	25.5692901045	0.0391094159	31
0.6719840728	26.2412741773	0.0381079056	32
0.6636879731	26.9049621504	0.0371678650	33
0.6554942944	27.5604564448	0.0362838693	34
0.6474017723	28.2078582171	0.0354511141	35
0.6394091578	28.8472673749	0.0346653285	36
0.6315152176	29.4787825925	0.0339227035	37
0.6237187334	30.1025013259	0.0332198308	38
0.6160185021	30.7185198281	0.0325536519	39
0.6084133355	31.3269331635	0.0319214139	40
0.6009020597	31.9278352233	0.0313206327	41
0.5934835158	32.5213187390	0.0307490606	42
0.5861565588	33.1074752978	0.0302046589	43
0.5789200581	33.6863953558	0.0296855745	44
0.5717728968	34.2581682527	0.0291901188	45
0.5647139722	34.8228822249	0.0287167499	46
0.5577421948	35.3806244196	0.0282640574	47
0.5508564886	35.9314809083	0.0278307483	48
0.5440557913	36.4755366995	0.0274156350	49
0.5373390531	37.0128757526	0.0270176251	50
0.5307052376	37.5435809902	0.0266357117	51
0.5241533211	38.0677343114	0.0262689655	52
0.5176822925	38.5854166038	0.0259165272	53
0.5112911530	39.0967077568	0.0255776012	54
0.5049789166	39.6016866734	0.0252514497	55
0.4987446090	40.1004312824	0.0249373877	56
0.4925872681	40.5930185505	0.0246347780	57
0.4865059438	41.0795244943	0.0243430276	58
0.4804996976	41.5600241919	0.0240615837	59
0.4745676026	42.0345917945	0.0237899301	60
0.2252144094	61.9828472474	0.0161334957	120
0.1068794623	71.4496430131	0.0139958712	180
0.0507215302	75.9422775836	0.0131678958	240
0.0240707950	78.0743364010	0.0128083061	300
0.0114232195	79.0861424425	0.0126444402	360
0.0054210899	79.5663128098	0.0125681330	420
0.0025726736	79.7941861099	0.0125322414	480
$\dfrac{1}{(1+i)^n}$	$p\,\overline{n}|$	$\dfrac{1}{p\,\overline{n}|}$	n

Rate

1.25%

ANNUALLY

If compounded annually, nominal annual rate is

$1\frac{1}{4}\%$

SEMIANNUALLY

If compounded semiannually, nominal annual rate is

$2\frac{1}{2}\%$

QUARTERLY

If compounded quarterly, nominal annual rate is

5%

MONTHLY

If compounded monthly, nominal annual rate is

15%

	n	Amount of \$1 at Comp. Int.	Amount Saved for \$1/Period	Payment to Save \$1
Rate	1	1.0150000000	1.0000000000	1.0000000000
	2	1.0302250000	2.0150000000	0.4962779156
1.5%	3	1.0456783750	3.0452250000	0.3283829602
	4	1.0613635506	4.0909033750	0.2444447860
	5	1.0772840039	5.1522669256	0.1940893231
	6	1.0934432639	6.2295509295	0.1605252146
	7	1.1098449129	7.3229941935	0.1365561645
	8	1.1264925866	8.4328391064	0.1185840246
	9	1.1433899754	9.5593316929	0.1046098234
	10	1.1605408250	10.7027216683	0.0934341779
	11	1.1779489374	11.8632624934	0.0842938442
	12	1.1956181715	13.0412114308	0.0766799929
	13	1.2135524440	14.2368296022	0.0702403574
	14	1.2317557307	15.4503820463	0.0647233186
	15	1.2502320667	16.6821377770	0.0599443557
	16	1.2689855477	17.9323698436	0.0557650778
	17	1.2880203309	19.2013553913	0.0520796569
	18	1.3073406358	20.4893757221	0.0488057818
	19	1.3269507454	21.7967163580	0.0458784701
ANNUALLY	20	1.3468550066	23.1236671033	0.0432457359
*If compounded **annually**,*	21	1.3670578316	24.4705221099	0.0408654950
	22	1.3875636991	25.8375799415	0.0387033152
nominal annual rate is	23	1.4083771546	27.2251436407	0.0367307520
	24	1.4295028119	28.6335207953	0.0349241020
1¹/₂%	25	1.4509453541	30.0630236072	0.0332634539
	26	1.4727095344	31.5139689613	0.0317319599
	27	1.4948001774	32.9866784957	0.0303152680
	28	1.5172221801	34.4814786732	0.0290010765
	29	1.5399805128	35.9987008533	0.0277787802
SEMIANNUALLY	30	1.5630802205	37.5386813661	0.0266391883
*If compounded **semiannually**,*	31	1.5865264238	39.1017615865	0.0255742954
	32	1.6103243202	40.6882880103	0.0245770970
nominal annual rate is	33	1.6344791850	42.2986123305	0.0236414375
	34	1.6589963727	43.9330915155	0.0227618855
3%	35	1.6838813183	45.5920878882	0.0219336303
	36	1.7091395381	47.2759692065	0.0211523955
	37	1.7347766312	48.9851087446	0.0204143673
	38	1.7607982806	50.7198853758	0.0197161329
	39	1.7872102548	52.4806836564	0.0190546298
QUARTERLY	40	1.8140184087	54.2678939113	0.0184271017
*If compounded **quarterly**,*	41	1.8412286848	56.0819123199	0.0178310610
	42	1.8688471151	57.9231410047	0.0172642571
nominal annual rate is	43	1.8968798218	59.7919881198	0.0167246488
	44	1.9253330191	61.6888679416	0.0162103801
6%	45	1.9542130144	63.6142009607	0.0157197604
	46	1.9835262096	65.5684139751	0.0152512458
	47	2.0132791028	67.5519401848	0.0148034238
	48	2.0434782893	69.5652192875	0.0143749996
	49	2.0741304637	71.6086975768	0.0139647841
MONTHLY	50	2.1052424206	73.6828280405	0.0135716832
*If compounded **monthly**,*	51	2.1368210569	75.7880704611	0.0131946887
	52	2.1688733728	77.9248915180	0.0128328700
nominal annual rate is	53	2.2014064734	80.0937648908	0.0124853664
	54	2.2344275705	82.2951713642	0.0121513812
18%	55	2.2679439840	84.5295989346	0.0118301756
	56	2.3019631438	86.7975429186	0.0115210635
	57	2.3364925909	89.0995060624	0.0112234068
	58	2.3715399798	91.4359986534	0.0109366116
	59	2.4071130795	93.8075386332	0.0106601241
	60	2.4432197757	96.2146517126	0.0103934274
	120	5.9693228723	331.2881914881	0.0030185199
	180	14.5843676891	905.6245126088	0.0011042104
	240	35.6328155540	2308.8543702679	0.0004331152
	300	87.0587996251	5737.2533083389	0.0001742994
	360	212.7037808918	14113.5853927876	0.0000708537
	420	519.6820838389	34578.8055892571	0.0000289194
	480	1269.6975443067	84579.8362871160	0.0000118231
n		$(1+i)^n$	$s\,\overline{n}\rceil$	$\dfrac{1}{s\,\overline{n}\rceil}$

Pres. Value of $1 at Comp. Int.	Amount Borrowed for $1 Payment	Payment to Borrow $1	n
0.9852216749	0.9852216749	1.0150000000	1
0.9706617486	1.9558834235	0.5112779156	2
0.9563169937	2.9122004173	0.3433829602	3
0.9421842303	3.8543846476	0.2594447860	4
0.9282603254	4.7826449730	0.2090893231	5
0.9145421925	5.6971871655	0.1755252146	6
0.9010267907	6.5982139561	0.1515561645	7
0.8877111238	7.4859250799	0.1335840246	8
0.8745922402	8.3605173201	0.1196098234	9
0.8616672317	9.2221845519	0.1084341779	10
0.8489332332	10.0711177851	0.0992938442	11
0.8363874219	10.9075052070	0.0916799929	12
0.8240270166	11.7315322236	0.0852403574	13
0.8118492775	12.5433815011	0.0797233186	14
0.7998515049	13.3432330060	0.0749443557	15
0.7880310393	14.1312640453	0.0707650778	16
0.7763852604	14.9076493057	0.0670796569	17
0.7649115866	15.6725608924	0.0638057818	18
0.7536074745	16.4261683669	0.0608784701	19
0.7424704182	17.1686387851	0.0582457359	20
0.7314979490	17.9001367341	0.0558654950	21
0.7206876345	18.6208243685	0.0537033152	22
0.7100370783	19.3308614468	0.0517307520	23
0.6995439195	20.0304053663	0.0499241020	24
0.6892058320	20.7196111984	0.0482634539	25
0.6790205242	21.3986317225	0.0467319599	26
0.6689857381	22.0676174606	0.0453152680	27
0.6590992494	22.7267167100	0.0440010765	28
0.6493588664	23.3760755763	0.0427787802	29
0.6397624299	24.0158380062	0.0416391883	30
0.6303078127	24.6461458189	0.0405742954	31
0.6209929189	25.2671387379	0.0395770970	32
0.6118156837	25.8789544216	0.0386414375	33
0.6027740726	26.4817284941	0.0377618855	34
0.5938660814	27.0755945755	0.0369336303	35
0.5850897353	27.6606843109	0.0361523955	36
0.5764430890	28.2371273999	0.0354143673	37
0.5679242256	28.8050516255	0.0347161329	38
0.5595312568	29.3645828822	0.0340546298	39
0.5512623219	29.9158452042	0.0334271017	40
0.5431155881	30.4589607923	0.0328310610	41
0.5350892494	30.9940500417	0.0322642571	42
0.5271815265	31.5212315681	0.0317246488	43
0.5193906665	32.0406222346	0.0312103801	44
0.5117149423	32.5523371770	0.0307197604	45
0.5041526526	33.0564898295	0.0302512458	46
0.4967021207	33.5531919503	0.0298034238	47
0.4893616953	34.0425536456	0.0293749996	48
0.4821297491	34.5246833947	0.0289647841	49
0.4750046789	34.9996880736	0.0285716832	50
0.4679849053	35.4676729789	0.0281946887	51
0.4610688722	35.9287418511	0.0278328700	52
0.4542550465	36.3829968977	0.0274853664	53
0.4475419178	36.8305388154	0.0271513812	54
0.4409279978	37.2714668132	0.0268301756	55
0.4344118205	37.7058786337	0.0265210635	56
0.4279919414	38.1338705751	0.0262234068	57
0.4216669373	38.5555375124	0.0259366116	58
0.4154354062	38.9709729186	0.0256601241	59
0.4092959667	39.3802688853	0.0253934274	60
0.1675231884	55.4984541085	0.0180185199	120
0.0685665653	62.0955623111	0.0161042104	180
0.0280640186	64.7957320905	0.0154331152	240
0.0114864896	65.9009006906	0.0151742994	300
0.0047013739	66.3532417412	0.0150708537	360
0.0019242534	66.5383831088	0.0150289194	420
0.0007875891	66.6141607238	0.0150118231	480
$\dfrac{1}{(1+i)^n}$	$p\,\overline{n|}$	$\dfrac{1}{p\,\overline{n|}}$	n

Rate

1.5%

ANNUALLY

If compounded annually,

nominal annual rate is

$1^1/_2\%$

SEMIANNUALLY

If compounded semiannually,

nominal annual rate is

3%

QUARTERLY

If compounded quarterly,

nominal annual rate is

6%

MONTHLY

If compounded monthly,

nominal annual rate is

18%

	n	Amount of $1 at Comp. Int.	Amount Saved for $1/Period	Payment to Save $1
Rate	1	1.0175000000	1.0000000000	1.0000000000
	2	1.0353062500	2.0175000000	0.4956629492
1.75%	3	1.0534241094	3.0528062500	0.3275674635
	4	1.0718590313	4.1062303594	0.2435323673
	5	1.0906165643	5.1780893907	0.1931214246
	6	1.1097023542	6.2687059550	0.1595225565
	7	1.1291221454	7.3784083092	0.1355305857
	8	1.1488817830	8.5075304546	0.1175429233
	9	1.1689872142	9.6564122376	0.1035581306
	10	1.1894444904	10.8253994517	0.0923753442
	11	1.2102597690	12.0148439421	0.0832303778
	12	1.2314393149	13.2251037111	0.0756137738
	13	1.2529895030	14.4565430261	0.0691728305
	14	1.2749168193	15.7095325290	0.0636556179
	15	1.2972278636	16.9844493483	0.0588773872
	16	1.3199293512	18.2816772119	0.0546995764
	17	1.3430281149	19.6016065631	0.0510162265
	18	1.3665311069	20.9446346779	0.0477449244
	19	1.3904454012	22.3111657848	0.0448206073
ANNUALLY	20	1.4147781958	23.7016111860	0.0421912246
If compounded annually,	21	1.4395368142	25.1163893818	0.0398146399
	22	1.4647287084	26.5559261960	0.0376563782
nominal annual rate is	23	1.4903614608	28.0206549044	0.0356879596
	24	1.5164427864	29.5110163652	0.0338856510
$1^3/_4\%$	25	1.5429805352	31.0274591516	0.0322295163
	26	1.5699826945	32.5704396868	0.0307026865
	27	1.5974573917	34.1404223813	0.0292907917
	28	1.6254128960	35.7378797730	0.0279815145
	29	1.6538576217	37.3632926690	0.0267642365
SEMIANNUALLY	30	1.6828001301	39.0171502907	0.0256297549
If compounded semiannually,	31	1.7122491324	40.6999504208	0.0245700545
	32	1.7422134922	42.4121995532	0.0235781216
nominal annual rate is	33	1.7727022283	44.1544130453	0.0226477928
	34	1.8037245173	45.9271152736	0.0217736297
$3^1/_2\%$	35	1.8352896963	47.7308397909	0.0209508151
	36	1.8674072660	49.5661294873	0.0201750673
	37	1.9000868932	51.4335367533	0.0194425673
	38	1.9333384138	53.3336236465	0.0187498979
	39	1.9671718361	55.2669620603	0.0180939926
QUARTERLY	40	2.0015973432	57.2341338963	0.0174720911
If compounded quarterly,	41	2.0366252967	59.2357312395	0.0168817026
	42	2.0722662394	61.2723565362	0.0163205735
nominal annual rate is	43	2.1085308986	63.3446227756	0.0157866596
	44	2.1454301893	65.4531536742	0.0152781026
7%	45	2.1829752176	67.5985838635	0.0147932093
	46	2.2211772839	69.7815590811	0.0143304336
	47	2.2600478864	72.0027363650	0.0138883611
	48	2.2995987244	74.2627842514	0.0134656950
	49	2.3398417021	76.5623829758	0.0130612445
MONTHLY	50	2.3807889319	78.9022246779	0.0126739139
If compounded monthly,	51	2.4224527382	81.2830136097	0.0123026935
	52	2.4648456611	83.7054663479	0.0119466511
nominal annual rate is	53	2.5079804602	86.1703120090	0.0116049249
	54	2.5518701182	88.6782924692	0.0112767169
21%	55	2.5965278453	91.2301625874	0.0109612871
	56	2.6419670826	93.8266904326	0.0106579481
	57	2.6882015065	96.4686575152	0.0103660611
	58	2.7352450329	99.1568590217	0.0100850310
	59	2.7831118210	101.8921040546	0.0098143032
	60	2.8318162778	104.6752158756	0.0095533598
	120	8.0191834313	401.0961960765	0.0024931675
	180	22.7088541757	1240.5059528978	0.0008061227
	240	64.3073029055	3617.5601660269	0.0002764294
	300	182.1064671506	10348.9409800323	0.0000966282
	360	515.6920579737	29410.9747413538	0.0000340009
	420	1460.3451641136	83391.1522350631	0.0000119917
	480	4135.4292069760	236253.0975414883	0.0000042327
	n	$(1+i)^n$	$s\,\overline{n|}$	$\dfrac{1}{s\,\overline{n|}}$

Pres. Value of $1 at Comp. Int.	Amount Borrowed for $1 Payment	Payment to Borrow $1	n
0.9828009828	0.9828009828	1.0175000000	1
0.9658977718	1.9486987546	0.5131629492	2
0.9492852794	2.8979840340	0.3450674635	3
0.9329585056	3.8309425396	0.2610323673	4
0.9169125362	4.7478550757	0.2106214246	5
0.9011425417	5.6489976174	0.1770225565	6
0.8856437756	6.5346413930	0.1530305857	7
0.8704115731	7.4050529661	0.1350429233	8
0.8554413495	8.2604943156	0.1210581306	9
0.8407285990	9.1012229146	0.1098753442	10
0.8262688934	9.9274918080	0.1007303778	11
0.8120578805	10.7395496884	0.0931137738	12
0.7980912830	11.5376409714	0.0866728305	13
0.7843648973	12.3220058687	0.0811556179	14
0.7708745919	13.0928804607	0.0763773872	15
0.7576163066	13.8504967672	0.0721995764	16
0.7445860507	14.5950828179	0.0685162265	17
0.7317799024	15.3268627203	0.0652449244	18
0.7191940073	16.0460567276	0.0623206073	19
0.7068245772	16.7528813048	0.0596912246	20
0.6946678891	17.4475491939	0.0573146399	21
0.6827202841	18.1302694780	0.0551563782	22
0.6709781662	18.8012476442	0.0531879596	23
0.6594380012	19.4606856454	0.0513856510	24
0.6480963157	20.1087819611	0.0497295163	25
0.6369496960	20.7457316571	0.0482026865	26
0.6259947872	21.3717264443	0.0467907917	27
0.6152282921	21.9869547364	0.0454815145	28
0.6046469701	22.5916017066	0.0442642365	29
0.5942476365	23.1858493431	0.0431297549	30
0.5840271612	23.7698765042	0.0420700545	31
0.5739824680	24.3438589722	0.0410781216	32
0.5641105336	24.9079695059	0.0401477928	33
0.5544083869	25.4623778928	0.0392736297	34
0.5448731075	26.0072510003	0.0384508151	35
0.5355018255	26.5427528258	0.0376750673	36
0.5262917204	27.0690445462	0.0369425673	37
0.5172400201	27.5862845663	0.0362498979	38
0.5083440001	28.0946285664	0.0355939926	39
0.4996009829	28.5942295493	0.0349720911	40
0.4910083370	29.0852378863	0.0343817026	41
0.4825634762	29.5678013625	0.0338205735	42
0.4742638586	30.0420652211	0.0332866596	43
0.4661069864	30.5081722075	0.0327781026	44
0.4580904043	30.9662626117	0.0322932093	45
0.4502116996	31.4164743113	0.0318304336	46
0.4424685008	31.8589428121	0.0313883611	47
0.4348584774	32.2938012895	0.0309656950	48
0.4273793390	32.7211806285	0.0305612445	49
0.4200288344	33.1412094629	0.0301739139	50
0.4128047513	33.5540142142	0.0298026935	51
0.4057049152	33.9597191294	0.0294466511	52
0.3987271894	34.3584463188	0.0291049249	53
0.3918694736	34.7503157925	0.0287767169	54
0.3851297038	35.1354454963	0.0284612871	55
0.3785058514	35.5139513477	0.0281579481	56
0.3719959228	35.8859472705	0.0278660611	57
0.3655979585	36.2515452290	0.0275850310	58
0.3593100329	36.6108552619	0.0273143032	59
0.3531302535	36.9639855154	0.0270533598	60
0.1247009759	50.0170870901	0.0199931675	120
0.0440356872	54.6265321579	0.0183061227	180
0.0155503334	56.2542666631	0.0177764294	240
0.0054912932	56.8290689615	0.0175966282	300
0.0019391418	57.0320490428	0.0175340009	360
0.0006847696	57.1037274504	0.0175119917	420
0.0002418129	57.1290392646	0.0175042327	480
$\dfrac{1}{(1+i)^n}$	$p\,\overline{n\rceil}$	$\dfrac{1}{p\,\overline{n\rceil}}$	n

Rate

1.75%

ANNUALLY
If compounded annually,
nominal annual rate is

$1\tfrac{3}{4}\%$

SEMIANNUALLY
If compounded semiannually,
nominal annual rate is

$3\tfrac{1}{2}\%$

QUARTERLY
If compounded quarterly,
nominal annual rate is

7%

MONTHLY
If compounded monthly,
nominal annual rate is

21%

	n	Amount of $1 at Comp. Int.	Amount Saved for $1/Period	Payment to Save $1
Rate	1	1.0200000000	1.0000000000	1.0000000000
	2	1.0404000000	2.0200000000	0.4950495050
2%	3	1.0612080000	3.0604000000	0.3267546726
	4	1.0824321600	4.1216080000	0.2426237527
	5	1.1040808032	5.2040401600	0.1921583941
	6	1.1261624193	6.3081209632	0.1585258123
	7	1.1486856676	7.4342833825	0.1345119561
	8	1.1716593810	8.5829690501	0.1165097991
	9	1.1950925686	9.7546284311	0.1025154374
	10	1.2189944200	10.9497209997	0.0913265279
	11	1.2433743084	12.1687154197	0.0821779428
	12	1.2682417946	13.4120897281	0.0745595966
	13	1.2936066305	14.6803315227	0.0681183527
	14	1.3194787631	15.9739381531	0.0626019702
	15	1.3458683383	17.2934169162	0.0578254723
	16	1.3727857051	18.6392852545	0.0536501259
	17	1.4002414192	20.0120709596	0.0499698408
	18	1.4282462476	21.4123123788	0.0467021022
	19	1.4568111725	22.8405586264	0.0437817663
ANNUALLY	20	1.4859473960	24.2973697989	0.0411567181
If compounded ***annually,***	21	1.5156663439	25.7833171949	0.0387847689
	22	1.5459796708	27.2989835388	0.0366314005
nominal annual rate is	23	1.5768992642	28.8449632096	0.0346680976
	24	1.6084372495	30.4218624738	0.0328710973
2%	25	1.6406059945	32.0302997232	0.0312204384
	26	1.6734181144	33.6709057177	0.0296992308
	27	1.7068864766	35.3443238321	0.0282930862
	28	1.7410242062	37.0512103087	0.0269896716
	29	1.7758446903	38.7922345149	0.0257783552
SEMIANNUALLY	30	1.8113615841	40.5680792052	0.0246499223
If compounded ***semiannually,***	31	1.8475888158	42.3794407893	0.0235963472
	32	1.8845405921	44.2270296051	0.0226106073
nominal annual rate is	33	1.9222314039	46.1115701972	0.0216865311
	34	1.9606760320	48.0338016011	0.0208186728
4%	35	1.9998895527	49.9944776331	0.0200022092
	36	2.0398873437	51.9943671858	0.0192328526
	37	2.0806850906	54.0342545295	0.0185067789
	38	2.1222987924	56.1149396201	0.0178205663
	39	2.1647447682	58.2372384125	0.0171711439
QUARTERLY	40	2.2080396636	60.4019831807	0.0165557478
If compounded ***quarterly,***	41	2.2522004569	62.6100228444	0.0159718836
	42	2.2972444660	64.8622233012	0.0154172945
nominal annual rate is	43	2.3431893553	67.1594677673	0.0148899334
	44	2.3900531425	69.5026571226	0.0143879391
8%	45	2.4378542053	71.8927102651	0.0139096161
	46	2.4866112894	74.3305644704	0.0134534159
	47	2.5363435152	76.8171757598	0.0130179220
	48	2.5870703855	79.3535192750	0.0126018355
	49	2.6388117932	81.9405896605	0.0122039639
MONTHLY	50	2.6915880291	84.5794014537	0.0118232097
If compounded ***monthly,***	51	2.7454197897	87.2709894828	0.0114585615
	52	2.8003281854	90.0164092724	0.0111090856
nominal annual rate is	53	2.8563347492	92.8167374579	0.0107739189
	54	2.9134614441	95.6730722070	0.0104522618
24%	55	2.9717306730	98.5865336512	0.0101433732
	56	3.0311652865	101.5582643242	0.0098465645
	57	3.0917885922	104.5894296107	0.0095611957
	58	3.1536243641	107.6812182029	0.0092866706
	59	3.2166968513	110.8348425669	0.0090224335
	60	3.2810307884	114.0515394183	0.0087679658
	n	$(1+i)^n$	$s\,\overline{n}|$	$\dfrac{1}{s\,\overline{n}|}$

Pres. Value of $1 at Comp. Int.	Amount Borrowed for $1 Payment	Payment to Borrow $1	n	
0.9803921569	0.9803921569	1.0200000000	1	**Rate**
0.9611687812	1.9415609381	0.5150495050	2	
0.9423223345	2.8838832726	0.3467546726	3	**2%**
0.9238454260	3.8077286987	0.2626237527	4	
0.9057308098	4.7134595085	0.2121583941	5	
0.8879713822	5.6014308907	0.1785258123	6	
0.8705601786	6.4719910693	0.1545119561	7	
0.8534903712	7.3254814405	0.1365097991	8	
0.8367552659	8.1622367064	0.1225154374	9	
0.8203482999	8.9825850062	0.1113265279	10	
0.8042630391	9.7868480453	0.1021779428	11	
0.7884931756	10.5753412209	0.0945595966	12	
0.7730325251	11.3483737460	0.0881183527	13	
0.7578750246	12.1062487706	0.0826019702	14	
0.7430147300	12.8492635006	0.0778254723	15	
0.7284458137	13.5777093143	0.0736501259	16	
0.7141625625	14.2918718768	0.0699698408	17	
0.7001593750	14.9920312517	0.0667021022	18	
0.6864307598	15.6784620115	0.0637817663	19	
0.6729713331	16.3514333446	0.0611567181	20	**ANNUALLY**
0.6597758168	17.0112091614	0.0587847689	21	*If compounded*
0.6468390361	17.6580481974	0.0566314005	22	***annually,***
0.6341559177	18.2922041151	0.0546680976	23	*nominal annual rate is*
0.6217214879	18.9139256031	0.0528710973	24	
0.6095308705	19.5234564736	0.0512204384	25	**2%**
0.5975792848	20.1210357584	0.0496992308	26	
0.5858620440	20.7068978024	0.0482930862	27	
0.5743745529	21.2812723553	0.0469896716	28	
0.5631123068	21.8443846620	0.0457783522	29	
0.5520708890	22.3964555510	0.0446499223	30	**SEMIANNUALLY**
0.5412459696	22.9377015206	0.0435963472	31	*If compounded*
0.5306333035	23.4683348241	0.0426106073	32	***semiannually,***
0.5202287289	23.9885635530	0.0416865311	33	*nominal annual rate is*
0.5100281656	24.4985917187	0.0408186728	34	
0.5000276134	24.9986193320	0.0400022092	35	**4%**
0.4902231504	25.4888424824	0.0392328526	36	
0.4806109317	25.9694534141	0.0385067789	37	
0.4711871880	26.4406406021	0.0378205663	38	
0.4619482235	26.9025888256	0.0371711439	39	
0.4528904152	27.3554792407	0.0365557478	40	**QUARTERLY**
0.4440102110	27.7994894517	0.0359718836	41	*If compounded*
0.4353041284	28.2347935801	0.0354172945	42	***quarterly,***
0.4267687533	28.6615623334	0.0348899334	43	*nominal annual rate is*
0.4184007386	29.0799630720	0.0343879391	44	
0.4101968025	29.4901598745	0.0339096161	45	**8%**
0.4021537280	29.8923136025	0.0334534159	46	
0.3942683607	30.2865819632	0.0330179220	47	
0.3865376086	30.6731195718	0.0326018355	48	
0.3789584398	31.0520780115	0.0322039639	49	
0.3715278821	31.4236058937	0.0318232097	50	**MONTHLY**
0.3642430217	31.7878489153	0.0314585615	51	*If compounded*
0.3571010017	32.1449499170	0.0311090856	52	***monthly,***
0.3500990212	32.4950489382	0.0307739189	53	*nominal annual rate is*
0.3432343345	32.8382832728	0.0304522618	54	
0.3365042496	33.1747875223	0.0301433732	55	**24%**
0.3299061270	33.5046936494	0.0298465645	56	
0.3234373794	33.8281310288	0.0295611957	57	
0.3170954700	34.1452264988	0.0292866706	58	
0.3108779118	34.4561044106	0.0290224335	59	
0.3047822665	34.7608866770	0.0287679658	60	
$\dfrac{1}{(1+i)^n}$	$p_{\overline{n}\rceil}$	$\dfrac{1}{p_{\overline{n}\rceil}}$	n	

	n	Amount of $1 at Comp. Int.	Amount Saved for $1/Period	Payment to Save $1
Rate	1	1.0225000000	1.0000000000	1.0000000000
	2	1.0455062500	2.0225000000	0.4944375773
2.25%	3	1.0690301406	3.0680062500	0.3259445772
	4	1.0930833188	4.1370363906	0.2417189277
	5	1.1176776935	5.2301197094	0.1912002125
	6	1.1428254416	6.3477974029	0.1575349584
	7	1.1685390140	7.4906228444	0.1335002470
	8	1.1948311418	8.6591618584	0.1154846181
	9	1.2217148425	9.8539930003	0.1014817039
	10	1.2492034265	11.0757078428	0.0902876831
	11	1.2773105036	12.3249112692	0.0811364868
	12	1.3060499899	13.6022217728	0.0735174015
	13	1.3354361147	14.9082717627	0.0670768561
	14	1.3654834272	16.2437078773	0.0615622989
	15	1.3962068044	17.6091913046	0.0567885250
	16	1.4276214575	19.0053981089	0.0526166300
	17	1.4597429402	20.4330195664	0.0489403926
	18	1.4925871564	21.8927625066	0.0456771958
	19	1.5261703674	23.3853496630	0.0427618152
ANNUALLY	20	1.5605092007	24.9115200304	0.0401420708
If compounded	21	1.5956206577	26.4720292311	0.0377757214
annually,	22	1.6315221225	28.0676498888	0.0356282056
nominal annual rate is	23	1.6682313703	29.6991720113	0.0336709724
	24	1.7057665761	31.3674033816	0.0318802289
2¹/₄%	25	1.7441463240	33.0731699577	0.0302359889
	26	1.7833896163	34.8173162817	0.0287213406
	27	1.8235158827	36.6007058980	0.0273218774
	28	1.8645449901	38.4242217807	0.0260252506
	29	1.9064972523	40.2887667708	0.0248208143
SEMIANNUALLY	30	1.9493934405	42.1952640232	0.0236993422
If compounded	31	1.9932547929	44.1446574637	0.0226527978
semiannually,	32	2.0381030258	46.1379122566	0.0216741493
nominal annual rate is	33	2.0839603439	48.1760152824	0.0207572169
	34	2.1308494516	50.2599756262	0.0198965477
4¹/₂%	35	2.1787935643	52.3908250778	0.0190873115
	36	2.2278164194	54.5696186421	0.0183252151
	37	2.2779422889	56.7974350615	0.0176064289
	38	2.3291959904	59.0753773504	0.0169275262
	39	2.3816029002	61.4045733408	0.0162854319
QUARTERLY	40	2.4351889654	63.7861762410	0.0156773781
If compounded	41	2.4899807171	66.2213652064	0.0151008666
quarterly,	42	2.5460052833	68.7113459235	0.0145536372
nominal annual rate is	43	2.6032904022	71.2573512068	0.0140336398
	44	2.6618644362	73.8606416090	0.0135390105
9%	45	2.7217563860	76.5225060452	0.0130680508
	46	2.7829959047	79.2442624312	0.0126192101
	47	2.8456133126	82.0272583359	0.0121910694
	48	2.9096396121	84.8728716484	0.0117823279
	49	2.9751065034	87.7825112605	0.0113917908
MONTHLY	50	3.0420463997	90.7576177639	0.0110183588
If compounded	51	3.1104924437	93.7996641636	0.0106610190
monthly,	52	3.1804785237	96.9101566073	0.0103188359
nominal annual rate is	53	3.2520392904	100.0906351309	0.0099909447
	54	3.3252101745	103.3426744214	0.0096765446
27%	55	3.4000274034	106.6678845958	0.0093748930
	56	3.4765280200	110.0679119993	0.0090853000
	57	3.5547499004	113.5444400192	0.0088071243
	58	3.6347317732	117.0991899197	0.0085397687
	59	3.7165132381	120.7339216929	0.0082826764
	60	3.8001347859	124.4504349310	0.0080353275
	n	$(1+i)^n$	$s\,\overline{n\rceil}$	$\dfrac{1}{s\,\overline{n\rceil}}$

Pres. Value of $1 at Comp. Int.	Amount Borrowed for $1 Payment	Payment to Borrow $1	n
0.9779951100	0.9779951100	1.0225000000	1
0.9564744352	1.9344695453	0.5169375773	2
0.9354273205	2.8698968658	0.3484445772	3
0.9148433453	3.7847402110	0.2642189277	4
0.8947123181	4.6794525291	0.2137002125	5
0.8750242720	5.5544768011	0.1800349584	6
0.8557694591	6.4102462602	0.1560002470	7
0.8369383464	7.2471846066	0.1379846181	8
0.8185216101	8.0657062167	0.1239817039	9
0.8005101322	8.8662163489	0.1127876831	10
0.7828949948	9.6491113436	0.1036364868	11
0.7656674765	10.4147788202	0.0960174015	12
0.7488190480	11.1635978681	0.0895768561	13
0.7323413672	11.8959392354	0.0840622989	14
0.7162262760	12.6121655113	0.0792885250	15
0.7004657956	13.3126313069	0.0751166300	16
0.6850521228	13.9976834298	0.0714403926	17
0.6699776262	14.6676610560	0.0681771958	18
0.6552348423	15.3228958983	0.0652618152	19
0.6408164717	15.9637123700	0.0626420708	20
0.6267153757	16.5904277457	0.0602757214	21
0.6129245728	17.2033523185	0.0581282056	22
0.5994372350	17.8027895536	0.0561709724	23
0.5862466846	18.3890362382	0.0543802289	24
0.5733463908	18.9623826291	0.0527359889	25
0.5607299666	19.5231125957	0.0512213406	26
0.5483911654	20.0715037610	0.0498218774	27
0.5363238781	20.6078276392	0.0485252506	28
0.5245221302	21.1323497693	0.0473208143	29
0.5129800784	21.6453298478	0.0461993422	30
0.5016920082	22.1470218560	0.0451527978	31
0.4906523308	22.6376741868	0.0441741493	32
0.4798555802	23.1175297670	0.0432572169	33
0.4692964110	23.5868261780	0.0423965477	34
0.4589695951	24.0457957731	0.0415873115	35
0.4488700197	24.4946657928	0.0408252151	36
0.4389926843	24.9336584771	0.0401064289	37
0.4293326985	25.3629911756	0.0394275262	38
0.4198852798	25.7828764554	0.0387854319	39
0.4106457504	26.1935222057	0.0381773781	40
0.4016095358	26.5951317416	0.0376008666	41
0.3927721622	26.9879039037	0.0370536372	42
0.3841292540	27.3720331577	0.0365336398	43
0.3756765320	27.7477096897	0.0360390105	44
0.3674098112	28.1151195009	0.0355680508	45
0.3593249988	28.4744444997	0.0351192101	46
0.3514180917	28.8258625913	0.0346910694	47
0.3436851753	29.1695477666	0.0342823279	48
0.3361224208	29.5056701874	0.0338917908	49
0.3287260839	29.8343962713	0.0335183588	50
0.3214925026	30.1558887739	0.0331610190	51
0.3144180954	30.4703068693	0.0328188359	52
0.3074993598	30.7778062291	0.0324909447	53
0.3007328703	31.0785390994	0.0321765446	54
0.2941152765	31.3726543760	0.0318748930	55
0.2876433022	31.6602976782	0.0315853000	56
0.2813137430	31.9416114212	0.0313071243	57
0.2751234651	32.2167348863	0.0310397687	58
0.2690694035	32.4858042898	0.0307826764	59
0.2631485609	32.7489528506	0.0305353275	60
$\dfrac{1}{(1+i)^n}$	$p_{\overline{n}\rceil}$	$\dfrac{1}{p_{\overline{n}\rceil}}$	n

Rate

2.25%

ANNUALLY

If compounded annually,

nominal annual rate is

$2^1/_4\%$

SEMIANNUALLY

If compounded semiannually,

nominal annual rate is

$4^1/_2\%$

QUARTERLY

If compounded quarterly,

nominal annual rate is

9%

MONTHLY

If compounded monthly,

nominal annual rate is

27%

479

n	Amount of $1 at Comp. Int.	Amount Saved for $1/Period	Payment to Save $1
1	1.0250000000	1.0000000000	1.0000000000
2	1.0506250000	2.0250000000	0.4938271605
3	1.0768906250	3.0756250000	0.3251371672
4	1.1038128906	4.1525156250	0.2408178777
5	1.1314082129	5.2563285156	0.1902468609
6	1.1596934182	6.3877367285	0.1565499711
7	1.1886857537	7.5474301467	0.1324954296
8	1.2184028975	8.7361159004	0.1144673458
9	1.2488629699	9.9545187979	0.1004568900
10	1.2800845442	11.2033817679	0.0892587632
11	1.3120866578	12.4834663121	0.0801059558
12	1.3448888242	13.7955529699	0.0724871270
13	1.3785110449	15.1404417941	0.0660482708
14	1.4129738210	16.5189528390	0.0605365249
15	1.4482981665	17.9319266599	0.0557664561
16	1.4845056207	19.3802248264	0.0515989886
17	1.5216182612	20.8647304471	0.0479277699
18	1.5596587177	22.3863487083	0.0446700805
19	1.5986501856	23.9460074260	0.0417606151
20	1.6386164403	25.5446576116	0.0391471287
21	1.6795818513	27.1832740519	0.0367873273
22	1.7215713976	28.8628559032	0.0346466061
23	1.7646106825	30.5844273008	0.0326963781
24	1.8087259496	32.3490379833	0.0309128204
25	1.8539440983	34.1577639329	0.0292759210
26	1.9002927008	36.0117080312	0.0277687467
27	1.9478000183	37.9120007320	0.0263768722
28	1.9964950188	39.8598007503	0.0250879327
29	2.0464073942	41.8562957690	0.0238912685
30	2.0975675791	43.9027031633	0.0227776407
31	2.1500067686	46.0002707424	0.0217390025
32	2.2037569378	48.1502775109	0.0207683123
33	2.2588508612	50.3540344487	0.0198593819
34	2.3153221327	52.6128853099	0.0190067508
35	2.3732051861	54.9282074426	0.0182055823
36	2.4325353157	57.3014126287	0.0174515767
37	2.4933486986	59.7339479444	0.0167408992
38	2.5556824161	62.2272966430	0.0160701180
39	2.6195744765	64.7829790591	0.0154361534
40	2.6850638384	67.4025535356	0.0148362332
41	2.7521904343	70.0876173740	0.0142678555
42	2.8209951952	72.8398078083	0.0137287567
43	2.8915200751	75.6608030035	0.0132168833
44	2.9638080770	78.5523230786	0.0127303683
45	3.0379032789	81.5161311556	0.0122675106
46	3.1138508609	84.5540344345	0.0118267568
47	3.1916971324	87.6678852954	0.0114066855
48	3.2714895607	90.8595824277	0.0110059938
49	3.3532767997	94.1310719884	0.0106234847
50	3.4371087197	97.4843487881	0.0102580569
51	3.5230364377	100.9214575078	0.0099086956
52	3.6111123486	104.4444939455	0.0095744635
53	3.7013901574	108.0556062942	0.0092544944
54	3.7939249113	111.7569964515	0.0089479856
55	3.8887730341	115.5509213628	0.0086541932
56	3.9859923599	119.4396943969	0.0083724260
57	4.0856421689	123.4256867568	0.0081020412
58	4.1877832231	127.5113289257	0.0078424404
59	4.2924778037	131.6991121489	0.0075930656
60	4.3997897488	135.9915899526	0.0073533959
n	$(1 + i)^n$	$s\,\overline{n|}$	$\dfrac{1}{s\,\overline{n|}}$

Rate

2.5%

ANNUALLY

If compounded
annually,

nominal annual rate is

$2^1/_2\%$

SEMIANNUALLY
If compounded
semiannually,

nominal annual rate is

5%

QUARTERLY

If compounded
quarterly,

nominal annual rate is

10%

MONTHLY

If compounded
monthly,

nominal annual rate is

30%

Pres. Value of $1 at Comp. Int.	Amount Borrowed for $1 Payment	Payment to Borrow $1	n
0.9756097561	0.9756097561	1.0250000000	1
0.9518143962	1.9274241523	0.5188271605	2
0.9285994109	2.8560235632	0.3501371672	3
0.9059506448	3.7619742080	0.2658178777	4
0.8838542876	4.6458284956	0.2152468609	5
0.8622968660	5.5081253616	0.1815499711	6
0.8412652351	6.3493905967	0.1574954296	7
0.8207465708	7.1701371675	0.1394673458	8
0.8007283618	7.9708655292	0.1254568900	9
0.7811984017	8.7520639310	0.1142587632	10
0,7621447822	9.5142087131	0.1051059558	11
0.7435558850	10.2577645982	0.0974871270	12
0.7254203757	10.9831849738	0.0910482708	13
0.7077271958	11.6909121696	0.0855365249	14
0.6904655568	12.3813777264	0.0807664561	15
0.6736249335	13.0550026599	0.0765989886	16
0.6571950571	13.7121977170	0.0729277699	17
0.6411659093	14.3533636264	0.0696700805	18
0.6255277164	14.9788913428	0.0667606151	19
0.6102709429	15.5891622856	0.0641471287	20
0.5953862857	16.1845485714	0.0617873273	21
0.5808646690	16.7654132404	0.0596466061	22
0.5666972380	17.3321104784	0.0576963781	23
0.5528753542	17.8849858326	0.0559128204	24
0.5393905894	18.4243764220	0.0542759210	25
0.5262347214	18.9506111434	0.0527687467	26
0.5133997282	19.4640108717	0.0513768722	27
0.5008777836	19.9648886553	0.0500879327	28
0.4886612523	20.4535499076	0.0488912685	29
0.4767426852	20.9302925928	0.0477776407	30
0.4651148148	21.3954074076	0.0467390025	31
0.4537705510	21.8491779586	0.0457683123	32
0.4427029766	22.2918809352	0.0448593819	33
0.4319053430	22.7237862783	0.0440067508	34
0.4213710664	23.1451573447	0.0432055823	35
0.4110937233	23.5562510680	0.0424515767	36
0.4010670471	23.9573181151	0.0417408992	37
0.3912849240	24.3486030391	0.0410701180	38
0.3817413893	24.7303444284	0.0404361534	39
0.3724306237	25.1027750521	0.0398362332	40
0.3633469499	25.4661220020	0.0392678555	41
0.3544848292	25.8206068313	0.0387287567	42
0.3458388578	26.1664456890	0.0382168833	43
0.3374037637	26.5038494527	0.0377303683	44
0.3291744036	26.8330238563	0.0372675106	45
0.3211457596	27.1541696159	0.0368267568	46
0.3133129362	27.4674825521	0.0364066855	47
0.3056711573	27.7731537094	0.0360059938	48
0.2982157632	28.0713694726	0.0356234847	49
0.2909422080	28.3623116805	0.0352580569	50
0.2838460566	28.6461577371	0.0349086956	51
0.2769229820	28.9230807191	0.0345744635	52
0.2701687629	29.1932494821	0.0342544944	53
0.2635792809	29.4568287630	0.0339479856	54
0.2571505180	29.7139792810	0.0336541932	55
0.2508785541	29.9648578351	0.0333724260	56
0.2447595650	30.2096174001	0.0331020412	57
0.2387898195	30.4484072196	0.0328424404	58
0.2329656776	30.6813728972	0.0325930656	59
0.2272835879	30.9086564851	0.0323533959	60
$\dfrac{1}{(1+i)^n}$	$p\,\overline{n|}$	$\dfrac{1}{p\,\overline{n|}}$	n

Rate

2.5%

ANNUALLY

If compounded annually,

nominal annual rate is

$2^1/_2\%$

SEMIANNUALLY

If compounded semiannually,

nominal annual rate is

5%

QUARTERLY

If compounded quarterly,

nominal annual rate is

10%

MONTHLY

If compounded monthly,

nominal annual rate is

30%

	n	Amount of \$1 at Comp. Int.	Amount Saved for \$1/Period	Payment to Save \$1
Rate	1	1.0300000000	1.0000000000	1.0000000000
	2	1.0609000000	2.0300000000	0.4926108374
3%	3	1.0927270000	3.0909000000	0.3235303633
	4	1.1255088100	4.1836270000	0.2390270452
	5	1.1592740743	5.3091358100	0.1883545714
	6	1.1940522965	6.4684098843	0.1545975005
	7	1.2298738654	7.6624621808	0.1305063538
	8	1.2667700814	8.8923360463	0.1124563888
	9	1.3047731838	10.1591061276	0.0984338570
	10	1.3439163793	11.4638793115	0.0872305066
	11	1.3842338707	12.8077956908	0.0780774478
	12	1.4257608868	14.1920295615	0.0704620855
	13	1.4685337135	15.6177904484	0.0640295440
	14	1.5125897249	17.0863241618	0.0585263390
	15	1.5579674166	18.5989138867	0.0537665805
	16	1.6047064391	20.1568813033	0.0496108493
	17	1.6528476323	21.7615877424	0.0459525294
	18	1.7024330612	23.4144353747	0.0427086959
	19	1.7535060531	25.1168684359	0.0398138806
ANNUALLY	20	1.8061112347	26.8703744890	0.0372157076
If compounded	21	1.8602945717	28.6764857236	0.0348717765
annually,	22	1.9161034089	30.5367802954	0.0327473948
nominal annual rate is	23	1.9735865111	32.4528837042	0.0308139027
	24	2.0327941065	34.4264702153	0.0290474159
3%	25	2.0937779297	36.4592643218	0.0274278710
	26	2.1565912675	38.5530422515	0.0259382903
	27	2.2212890056	40.7096335190	0.0245642103
	28	2.2879276757	42.9309225246	0.0232932334
	29	2.3565655060	45.2188502003	0.0221146711
SEMIANNUALLY	30	2.4272624712	47.5754157063	0.0210192593
If compounded	31	2.5000803453	50.0026781775	0.0199989288
semiannually,	32	2.5750827557	52.5027585228	0.0190466183
nominal annual rate is	33	2.6523352384	55.0778412785	0.0181561219
	34	2.7319052955	57.7301765169	0.0173219633
6%	35	2.8138624544	60.4620818124	0.0165392916
	36	2.8982783280	63.2759442668	0.0158037942
	37	2.9852266778	66.1742225948	0.0151116244
	38	3.0747834782	69.1594492726	0.0144593401
	39	3.1670269825	72.2342327508	0.0138438516
QUARTERLY	40	3.2620377920	75.4012597333	0.0132623779
If compounded	41	3.3598989258	78.6632975253	0.0127124089
quarterly,	42	3.4606958935	82.0231964511	0.0121916731
nominal annual rate is	43	3.5645167703	85.4838923446	0.0116981103
	44	3.6714522734	89.0484091149	0.0112298469
12%	45	3.7815958417	92.7198613884	0.0107851757
	46	3.8950437169	96.5014572300	0.0103625378
	47	4.0118950284	100.3965009469	0.0099605065
	48	4.1322518793	104.4083959753	0.0095777738
	49	4.2562194356	108.5406478546	0.0092131383
MONTHLY	50	4.3839060187	112.7968672902	0.0088654944
If compounded	51	4.5154231993	117.1807733089	0.0085338232
monthly,	52	4.6508858952	121.6961965082	0.0082171837
nominal annual rate is	53	4.7904124721	126.3470824035	0.0079147059
	54	4.9341248463	131.1374948756	0.0076255841
36%	55	5.0821485917	136.0716197218	0.0073490710
	56	5.2346130494	141.1537683135	0.0070844726
	57	5.3916514409	146.3883813629	0.0068311432
	58	5.5534009841	151.7800328038	0.0065884819
	59	5.7200030136	157.3334337879	0.0063559281
	60	5.8916031040	163.0534368015	0.0061329587
	n	$(1 + i)^n$	$s\,\overline{n}\rceil$	$\dfrac{1}{s\,\overline{n}\rceil}$

Pres. Value of $1 at Comp. Int.	Amount Borrowed for $1 Payment	Payment to Borrow $1	n
0.9708737864	0.9708737864	1.0300000000	1
0.9425959091	1.9134696955	0.5226108374	2
0.9151416594	2.8286113549	0.3535303633	3
0.8884870479	3.7170984028	0.2690270452	4
0.8626087844	4.5797071872	0.2183545714	5
0.8374842567	5.4171914439	0.1845975005	6
0.8130915113	6.2302829552	0.1605063538	7
0.7894092343	7.0196921895	0.1424563888	8
0.7664167323	7.7861089219	0.1284338570	9
0.7440939149	8.5302028368	0.1172305066	10
0.7224212766	9.2526241134	0.1080774478	11
0.7013798802	9.9540039936	0.1004620855	12
0.6809513400	10.6349553336	0.0940295440	13
0.6611178058	11.2960731394	0.0885263390	14
0.6418619474	11.9379350868	0.0837665805	15
0.6231669392	12.5611020260	0.0796108493	16
0.6050164458	13.1661184718	0.0759525294	17
0.5873946076	13.7535130795	0.0727086959	18
0.5702860268	14.3237991063	0.0698138806	19
0.5536757542	14.8774748605	0.0672157076	20
0.5375492759	15.4150241364	0.0648717765	21
0.5218925009	15.9369166372	0.0627473948	22
0.5066917484	16.4436083857	0.0608139027	23
0.4919337363	16.9355421220	0.0590474159	24
0.4776055693	17.4131476913	0.0574278710	25
0.4636947274	17.8768424187	0.0559382903	26
0.4501890558	18.3270314745	0.0545642103	27
0.4370767532	18.7641082277	0.0532932334	28
0.4243463623	19.1884545900	0.0521146711	29
0.4119867595	19.6004413495	0.0510192593	30
0.3999871452	20.0004284946	0.0499989288	31
0.3883370341	20.3887655288	0.0490466183	32
0.3770262467	20.7657917755	0.0481561219	33
0.3660448997	21.1318366752	0.0473219633	34
0.3553833978	21.4872200731	0.0465392916	35
0.3450324251	21.8322524981	0.0458037942	36
0.3349829369	22.1672354351	0.0451116244	37
0.3252261524	22.4924615874	0.0444593401	38
0.3157535460	22.8082151334	0.0438438516	39
0.3065568408	23.1147719742	0.0432623779	40
0.2976280008	23.4123999750	0.0427124089	41
0.2889592240	23.7013591990	0.0421916731	42
0.2805429360	23.9819021349	0.0416981103	43
0.2723717825	24.2542739174	0.0412298469	44
0.2644386238	24.5187125412	0.0407851757	45
0.2567365279	24.7754490691	0.0403625378	46
0.2492587650	25.0247078341	0.0399605065	47
0.2419988009	25.2667066350	0.0395777738	48
0.2349502922	25.5016569272	0.0392131383	49
0.2281070798	25.7297640070	0.0388654944	50
0.2214631843	25.9512271913	0.0385338232	51
0.2150128003	26.1662399915	0.0382171837	52
0.2087502915	26.3749902830	0.0379147059	53
0.2026701859	26.5776604690	0.0376255841	54
0.1967671708	26.7744276398	0.0373490710	55
0.1910360882	26.9654637279	0.0370844726	56
0.1854719303	27.1509356582	0.0368311432	57
0.1800698352	27.3310054934	0.0365884819	58
0.1748250827	27.5058305761	0.0363559281	59
0.1697330900	27.6755636661	0.0361329587	60
$\dfrac{1}{(1+i)^n}$	$p\,\overline{n}|$	$\dfrac{1}{p\,\overline{n}|}$	n

Rate

3%

ANNUALLY

If compounded annually,

nominal annual rate is

3%

SEMIANNUALLY

If compounded semiannually,

nominal annual rate is

6%

QUARTERLY

If compounded quarterly,

nominal annual rate is

12%

MONTHLY

If compounded monthly,

nominal annual rate is

36%

	n	Amount of $1 at Comp. Int.	Amount Saved for $1 / Period	Payment to Save $1
Rate	1	1.0350000000	1.0000000000	1.0000000000
	2	1.0712250000	2.0350000000	0.4914004914
3.5%	3	1.1087178750	3.1062250000	0.3219341806
	4	1.1475230006	4.2149428750	0.2372511395
	5	1.1876863056	5.3624658756	0.1864813732
	6	1.2292553263	6.5501521813	0.1526682087
	7	1.2722792628	7.7794075076	0.1285444938
	8	1.3168090370	9.0516867704	0.1104766465
	9	1.3628973533	10.3684958073	0.0964460051
	10	1.4105987606	11.7313931606	0.0852413679
	11	1.4599697172	13.1419919212	0.0760919658
	12	1.5110686573	14.6019616385	0.0684839493
	13	1.5639560604	16.1130302958	0.0620615726
	14	1.6186945225	17.6769863562	0.0565707287
	15	1.6753488308	19.2956808786	0.0518250694
	16	1.7339860398	20.9710297094	0.0476848306
	17	1.7946755512	22.7050157492	0.0440431317
	18	1.8574891955	24.4996913004	0.0408168408
ANNUALLY	19	1.9225013174	26.3571804960	0.0379403252
	20	1.9897888635	28.2796818133	0.0353610768
If compounded	21	2.0594314737	30.2694706768	0.0330365870
annually,	22	2.1315115753	32.3289021505	0.0309320742
nominal annual rate is	23	2.2061144804	34.4604137257	0.0290188042
	24	2.2833284872	36.6665282061	0.0272728303
3$\frac{1}{2}$%	25	2.3632449843	38.9498566933	0.0256740354
	26	2.4459585587	41.3131016776	0.0242053963
	27	2.5315671083	43.7590602363	0.0228524103
	28	2.6201719571	46.2906273446	0.0216026452
SEMIANNUALLY	29	2.7118779756	48.9107993017	0.0204453825
	30	2.8067937047	51.6226772772	0.0193713316
If compounded	31	2.9050314844	54.4294709819	0.0183723998
semiannually,	32	3.0067075863	57.3345024663	0.0174415048
nominal annual rate is	33	3.1119423518	60.3412100526	0.0165724221
	34	3.2208603342	63.4531524044	0.0157596583
7%	35	3.3335904459	66.6740127386	0.0149983473
	36	3.4502661115	70.0076031845	0.0142841628
	37	3.5710254254	73.4578692959	0.0136132454
	38	3.6960113152	77.0288947213	0.0129821414
	39	3.8253717113	80.7249060365	0.0123877506
QUARTERLY	40	3.9592597212	84.5502777478	0.0118272823
If compounded	41	4.0978338114	88.5095374690	0.0112982174
quarterly,	42	4.2412579948	92.6073712804	0.0107982765
nominal annual rate is	43	4.3897020246	96.8486292752	0.0103253914
	44	4.5433415955	101.2383312998	0.0098776816
14%	45	4.7023585513	105.7816728953	0.0094534334
	46	4.8669411006	110.4840314467	0.0090510817
	47	5.0372840392	115.3509725473	0.0086691944
	48	5.2135889805	120.3882565864	0.0083064580
MONTHLY	49	5.3960645948	125.6018455670	0.0079616665
	50	5.5849268557	130.9979101618	0.0076337096
If compounded	51	5.7803992956	136.5828370175	0.0073215641
monthly,	52	5.9827132710	142.3632363131	0.0070242854
nominal annual rate is	53	6.1921082354	148.3459495840	0.0067409997
	54	6.4088320237	154.5380578195	0.0064708979
42%	55	6.6331411445	160.9468898432	0.0062132297
	56	6.8653010846	167.5800309877	0.0059672981
	57	7.1055866225	174.4453320722	0.0057324549
	58	7.3542821543	181.5509186948	0.0055080966
	59	7.6116820297	188.9052008491	0.0052936605
	60	7.8780909008	196.5168828788	0.0050886213
	n	$(1 + i)^n$	$s\,\overline{n\rvert}$	$\dfrac{1}{s\,\overline{n\rvert}}$

Pres. Value of $1 at Comp. Int.	Amount Borrowed for $1 Payment	Payment to Borrow $1	n
0.9661835749	0.9661835749	1.0350000000	1
0.9335107004	1.8996942752	0.5264004914	2
0.9019427057	2.8016369809	0.3569341806	3
0.8714422277	3.6730792086	0.2722511395	4
0.8419731669	4.5150523755	0.2214813732	5
0.8135006443	5.3285530198	0.1876682087	6
0.7859909607	6.1145439805	0.1635444938	7
0.7594115562	6.8739555367	0.1454766465	8
0.7337309722	7.6076865089	0.1314460051	9
0.7089188137	8.3166053226	0.1202413679	10
0.6849457137	9.0015510363	0.1110919658	11
0.6617832983	9.6633343346	0.1034839493	12
0.6394041529	10.3027384875	0.0970615726	13
0.6177817903	10.9205202778	0.0915707287	14
0.5968906186	11.5174108964	0.0868250694	15
0.5767059117	12.0941168081	0.0826848306	16
0.5572037794	12.6513205876	0.0790431317	17
0.5383611396	13.1896817271	0.0758168408	18
0.5201556904	13.7098374175	0.0729403252	19
0.5025658844	14.2124033020	0.0703610768	20
0.4855709028	14.6979742048	0.0680365870	21
0.4691506308	15.1671248355	0.0659320742	22
0.4532856336	15.6204104691	0.0640188042	23
0.4379571339	16.0583676030	0.0622728303	24
0.4231469893	16.4815145923	0.0606740354	25
0.4088376708	16.8903522631	0.0592053963	26
0.3950122423	17.2853645054	0.0578524103	27
0.3816543404	17.6670188458	0.0566026452	28
0.3687481550	18.0357670008	0.0554453825	29
0.3562784106	18.3920454114	0.0543713316	30
0.3442303484	18.7362757598	0.0533723998	31
0.3325897086	19.0688654684	0.0524415048	32
0.3213427136	19.3902081820	0.0515724221	33
0.3104760518	19.7006842338	0.0507596583	34
0.2999768617	20.0006610955	0.0499983473	35
0.2898327166	20.2904938121	0.0492841628	36
0.2800316102	20.5705254223	0.0486132454	37
0.2705619422	20.8410873645	0.0479821414	38
0.2614125046	21.1024998691	0.0473877506	39
0.2525724682	21.3550723373	0.0468272823	40
0.2440313702	21.5991037075	0.0462982174	41
0.2357791017	21.8348828092	0.0457982765	42
0.2278058953	22.0626887046	0.0453253914	43
0.2201023143	22.2827910189	0.0448776816	44
0.2126592409	22.4954502598	0.0444534334	45
0.2054678656	22.7009181254	0.0440510817	46
0.1985196769	22.8994378023	0.0436691944	47
0.1918064511	23.0912442535	0.0433064580	48
0.1853202426	23.2765644961	0.0429616665	49
0.1790533745	23.4556178706	0.0426337096	50
0.1729984295	23.6286163001	0.0423215641	51
0.1671482411	23.7957645412	0.0420242854	52
0.1614958851	23.9572604263	0.0417409997	53
0.1560346716	24.1132950978	0.0414708979	54
0.1507581368	24.2640532346	0.0412132297	55
0.1456600355	24.4097132702	0.0409672981	56
0.1407343339	24.5504476040	0.0407324549	57
0.1359752018	24.6864228058	0.0405080966	58
0.1313770066	24.8177998124	0.0402936605	59
0.1269343059	24.9447341182	0.0400886213	60
$\dfrac{1}{(1+i)^n}$	$p\,\overline{n}|$	$\dfrac{1}{p\,\overline{n}|}$	n

Rate

3.5%

ANNUALLY

If compounded annually,

nominal annual rate is

$3^1/_2\%$

SEMIANNUALLY

If compounded semiannually,

nominal annual rate is

7%

QUARTERLY

If compounded quarterly,

nominal annual rate is

14%

MONTHLY

If compounded monthly,

nominal annual rate is

42%

	n	Amount of $1 at Comp. Int.	Amount Saved for $1/Period	Payment to Save $1
Rate	1	1.0400000000	1.0000000000	1.0000000000
	2	1.0816000000	2.0400000000	0.4901960784
4%	3	1.1248640000	3.1216000000	0.3203485392
	4	1.1698585600	4.2464640000	0.2354900454
	5	1.2166529024	5.4163225600	0.1846271135
	6	1.2653190185	6.6329754624	0.1507619025
	7	1.3159317792	7.8982944809	0.1266096120
	8	1.3685690504	9.2142262601	0.1085278320
	9	1.4233118124	10.5827953105	0.0944929927
	10	1.4802442849	12.0061071230	0.0832909443
	11	1.5394540563	13.4863514079	0.0741490393
	12	1.6010322186	15.0258054642	0.0665521727
	13	1.6650735073	16.6268376828	0.0601437278
	14	1.7316764476	18.2919111901	0.0546689731
	15	1.8009435055	20.0235876377	0.0499411004
	16	1.8729812457	21.8245311432	0.0458199992
	17	1.9479004956	23.6975123889	0.0421985221
	18	2.0258165154	25.6454128845	0.0389933281
	19	2.1068491760	27.6712293998	0.0361386184
ANNUALLY	20	2.1911231430	29.7780785758	0.0335817503
If compounded	21	2.2787680688	31.9692017189	0.0312801054
annually,	22	2.3699187915	34.2479697876	0.0291988111
nominal annual rate is	23	2.4647155432	36.6178885791	0.0273090568
	24	2.5633041649	39.0826041223	0.0255868313
4%	25	2.6658363315	41.6459082872	0.0240119628
	26	2.7724697847	44.3117446187	0.0225673805
	27	2.8833685761	47.0842144034	0.0212385406
	28	2.9987033192	49.9675829796	0.0200129752
	29	3.1186514519	52.9662862987	0.0188799342
SEMIANNUALLY	30	3.2433975100	56.0849377507	0.0178300991
If compounded	31	3.3731334104	59.3283352607	0.0168553524
semiannually,	32	3.5080587468	62.7014686711	0.0159485897
nominal annual rate is	33	3.6483810967	66.2095274180	0.0151035665
	34	3.7943163406	69.8579085147	0.0143147715
8%	35	3.9460889942	73.6522248553	0.0135773224
	36	4.1039325540	77.5983138495	0.0128868780
	37	4.2680898561	81.7022464035	0.0122395655
	38	4.4388134504	85.9703362596	0.0116319191
	39	4.6163659884	90.4091497100	0.0110608274
QUARTERLY	40	4.8010206279	95.0255156984	0.0105234893
If compounded	41	4.9930614531	99.8265363264	0.0100173765
quarterly,	42	5.1927839112	104.8195977794	0.0095402007
nominal annual rate is	43	5.4004952676	110.0123816906	0.0090898859
	44	5.6165150783	115.4128769582	0.0086645444
16%	45	5.8411756815	121.0293920365	0.0082624558
	46	6.0748227087	126.8705677180	0.0078820488
	47	6.3178156171	132.9453904267	0.0075218855
	48	6.5705282418	139.2632060438	0.0071806476
	49	6.8333493714	145.8337342855	0.0068571240
MONTHLY	50	7.1066833463	152.6670836570	0.0065502004
If compounded	51	7.3909506801	159.7737670032	0.0062588497
monthly,	52	7.6865887073	167.1647176834	0.0059821236
nominal annual rate is	53	7.9940522556	174.8513063907	0.0057191451
	54	8.3138143459	182.8453586463	0.0054691025
48%	55	8.6463669197	191.1591729922	0.0052312426
	56	8.9922215965	199.8055399119	0.0050048662
	57	9.3519104603	208.7977615083	0.0047893234
	58	9.7259868787	218.1496719687	0.0045840087
	59	10.1150263539	227.8756588474	0.0043883581
	60	10.5196274081	237.9906852013	0.0042018451
	n	$(1 + i)^n$	$s\,\overline{n|}$	$\dfrac{1}{s\,\overline{n|}}$

Pres. Value of $1 at Comp. Int.	Amount Borrowed for $1 Payment	Payment to Borrow $1	n
0.9615384615	0.9615384615	1.0400000000	1
0.9245562130	1.8860946746	0.5301960784	2
0.8889963587	2.7750910332	0.3603485392	3
0.8548041910	3.6298952243	0.2754900454	4
0.8219271068	4.4518223310	0.2246271135	5
0.7903145257	5.2421368567	0.1907619025	6
0.7599178132	6.0020546699	0.1666096120	7
0.7306902050	6.7327448750	0.1485278320	8
0.7025867356	7.4353316105	0.1344929927	9
0.6755641688	8.1108957794	0.1232909443	10
0.6495809316	8.7604767109	0.1141490393	11
0.6245970496	9.3850737605	0.1065521727	12
0.6005740861	9.9856478466	0.1001437278	13
0.5774750828	10.5631229295	0.0946689731	14
0.5552645027	11.1183874322	0.0899411004	15
0.5339081757	11.6522956079	0.0858199992	16
0.5133732459	12.1656688537	0.0821985221	17
0.4936281210	12.6592969747	0.0789933281	18
0.4746424240	13.1339393988	0.0761386184	19
0.4563869462	13.5903263450	0.0735817503	20
0.4388336021	14.0291599471	0.0712801054	21
0.4219553867	14.4511153337	0.0691988111	22
0.4057263333	14.8568416671	0.0673090568	23
0.3901214743	15.2469631414	0.0655868313	24
0.3751168023	15.6220799437	0.0640119628	25
0.3606892329	15.9827691766	0.0625673805	26
0.3468165701	16.3295857467	0.0612385406	27
0.3334774713	16.6630632180	0.0600129752	28
0.3206514147	16.9837146327	0.0588799342	29
0.3083186680	17.2920333007	0.0578300991	30
0.2964602577	17.5884935583	0.0568553524	31
0.2850579401	17.8735514984	0.0559485897	32
0.2740941731	18.1476456715	0.0551035665	33
0.2635520896	18.4111977611	0.0543147715	34
0.2534154707	18.6646132318	0.0535773224	35
0.2436687219	18.9082819537	0.0528868780	36
0.2342968479	19.1425788016	0.0522395655	37
0.2252854307	19.3678642323	0.0516319191	38
0.2166206064	19.5844848388	0.0510608274	39
0.2082890447	19.7927738834	0.0505234893	40
0.2002779276	19.9930518110	0.0500173765	41
0.1925749303	20.1856267413	0.0495402007	42
0.1851682023	20.3707949436	0.0490898859	43
0.1780463483	20.5488412919	0.0486645444	44
0.1711984118	20.7200397038	0.0482624558	45
0.1646138575	20.8846535613	0.0478820488	46
0.1582825553	21.0429361166	0.0475218855	47
0.1521947647	21.1951308814	0.0471806476	48
0.1463411199	21.3414720013	0.0468571240	49
0.1407126153	21.4821846167	0.0465502004	50
0.1353005917	21.6174852083	0.0462588497	51
0.1300967228	21.7475819311	0.0459821236	52
0.1250930027	21.8726749337	0.0457191451	53
0.1202817333	21.9929566671	0.0454691025	54
0.1156555128	22.1086121799	0.0452312426	55
0.1112072239	22.2198194037	0.0450048662	56
0.1069300229	22.3267494267	0.0447893234	57
0.1028173297	22.4295667564	0.0445840087	58
0.0988628171	22.5284295735	0.0443883581	59
0.0950604010	22.6234899745	0.0442018451	60
$\dfrac{1}{(1+i)^n}$	$p\,\overline{n}|$	$\dfrac{1}{p\,\overline{n}|}$	n

Rate

4%

ANNUALLY

If compounded
annually,

nominal annual rate is

4%

SEMIANNUALLY

If compounded
semiannually,

nominal annual rate is

8%

QUARTERLY

If compounded
quarterly,

nominal annual rate is

16%

MONTHLY

If compounded
monthly,

nominal annual rate is

48%

	n	Amount of $1 at Comp. Int.	Amount Saved for $1/Period	Payment to Save $1
Rate	1	1.0450000000	1.0000000000	1.0000000000
	2	1.0920250000	2.0450000000	0.4889975550
4.5%	3	1.1411661250	3.1370250000	0.3187733601
	4	1.1925186006	4.2781911250	0.2337436479
	5	1.2461819377	5.4707097256	0.1827916395
	6	1.3022601248	6.7168916633	0.1488783875
	7	1.3608618305	8.0191517881	0.1247014680
	8	1.4221006128	9.3800136186	0.1066096533
	9	1.4860951404	10.8021142314	0.0925744700
	10	1.5529694217	12.2882093718	0.0813788217
	11	1.6228530457	13.8411787936	0.0722481817
	12	1.6958814328	15.4640318393	0.0646661886
	13	1.7721960972	17.1599132721	0.0582753528
	14	1.8519449216	18.9321093693	0.0528203160
	15	1.9352824431	20.7840542909	0.0481138081
	16	2.0223701530	22.7193367340	0.0440153694
	17	2.1133768099	24.7417068870	0.0404175833
	18	2.2084787664	26.8550836970	0.0372368975
	19	2.3078603108	29.0635624633	0.0344073443
ANNUALLY	20	2.4117140248	31.3714227742	0.0318761443
If compounded	21	2.5202411560	33.7831367990	0.0296005669
annually,	22	2.6336520080	36.3033779550	0.0275456461
nominal annual rate is	23	2.7521663483	38.9370299629	0.0256824930
	24	2.8760138340	41.6891963113	0.0239870280
4$\frac{1}{2}$%	25	3.0054344565	44.5652101453	0.0224390280
	26	3.1406790071	47.5706446018	0.0210213674
	27	3.2820095624	50.7113236089	0.0197194616
	28	3.4296999927	53.9933331713	0.0185208051
	29	3.5840364924	57.4230331640	0.0174146147
SEMIANNUALLY	30	3.7453181345	61.0070696564	0.0163915429
If compounded	31	3.9138574506	64.7523877909	0.0154434459
semiannually,	32	4.0899810359	68.6662452415	0.0145631962
nominal annual rate is	33	4.2740301825	72.7562262774	0.0137445281
	34	4.4663615407	77.0302564599	0.0129819119
9%	35	4.6673478100	81.4966180005	0.0122704478
	36	4.8773784615	86.1639658106	0.0116057796
	37	5.0968604922	91.0413442720	0.0109840206
	38	5.3262192144	96.1382047643	0.0104016920
	39	5.5658990790	101.4644239787	0.0098556712
QUARTERLY	40	5.8163645376	107.0303230577	0.0093431466
If compounded	41	6.0781009418	112.8466875953	0.0088615804
quarterly,	42	6.3516154842	118.9247885371	0.0084086759
nominal annual rate is	43	6.6374381810	125.2764040213	0.0079823492
	44	6.9361228991	131.9138422022	0.0075807056
18%	45	7.2482484296	138.8499651013	0.0072020184
	46	7.5744196089	146.0982135309	0.0068447107
	47	7.9152684913	153.6726331398	0.0065073395
	48	8.2714555734	161.5879016311	0.0061885821
	49	8.6436710742	169.8593572045	0.0058872235
MONTHLY	50	9.0326362725	178.5030282787	0.0056021459
If compounded	51	9.4391049048	187.5356645512	0.0053323191
monthly,	52	9.8638646255	196.9747694560	0.0050767923
nominal annual rate is	53	10.3077385337	206.8386340815	0.0048346867
	54	10.7715867677	217.1463726152	0.0046051886
54%	55	11.2563081722	227.9179593829	0.0043875437
	56	11.7628420400	239.1742675551	0.0041810518
	57	12.2921699318	250.9371095951	0.0039850622
	58	12.8453175787	263.2292795269	0.0037989695
	59	13.4233568698	276.0745971056	0.0036222094
	60	14.0274079289	289.4979539753	0.0034542558
	n	$(1+i)^n$	$s\,\overline{n}|$	$\dfrac{1}{s\,\overline{n}|}$

Pres. Value of $1 at Comp. Int.	Amount Borrowed for $1 Payment	Payment to Borrow $1	n	
0.9569377990	0.9569377990	1.0450000000	1	Rate
0.9157299512	1.8726677503	0.5339975550	2	
0.8762966041	2.7489643543	0.3637733601	3	**4.5%**
0.8385613436	3.5875256979	0.2787436479	4	
0.8024510465	4.3899767444	0.2277916395	5	
0.7678957383	5.1578724827	0.1938783875	6	
0.7348284577	5.8927009404	0.1697014680	7	
0.7031851270	6.5958860674	0.1516096533	8	
0.6729044277	7.2687904951	0.1375744700	9	
0.6439276820	7.9127181771	0.1263788217	10	
0.6161987388	8.5289169159	0.1172481817	11	
0.5896638649	9.1185807808	0.1096661886	12	
0.5642716410	9.6828524218	0.1032753528	13	
0.5399728622	10.2228252840	0.0978203160	14	
0.5167204423	10.7395457263	0.0931138081	15	
0.4944693228	11.2340150491	0.0890153694	16	
0.4731763854	11.7071914346	0.0854175833	17	
0.4528003688	12.1599918034	0.0822368975	18	
0.4333017884	12.5932935918	0.0794073443	19	
0.4146428597	13.0079364515	0.0768761443	20	**ANNUALLY**
0.3967874255	13.4047238770	0.0746005669	21	*If compounded*
0.3797008857	13.7844247627	0.0725456461	22	***annually,***
0.3633501298	14.1477748925	0.0706824930	23	nominal annual rate is
0.3477034735	14.4954783660	0.0689870299	24	
0.3327305967	14.8282089627	0.0674390280	25	$4^1/_2\%$
0.3184024849	15.1466114476	0.0660213674	26	
0.3046913731	15.4513028206	0.0647194616	27	
0.2915706919	15.7428735126	0.0635208051	28	
0.2790150162	16.0218885288	0.0624146147	29	
0.2670000155	16.2888885443	0.0613915429	30	**SEMIANNUALLY**
0.2555024072	16.5443909515	0.0604434459	31	*If compounded*
0.2444999112	16.7888908627	0.0595631962	32	***semiannually,***
0.2339712069	17.0228620695	0.0587445281	33	nominal annual rate is
0.2238958917	17.2467579613	0.0579819119	34	
0.2142544419	17.4610124031	0.0572704478	35	**9%**
0.2050281740	17.6660405772	0.0566057796	36	
0.1961992096	17.8622397868	0.0559840206	37	
0.1877504398	18.0499902266	0.0554016920	38	
0.1796654926	18.2296557192	0.0548556712	39	
0.1719287011	18.4015844203	0.0543431466	40	**QUARTERLY**
0.1645250728	18.5661094931	0.0538615804	41	*If compounded*
0.1574402611	18.7235497542	0.0534086729	42	***quarterly,***
0.1506605369	18.8742102911	0.0529823492	43	nominal annual rate is
0.1441727626	19.0183830536	0.0525807056	44	
0.1379643661	19.1563474198	0.0522020184	45	**18%**
0.1320233169	19.2883707366	0.0518447107	46	
0.1263381023	19.4147088389	0.0515073395	47	
0.1208977055	19.5356065444	0.0511885821	48	
0.1156915842	19.6512981286	0.0508872235	49	
0.1107096500	19.7620077785	0.0506021459	50	**MONTHLY**
0.1059422488	19.8679500273	0.0503323191	51	*If compounded*
0.1013801424	19.9693301697	0.0500767923	52	***monthly,***
0.0970144903	20.0663446600	0.0498346867	53	nominal annual rate is
0.0928368328	20.1591814928	0.0496051886	54	
0.0888390745	20.2480205673	0.0493875437	55	**54%**
0.0850134684	20.3330340357	0.0491810518	56	
0.0813526013	20.4143866370	0.0489850622	57	
0.0778493793	20.4922360163	0.0487989695	58	
0.0744970137	20.5667330299	0.0486222094	59	
0.0712890083	20.6380220382	0.0484542558	60	
$\dfrac{1}{(1+i)^n}$	$p\,\overline{n}\rceil$	$\dfrac{1}{p\,\overline{n}\rceil}$	n	

	n	Amount of $1 at Comp. Int.	Amount Saved for $1/Period	Payment to Save $1
Rate	1	1.0500000000	1.0000000000	1.0000000000
	2	1.1025000000	2.0500000000	0.4878048780
5%	3	1.1576250000	3.1525000000	0.3172085646
	4	1.2155062500	4.3101250000	0.2320118326
	5	1.2762815625	5.5256312500	0.1809747981
	6	1.3400956406	6.8019128125	0.1470174681
	7	1.4071004227	8.1420084531	0.1228198184
	8	1.4774554438	9.5491088758	0.1047218136
	9	1.5513282160	11.0265643196	0.0906900800
	10	1.6288946268	12.5778925355	0.0795045750
	11	1.7103393581	14.2067871623	0.0703888915
	12	1.7958563260	15.9171265204	0.0628254100
	13	1.8856491423	17.7129828465	0.0564557652
	14	1.9799315994	19.5986319888	0.0510239695
	15	2.0789281794	21.5785635882	0.0463422876
	16	2.1828745884	23.6574917676	0.0422699080
	17	2.2920183178	25.8403663560	0.0386991417
	18	2.4066192337	28.1323846738	0.0355462223
	19	2.5269501954	30.5390039075	0.0327450104
ANNUALLY	20	2.6532977051	33.0659541029	0.0302425872
If compounded	21	2.7859625904	35.7192518080	0.0279961071
annually,	22	2.9252607199	38.5052143984	0.0259705086
nominal annual rate is	23	3.0715237559	41.4304751184	0.0241368219
	24	3.2250999437	44.5019988743	0.0224709008
5%	25	3.3863549409	47.7270988180	0.0209524573
	26	3.5556726879	51.1134537589	0.0195643207
	27	3.7334563223	54.6691264468	0.0182918599
	28	3.9201291385	58.4025827692	0.0171225304
	29	4.1161355954	62.3227119076	0.0160455149
SEMIANNUALLY	30	4.3219423752	66.4388475030	0.0150514351
If compounded	31	4.5380394939	70.7607898782	0.0141321204
semiannually,	32	4.7649414686	75.2988293721	0.0132804189
nominal annual rate is	33	5.0031885420	80.0637708407	0.0124900437
	34	5.2533479691	85.0669593827	0.0117554454
10%	35	5.5160153676	90.3203073518	0.0110717072
	36	5.7918161360	95.8363227194	0.0104344571
	37	6.0814069428	101.6281388554	0.0098397945
	38	6.3854772899	107.7095457982	0.0092842282
	39	6.7047511544	114.0950230881	0.0087646242
QUARTERLY	40	7.0399887121	120.7997742425	0.0082781612
If compounded	41	7.3919881477	127.8397629546	0.0078222924
quarterly,	42	7.7615875551	135.2317511023	0.0073947131
nominal annual rate is	43	8.1496669329	142.9933386575	0.0069933328
	44	8.5571502795	151.1430055903	0.0066162506
20%	45	8.9850077935	159.7001558699	0.0062617347
	46	9.4342581832	168.6851636633	0.0059282036
	47	9.9059710923	178.1194218465	0.0056142109
	48	10.4012696469	188.0253929388	0.0053184306
	49	10.9213331293	198.4266625858	0.0050396453
MONTHLY	50	11.4673997858	209.3479957151	0.0047767355
If compounded	51	12.0407697750	220.8153955008	0.0045286697
monthly,	52	12.6428082638	232.8561652759	0.0042944966
nominal annual rate is	53	13.2749486770	245.4989735397	0.0040733368
	54	13.9386961108	258.7739222166	0.0038643770
60%	55	14.6356309164	272.7126183275	0.0036668637
	56	15.3674124622	287.3482492439	0.0034800978
	57	16.1357830853	302.7156617060	0.0033034300
	58	16.9425722396	318.8514447913	0.0031362568
	59	17.7897008515	335.7940170309	0.0029780161
	60	18.6791858941	353.5837178825	0.0028281845
	n	$(1+i)^n$	$s\,\overline{n}|$	$\frac{1}{s\,\overline{n}|}$

490

Pres. Value of $1 at Comp. Int.	Amount Borrowed for $1 Payment	Payment to Borrow $1	n	
0.9523809524	0.9523809524	1.0500000000	1	**Rate**
0.9070294785	1.8594104308	0.5378048780	2	
0.8638375985	2.7232480294	0.3672085646	3	**5%**
0.8227024748	3.5459505042	0.2820118326	4	
0.7835261665	4.3294766706	0.2309747981	5	
0.7462153966	5.0756920673	0.1970174681	6	
0.7106813301	5.7863733974	0.1728198184	7	
0.6768393620	6.4632127594	0.1547218136	8	
0.6446089162	7.1078216756	0.1406900080	9	
0.6139132535	7.7217349292	0.1295045750	10	
0.5846792891	8.3064142183	0.1203888915	11	
0.5568374182	8.8632516364	0.1128254100	12	
0.5303213506	9.3935729871	0.1064557652	13	
0.5050679530	9.8986409401	0.1010239695	14	
0.4810170981	10.3796580382	0.0963422876	15	
0.4581115220	10.8377695602	0.0922699080	16	
0.4362966876	11.2740662478	0.0886991417	17	
0.4155206549	11.6895869027	0.0855462223	18	
0.3957339570	12.0853208597	0.0827450104	19	
0.3768894829	12.4622103425	0.0802425872	20	**ANNUALLY**
0.3589423646	12.8211527072	0.0779961071	21	*If compounded*
0.3418498711	13.1630025783	0.0759705086	22	***annually,***
0.3255713058	13.4885738841	0.0741368219	23	*nominal annual rate is*
0.3100679103	13.7986417943	0.0724709008	24	
0.2953027717	14.0939445660	0.0709524573	25	**5%**
0.2812407350	14.3751853010	0.0695643207	26	
0.2678483190	14.6430336200	0.0682918599	27	
0.2550936371	14.8981272571	0.0671225304	28	
0.2429463211	15.1410735782	0.0660455149	29	
0.2313774487	15.3724510269	0.0650514351	30	**SEMIANNUALLY**
0.2203594749	15.5928105018	0.0641321204	31	*If compounded*
0.2098661666	15.8026766684	0.0632804189	32	***semiannually,***
0.1998725396	16.0025492080	0.0624900437	33	*nominal annual rate is*
0.1903547996	16.1929040076	0.0617554454	34	
0.1812902854	16.3741942929	0.0610717072	35	**10%**
0.1726574146	16.5468517076	0.0604344571	36	
0.1644356330	16.7112873405	0.0598397945	37	
0.1566053647	16.8678927053	0.0592842282	38	
0.1491479664	17.0170406717	0.0587646242	39	
0.1420456823	17.1590863540	0.0582781612	40	**QUARTERLY**
0.1352816022	17.2943679562	0.0578222924	41	*If compounded*
0.1288396211	17.4232075773	0.0573947131	42	***quarterly,***
0.1227044011	17.5459119784	0.0569933328	43	*nominal annual rate is*
0.1168613344	17.6627733128	0.0566162506	44	
0.1112965089	17.7740698217	0.0562617347	45	**20%**
0.1059966752	17.8800664968	0.0559282036	46	
0.1009492144	17.9810157113	0.0556142109	47	
0.0961421090	18.0771578203	0.0553184306	48	
0.0915639133	18.1687217336	0.0550396453	49	
0.0872037270	18.2559254606	0.0547767355	50	**MONTHLY**
0.0830511685	18.3389766291	0.0545286697	51	*If compounded*
0.0790963510	18.4180729801	0.0542944966	52	***monthly,***
0.0753298581	18.4934028382	0.0540733368	53	*nominal annual rate is*
0.0717427220	18.5651455602	0.0538643770	54	
0.0683264019	18.6334719621	0.0536668637	55	**60%**
0.0650727637	18.6985447258	0.0534800978	56	
0.0619740607	18.7605187865	0.0533034300	57	
0.0590229149	18.8195417014	0.0531362568	58	
0.0562122999	18.8757540013	0.0529780161	59	
0.0535355237	18.9292895251	0.0528281845	60	
$\dfrac{1}{(1+i)^n}$	$p\,\overline{n}\rceil$	$\dfrac{1}{p\,\overline{n}\rceil}$	n	

	n	Amount of \$1 at Comp. Int.	Amount Saved for \$1/Period	Payment to Save \$1
Rate	1	1.0600000000	1.0000000000	1.0000000000
	2	1.1236000000	2.0600000000	0.4854368932
6%	3	1.1910160000	3.1836000000	0.3141098128
	4	1.2624769600	4.3746160000	0.2285914924
	5	1.3382255776	5.6370929600	0.1773964004
	6	1.4185191123	6.9753185376	0.1433626285
	7	1.5036302590	8.3938376499	0.1191350181
	8	1.5938480745	9.8974679088	0.1010359426
	9	1.6894789590	11.4913159834	0.0870222350
	10	1.7908476965	13.1807949424	0.0758679582
	11	1.8982985583	14.9716426389	0.0667929381
	12	2.0121964718	16.8699411973	0.0592770294
	13	2.1329282601	18.8821376691	0.0529601053
	14	2.2609039558	21.0150659292	0.0475849090
	15	2.3965581931	23.2759698850	0.0429627640
	16	2.5403516847	25.6725280781	0.0389521436
	17	2.6927727858	28.2128797628	0.0354448042
	18	2.8543391529	30.9056525485	0.0323565406
	19	3.0255995021	33.7599917015	0.0296208604
ANNUALLY	20	3.2071354722	36.7855912035	0.0271845570
If compounded ***annually,***	21	3.3995636005	39.9927266758	0.0250045467
	22	3.6035374166	43.3922902763	0.0230455685
nominal annual rate is	23	3.8197496616	46.9958276929	0.0212784847
	24	4.0489346413	50.8155773545	0.0196790050
6%	25	4.2918707197	54.8645119957	0.0182267182
	26	4.5493829629	59.1563827155	0.0169043467
	27	4.8223459407	63.7057656784	0.0156971663
	28	5.1116866971	68.5281116191	0.0145925515
	29	5.4183878990	73.6397983162	0.0135796135
SEMIANNUALLY	30	5.7434911729	79.0581862152	0.0126489115
If compounded ***semiannually,***	31	6.0881006433	84.8016773881	0.0117922196
	32	6.4533866819	90.8897780314	0.0110023374
nominal annual rate is	33	6.8405898828	97.3431647133	0.0102729350
	34	7.2510252758	104.1837545961	0.0095984254
12%	35	7.6860867923	111.4347798719	0.0089738590
	36	8.1472519999	119.1208666642	0.0083948348
	37	8.6360871198	127.2681186640	0.0078574274
	38	9.1542523470	135.9042057839	0.0073581240
	39	9.7035074879	145.0584581309	0.0068937724
QUARTERLY	40	10.2857179371	154.7619656188	0.0064615359
If compounded ***quarterly,***	41	10.9028610134	165.0476835559	0.0060588551
	42	11.5570326742	175.9505445692	0.0056834152
nominal annual rate is	43	12.2504546346	187.5075772434	0.0053331178
	44	12.9854819127	199.7580318780	0.0050060565
24%	45	13.7646108274	212.7435137907	0.0047004958
	46	14.5904874771	226.5081246181	0.0044148527
	47	15.4659167257	241.0986120952	0.0041476805
	48	16.3938717293	256.5645288209	0.0038976549
	49	17.3775040330	272.9584005502	0.0036635619
MONTHLY	50	18.4201542750	290.3359045832	0.0034442864
If compounded ***monthly,***	51	19.5253635315	308.7560588582	0.0032388028
	52	20.6968853434	328.2814223897	0.0030461669
nominal annual rate is	53	21.9386984640	348.9783077331	0.0028655076
	54	23.2550203718	370.9170061970	0.0026960209
72%	55	24.6503215941	394.1720265689	0.0025369634
	56	26.1293408898	418.8223481630	0.0023876472
	57	27.6971013432	444.9516890528	0.0022474350
	58	29.3589274238	472.6487903959	0.0021157359
	59	31.1204630692	502.0077178197	0.0019920012
	60	32.9876908533	533.1281808889	0.0018757215
	n	$(1+i)^n$	$s\,\overline{n}$	$\dfrac{1}{s\,\overline{n}}$

Pres. Value of $1 at Comp. Int.	Amount Borrowed for $1 Payment	Payment to Borrow $1	n	
0.9433962264	0.9433962264	1.0600000000	1	**Rate**
0.8899964400	1.8333926664	0.5454368932	2	
0.8396192830	2.6730119495	0.3741098128	3	**6%**
0.7920936632	3.4651056127	0.2885914924	4	
0.7472581729	4.2123637856	0.2373964004	5	
0.7049605404	4.9173243260	0.2033626285	6	
0.6650571136	5.5823814396	0.1791350181	7	
0.6274123713	6.2097938110	0.1610359426	8	
0.5918984635	6.8016922745	0.1470222350	9	
0.5583947769	7.3600870514	0.1358679582	10	
0.5267875254	7.8868745768	0.1267929381	11	
0.4969693636	8.3838439404	0.1192770294	12	
0.4688390222	8.8526829626	0.1129601053	13	
0.4423009644	9.2949839270	0.1075849090	14	
0.4172650607	9.7122489877	0.1029627640	15	
0.3936462837	10.1058952715	0.0989521436	16	
0.3713644186	10.4772596901	0.0954448042	17	
0.3503437911	10.8276034812	0.0923565406	18	
0.3305130105	11.1581164917	0.0896208604	19	
0.3118047269	11.4699212186	0.0871845570	20	**ANNUALLY**
0.2941554027	11.7640766213	0.0850045467	21	*If compounded*
0.2775050969	12.0415817182	0.0830455685	22	***annually***,
0.2617972612	12.3033789794	0.0812784847	23	nominal annual rate is
0.2469785483	12.5503575278	0.0796790050	24	
0.2329986305	12.7833561583	0.0782267182	25	**6%**
0.2198100288	13.0031661870	0.0769043467	26	
0.2073679517	13.2105341387	0.0756971663	27	
0.1956301431	13.4061642818	0.0745925515	28	
0.1845567388	13.5907210206	0.0735796135	29	
0.1741101309	13.7648311515	0.0726489115	30	**SEMIANNUALLY**
0.1642548405	13.9290859920	0.0717922196	31	*If compounded*
0.1549573967	14.0840433887	0.0710023374	32	***semiannually***,
0.1461862233	14.2302296119	0.0702729350	33	nominal annual rate is
0.1379115314	14.3681411433	0.0695984254	34	
0.1301052183	14.4982463616	0.0689738590	35	**12%**
0.1227407720	14.6209871336	0.0683948348	36	
0.1157931811	14.7367803147	0.0678574274	37	
0.1092388501	14.8460191648	0.0673581240	38	
0.1030555190	14.9490746838	0.0668937724	39	
0.0972221877	15.0462968715	0.0664615359	40	**QUARTERLY**
0.0917190450	15.1380159165	0.0660588551	41	*If compounded*
0.0865274010	15.2245433175	0.0656834152	42	***quarterly***,
0.0816296235	15.3061729410	0.0653331178	43	nominal annual rate is
0.0770090788	15.3831820198	0.0650060565	44	
0.0726500743	15.4558320942	0.0647004958	45	**24%**
0.0685378060	15.5243699002	0.0644148527	46	
0.0646583075	15.5890282077	0.0641476805	47	
0.0609984033	15.6500266110	0.0638976549	48	
0.0575456635	15.7075722746	0.0636635619	49	
0.0542883618	15.7618606364	0.0634442864	50	**MONTHLY**
0.0512154357	15.8130760721	0.0632388028	51	*If compounded*
0.0483164488	15.8613925208	0.0630461669	52	***monthly***,
0.0455815554	15.9069740762	0.0628655076	53	nominal annual rate is
0.0430014674	15.9499755436	0.0626960209	54	
0.0405674221	15.9905429657	0.0625369634	55	**72%**
0.0382711529	16.0288141186	0.0623876472	56	
0.0361048612	16.0649189798	0.0622474350	57	
0.0340611898	16.0989801696	0.0621157359	58	
0.0321331979	16.1311133676	0.0619920012	59	
0.0303143377	16.1614277052	0.0618757215	60	
$\dfrac{1}{(1+i)^n}$	$p\,\overline{n}|$	$\dfrac{1}{p\,\overline{n}|}$	n	

	n	Amount of $1 at Comp. Int.	Amount Saved for $1/Period	Payment to Save $1
Rate	1	1.0700000000	1.0000000000	1.0000000000
	2	1.1449000000	2.0700000000	0.4830917874
7%	3	1.2250430000	3.2149000000	0.3110516657
	4	1.3107960100	4.4399430000	0.2252281167
	5	1.4025517307	5.7507390100	0.1738906944
	6	1.5007303518	7.1532907407	0.1397957998
	7	1.6057814765	8.6540210925	0.1155532196
	8	1.7181861798	10.2598025690	0.0974677625
	9	1.8384592124	11.9779887489	0.0834864701
	10	1.9671513573	13.8164479613	0.0723775027
	11	2.1048519523	15.7835993186	0.0633569048
	12	2.2521915890	17.8884512709	0.0559019887
	13	2.4098450002	20.1406428598	0.0496508481
	14	2.5785341502	22.5504878600	0.0443449386
	15	2.7590315407	25.1290220102	0.0397946247
	16	2.9521637486	27.8880535509	0.0358576477
	17	3.1588152110	30.8402172995	0.0324251931
	18	3.3799322757	33.9990325105	0.0294126017
	19	3.6165275350	37.3789647862	0.0267530148
ANNUALLY	20	3.8696844625	40.9954923212	0.0243929257
If compounded	21	4.1405623749	44.8651767837	0.0222890017
annually,	22	4.4304017411	49.0057391586	0.0204057732
nominal annual rate is	23	4.7405298630	53.4361408997	0.0187139263
	24	5.0723669534	58.1766707627	0.0171890207
7%	25	5.4274326401	63.2490377160	0.0158105172
	26	5.8073529249	68.6764703562	0.0145610279
	27	6.2138676297	74.4838232811	0.0134257340
	28	6.6488383638	80.6976909108	0.0123919283
	29	7.1142570492	87.3465292745	0.0114486518
SEMIANNUALLY	30	7.6122550427	94.4607863237	0.0105864035
If compounded	31	8.1451128956	102.0730413664	0.0097969061
semiannually,	32	8.7152707983	110.2181542621	0.0090729155
nominal annual rate is	33	9.3253397542	118.9334250604	0.0084080653
	34	9.9781135370	128.2587648146	0.0077967381
14%	35	10.6765814846	138.2368783516	0.0072339596
	36	11.4239421885	148.9134598363	0.0067153097
	37	12.2236181417	160.3374020248	0.0062368480
	38	13.0792714117	172.5610201665	0.0057950515
	39	13.9948204105	185.6402915782	0.0053867616
QUARTERLY	40	14.9744578392	199.6351119887	0.0050091389
If compounded	41	16.0226698880	214.6095698279	0.0046596245
quarterly,	42	17.1442567801	230.6322397158	0.0043359072
nominal annual rate is	43	18.3443547547	247.7764964959	0.0040358953
	44	19.6284595875	266.1208512507	0.0037576913
28%	45	21.0024517587	285.7493108382	0.0034995710
	46	22.4726233818	306.7517625969	0.0032599650
	47	24.0457070185	329.2243859787	0.0030374421
	48	25.7289065098	353.2700929972	0.0028306953
	49	27.5299299655	378.9989995070	0.0026385294
MONTHLY	50	29.4570250631	406.5289294724	0.0024598495
If compounded	51	31.5190168175	435.9859545355	0.0022936519
monthly,	52	33.7253479947	467.5049713530	0.0021390147
nominal annual rate is	53	36.0861223543	501.2303193477	0.0019950908
	54	38.6121509191	537.3164417021	0.0018611007
84%	55	41.3150014835	575.9285926212	0.0017363264
	56	44.2070515873	617.2435941047	0.0016201059
	57	47.3015451984	661.4506456920	0.0015118286
	58	50.6126533623	708.7521908905	0.0014109304
	59	54.1555390977	759.3648442528	0.0013168900
	60	57.9464268345	813.5203833505	0.0012292255
	n	$(1+i)^n$	$s\,\overline{n}|$	$\dfrac{1}{s\,\overline{n}|}$

Pres. Value of $1 at Comp. Int.	Amount Borrowed for $1 Payment	Payment to Borrow $1	n	
0.9345794393	0.9345794393	1.0700000000	1	**Rate**
0.8734387283	1.8080181675	0.5530917874	2	
0.8162978769	2.6243160444	0.3810516657	3	**7%**
0.7628952120	3.3872112565	0.2952281167	4	
0.7129861795	4.1001974359	0.2438906944	5	
0.6663422238	4.7665396598	0.2097957998	6	
0.6227497419	5.3892894016	0.1855532196	7	
0.5820091046	5.9712985062	0.1674677625	8	
0.5439337426	6.5152322488	0.1534864701	9	
0.5083492921	7.0235815409	0.1423775027	10	
0.4750927964	7.4986743373	0.1333569048	11	
0.4440119592	7.9426862966	0.1259019887	12	
0.4149644479	8.3576507444	0.1196508481	13	
0.3878172410	8.7454679855	0.1143449386	14	
0.3624460196	9.1079140051	0.1097946247	15	
0.3387345978	9.4466486029	0.1058576477	16	
0.3165743905	9.7632229934	0.1024251931	17	
0.2958639163	10.0590869097	0.0994126017	18	
0.2765083330	10.3355952427	0.0967530148	19	
0.2584190028	10.5940142455	0.0943929257	20	**ANNUALLY**
0.2415130867	10.8355273323	0.0922890017	21	*If compounded annually,*
0.2257131652	11.0612404974	0.0904057732	22	nominal annual rate is
0.2109468833	11.2721873808	0.0887139263	23	
0.1971466199	11.4693340007	0.0871890207	24	**7%**
0.1842491775	11.6535831783	0.0858105172	25	
0.1721954930	11.8257786713	0.0845610279	26	
0.1609303673	11.9867090386	0.0834257340	27	
0.1504022124	12.1371112510	0.0823919283	28	
0.1405628154	12.2776740664	0.0814486518	29	
0.1313671172	12.4090411835	0.0805864035	30	**SEMIANNUALLY**
0.1227730067	12.5318141902	0.0797969061	31	*If compounded semiannually,*
0.1147411277	12.6465553179	0.0790729155	32	nominal annual rate is
0.1072346988	12.7537900168	0.0784080653	33	
0.1002193447	12.8540093615	0.0777967381	34	**14%**
0.0936629390	12.9476723004	0.0772339596	35	
0.0875354570	13.0352077574	0.0767153097	36	
0.0818088383	13.1170165957	0.0762368480	37	
0.0764568582	13.1934734539	0.0757950515	38	
0.0714550077	13.2649284616	0.0753867616	39	
0.0667803810	13.3317088426	0.0750091389	40	**QUARTERLY**
0.0624115710	13.3941204137	0.0746596245	41	*If compounded quarterly,*
0.0583285711	13.4524489847	0.0743359072	42	nominal annual rate is
0.0545126832	13.5069616680	0.0740358953	43	
0.0509464329	13.5579081009	0.0737576913	44	**28%**
0.0476134887	13.6055215896	0.0734995710	45	
0.0444985876	13.6500201772	0.0732599650	46	
0.0415874650	13.6916076423	0.0730374421	47	
0.0388667898	13.7304744320	0.0728306953	48	
0.0363241026	13.7667985346	0.0726385294	49	
0.0339477594	13.8007462940	0.0724598495	50	**MONTHLY**
0.0317268780	13.8324731720	0.0722936519	51	*If compounded monthly,*
0.0296512878	13.8621244598	0.0721390147	52	nominal annual rate is
0.0277114839	13.8898359437	0.0719950908	53	
0.0258985831	13.9157345269	0.0718611007	54	**84%**
0.0242042833	13.9399388102	0.0717363264	55	
0.0226208255	13.9625596357	0.0716201059	56	
0.0211409584	13.9837005941	0.0715118286	57	
0.0197579051	14.0034584991	0.0714109304	58	
0.0184653318	14.0219238310	0.0713168900	59	
0.0172573195	14.0391811504	0.0712292255	60	
$\dfrac{1}{(1+i)^n}$	$p\,\overline{n}$	$\dfrac{1}{p\,\overline{n}}$	n	

	n	Amount of $1 at Comp. Int.	Amount Saved for $1/Period	Payment to Save $1
Rate	1	1.0800000000	1.0000000000	1.0000000000
	2	1.1664000000	2.0800000000	0.4807692308
8%	3	1.2597120000	3.2464000000	0.3080335140
	4	1.3604889600	4.5061120000	0.2219208045
	5	1.4693280768	5.8666009600	0.1704564546
	6	1.5868743229	7.3359290368	0.1363153862
	7	1.7138242688	8.9228033597	0.1120724014
	8	1.8509302103	10.6366276285	0.0940147606
	9	1.9990046271	12.4875578388	0.0800797092
	10	2.1589249973	14.4865624659	0.0690294887
	11	2.3316389971	16.6454874632	0.0600763421
	12	2.5181701168	18.9771264602	0.0526950169
	13	2.7196237262	21.4952965771	0.0465218052
	14	2.9371936243	24.2149203032	0.0412968528
	15	3.1721691142	27.1521139275	0.0368295449
	16	3.4259426433	30.3242830417	0.0329768720
	17	3.7000180548	33.7502256850	0.0296294315
	18	3.9960194992	37.4502437398	0.0267020959
	19	4.3157010591	41.4462632390	0.0241276275
ANNUALLY	20	4.6609571438	45.7619642981	0.0218522088
If compounded	21	5.0338337154	50.4229214420	0.0198322503
annually,	22	5.4365404126	55.4567551573	0.0180320684
nominal annual rate is	23	5.8714636456	60.8932955699	0.0164221692
	24	6.3411807372	66.7647592155	0.0149779616
8%	25	6.8484751962	73.1059399527	0.0136787791
	26	7.3963532119	79.9544151490	0.0125071267
	27	7.9880614689	87.3507683609	0.0114480962
	28	8.6271063864	95.3388298297	0.0104889057
	29	9.3172748973	103.9659362161	0.0096185350
SEMIANNUALLY	30	10.0626568891	113.2832111134	0.0088274334
If compounded	31	10.8676694402	123.3458680025	0.0081072841
semiannually,	32	11.7370829954	134.2135374427	0.0074508132
nominal annual rate is	33	12.6760496350	145.9506204381	0.0068516324
	34	13.6901336059	158.6266700732	0.0063041101
16%	35	14.7853442943	172.3168036790	0.0058032646
	36	15.9681718379	187.1021479733	0.0053446741
	37	17.2456255849	203.0703198112	0.0049244025
	38	18.6252756317	220.3159453961	0.0045389361
	39	20.1152976822	238.9412210278	0.0041851297
QUARTERLY	40	21.7245214968	259.0565187100	0.0038601615
If compounded	41	23.4624832165	280.7810402068	0.0035614940
quarterly,	42	25.3394818739	304.2435234233	0.0032868407
nominal annual rate is	43	27.3666404238	329.5830052972	0.0030341370
	44	29.5559716577	356.9496457210	0.0028015156
32%	45	31.9204493903	386.5056173787	0.0025872845
	46	34.4740853415	418.4260667690	0.0023899085
	47	37.2320121688	452.9001521105	0.0022079922
	48	40.2105731423	490.1321642793	0.0020402660
	49	43.4274189937	530.3427374217	0.0018855731
MONTHLY	50	46.9016125132	573.7701564154	0.0017428582
If compounded	51	50.6537415143	620.6717689286	0.0016111575
monthly,	52	54.7060408354	671.3255104429	0.0014895903
nominal annual rate is	53	59.0825241023	726.0315512783	0.0013773506
	54	63.8091260304	785.1140753806	0.0012737003
96%	55	68.9138561129	848.9232014111	0.0011779629
	56	74.4269646019	917.8370575239	0.0010895180
	57	80.3811217701	992.2640221259	0.0010077963
	58	86.8116115117	1072.6451438959	0.0009322748
	59	93.7565404326	1159.4567554076	0.0008624729
	60	101.2570636672	1253.2132958402	0.0007979488
	n	$(1+i)^n$	$s\,\overline{n|}$	$\dfrac{1}{s\,\overline{n|}}$

Pres. Value of $1 at Comp. Int.	Amount Borrowed for $1 Payment	Payment to Borrow $1	n
0.9259259259	0.9259259259	1.0800000000	1
0.8573388203	1.7832647462	0.5607692308	2
0.7938322410	2.5770969872	0.3880335140	3
0.7350298528	3.3121268400	0.3019208045	4
0.6805831970	3.9927100371	0.2504564546	5
0.6301696269	4.6228796640	0.2163153862	6
0.5834903953	5.2063700592	0.1920724014	7
0.5402688845	5.7466389437	0.1740147606	8
0.5002489671	6.2468879109	0.1600797092	9
0.4631934881	6.7100813989	0.1490294887	10
0.4288828593	7.1389642583	0.1400763421	11
0.3971137586	7.5360780169	0.1326950169	12
0.3676979247	7.9037759416	0.1265218052	13
0.3404610414	8.2442369830	0.1212968528	14
0.3152417050	8.5594786879	0.1168295449	15
0.2918904676	8.8513691555	0.1129768720	16
0.2702689514	9.1216381069	0.1096294315	17
0.2502490291	9.3718871360	0.1067020959	18
0.2317120640	9.6035992000	0.1041276275	19
0.2145482074	9.8181474074	0.1018522088	20
0.1986557476	10.0168031550	0.0998322503	21
0.1839405070	10.2007436621	0.0980320684	22
0.1703152843	10.3710589464	0.0964221692	23
0.1576993373	10.5287582837	0.0949779616	24
0.1460179049	10.6747761886	0.0936787791	25
0.1352017638	10.8099779524	0.0925071267	26
0.1251868183	10.9351647707	0.0914480962	27
0.1159137207	11.0510784914	0.0904889057	28
0.1073275192	11.1584060106	0.0896185350	29
0.0993773325	11.2577833431	0.0888274334	30
0.0920160487	11.3497993918	0.0881072841	31
0.0852000451	11.4349994368	0.0874508132	32
0.0788889306	11.5138883674	0.0868516324	33
0.0730453061	11.5869336736	0.0863041101	34
0.0676345427	11.6545682163	0.0858032646	35
0.0626245766	11.7171927928	0.0853446741	36
0.0579857190	11.7751785119	0.0849244025	37
0.0536904806	11.8288689925	0.0845389361	38
0.0497134080	11.8785824004	0.0841851297	39
0.0460309333	11.9246133337	0.0838601615	40
0.0426212345	11.9672345683	0.0835614940	41
0.0394641061	12.0066986743	0.0832868407	42
0.0365408389	12.0432395133	0.0830341370	43
0.0338341101	12.0770736234	0.0828015156	44
0.0313278797	12.1084015032	0.0825872845	45
0.0290072961	12.1374087992	0.0823899085	46
0.0268586075	12.1642674067	0.0822079922	47
0.0248690810	12.1891364877	0.0820402660	48
0.0230269268	12.2121634145	0.0818855731	49
0.0213212286	12.2334846431	0.0817428582	50
0.0197418783	12.2532265214	0.0816111575	51
0.0182795169	12.2715060383	0.0814895903	52
0.0169254786	12.2884315169	0.0813773506	53
0.0156717395	12.3041032564	0.0812737003	54
0.0145108699	12.3186141263	0.0811779629	55
0.0134359906	12.3320501170	0.0810895180	56
0.0124407321	12.3444908490	0.0810077963	57
0.0115191964	12.3560100454	0.0809322748	58
0.0106659226	12.3666759680	0.0808624729	59
0.0098758542	12.3765518222	0.0807979488	60
$\dfrac{1}{(1+i)^n}$	$p\,\overline{n|}$	$\dfrac{1}{p\,\overline{n|}}$	n

Rate

8%

ANNUALLY

If compounded
annually,
nominal annual rate is

8%

SEMIANNUALLY

If compounded
semiannually,
nominal annual rate is

16%

QUARTERLY

If compounded
quarterly,
nominal annual rate is

32%

MONTHLY

If compounded
monthly,
nominal annual rate is

96%

	n	Amount of \$1 at Comp. Int.	Amount Saved for \$1/Period	Payment to Save \$1
Rate	1	1.0900000000	1.0000000000	1.0000000000
	2	1.1881000000	2.0900000000	0.4784688995
9%	3	1.2950290000	3.2781000000	0.3050547573
	4	1.4115816100	4.5731290000	0.2186686621
	5	1.5386239549	5.9847106100	0.1670924570
	6	1.6771001108	7.5233345649	0.1329197833
	7	1.8280391208	9.2004346757	0.1086905168
	8	1.9925626417	11.0284737966	0.0906743778
	9	2.1718932794	13.0210364382	0.0767988021
	10	2.3673636746	15.1929297177	0.0658200899
	11	2.5804264053	17.5602933923	0.0569466567
	12	2.8126647818	20.1407197976	0.0496506585
	13	3.0658046121	22.9533845794	0.0435665597
	14	3.3417270272	26.0191891915	0.0384331730
	15	3.6424824597	29.3609162188	0.0340588827
	16	3.9703058811	33.0033986784	0.0302999097
	17	4.3276334104	36.9737045595	0.0270462485
	18	4.7171204173	41.3013379699	0.0242122907
	19	5.1416612548	46.0184583871	0.0217304107
ANNUALLY	20	5.6044107678	51.1601196420	0.0195464750
if compounded	21	6.1088077369	56.7645304098	0.0176166348
annually	22	6.6586004332	62.8733381466	0.0159049930
nominal annual rate is	23	7.2578744722	69.5319385798	0.0143818800
	24	7.9110831747	76.7898130520	0.0130225607
9%	25	8.6230806604	84.7008962267	0.0118062505
	26	9.3991579198	93.3239768871	0.0107153599
	27	10.2450821326	102.7231348069	0.0097349054
	28	11.1671395246	112.9682169396	0.0088520473
	29	12.1721820818	124.1353564641	0.0080557226
SEMIANNUALLY	30	13.2676784691	136.3075385459	0.0073363514
if compounded	31	14.4617695314	149.5752170150	0.0066855995
semiannually	32	15.7633287892	164.0369865464	0.0060961861
nominal annual rate is	33	17.1820283802	179.8003153356	0.0055617255
	34	18.7284109344	196.9823437158	0.0050765971
18%	35	20.4139679185	215.7107546502	0.0046358375
	36	22.2512250312	236.1247225687	0.0042350500
	37	24.2538352840	258.3759475999	0.0038703293
	38	26.4366804595	282.6297828839	0.0035381975
	39	28.8159817009	309.0664633434	0.0032355500
QUARTERLY	40	31.4094200540	337.8824450443	0.0029596092
if compounded	41	34.2362678588	369.2918650983	0.0027078853
quarterly	42	37.3175319661	403.5281329572	0.0024781420
nominal annual rate is	43	40.6761098431	440.8456649233	0.0022683675
	44	44.3369597290	481.5217747664	0.0020767493
36%	45	48.3272861046	525.8587344954	0.0019016514
	46	52.6767418540	574.1860206000	0.0017415959
	47	57.4176486209	626.8627624540	0.0015952455
	48	62.5852369967	684.2804110748	0.0014613892
	49	68.2179083264	746.8656480716	0.0013389289
MONTHLY	50	74.3575200758	815.0835563980	0.0012268681
if compounded	51	81.0496968826	889.4410764738	0.0011243016
monthly	52	88.3441696021	970.4907733565	0.0010304065
nominal annual rate is	53	96.2951448663	1058.8349429585	0.0009444343
	54	104.9617079042	1155.1300878248	0.0008657034
108%	55	114.4082616156	1260.0917957290	0.0007935930
	56	124.7050051610	1374.5000573447	0.0007275373
	57	135.9284556255	1499.2050625057	0.0006670202
	58	148.1620166318	1635.1335181312	0.0006115709
	59	161.4965981287	1783.2955347630	0.0005607595
	60	176.0312919602	1944.7921328917	0.0005141938
	n	$(1+i)^n$	$s\,\overline{n}$	$\dfrac{1}{s\,\overline{n}}$

Pres. Value of $1 at Comp. Int.	Amount Borrowed for $1 Payment	Payment to Borrow $1	n	
0.9174311927	0.9174311927	1.0900000000	1	Rate
0.8416799933	1.7591111859	0.5684688995	2	
0.7721834801	2.5312946660	0.3950547573	3	**9%**
0.7084252111	3.2397198771	0.3086686621	4	
0.6499313863	3.8896512634	0.2570924570	5	
0.5962673269	4.4859185902	0.2229197833	6	
0.5470342448	5.0329528351	0.1986905168	7	
0.5018662797	5.5348191147	0.1806743778	8	
0.4604277795	5.9952468943	0.1667988021	9	
0.4224108069	6.4176577012	0.1558200899	10	
0.3875328504	6.8051905515	0.1469466567	11	
0.3555347251	7.1607252766	0.1396506585	12	
0.3261786469	7.4869039235	0.1335665597	13	
0.2992464650	7.7861503885	0.1284331730	14	
0.2745380413	8.0606884299	0.1240588827	15	
0.2518697627	8.3125581925	0.1202999097	16	
0.2310731768	8.5436313693	0.1170462485	17	
0.2119937402	8.7556251094	0.1142122907	18	
0.1944896699	8.9501147793	0.1117304107	19	
0.1784308898	9.1285456691	0.1095464750	20	**ANNUALLY**
0.1636980640	9.2922437331	0.1076166348	21	*if compounded*
0.1501817101	9.4424254432	0.1059049930	22	***annually***
0.1377813854	9.5802068286	0.1043818800	23	*nominal annual rate is*
0.1264049408	9.7066117694	0.1030225607	24	
0.1159678356	9.8225796049	0.1018062505	25	**9%**
0.1063925097	9.9289721146	0.1007153599	26	
0.0976078070	10.0265799217	0.0997349054	27	
0.0895484468	10.1161283685	0.0988520473	28	
0.0821545384	10.1982829069	0.0980557226	29	
0.0753711361	10.2736540430	0.0973363514	30	**SEMIANNUALLY**
0.0691478313	10.3428018743	0.0966855995	31	*if compounded*
0.0634383773	10.4062402517	0.0960961861	32	***semiannually***
0.0582003462	10.4644405979	0.0955617255	33	*nominal annual rate is*
0.0533948130	10.5178354109	0.0950765971	34	
0.0489860670	10.5668214779	0.0946358375	35	**18%**
0.0449413459	10.6117628237	0.0942350500	36	
0.0412305925	10.6529934163	0.0938703293	37	
0.0378262317	10.6908196480	0.0935381975	38	
0.0347029648	10.7255226128	0.0932355500	39	
0.0318375824	10.7573601952	0.0929596092	40	**QUARTERLY**
0.0292087912	10.7865689865	0.0927078853	41	*if compounded*
0.0267970562	10.8133660426	0.0924781420	42	***quarterly***
0.0245844552	10.8379504978	0.0922683675	43	*nominal annual rate is*
0.0225545461	10.8605050439	0.0920767493	44	
0.0206922441	10.8811972880	0.0919016514	45	**36%**
0.0189837102	10.9001809981	0.0917415959	46	
0.0174162479	10.9175972460	0.0915952455	47	
0.0159782090	10.9335754550	0.0914613892	48	
0.0146589074	10.9482343624	0.0913389289	49	
0.0134485389	10.9616829013	0.0912268681	50	**MONTHLY**
0.0123381091	10.9740210104	0.0911243016	51	*if compounded*
0.0113193661	10.9853403765	0.0910304065	52	***monthly***
0.0103847396	10.9957251160	0.0909444343	53	*nominal annual rate is*
0.0095272840	11.0052524000	0.0908657034	54	
0.0087406275	11.0139930276	0.0907935930	55	**108%**
0.0080189243	11.0220119519	0.0907275373	56	
0.0073568113	11.0293687632	0.0906670202	57	
0.0067493682	11.0361181314	0.0906115709	58	
0.0061920809	11.0423102123	0.0905607595	59	
0.0056808082	11.0479910204	0.09051419308	60	
$\dfrac{1}{(1+i)^n}$	$p\,\overline{n|}$	$\dfrac{1}{p\,\overline{n|}}$	n	

Answers to Selected Exercises

Page 4
1. hundreds 3. tenths 5. hundredths 7. hundred thousands 9. ten-thousandths 11. millions 13. 50 15. 500 17. 200,000 19. 6 21. .07 23. 90

Page 5
1. 641 3. 53,242 5. 305 7. 1,281 9. 265.593 11. 43.7059 13. 3.21 15. 113.54

Page 7
Oral: 1. 180 3. 49.8 5. 685 7. 56,000 9. 436,210
Written: 1. 966 3. 15,764 5. 15,405,390 7. 512.4 9. 100,533.98 11. 91.8932

Page 9
Oral: 1. 7.5 3. 9.36 5. 362.415 7. 4.3578 9. 7.224
Written: 1. $6\overline{)48}$, $48 \div 6$, $\frac{48}{6}$ 3. $5\overline{)365}$, $365 \div 5$, $\frac{365}{5}$
5. 35 7. 31 9. 28 11. 233 13. 2.65 15. 22.58 17. 31.6

Page 12
1. 6,330 3. 420 5. 7,400 7. 2,400 9. 65.25 11. 37.70 13. 2.4 15. 534.9 17. 300,000 19. 256,000 21. 256,370 23. 256,372.7 25. 256,372.684

Page 13
27. 11.60 29. 1,085 31. 1,626 33. 223 35. 3,045 37. 65,861 39. 128

Page 14
1. −23 3. 125 5. −58 7. 77 9. 481   1. 12 3. 3 5. 34 7. 92 9. 309 11. 21

Page 15
13. 10 15. 18 17. 31 19. 11 21. 50 23. 4 25. 39 27. 72

Page 18
1. −2 3. −11 5. −9 7. −2 9. 5   1. 22 3. −44 5. 13 7. 87 9. −4 11. 12 13. −39 15. 64 17. −58 19. 8

Page 21
1. −3 3. −21 5. 9 7. −10 9. −25 11. 13 13. −4 15. 13 17. 8 19. −9

Page 23
1. 60 3. −196 5. 322 7. −756 9. 108 11. −125 13. 667 15. 124 17. −1,710 19. 12,225

Page 24
1. 5 3. −6 5. −7 7. 9 9. −14 11. −8 13. −10 15. −16 17. −22 19. 19

Page 26
1. 11 3. 14 5. 20 7. 22 9. 15 11. 42 13. 24 15. 43 17. 84 19. 9   1. tens 3. thousands 5. 4 thousandths 7. 944 9. 1,497 11. 566 13. 26,675 15. 18,972 17. 296.57376

Page 27
19. 41 21. 3.14 23. 6,800 25. 500 27. 65.30 29. −72 31. 2 33. 19 35. 8 37. 6 39. −12 41. −15 43. 68 45. 60 47. 6 49. 3 51. 18 − 3, or 15 53. 12 ÷ 2 + 6, or 6 + 6, or 12

Page 31
Oral: 1. improper 3. proper 5. improper 7. mixed
Written: 1. 7, sevenths 3 3. 5, fifths, 4 5. 10, tenths, 7 7. $1\frac{1}{3}$ 9. $4\frac{1}{4}$ 11. 9 13. $6\frac{13}{18}$ 15. 2

Page 32
17. $\frac{90}{7}$ 19. $\frac{73}{7}$ 21. $\frac{103}{13}$ 23. $\frac{67}{7}$

Page 33
1. no 3. yes 5. no 7. yes 9. no

Page 34
1. 1, 2, 4, 8, 16 3. 1, 3, 5, 15, 25, 75 5. 1, 2, 3, 4, 6, 8, 9, 12, 16, 18, 24, 36, 48, 72, 144 7. 1, 2, 3, 4, 6, 11, 12, 22, 33, 44, 66, 132 9. $2^3 \cdot 3$ 11. $3^2 \cdot 7^2$ 13. $2 \cdot 3^3 \cdot 7$ 15. $2 \cdot 3^4 \cdot 5$ 17. $3 \cdot 5 \cdot 7^3$

Page 37
1. 5, 10, 15, 20, 25, 30 3. 12, 24, 36, 48, 60, 72 5. 7, 14, 21, 28, 35, 42 7. 18, 36, 54, 72, 90, 108 9. 18; 108 11. 28; 1,176 13. 27; 22,680 15. 44; 72,600 17. 60; 12,600 19. 5; 3,464,175

Page 40
1. Answers vary. 3. Answers vary. 5. Answers vary. 7. Answers vary. 9. $\frac{1}{3}$ 11. $\frac{1}{2}$ 13. $\frac{1}{2}$ 15. $\frac{2}{3}$ 17. $7\frac{2}{5}$ 19. $12\frac{1}{4}$ 21. = 23. ≠ 25. = 27. ≠

Page 42
1. $7\frac{7}{9}$ 3. $\frac{8}{15}$ 5. $\frac{5}{9}$ 7. $\frac{1}{8}$ 9. $\frac{2}{33}$ 11. $\frac{5}{9}$ 13. 24 15. $\frac{4}{15}$ 17. $\frac{20}{27}$ 19. $1\frac{1}{3}$ hr.

Page 43

Oral: 1. $\frac{4}{3}$ 3. $\frac{5}{6}$ 5. $\frac{12}{7}$ Written: 1. 20 3. $\frac{7}{12}$
5. $2\frac{1}{2}$ 7. 14 9. $3\frac{1}{9}$ 11. $1\frac{3}{7}$

Page 44

13. $1\frac{11}{16}$ 15. $1\frac{1}{6}$ 17. 1 19. 32 copies

Page 45

1. 32 3. $52\frac{4}{5}$ 5. $91\frac{1}{5}$ 7. $40\frac{2}{15}$ 9. 2 11. $2\frac{5}{9}$ 13. $2\frac{9}{25}$ 15. 6 pieces

Page 48

1. $\frac{4}{6}$ 3. $\frac{9}{15}$ 5. 24 7. 84

Page 49

9. $\frac{3}{5}$ 11. $\frac{8}{9}$ 13. $\frac{1}{4}$ 15. $1\frac{5}{16}$ 17. $1\frac{1}{3}$ 19. $\frac{1}{4}$ 21. $\frac{7}{15}$
23. $\frac{23}{24}$ 25. $\frac{19}{40}$ 27. $\frac{13}{15}$ in. 29. $2\frac{1}{4}$ yd.

Page 51

1. $10\frac{3}{5}$ 3. $4\frac{1}{2}$ 5. $62\frac{1}{2}$ 7. $20\frac{1}{2}$ 9. $8\frac{7}{12}$ 11. $107\frac{5}{12}$ 13. $78\frac{8}{21}$
15. $100\frac{1}{12}$ 17. $35\frac{4}{5}$ 19. $355\frac{11}{36}$ 21. 13 hr. 23. $48\frac{5}{6}$ cups

Page 53

1. $\frac{7}{10}$ 3. $\frac{1}{2}$ 5. $\frac{31}{250}$ 7. $\frac{3}{8}$ 9. $\frac{5}{8}$ 11. $\frac{3}{4}$ 13. $6\frac{1}{5}$ 15. $23\frac{21}{50}$ 17. $26\frac{1}{20}$
19. $12\frac{23}{40}$ 21. $43\frac{1}{250}$ 23. $28\frac{18}{125}$ 25. $\frac{17}{20}$ 27. $1\frac{3}{4}$ 29. $1\frac{3}{4}$

Page 55

1. .3 3. .35 5. .003 7. .6 9. .375 11. .548 13. .28 15. .025
17. $.\overline{6}$ 19. 1.131 21. 1.833

Page 56

1. > 3. < 5. = 7. > 9. = 11. > 13. 0.30, 0.03, 0.003
15. 7.75, 7.7, 7.075 17. 12.73, 12.7, 12.63 19. 401.25, 400.48, 399.87

Page 57

1. $2\frac{1}{2}$ 3. 4 5. 6 7. $\frac{32}{5}$ 9. $\frac{249}{7}$ 11. $\frac{75}{4}$ 13. $2 \cdot 3^3 \cdot 5$
15. $3^2 \cdot 5^2 \cdot 7$ 17. 30; 2,700 19. 10; 163,800 21. $\frac{1}{3}$ 23. $\frac{1}{2}$
25. $\frac{25}{38}$ 27. = 29. = 31. ≠ 33. 24 35. 35 37. 16

Page 58

39. $\frac{5}{8}$ 41. $\frac{31}{40}$ 43. $\frac{1}{20}$ 45. $\frac{4}{9}$ 47. $\frac{3}{26}$ 49. 1 51. 21 53. $18\frac{17}{30}$
55. $10\frac{5}{8}$ 57. $20\frac{5}{21}$ 59. $39\frac{13}{36}$ 61. $3\frac{283}{343}$ 63. $\frac{1}{2}$ 65. $\frac{37}{50}$ 67. $12\frac{1}{40}$
69. .7 71. .15 73. $.\overline{03}$ 75. > 77. =

Page 63

1. 3 3. 1 5. 21 7. 19 9. 1 11. $15x$, $2y$ 13. $26xyz$, $16xy$,
$4x$, $5y$ 15. $53a$, $21b$, $5c$ 17. $25x$, $5y$ 19. $61xy$, $32y$

Page 65

1. 18 3. 14 5. 323 7. 18 9. 16 11. 18 13. 70 15. 5 17. 504
19. 66

Page 66

1. 1,984 sq. ft. 3. 138 in. 5. 225 mi. 7. 40 ft.

Page 67

9. 260 mi.

Page 69

1. $x + 6$ 3. $\frac{x}{4}$ 5. $x + 4$ 7. $\frac{x}{9}$ 9. $\frac{3}{5} \cdot x$
11. $7x = 28$ 13. $x + 28 = 174$ 15. $4(7 + n) = 5 \cdot 8$
17. $\frac{1}{3}x + \frac{1}{2}x > 4$ 19. $5x + 4x < 40$

Page 70

1. O 3. O 5. T 7. O 9. T 11. $x = 3$ 13. $x = 1$ 15. $x = 4$
17. $x = 3$ 19. $x = 6$

Page 72

1. subtraction 3. addition 5. addition 7. subtraction
9. addition

Page 73

11. $x = 38$ 13. $x = 74$ 15. $x = 39$ 17. $x = 113$ 19. $x =$
115 21. $x = 378$ 23. $x = 117$

Page 75

1. multiplication 3. division 5. subtraction 7. division
9. multiplication 11. $x = 9$ 13. $x = 252$ 15. $x = 7$ 17. x
$= 729$ 19. $x = 16$ 21. $x = 207$ 23. $x = 114$ 25. $x = 388$
27. $x = 26$

Page 77

1. $x = 7$ 3. $x = 7$ 5. $x = 18$ 7. $x = 6$ 9. $x = 16$ 11. $x =$
20

Page 78

13. $x = 45$ 15. $x = 161$ 17. $x = 84$ 19. $x = 272$ 21. $x =$
8 23. $x = 1,176$ 25. $x = 3$ 27. $x = 8$ 29. $x = 41$

Page 58

39. $\frac{5}{8}$ 41. $\frac{31}{40}$ 43. $\frac{1}{20}$ 45. $\frac{4}{9}$ 47. $\frac{3}{26}$ 49. 1 51. 21 53. $18\frac{17}{30}$
55. $10\frac{5}{8}$ 57. $20\frac{5}{21}$ 59. $39\frac{13}{36}$ 61. $3\frac{283}{343}$ 63. $\frac{1}{2}$ 65. $\frac{37}{50}$ 67. $12\frac{1}{40}$
69. .7 71. .15 73. $.\overline{03}$ 75. > 77. =

Page 57

1. $2\frac{1}{2}$ 3. 4 5. 6 7. $\frac{32}{5}$ 9. $\frac{249}{7}$ 11. $\frac{75}{4}$ 13. $2 \cdot 3^3 \cdot 5$
15. $3^2 \cdot 5^2 \cdot 7$ 17. 30; 2,700 19. 10; 163,800 21. $\frac{1}{3}$ 23. $\frac{1}{2}$
25. $\frac{25}{38}$ 27. = 29. = 31. ≠ 33. 24 35. 35 37. 16

Page 80

1. $x + 33 = 84$, $x = 51$ **3.** $12 x = 96$, $x = 8$ **5.** $x - 23 = 47$, $x = 70$ **7.** $22 x = 132$, $x = 6$ **9.** $x + 24 = 42$, $x = 18$ **11.** $18 + 6 x = 66$, $x = 8$ **13.** $\frac{x}{9} + 15 = 78$, $x = 567$ **15.** $5 x - 12 = 68$, $x = 16$ **17.** $2 x - 7 = 15$, $x = 11$ years old **19.** $3 x + 17 = 59$, $x = 14$

Page 81

1. 1:2 **3.** 1:4 **5.** 2:3 **7.** 3:10 **9.** 9:16 **11.** 3:8 **13.** 4:5 **15.** 11:12

Page 84

1. = **3.** = **5.** > **7.** < **9.** < **11.** = **13.** > **15.** < **17.** > **19.** = **20.** < **1.** 21 **3.** 7 **5.** 11 **7.** 4

Page 85

9. 3,358 square feet **11.** 318 miles **13.** $n + 8$ **15.** $n + 18$ **17.** $n + 6 = 19$ **19.** $\frac{n}{3} = 7$ **21.** True **23.** Open **25.** True **27.** 157 **29.** 28 **31.** 258 **33.** 100 **35.** 7 **37.** 42 **39.** 84

Page 86

41. $6 x = 144$, $x = 24$ **43.** $3 x + 6 = 30$, $x = 8$ **45.** 1:2 **47.** 7:4 **49.** > **51.** = **53.** > **55.** >

Page 90

1. $\frac{3}{10}$ **3.** $\frac{4}{25}$ **5.** $\frac{3}{4}$ **7.** $\frac{19}{50}$ **9.** $\frac{1}{2}$

Page 92

1. 0.28 **3.** 0.05 **5.** 0.04 **7.** 0.845 **9.** 0.76 **11.** 0.16 **13.** 1.25 **15.** 9.46 **17.** 21% **19.** 3% **21.** 7% **23.** 73% **25.** 67.2% **27.** 960% **29.** 2.5%

Page 94

1. $\frac{1}{20}$ **3.** $\frac{63}{100}$ **5.** $\frac{7}{25}$ **7.** $1\frac{1}{4}$ **9.** $\frac{9}{25}$

Page 95

11. 34% **13.** $37\frac{1}{2}$% **15.** 50% **17.** $44\frac{4}{9}$% **19.** 420% **21.** 60% **23.** 19% **25.** 25% **27.** $33\frac{1}{3}$% **29.** $62\frac{1}{2}$%

Page 97

1. $b = 50$ **3.** $b = 20$ **5.** $r = 50\%$ **7.** $r = 46\%$ **9.** $p = 4.48$ **11.** $p = 20.06$ **13.** 80% **15.** 40% **17.** 116 **19.** 11 **21.** 60% **23.** 32 **25.** 47 **27.** 20% **29.** 325 **31.** 7.3 **33.** 48.72

Page 99

1. 80% **3.** $33.60 **5.** $49.00 **7.** $134.13 **9.** $19.44

Page 101

1. $24,150 **3.** 299 employees **5.** $132.30 **7.** $28.25 **9.** $9,618.96

Page 102

1. 0.36 **3.** 0.06 **5.** 0.485 **7.** 3.85 **9.** 86% **11.** 27% **13.** 562% **15.** 96% **17.** $\frac{3}{50}$ **19.** $\frac{27}{100}$ **21.** $\frac{6}{25}$ **23.** $1\frac{4}{25}$ **25.** 71% **27.** 80% **29.** 6% **31.** 75% **33.** $b = 36$ **35.** $r = .12$ **37.** $p = 16$ **39.** 40% **41.** 75 **43.** 56.07

Page 103

45. $15.00 **47.** 70% **49.** 176 lb.

Page 108

1. divide, 12 **3.** multiply, 320 **5.** multiply, 16 **7.** multiply, 2 **9.** divide, 32,000 **11.** multiply, 32 **13.** divide, 16.5 **15.** multiply, 2,000 **17.** 144 oz. **19.** 18 pt. **21.** 4 T. **23.** 17.3 bu. **25.** 6,000 lb. **27.** 15,840 yd. **29.** 6.21 qt.

Page 110

1. centimeter **3.** kilogram **5.** centigram **7.** decimeter **9.** milliliter

Page 112

1. multiply, 1,000 **3.** divide, 100,000 **5.** multiply, 10 **7.** divide, 10,000 **9.** .0347 hm **11.** 4,320 dkl **13.** 34,200 mg **15.** 642 cg **17.** .04675 kg **19.** .983 hg **21.** 846.2 cl

Page 114

1. 11.5 ft. **3.** 453.28 g **5.** 2,700 g **7.** 113.7 dl **9.** 3.08 l

Page 117

1. 52 m **3.** 66 ft. **5.** 100 m **7.** 160 m, or 16 dkm **9.** 1220 cm, or 122 dm **11.** 48 **13.** 28 mm **15.** 76 in. **17.** 37.68 cm **19.** 109.9 dm **21.** 207.24 m **23.** 182.12 km **25.** 703.36 ft. **27.** (a) 8 linear ft., (b) 21 linear ft., (c) 116 ft., (d) 2 linear ft.

Page 122

1. 27 cm^2 **3.** 180.8 dkm^2 **5.** 342.4 yd.^{2} **7.** 414 dm^2 or 41,400 cm^2 **9.** 925 km^2 or 92,500 hm^2 **11.** 49 in.^{2} **13.** 144 dm^2 **15.** 400 ft.^{2} **17.** 198 yd.^{2} **19.** 27 mm^2 **21.** 480 cm^2

Page 123

23. 424 m^2 **25.** 558 ft.^{2}

Page 125

1. 1,080 ft.^{3} **3.** 24,192 cm^3 **5.** 756 km^3 **7.** 43,092 ft.^{3} **9.** 945 m^3, or 945,000 dm^3, or 945,000,000 cm^3 **11.** 216 in.^{3} **13.** 729 m^3 **15.** 12,167 dm^3

Page 126

1. 192 in. **3.** 15 lb. **5.** 570,240 in. **7.** 7,200 dkl **9.** 0.0416 hg **11.** 4,300 cl **13.** 339.96 g **15.** .62 ft. **17.** 5.685 l **19.** 66 ft. **21.** 32 m **23.** 24 cm **25.** 56 yd. **27.** 34.54 cm **29.** 31.4 in. **31.** 48 cm^2 **33.** 272 m^2 **35.** 36 ft.^{2} **37.** 121 m^2 **39.** 66 in.^{2} **41.** 294 cm^2

Page 127

43. 1,512 in.^{3} **45.** 17,576 m^3 **47.** 434,112 in.^{3}

Page 131

1. $342.00 **3.** $262.20 **5.** $6.15; $155.80; $0; $155.80 **7.** $6.30; $252.00; $47.25; $299.25 **9.** $18.69; 37; $461.02 **11.** $4.26; $6.39; $119.28; $0

Page 138

1. 4 hr., 15 min. **3.** 3 hr., 50 min. **5.** 3 hr., 15 min. **7.** 3 hr., 25 min. **9.** 4 hr., 5 min. **11.** 7:00 = 7:00; 2:56 = 2:45; 6:53 = 7:00; 3:04 = 3:00; 7:02 = 7:15; 3:00 = 3:00; 7:05 = 7:05; 2:58 = 2:45; 6:57 = 7:00; 3:01 = 3:00

Page 139

13. (a) 39 hr., 15 min.; (b) $255.13 **15.** 4 hr. **17.** 3 hr., 45 min. **19.** 1 hr., 15 min. **21.** 2 hr., 45 min. **23.** 13 hr., 15 min.

Page 141

1. $332.15 **3.** $228.80 **5.** $174 **7.** $290.50 **9.** $252.85 **11.** $268.60

Page 144

1. $588 **3.** $310 **5.** $299 **7.** $1,025 **9.** $9,984 **11.** $11,736 **13.** $22,980 **15.** $16,200 **17.** A: $34,992, B: $35,834 (pays most), C: $34,260 **19.** $105 weekly

Page 147

1. $1,537.50 **3.** $1,140 **5.** $842 **7.** $172.38 **9.** $197.50 **11.** $26.40 (Price); $10.56 (Commission)

Page 148

1. $362.60 **3.** 34 hr., 55 min. **5.** 8:00—12:00; 4 hr. **7.** 1:15—5:00; 3 hr., 45 min. **9.** $207 **11.** $250

Page 149

13. $28.31 (total price); $9.91 (commission) **15.** $72

Page 154

1. $184.47 **3.** $107.25 **5.** $117.83 **7.** $92.02 **9.** $2,717 **11.** $1,930.50 **13.** $2,589.02 **15.** $3,609.32

Page 157

1. $933.34 **3.** $552.49 **5.** $557.60

Page 158

7. $339.35 **5.** $174 **7.** $290.50 **9.** $252.85 **11.** $268.60

Page 159

1. $380 **3.** $383.55 **5.** $1,011.67 **7.** $332.28 **9.** $324

Page 160

11. $172 **13.** $1,206.50 **15.** $123.20 **17.** $19.40 **19.** $53.50

Page 165

1. $9,101.20 **3.** $15,527.45 **5.** $5,669.70

Page 166

7. $12,900 **9.** $12,760 **11.** $915 **13.** $1,252.50 **15.** $6,572.30 **17.** tax liability: $1,778.60; tax refund: $574.00

Page 168

1. $.24 **3.** $1.25 **5.** $.13 **7.** $1.53 **9.** $14.45 **11.** $56.73 **13.** $28.60 **15.** $166.11

Page 169

17. $51.31 **19.** $99.67

Page 170

1. $10,920 **3.** $12,600 **5.** $64,929 **7.** $5,931.50 **9.** $39,127.80 **11.** $278.27 **13.** $1,259.68 **15.** $1,851.93 **17.** $1,800.28 **19.** $1,474.19

Page 171

1. $2,323.75 **3.** $1,307.38 **5.** $31.07 **7.** $392.96 **9.** $317 **11.** $22.30 **13.** $836.72

Page 178

1. 182 **3.** 150 **5.** 85 **7.** $37.50 **9.** $110.83 **11.** $10.91 **13.** $180.50, $1,130.50 **15.** $18.03, $768.03 **17.** $46.67, $846.67 **19.** $2,400, $6,400.00 **21.** $41.56, $736.56 **23.** July 7, 1986, $1,640

Page 179

25. $880

Page 181

1. I = $108.56; pymt. = $59.64 **3.** I = $600; pymt. = $129.17 **5.** I = $78.75; pymt. = $92.08 **7.** 34% **9.** 29% **11.** 26% **13.** 16% **15.** 19% **17.** 22%

Page 185

1. $445.00 **3.** $619.94 **5.** $864.00 **7.** $1,155 **9.** $1,963.70

Page 186

11. $909.09 **13.** $1,371.43 **15.** $2,553.16 **17.** $1,933.49
19. $8\frac{1}{2}$% **21.** 20.3% **23.** 11.4% **25.** $4,531.50

Page 191

1. $153.96; $23.76 **3.** $124.92; $747.60 **5.** $216.28;
$1,183.76 **7.** $594.82; $64,567.60 **9.** $1,460 **11.** $5,808
13. $56,344 **15.** $65,082 **17.** (a) $584.45; $93,268
(b) $556.89; $153,480.40

Page 192

19. (a) $89.13 (b) $2,673.90 (c) $373.90

Page 194

1. $25.00 **3.** $134.46 **5.** $71.29 **7.** $35.00 **9.** $299.63
11. bal.: $660.80; min. pymt.: $132.16

Page 196

1. $296.28, $4.44 **3.** $72.64, $1.09 **5.** $43.18, $.65
7. $91.12, $1.37 **9.** $633.77, $9.51 **11.** $646.42, $9.70
13. Dec. bal. = $679.74; Dec. pymt. = $135.95; total
pymt. = $21.49

Page 198

1. (a) 187, (b) 190, (c) 240, (d) 229, (e) 180, (f) 103
3. (a) 17.1%, (b) 12%, (c) 10%

Page 199

5. (a) 14.2%, (b) 17.3%, (c) 19.4%, (d) 25.8%,
(e) 15.9%, (f) 21.6% **7.** (a) p: $182.95; i: $293.10,
(b) p: $225.32; i: $1,611.52, (c) p: $978.84; i: $5,492.16,
(d) p: $381.65; i: $72,495 **9.** int: $1,581.08; amt.:
$6.081.08 **11.** $5,033.52

Page 205

1. Thirty-five and $\frac{no}{100}$ **3.** Two hundred fifty-three
and $\frac{no}{100}$ **5.** Fifty-eight and $\frac{84}{100}$

Page 209

1. Currency: $133.00; Coin: $1.80 **3.** Currency: $146.00;
Coin: $7.48

Page 212

1. $237.05 **3.** $719.89 **5.** $314.12 **7.** $680.83

Page 214

9. $46.34 **11.** yes; a withdrawal: $30.00. no

Page 218

1. 5 **3.** 8 **5.** 18 **7.** 40

Page 219

9. $1,113.31; $153.31 **11.** $1,008.84; $213.84
13. $3,146.89; $586.89 **15.** $1,763.68; $366.68
17. $394.02 **19.** $1,198.78 **21.** $4,490.43 **23.** $6,819.34

Page 223

1. 6.09; 6.14; 6.17 **3.** 8.16; 8.24; 8.30 **5.** 10.25; 10.38;
10.47 **7.** 14.49; 14.75; 14.93

Page 224

9. 5.35; 5.38; 5.39 **11.** 13.65; 13.80; 13.88 **13.** 19.25;
19.56; 19.72 **15.** 26.25; 26.82; 23.36 **17.** Banker's Rule
method gives $12.04 more.

Page 228

1. $487.85 **3.** $677.85 **5.** $787.80 **7.** $1,212.80
9. $1,127.80 **11.** $6.93

Page 229

13. $1.09 **15.** $4.10 **17.** $15.68

Page 233

1. $590.04 **3.** $1,093.38 **5.** $151,873.77 **7.** $2,204.97

Page 234

9. $109.32 **11.** $144.44 **13.** $74.62 **15.** $135.71
17. $2,845.64 **19.** $58,383.53

Page 237

1. $19,019.32 **3.** $5,058.17 **5.** $57,929.21

Page 238

7. $155.54 per month **9.** $89.99 per quarter **11.** $93.22
per month **13.** $374.30 per month **15.** $10,914.62 per
quarter **17.** $4,566.98 **19.** $21,158.49

Page 239

1. Twenty-five and $\frac{50}{100}$ **3.** Two thousand four hundred
fifty-six and $\frac{00}{100}$ **5.** Five hundred thirty-nine and $\frac{15}{100}$
7. $1,127.43; $237.42 **9.** $1,647.42; $185.42 **11.** $185.43;
$97.43 **13.** $9,962.23; $562.23

Page 240

15. $748.33 **17.** $2,338.97 **19.** $906.28 **21.** $11,430.42
23. $1,858.89 **25.** $674.86 **27.** 2.01% **29.** 26.82%
31. $871.40 **33.** $26,572.35 **35.** $504.38

37. $.78 39. $.97

1. $6,419; $320.95 3. $8,787.50; $439.38 5. $10,814.60;
$540.73 7. $12,093.90; $604.70 9. $13,752; $687.60
11. $15 13. $84 15. $28 17. $0.3617/mi.; large
19. $0.2336/mi.; compact 21. $6,557.16 23. no options,
$5,034.75

25. (a) $7,596.57, (b) $7,508.43 (best value)

1. $1,013.39 3. $4,523.07 5. $15,839.07

7. $92.43 9. $157.95 11. $195.62 13. $138.43
15. $249.11 17. $267.18 19. $322.32 21. $1,467.96
23. $3,224.64 25. Answers may vary: You earn interest,
which helps pay for car; it costs much less—good
stewardship; you don't have to pay interest; you can
buy the car at today's prices.

1. $6,700 3. $8,400

5. $1,175 (18%) 7. $2,200 (21%) 9. $3,705 11. $1,235
13. 15.8% 15. $4,692.50 17. $1,200; 14.1% 19. $7,349

1. $426.50 3. $218.00 5. $267.50 7. $4,427.50
9. $4,252.50

1. $6,264 3. $11,040 5. $9,504 7. $348 9. $432 11. $480
13. $3,360 15. $312 owed 17. $294 refund
19. subcompact 21. 5 years

1. $73.46 3. $103.27 5. $93.92 7. $133.20 9. $174.90
11. $115.40 13. The $5,000 would not be enough.
15. $164.60 17. $\frac{100}{10.5}$ = 9.5 half-years = 4.75 years
19. Yes, it would cost $8.82/week; No, it would cost
$11.75/week.

1. 31.22 mpg 3. 11.57 km/l 5. 42.89 mpg 7. 20.96 mpg;
$0.95/gal.

9. 44.4 gal.; $52.39 11. 158.3 l; $186.79 13. 367.95 gal.;
$434.18 15. 462 miles 17. 360 miles 19. $21.03
21. $24.04 23. A: $0.0054/mile; B: $0.0045/mile. Best
= B 25. $37.91

1. $55.50 3. $151.20 5. $57.75 7. $72.75 9. $88.50
11. $345.45 13. $101.25 15. $45.00 17. $100.82

1. $3,682.74 3. $1,893.42 5. $300 7. $276.36 9. $547.65
11. 21 cents/mi.

13. $9,375 15. foregone int.: $872.13; fin. charge:
$1,447.90 17. $575 19. $4,533.33 21. $1,075.80 23. $25
25. 32¢/mi.

1. 553 3. 482 5. 713 7. 11.8 hr. 9. 31.8 hr. 11. 5 hr.
13. 2:18 P.M. Central 15. 9:12 A.M. Central 2 days later
17. 4 hr., 6 min. 19. 1:20 P.M. Pacific

1. $158.10 3. $394.50 5. $78.32 7. $1,440

9. $379.50 11. $112.94 13. $25.62 savings per week
15. $1,864; 2:00-2:30 P.M. MST on June 19 17. $1,080;
11 P.M. EST on July 12

19. $147 21. 8.7% 23. 12.9% 25. 8.8% 1. $9,503.24
3. $7,455 5. $5,840.10

7. $475 9. $294 11. $244 13. $5,900.42 15. $4,789.74
17. $3,139.65 19. $184.58, $429.92 21. $327.39,
$1,786.04 23. $150.14, $202.52 25. $1,630, 14.1%
27. $941.67, 10.67% 29. $2,426.67, 17.6% 31. $8,928
33. $13,872 35. $248.40 37. $1,396.00

39. 16.17 mpg 41. 10 km/l 43. 12 mpg 45. 107 gal., 53
hr. 47. 46 gal., 21 hr. 49. 5:08 A.M. 51. 8:20 P.M.
53. weekend, save $31.25

Page 296

1. 4.5¢/oz. **3.** 79.2¢/lb. **5.** 99.1¢/lb. **7.** 4.7¢/oz.*; 5.7¢/oz. **9.** $2.25/lb.*; $2.83/lb. **11.** 9.9¢/oz.; 9.3¢/oz.*

Page 297

13. 35.6¢/serving **15.** 24¢/serving **17.** 50.85¢/serving **19.** frozen: 1.8¢/fl. oz.*; bottled: 2¢/fl. oz.; canned: 2.46¢/fl. oz. **21.** small pkg. = $2.59/lb., 78.9¢/chop, 0.3 lb./chop; large pkg. = $2.49/lb., 90.5¢/chop, 0.36 lb./chop

Page 302

1. $25.79; 16.9% **3.** $47.32; 17.3% **5.** $57.46; 12% **7.** $83.98; $5.88 **9.** $58.93; $5.60 **11.** $62.11; $4.97

Page 303

13. $4.26 **15.** $3.64 **17.** $2.33

Page 304

19. 21.9%, $655.20 **21.** 25.1%, $906.36 **23.** 24.6%, $1,406.08

Page 309

1. $83.37 **3.** $60.02 **5.** $66.29 **7.** $136.20 **9.** $126.29 **11.** $127.05 **13.** 4.7 years **15.** 2.06 years **17.** 1.03 years

Page 310

19. $21.60 **21.** $8.00 **23.** $6.67 **25.** $9.82 **27.** year 1: lost $94; year 2: saved $482. **29.** $149.40

Page 315

1. total: 500 **3.** total: 620 **5.** total: 608

Page 316

7. total: 1,270 **9.** total: 575 **11.** 1,023 calories **13.** 1,075 calories **15.** 1,436.2 calories **17.** Shad; the exercise expends only about 100 calories.

Page 317

19. no dairy products **21.** cake, rolls, steak **23.** less than 1,868.8 **25.** 2,187 calories

Page 321

1. $30.03; $4.58 **3.** $174.83; $45.33 **5.** $19.98; $4.73 **7.** $7.75; 69% **9.** $40; 73% **11.** $40.49; 82%

Page 322

13. $14.46 **15.** $7,841.53 **17.** $72.57 **19.** 436 at $21.22 **21.** 128 at $203.68 **23.** 263 at $11.08 **25.** $29.55, $12.28

27. If he's broken even on the lot, he can sell the rest cheaply.

Page 326

1. $6.66 **3.** $18.75 **5.** $107.96 **7.** $34.71 **9.** $99 **11.** 25% **13.** 33% **15.** 37% **17.** 15% **19.** 40% **21.** $86\frac{2}{3}$%

Page 331

1. $44.50 savings; 21.4% **3.** $27.80 savings; 18.1% **5.** no savings; catalog costs 84 cents more

Page 332

13. pymt. = $48.50 **15.** pymt. = $28.17 **17.** order: $161.96; monthly pymt.: $44.49; initial pymt.: $32.39; int. $3.91

Page 334

1. $12.97 **3.** $8.91 **5.** $10.97 **7.** $85.71 **9.** $102.31 **11.** $87.58

Page 335

13. cost: $43.36; savings: $39.64 **15.** cost: $18.72; loss: $2.77

Page 336

1. 2nd: (20¢/lb.), (23¢/lb.)* **3.** 1st: (99¢/lb.)*, ($1.19/lb.) **5.** 1st: (9¢/oz.)*, (10.6¢/oz.) **7.** 23¢ **9.** $10\frac{1}{2}$¢ **11.** $54.11; 12.3% **13.** $35.20; 13.5% **15.** $37.67; $1.13 **17.** $56.56, $3.68

Page 337

19. $153.13 **21.** $170.46 **23.** $5\frac{1}{2}$ years **25.** 624 calories **27.** 2,464 calories **29.** 3,260 calories

Page 338

31. $2.78; $21.28 **33.** $5.20; $70.20 **35.** $26.04 **37.** $1,299.18 **39.** $27\frac{1}{4}$% **41.** 35% **43.** $14.39; 24% **45.** $5.30; 6% **47.** $235.29 **49.** 852 settings

Page 345

1. $510 **3.** $430 **5.** $303 **7.** $544 **9.** $500 **11.** $1,398 **13.** $90.23 **15.** $119.54 **17.** $316.44 **19.** 42 mo. = $3\frac{1}{2}$ yr.; amount to save/mo. = $277.08

Page 350

1. $480 **3.** $2,025 **5.** $1,852.50 **7.** 3 points **9.** $4\frac{1}{2}$ points **11.** $5\frac{1}{4}$ points **13.** $2,175.50 **15.** $3,985.76 **17.** $39,750 **19.** $40,500 **21.** $72,800 **23.** closing costs $3,124; needs $1,624

Page 354

1. $1,625 **3.** $2,097 **5.** $12,000 **7.** $249.44 *I:* $232.50 *Pr:* $16.94 **9.** $845.60 *I:* $793.33 *Pr:* $52.27 **11.** $652.27 *I:* $640.00 *Pr:* $12.27 **15.** $278.92 **17.** $1,118.67 **19.** pay it off sooner; reduce interest paid **21.** $\frac{1}{4}$ income = $375 per month; 2.5 rule gives $45,000 max. debit and $462.88/mo. **23.** annual income: $39,600; could borrow: $62,652.38

Page 356

1. $257.91, $22,423.80 **3.** $525.56, $107,768 **5.** $690.96, $149,888 **7.** $I = $14,060.40$; savings = $8,363.40 **9.** $I = $110,877.38$; savings = $71,042.22 **11.** $I = $86,132.50$; savings = $21,635.50

Page 359

1. Out. bal.: $64,848.49

Page 360

3. Out. bal.: $28,591.89 **5.** Out. bal.: $21,493.34 **7.** (1) $1,551.51; (2) $22,301.51 **9.** (1) $11,663.11; (2) $24,113.11 **11.** (1) $28,761.66; (2) $50,450.66 **13.** $39,428.49 **15.** $31,799.69 **17.** $80,839.14 **19.** Out bal.: $60,918.97—6%; *I:* $38,386.77—2.6% **21.** Most of the payment goes to interest at the first of the loan. At the 15th year, or 60% of the way through the loan, only 20.6% of the principal has been repaid.

Page 365

1. 23′ 3″ **3.** 25′ 6″ **5.** 15′ 6″ **7.** $3\frac{5}{8}$″ **9.** $3\frac{1}{16}$″ **11.** $1\frac{1}{8}$″ × $1\frac{3}{4}$″ **13.** 66 ft.^{2} **15.** 16 yd.^{2} **17.** 4

Page 366

19. 0.52 A. **21.** 0.57 A. **23.** $16\frac{2}{3}$ yd.^{3} **25.** $250 (10 boxes) + $89.40 (installation) = $334.40 **27.** $605 (10 int.) + $180 (3 bi-fold) + $270 (2 ext.) + $630 (2 garage) = $1,685 **29.** 8 gal.

Page 368

1. $613 **3.** $455 **5.** $1,024 **7.** $1,800 **9.** $1,312.50 **11.** $1\frac{1}{4}$ points **13.** $4\frac{1}{4}$ points

Page 369

15. $5,235 **17.** $18,750 **19.** $278.66 **21.** $501.82 **23.** $543.44; $30,212.80 **25.** $550.07; $75,016.80 **27.** $23.355.43 **29.** $25,889.25 **31.** $20.961.83 **33.** $67,901.85 **35.** 26′ × $32\frac{1}{2}$′ **37.** 12′-9″ **39.** $2\frac{3}{8}$″ × $2\frac{13}{16}$″ **41.** $2\frac{1}{8}$″ × $3\frac{3}{4}$″ **43.** 0.54 A. **45.** 0.80 A.

Page 373

1. $642.39 **3.** $366.76 **5.** $517.92 **7.** $413.78 **9.** $5,350.40 **11.** $1,771.58 **13.** $1.52/$100 and 15.2 mils

Page 379

1. $70.10 **3.** $246.00

Page 382

1. 8,135

Page 383

3. 7,362 **5.** 1837; $132.72 **7.** 852; $73.62 **9.** 1003; $82.68 **11.** 30; $4.42/day **13.** 30; $2.45/day **15.** 27; $3.06/day **17.** 7.5¢/kWh

Page 385

1. 3514 CCF **3.** 6214 CCF

Page 386

5. 29; $16.35 **7.** 54: $29.82 **9.** 81; $43.23 **11.** 30; 54.5¢/day **13.** 31; 96.2¢/day **15.** 32; $1.35/day

Page 389

1. 21.2; W: 18.42; S: 16.70 **3.** 121.3; W: 119.78; S: 91.78 **5.** 15.4; W: 20.05; S: 12.35 **7.** 41.2; W: 35.06; S: 31.70 **9.** 90; W: 20.5¢/day, S: 18.6¢/day **11.** 92; W: $1.30/day, S: 99.7¢/day **13.** 90; W: 22.3¢/day, S: 13.7¢/day **15.** 88; W: 39.8¢/day, S: 36¢/day **17.** W: $31; S: $27.80

Page 393

1. $26.73 **3.** $21.04 **5.** $22.52 **7.** $4.12 **9.** $3.28 **11.** $9.97

Page 399

1. 10.9 hr./mo.; 22 min./day **3.** 315.9 hr./mo.; 10.5 hr./day **5.** 18.4 kWh; $1.49 **7.** 80.2 kWh; $6.50 **9.** 82.1 kWh; $6.65 **11.** $1.10 **13.** $55.05 **15.** $6.71

Page 400

17. $44/month

Page 404

1. 1,280 ft.^{2}; 3.4 gallons **3.** 1,696 ft.^{2}; 4.5 gallons **5.** 2,112 ft.^{2}; 5.6 gallons **7.** 19.7 hours; $315.20 **9.** 52.2 hours; $835.20 **11.** 32.5 hours; $520 **13.** $24.83 **15.** $99.75

Page 405

17. $85.25 $36.60 + $33.60 + $8.50 + $4.25 + $3.75 + $25.50 = $197.45

Page 409

1. 1,440 ft.^{2}; 30 bundles **3.** 2,588 ft.^{2}; 53 bundles
5. 2,869 ft.^{2}; 59 bundles **7.** 14 rolls **9.** 9 rolls **11.** 22 rolls

Page 410

13. 65 intermediate posts, 5 special posts, 690′ fencing
15. 11.6 yd.^{3} **17.** 2.7 yd.^{3} **19.** 1.24 yd.^{3}

Page 411

1. $911.95 **3.** $1,152.58 **5.** $979.32 **7.** $60.80 **9.** $239
11. $138.38 **13.** $610.88 **15.** 952; $79.62 **17.** 580; $56.10

Page 412

19. 52 CCF; $22.14 **21.** 97 CCF; $47.95 **23.** $13.60;
$12.50 **25.** $30.55; $18.65 **27.** $36.22; $33.28 **29.** $19.23
31. $25.11 **33.** $3.35

Page 413

35. 240.6 hr./mo., 8 hr./day **37.** 240 hr./mo., 8 hr./day
39. $2.14 **41.** $8.00 **43.** paint $100; labor $890.09
45. paint $60; labor $512 **47.** 26 bundles; 1,266 ft.^{2}
49. 150 ft. of fencing, 16 posts (and 1 gate)

Page 420

1. 9,575,636 **3.** 17,300 **5.** 8,331,317 **7.** 1.93 **9.** 20.34
11. 362 **13.** 967 **15.** 884 **17.** 794 **19.** 19 **21.** 16 **23.** 864
25. $133,200 **27.** $111,000 **29.** $115,916 **31.** $135,569

Page 423

1. $70.50 **3.** $153 **5.** $280.80 **7.** $297 **9.** $152.55

Page 428

1. $96.40 **3.** $234.15 **5.** $139.16 **7.** $795.60 **9.** $1,672.80
11. $9,170; $8,960 **13.** $15,725; $16,320 **15.** $10,950;
$10,560 **17.** $16,000 **19.** $11,000 **21.** $3,990 **23.** cash
value: $6,325; loan value: $5,692.50

Page 433

1. $15,000 **3.** $30,000 **5.** $25,000 **7.** $35,000 **9.** $40,000
11. $7,710 **13.** $33,228 **15.** $18,885 **17.** $1,162 **19.** $685

Page 434

21. $1,162 **23.** $1,066 **25.** $3,394 **27.** (a) $1,824,
(b) $152, (c) $384, (d) $33, (e) $119, (f) $39,300,
(g) $79,479, (h) $7,500, (i) $86,979, (j) $189,300

Page 439

1. $3,490; $740 **3.** $3,880; $610 **5.** $7,280; $215
7. $19,264; $2,366 **9.** $5,000; $3,095 **11.** 26% or $4,560
13. total: $43,570; auto ins.: $30,000; Plan C: $12,816;
Caldwells: $754

Page 445

1. $340.46 **3.** $601.29 **5.** $662.18 **7.** $734.86 **9.** $684.00
11. $17,224.20 **13.** $843.04

Page 446

1. 519 **3.** 923 **5.** 335 **7.** 977 **9.** 815 **11.** $72 **13.** $361.50
15. $64.20 **17.** $248,000 **19.** $143,000 **21.** $143.50;
$1,300 **23.** $652.40; $15,120 **25.** $1,576; $22,100

Page 447

27. $17,000 **29.** $17,000 **31.** $12,000 **33.** $28,000
35. $64,000 **37.** $1,066 **39.** $578 **41.** $4,060; $880
43. $7,170; $750 **45.** $13,360; $1,140

Page 448

47. $607.54 **49.** $667.59

Glossary

absolute value The number of units a number is from zero.

add-on loan A simple-interest loan that is paid off by installments.

adjustable-rate mortgages (ARM) A loan for which the interest rate changes every year or two, according to current prime-rate interest.

adjusted gross income The gross income minus all allowable adjustments.

adjustment to income A cost incurred by the taxpayer that can be subtracted directly from the gross income. It includes expenses not paid by employer, payments to a retirement plan up to a maximum amount, alimony, and interest penalties for early withdrawal.

algebraic expression A string of one or more variables and constants or products of variables and constants connected by + and − signs.

amortization Calculating monthly payments, giving the size of the loan, the interest rate per month, and the number of payments.

amortization schedule A table showing how to pay back a loan through installments that periodically decrease the outstanding principal.

annual percentage rate (APR)

$$APR = \frac{2ml}{P(n+1)}, \text{ where } \dots$$

m = number of payments per year, l = amount of interest, P = principal, and n = total number of payments.

annuity Equal amounts of money deposited at equally spaced periods of time.

approximate time When the time of a loan or when the date of a note and the maturity date is given in months and years.

area The number of square units needed to cover a region completely.

assessed valuation The value of property that is established by the officials of city or county government to determine property-tax liability. Determined by a certain percentage of the market value and also called "assessed value."

average indexed monthly earnings (AIME) An average value of the income the employee earned during the working years.

back order A company's procedure for forwarding to the customer an item that is not currently in stock as soon as the supply is replenished.

Banker's Rule Used by bankers to make use of ordinary interest and exact time.

basic coverage Insurance that pays for hospital room-and-board, laboratory fees, x-rays, drugs, and medical equipment. (Sometimes surgical and outpatient fees are paid.)

beneficiary The person named in an insurance policy to receive the money.

benefits Money paid as agreed in an insurance policy.

blank endorsement A person's signature on the back of a check written to him.

blueprint An artist's view of the exterior of a building and a simplified plan of the floor layout.

break-even point The time when a life-insurance policy exceeds the accumulated premiums. Also, the point when merchandise sold has covered the merchant's cost and overhead.

buyer's guide A piece of paper on the window of a new vehicle that lists warranties.

buying cooperative A group of families that buys groceries in large quantities in order to take advantage of wholesale prices.

calorie A unit expressing the amount of energy provided by a food and burned by the body.

canceled check A check for which the financial institution has paid.

capacity The amount that a container can hold.

cash value The money the insured has actually paid on an insurance policy.

check An order to a bank to pay a certain amount of money to the person or place designated.

checkbook register The place in the checkbook where a record is kept of the check number, check amount, and balance.

circumference The distance around a circle. $C = 2\pi r$.

claim A customer's report of an accident to an insurance company for the purpose of receiving money as compensation.

closed-end lease An auto lease in which the vehicle is turned in at the end of the lease time without any price adjustment.

closing date The time of the legal transfer of property when closing costs are paid.

coefficient The numerical factor accompanying the variable in a term.

coinsurance A policy in which the insured pays about 20% of the covered expenses and the insurer pays the other 80%.

collateral A guarantee of ability to pay back a loan.

collision The type of coverage that pays for damages to the policyholder's own vehicle due to a collision with another object or upset of that vehicle.

commission Income earned by a certain percentage of total sales.

comparison shopping Comparing the prices of items among grocery stores by sample shopping and by newspaper ads.

compound amount The amount of money after n compounding periods.

compound interest Interest added to the principal at designated intervals.

comprehensive The type of coverage that pays for loss or damage to the vehicle of the insured due to causes other than collision or upset—for example, theft, fire, wind, or vandalism.

constant A symbol that represents a fixed number.

constant-ratio formula Used to learn how the annual percentage rate can be more than the stated note of an add-on loan.

contract A signed legal document.

conventional loan A loan that belongs to a commercial bank, usually requiring a 20% down payment.

conversion factor A number used to multiply or divide a quantity in order to express it in a different unit.

cost of operation Actual cost of keeping a vehicle in running condition—for example, gas, oil, tires, maintenance, and repairs.

cost of ownership Money which an owner of a vehicle pays for depreciation, insurance, finance charges, fees, plates, and taxes.

cost per $100 A method of expressing a tax rate.

coverage The amount and type of insurance.

credit Money added to bank balance. Also, the ability to borrow money.

credit card A plastic card from a financial institution authorizing the bearer to make purchases on credit. A method of borrowing money.

credit union A financial institution owned and controlled by a corporation.

currency Paper money.

customary system The non-metric system of measurement used in the United States.

daily interest A method of figuring interest that accounts for the actual number of days during which the money is on deposit.

date of the note The date a note is signed.

debit A figure subtracted from the amount in a bank account.

decimal Numbered by tens.

deductible The part of a liability policy that the insured agrees to pay when a claim is made.

deduction The amount subtracted from the adjusted gross income before calculation of tax liability.

default Failure to pay.

dependent A member of a household who depends on the head of the household for more than half of his support and whose gross income is very low.

depreciation Loss in value of a vehicle during any part of its lifetime.

disability-income coverage Insurance that pays for loss of income due to injuries.

discount interest (discounting) Loan made to a customer for which the bank calculates the interest. Interest charges are subtracted from the face value of the loan, and the customer receives the balance, or *proceeds*.

do-it-yourself (DIY) Performing one's own home repairs.

drive-away cost The amount a person will pay for a new car, which includes discounts made and sales tax added, but not including a trade-in.

effective-interest rate The simple-interest equivalent of a compound interest rate.

electronic teller A computerized system for which a person uses a special card to transact different types of banking business.

empty calories Food in which there are no nutrients or vitamins, just calories.

endorse To sign a check before depositing or cashing it.

endowment life insurance A limited-payment, whole-life policy with a rapid built-in cash value growth that will provide retirement income.

energy efficiency ratio (EER) The factor by which appliances have the potential to save energy.

equation A mathematical sentence stating that two expressions are equal.

equivalent fractions Fractions with the same value.

estimate Rough calculation done to save time or to give some idea of what will be needed in the future.

exact interest Using a 365-day year to figure compound interest.

exact time The time for a loan, given in days.

exemption Any of several kinds of allowances that a taxpayer can claim in order to have fewer withholdings taken out of his paychecks.

exponent A number that tells how many times the base is used as a factor.

face value (principal) The amount of money that is borrowed.

factor One of two or more numbers multiplied together.

federal income tax Money withheld by an employer to be paid to the federal government.

Federal Trade Commission (FTC) The federal agency that, among other duties, controls and enforces policies on new and used vehicles.

FHA loan A loan backed by the Federal Housing Administration (FHA), requiring as low as 3% to 5% down payment.

FICA tax Federal Insurance Contributions Act tax, which requires employers to deduct a certain amount of an employee's earnings to go toward the support of the Social Security program.

filing status A taxpayer's status for purposes of computing tax liability: single, single head of house, married with joint return, married with separate returns, and widow or widower with dependents.

finance charge The interest paid to a credit company.

fixed rate An interest rate guaranteed to remain the same for the term of the loan.

foregone interest Potential interest that is lost when a purchase is made with borrowed money rather than saved money.

Form W-2 (Wage and Tax Statement) The form used to inform the IRS about a person's income, filed by the employer.

Form W-4 (Employee's Withholding Allowance Certificate) The form used by the employer to figure how much of a person's gross income should be withheld for federal income tax.

formula An equation that describes a rule or principle.

furnished housing Rental housing that has appliances and furniture but no dishes or linens.

graduated commission A rate of commission that increases as the sales increase.

greatest common factor (GCF) The greatest number that will divide evenly into two numbers.

gross income Total income.

home improvement Labor performed in order to beautify, improve efficiency, or expand household functions.

home-owner's insurance policy A contract between the home owner and the insurance company.

home repairs Repairs done on items that have deteriorated or broken and which inhibit household functions.

hourly wages Wages paid to an employee on the basis of the hours he works.

improper fraction A fraction with a value equal to or greater than 1.

income Wages, bonuses, commissions, tips, dividends, interest, and profits from business or sale of real property.

income exclusion An item that is not income; e.g., welfare, insurance benefits because of death or property loss, gifts, interest on tax-free bonds, and child support.

income-tax return A form that reconciles the amount of money withheld for taxes with the taxpayer's actual tax obligation.

indemnity-basis coverage Insurance that provides cash reimbursements for medical expenses.

individual retirement account (IRA) An account in which a person can save up to $2000 per year and defer the payment of taxes until retirement.

insurance premium The fee that the policyholder pays an insurance company.

insured The person who has insurance.

insurer The insurance company who issues insurance.

integers The set of whole and negative numbers (excluding proper fractions).

interest period A given period of time during which interest accrues at a stated rate.

interest rate A percent of the principal that must be paid for its use.

Internal Revenue Service (IRS) The tax-collection agency of the federal government in the United States.

International System (S.I.) A measurement system based on the decimal system. Also known as the *metric system*.

isolate the variable The process of finding those values that replace the variable to make the equation true; getting the variable by itself on one side of the equal sign and its numerical value on the other side.

junk food Edibles lacking in nutrition.

Keogh plan A tax-deferred savings plan for self-employed people.

kilowatt-hours (kWh) 1,000 watts used for one hour.

landlord Owner of rental housing.

lease A rental agreement for a specific length of time and at an agreed-upon rate per month.

least common multiple (LCM) The smallest number that two numbers will divide into evenly.

lessee The person who leases an item from someone else.

lessor The person who owns the leased item.

liability The amount of tax to be paid.

liability coverage Insurance that pays for personal damage to others, including medical payments.

limited-payment policy A whole-life insurance policy that has a fixed number of years over which the premiums are paid.

linear unit A unit of length.

loading-insurance company A company that serves as a manager of funds and uses the yearly premiums to pay fees, buy term insurance for the insured, and invest the rest for growth.

local measured service Telephone billing system using a low base rate but measuring all calls for time and distance, as with long-distance calls.

lot A building site.

maintenance The repair and upkeep of a vehicle or property.

major-medical coverage Insurance that protects the insured against catastrophic medical expenses associated with traumatic accidents and complicated surgery.

maker A person who signs a promissory note.

manufacturer's (product) coupons Certificates with the value, product size, and sometimes the expiration date, allowing discounts for specific items.

mark up To add to the wholesale cost of goods to make a profit.

maturity date The date at which a loan must be repaid.

maturity value The amount of money that will be repaid (the sum of the original principal plus the interest).

Medicare Insurance for retired people; it includes hospital insurance and supplemental medical insurance.

mil One tenth of a cent.

mils per $1 A method of expressing tax rate.

minimum balance An account paying interest on the lowest balance in the account during the compound period.

minimum payment The amount of a bill that must be paid immediately.

mixed number A number that is the sum of a whole number and a fraction.

mortality table A chart that predicts the number of deaths in certain groups by each age.

mortgage A home loan in which you pay interest to a bank for the use of their money.

National Dealers Association (NADA) An organization that publishes a book giving the wholesale value of vehicles.

net income The amount of money in income after the withholdings are subtracted from the gross income.

nutrition The process of meeting the body's need for food.

open-ended lease A lease calling for a price adjustment above or below the predicted residual value of a leased vehicle at the time it is turned in.

open sentence A mathematical sentence that contains at least one variable and as a result is neither true nor false.

opposites Two different numbers that have the same absolute value. They are the same distance from zero but in opposite directions.

ordinary interest Interest figured by using a 360-day year to convert time to years.

origination fee The lender's charge to originate, or create, a loan; it includes all paperwork and documentation.

outstanding balance The amount of a loan that remains to be paid.

outstanding check A check that has been written but that has not cleared the bank and been returned to the issuer.

outstanding deposit A deposit that has not been credited to an account.

overhead The expenses for running a business.

overtime Time worked in excess of regular time.

owner's equity The part of the house's value that belongs to the owner.

passbook savings A savings account for which all transactions are recorded in a book.

pay-back period The amount of time required to pay for items or services.

payee The one to whom money is paid.

payer Person or institution that must pay money to another.

payroll period The time for which an employee receives a paycheck.

percent The ratio of a given number to 100.

percentage A part of the base, expressed in parts per 100.

perimeter The distance around a figure.

piecework wages Wages paid according to the number of items (pieces) of work completed.

place value The value that a digit gets as a result of the place it occupies in a numeral.

points The amount of discount the lender will subtract from the face value of the loan.

policyholder A person who owns insurance.

premium Money paid for insurance.

present value The principal (money) invested at a given time.

primary insurance amount (PIA) The retirement benefit that a person receives from Social Security.

prime factorization The process of finding all the prime factors of a number.

prime number A whole number greater than one whose only positive factors are one and itself.

principal The amount of money that is borrowed.

proceeds The amount of money a customer receives after the interest charges have been subtracted.

profit The money made after expenses have been paid.

promissory note A signed paper recording a loan between individuals.

proper fraction A fraction with a value of less than one, representing part of a whole.

property-damage coverage Insurance that pays for damage to dwellings and personal effects.

property tax Tax paid to a local government by those who own real estate.

proportion An equation that states that two ratios are equal (the product of the means equals the product of the extremes).

quarterly The compounding of interest to the principal four times a year.

rate of interest Percentage of principal added to payments.

rate per period The percentage paid within a period of time.

ratio A comparison of two different numbers or quantities.

rational numbers Numbers that can be written by placing one integer over another integer.

reciprocals Two numbers whose product is 1.

reconcile To compare checking account records with the bank statement and resolve any conflicts.

regular time The number of hours an employee is expected to work each week.

renaming fractions Writing fractions in higher or lower terms.

repeating decimal A decimal in which a pattern of digits repeats itself.

resale value The amount a vehicle is worth when it is traded in.

residual value The depreciated value of a leased vehicle at the time it is returned to the owner.

restricted endorsement An endorsement limiting what can be done with a check; it is usually stamped with "For deposit only."

salary A fixed amount of money paid to an employee in equal payments.

sales tax A tax paid in many cities and states when a person purchases merchandise or a service.

savings program A plan whereby a set amount of money is deposited on a regular basis.

scale drawing Blueprints drawn so that all the sides are in the same ratio with the actual measurements.

seamstress A woman who sews for a living.

seconds Flawed merchandise that is still acceptable to the consumer.

service-basis coverage Medical coverage within the guidelines of the insurance program for which the insured pays no extras.

simple interest Interest computed on the original principal, without consideration of previous interest.

solution The number(s) that make(s) an open sentence true.

special (full) endorsement Endorsement that transfers ownership of a check.

square units Area.

state income tax Money withheld by an employer from employees' earnings for the state.

sticker price The paper on the left rear window of an automobile that explains the price of the vehicle. (This price includes a base price and all the options.)

straight commission An arrangement whereby a person is paid only for sales made.

tailor A man who sews for a living.

tax-deferred Accounts for which taxes are not paid until a later time.

taxable income The adjusted gross income minus all allowable deductions.

tax rate The ratio used to establish property tax.

tenant A person who rents a dwelling.

term The length of time for which a loan is given.

term insurance Insurance that provides protection against the loss of income for a specified period of time and pays only in case of death of the insured.

terminating decimal A decimal with an eventual remainder of zero.

terms The parts of an algebraic expression that are separated by $+$ and $-$ signs.

therms Units used to measure gas consumption.

timecard A method of keeping track of the hours a person works (sometimes *time sheets* are used).

time clock A device that stamps the time on a timecard.

tips Money added to the hourly wage by a customer.

trade-in The selling of an old vehicle as part of the payment for a newer one.

transaction A deposit or withdrawal on an account.

Transatlantic Real Estate Tax Service (TRETS) A fee that ensures that the taxes on the property get paid during the period of the loan.

translate To express in another language. Also, to express English sentences in algebraic equations.

unfurnished housing Rental housing that has kitchen appliances but no furniture.

uninsured-motorist coverage Liability insurance that covers bodily injury and property damage losses that the policyholder sustains because of a motorist who has no liability insurance.

unit price Cost per ounce, per pound, per gallon, and so forth.

universal-life insurance Insurance that provides the insured the flexibility of making payments to a cash fund that is tied to the money market or other securities.

unlimited telephone service Service for which a set fee is charged.

VA loan Loans backed by the Veteran's Administration and available only to military veterans; often no down payment is required.

variable A letter or symbol in algebra used to represent an unknown number.

void To destroy a check if a mistake is made while it is being written.

volume The measure of a solid object in cubic units (the number of cubic units needed to fill the interior of a solid object).

warranty A guarantee that specified items are under a contract for a specific length of time.

whole-life insurance Insurance whose rates stay the same for as long as the insured lives.

withholdings The amount of money deducted from an employee's gross income before his check is written.

worker's compensation A plan that provides benefits for injuries or disease caused from one's employment.

Index